McGRAW-HILL SERIES IN GEOGRAPHY

V. C. FINCH, *Consulting Editor*

# ECONOMIC GEOGRAPHY

## McGRAW-HILL SERIES
## IN GEOGRAPHY

*Bennett*—SOIL CONSERVATION

*Finch and Trewartha*—ELEMENTS OF GEOGRAPHY

*Raisz*—GENERAL CARTOGRAPHY

*Trewartha*—AN INTRODUCTION TO WEATHER AND CLIMATE

*Whitbeck and Finch*—ECONOMIC GEOGRAPHY

*Whitbeck and Williams*—ECONOMIC GEOGRAPHY OF SOUTH AMERICA

# ECONOMIC GEOGRAPHY

## A REGIONAL SURVEY

*By*

### R. H. WHITBECK

*Late Professor of Geography*
*University of Wisconsin*

*and*

### V. C. FINCH

*Professor of Geography*
*University of Wisconsin*

FOURTH EDITION

McGRAW-HILL BOOK COMPANY, Inc.

NEW YORK AND LONDON

1941

ECONOMIC GEOGRAPHY

THE MAPLE PRESS COMPANY, YORK, PA.

# PREFACE
# TO THE FOURTH EDITION

The preparation of a fourth edition of this book has not been an easy task. Two circumstances in particular have made it more difficult in some respects than the original writing. One of these was the death of the senior author, Prof. R. H. Whitbeck, in July, 1939. The other was the outbreak of war in Europe just as the task was undertaken. Changes in world economy since the book was last revised made necessary a complete rewriting of large parts of the text. These changes have, of necessity, been made without benefit of the wide understanding, skillful phrasing, and pedagogical technique of Prof. Whitbeck. The junior author accepts full responsibility for them. The progress of the war in Europe during the period in which the book was undergoing revision has further complicated the task. It has wrought catastrophic changes in world economy. Customary productions have been held in abeyance, producing centers have been destroyed, and the normal movement of trade has been disrupted by financial restrictions, naval blockade, and the loss of merchant shipping. The end of these things and their ultimate effect on world economy cannot yet be seen.

Devastating as war may be in its influence on production and trade, it does not greatly alter the inherent capacities of the world's regions to produce. Therefore, the basic elements of land, energy, and resources and the complexities of their regional association still may be discussed with some assurance. For the rest, it must suffice for the present to consider the facts of production and trade as they have recently been. It must be left to the student and his instructor to supply from current events the rapidly changing facts that bear upon the use of resources and trends in production and trade.

In revising the text, numerous changes have been made. The factual materials have been restated and all statistical and graphic data have

3104

been revised in agreement with the latest available information or with such as represents the status of production and trade just before the onset of the turbulence of war. Most of the above changes are in the nature of routine revision, but certain others have been made that seem to the author even more significant for the usefulness of the book. Several of the chapters have been completely rewritten. This gave opportunity for the rearrangement of the former material and the introduction of much new material in greater conformance with the regional manner of approach. The facts concerning production and trade have been, so far as feasible, arranged to present regional contrasts within the continents and their larger political subdivisions. The chapter formerly entitled "Agriculture in the United States and Canada" has been replaced by one entitled "Regional Contrasts in the United States and Canada." Its purpose is to distinguish the basic geographical regions of Anglo-America prior to taking up the study of the more important American crops and industries from the topical viewpoint. In the section on Europe the instability of the present political situation has made advisable some rearranging and recombining of the sections of text dealing with various of the political units. It is not presumed that these changes are more in harmony with any probable realignment that may be the outgrowth of the European war; they have only the justification of convenience. The chapters on Russia, China, and Japan have been almost completely rewritten with much greater emphasis on regional contrasts than formerly was the case. Further emphasis on the regional viewpoint is given by the introduction of new maps and diagrams showing the regional subdivisions of various countries and areas, characteristic railway patterns, road patterns, and the distribution of other cultural features.

The facts presented in this edition of the book, as in those of earlier dates, derive from many sources, and the author appreciates the depth of his obligation to them all. Among them are those who have prepared research publications, textbooks, periodical literature, and statistical and other government documents. They have, by their painstaking labor, enriched and illuminated many of the complicated relationships of the geography of regions and of world production and trade. Particular appreciation is expressed to G. T. Trewartha and H. S. Sterling, for their criticisms of certain parts of the manuscript, and to J. V. Finch, E. M. Scott, and Margaret Bowen, who helped in the assembling of statistical and illustrative materials and with the mechanical aspects of preparing the manuscript.

V. C. FINCH.

UNIVERSITY OF WISCONSIN,
*February*, 1941.

# PREFACE
# TO THE THIRD EDITION

This volume is devoted to the presentation of economic geography upon a topical-regional basis at the level of beginning college classes. In chapter I, under the heading "The Field of Modern Geography," the authors have set forth the relation of this treatment to the whole field of the subject. In writing the book the authors have not only been concerned with an account of the material things of areas and the economic activities of peoples but have attempted to interpret their significance; for example, to indicate *why* particular crops are raised in certain places and others in other places, and *why* one nation has directed its economic life along certain lines and another along other lines. The idea of the differences between parts of the world and the reasons for those differences is fundamental in modern geography. The interpretation of areal differences is a function of geography that requires the reasoned association of facts of many kinds and gives the subject a considerable part of its educational value.

But the body of knowledge included in Economic Geography has also a high utilitarian value. It has something to contribute to those citizens who would have a world outlook and an international point of view. A knowledge of the poverty or plenitude of the resources of the various countries, of their stage of industrial development, and of their elements of economic strength or weakness, is a kind of knowledge that educated people need and use.

The book naturally divides into two parts. Chapters I to XVII, inclusive, treat of the United States and Canada. So similar are the conditions of environment, the people, and the economic life of sections of the United States and adjacent parts of southern Canada that it seems wise to treat the two countries together at many points in these chapters. However, there is need for a summary chapter dealing with Canada as a whole, and it is provided in chapter XVII.

It is commonly recognized that Economic Geography includes two different and distinct types of units of study; they are (1) commodities or products, and (2) regions. The former include any or all of the commodities whose production and distribution are significant matters in industry and commerce, notably the food materials, textile fibers, and minerals. The serious student of Economic Geography desires to know the conditions under which the agricultural staples are produced in various parts of the world, where the world's great mineral deposits are located and how they are obtained, and under what conditions the raw materials of industry are economically produced and marketed.

A majority of the significant commodities of commerce are produced in the United States; consequently their detailed treatment is found in the various chapters devoted to this country. Other commodities of which the United States is not a large producer—for example, raw silk, raw rubber, coffee, tea—receive detailed treatment in connection with the countries in which they are respectively important.

The second part of the book deals with foreign countries. Among geographers there is some disposition to favor the divisions of the continents into *natural* or *geographical* regions and to make these the units of treatment. Such a plan might treat, for example, the North European Plain, extending from northern France, through Belgium, the Netherlands, Prussia, Denmark, and southern Sweden, as a single geographical unit, largely disregarding national boundaries. For the specialist in geography such a plan has certain attractions and advantages. Such natural regions, however, are not the ones with which the commercial world in practice has to deal. The reading and traveling public, the business world, the international news, statistical reports, and international relations generally, take account of countries or nations as units. So universally do people think and speak and write of foreign lands in terms of political units—France, Italy, Japan—that they seem unquestionably to form the appropriate regional units for this study in the Economic Geography of foreign lands.

The book contains no treatment of climate or physiography as such, although the importance of the physical environment is constantly stressed. It is expected that the students who enter upon the study of Economic Geography at the college level will already have acquired a knowledge of the elements of physical geography. Students should regularly use a school atlas in connection with the text.

Careful attention has been given to the selecting and preparing of illustrations; they are believed to have as much teaching value as corresponding parts of the text, and it is hoped that they will be used.

Doubtless it is unnecessary to say that the lists of reference materials at ends of chapters and at the end of the book are not intended to be exhaustive. These lists include only a few of many references that might profitably be given. The lists do, however, include some of the recent and readily available books, reports, documents, and articles. Purposely, very few references to periodical literature are made.

The authors are indebted to many people in many ways—too many to enumerate specifically. Thanks are especially due to Dr. Selma L. Schubring for helpful suggestions and painstaking reading of parts of the proof.

To various departments of government in Washington, and particularly to the publications of the departments of Agriculture and Commerce, hearty acknowledgment is due. We desire to make special reference to the work of Dr. O. E. Baker, Bureau of Agricultural Economics, Department of Agriculture. From the excellent illustrative matter issued by this Department we have borrowed freely and appreciatively

R. H. WHITBECK.
V. C. FINCH.

UNIVERSITY OF WISCONSIN,
    January, 1924.
        REVISED, 1929
        REVISED, 1934

# CONTENTS

xii CONTENTS

# INTRODUCTION

# Chapter I. The Nature of Economic Geography

The peoples of the earth are engaged in the production of economic goods and services. This they do by farming, fishing, lumbering, mining, manufacturing, and trading and in many other ways. Not only are individuals and groups of people differently employed, but they are very unequally distributed over the earth (Fig. 5), they build different kinds of structures, and they arrange their settlements in widely differing forms and patterns. These differences in population density, occupation, and manner of living arise from many causes. Some of them spring from differences in the history and cultural backgrounds of the peoples concerned, and some are related to the manner of their political administration. Still others depend upon the use made by people of the materials and advantages with which nature has endowed the regions in which they live. The nations bordering the North Sea long have derived a part of their income from fishing. A shallow sea with abundant fish resources lies at their doors. However, the possession of similar natural endowments does not inevitably lead to identical means for their use in different places. The fertile soils of the Danube Basin yielded grain for centuries, but similar soils in North America were grazed only by bison, because their Indian inhabitants had not yet developed extensive methods of agriculture. On the other hand, similar conditions of natural surroundings do, in some cases, encourage people of unlike backgrounds to gain their living in similar manner. Steppe lands generally are grazing lands. The deeply fiorded mountain coasts of Norway, British Columbia, and southern Chile are physically much alike in that climate, landforms, and soils discourage agriculture, but numerous quiet bays invite to the sea. This invitation the fishing and seafaring inhabitants of the three regions have accepted, each in its own manner, in spite of the fact that they are widely separated and of different racial origins and cultural backgrounds.

It is a matter of common observation that people everywhere tend to engage in occupations that are made possible by the resources that they have at hand and by their commercial situation with respect to other regions. In generations past, when means of communication were poor and slow, the people of most regions satisfied the larger part of their requirements by means of goods and services produced at home, and they either did not know of or were forced to do without the products of other regions. Economically primitive peoples there still are, and they occupy a considerable part of the earth. In growing degree, however, modern commerce tends to encourage the production of goods in regions where they can be produced efficiently. This is true in spite of the opposing and restricting forces of nationalistic pride and protective tariffs.

GEOGRAPHY AND ECONOMIC PRODUCTION AND TRADE. Modern geography is concerned primarily with the different parts or regions of the earth and with those things, both natural or man-made, which exist together in and are characteristic or distinctive of each of the different regions. It is the purpose of geography not only to discover, describe, and explain these things, which are the elements of geography, but also to understand their functions and their characteristic arrangements in the various regions, the ways in which they are associated with and related to each other. This purpose involves a study of the features or elements of natural earth and also those features created by man in his endeavor to fit himself with the greatest advantage into the natural environment of his locality. It is also a purpose of geography to provide the basis for comparing one region with another and to seek to understand the likenesses and differences between them, for these are basic to the inter-regional exchange that is world trade.

THE ELEMENTS OF GEOGRAPHY. It was noted above that the things that, taken together, make up the characteristics of a region may be called the "elements of geography" and that they may be divided into two main classes: (I) the natural features or elements that, studied together, may be thought of as comprising *physical geography*, (II) the cultural, or man-made, features, the study of which in their physical association may be called *cultural*, or *human*, *geography*.

The items of the first, or physical, category include the following:

1. Climate.
    *a.* Conditions of temperature, such as the average temperatures of the warmest and coldest months or the length of the frost-free season.
    *b.* Precipitation, its average annual amount, its seasonal distribution, its manner of occurrence, dependability, etc.
    *c.* Storms and other winds.
2. Surface configuration and drainage.
    *a.* The kind of underlying rock and its structure.
    *b.* The major classes of landforms, especially such contrasting features as plains, plateaus, hill lands, and mountains.
    *c.* Smaller surface features and the pattern and steepness of their slopes.
    *d.* Condition of water drainage.

3. Earth resources.
    *a.* Water resources of the land, such as water for personal and industrial use, water for power, for navigation.
    *b.* Natural vegetation and animal-life resources, such as forests, grasslands, and wild game.
    *c.* Soil types.
    *d.* Economic minerals.

Some of the major elements in the second, or cultural, category are stated below.

1. Population, its relative density and distribution over the earth.
2. Houses and other buildings, their functions, types, and groupings, whether scattered or clustered in villages and cities.
3. Features resulting from economic production. These include
    *a.* All the forms and patterns of agriculture associated with the production of crops and livestock in whatever manner.
    *b.* All those features required in the production of goods by manufacture.
    *c.* Features associated with the extractive industries, such as logging, mining, hunting, and fishing.
4. Features associated with the development of modern transportation and commerce. These include the routes of travel, their spacing and pattern, the types of carriers employed, and the things transported.

ECONOMIC GEOGRAPHY. Within the broad field of general geography, as outlined above, may be distinguished a more restricted field which may be called "economic geography." This obviously is a part of the human, or cultural, aspect of geography. It places special emphasis upon the features of economic production and trade.

Economic geography may be approached from various points of view. The whole earth and the multiplicity of cultural features on it are too vast to be grasped as a unit. It must be studied in parts. One way to do this is to study the entire complex of land and life in a small region or part of the earth. Another way is to study a single limited aspect of economic production, such as a given crop or type of manufacture, in its principal places of occurrence all over the world. The first of these methods attempts to picture all the essential features of a selected area, such as a country or part of a country, and to explain the distribution of the people, their industries, and the things that they have created, in terms of each other and of the natural features of the area. The second method is essentially an interpretative study of geographical distributions. Such a study may be conducted within the limits of a small area or a large one, or it may be extended to the limits of the earth. In a study of this kind a single aspect of human culture may be considered, as, for example, an agricultural crop, a type of manufacturing industry, or the movement of a given commodity in trade. Whatever the subject, it will be analyzed for the purpose of discovering the location of its various parts and the explanation of them and their densities with respect to each other and to the environmental conditions with which they may be associated.

We observe, therefore, that any part of the earth may be studied from either or both of two ways: (1) as if it were a unit, a composite of many things all of which are studied together and in their interrelations; or (2) as if it were comprised of many separate conditions and industries each of which is studied separately, by and for itself, over this and any other part of the earth where it may be found. The first is sometimes called the "regional approach" to the study of geography, and the second the "topical approach." In the present volume both will be employed. The primary subdivision will be regional in the sense that the larger political subdivisions of the earth or physically related groups of them constitute regions. The discussion within this larger framework will be either topical or subregional, as brevity and convenience may dictate. The theme will be always *the economic activities of man in their physical and cultural setting.*

DESCRIPTION AND EXPLANATION IN ECONOMIC GEOGRAPHY. The subject matter of economic geography is made up largely of two classes of statements: those which are descriptive in nature and those whose purpose is to explain. Description, in geography, is concerned primarily with facts about the contents of and activities within regions. These include such facts as the nature and appearance of the elements of local earth environment, the distribution and relative importance of agricultural products, manufacturing industries, or the movement of goods from one region to another. It is by means of such description that one obtains a picture of the things and activities that are in an area, of their relative importance, and of where they are within the area with respect to each other. The use of pictures, maps, and diagrams supplements this kind of description.

The explanatory part of geography is intended to make clear *why* certain crops grow where they do and *why* certain regions are characterized by outstanding manufactures or special modes of transportation. Explanations in economic geography seldom are simple, and they often involve facts of widely different natures gathered from the fields of both the physical sciences and the social studies. In some cases the causes and relationships that explain facts of distribution are immediate and direct; in others they are remote and indirect. In the study of most countries and most industries it will be found that a full explanation of their characteristics and distributions will involve conditions that reach, on the one hand, into the realm of earth environment and, on the other, into conditions of social environment, such as racial traits, historical background, economic condition, and political status.

PRACTICAL ASPECTS OF GEOGRAPHY.   Geography has been considered a subject that contributes mainly to the culture and general information of its students. Although this is in large measure true, there are practical aspects of the subject that deserve attention. Europeans were earlier than Americans in developing the field of modern geography. This may be attributed in part to their earlier acquaintance with and practical interest in foreign lands, their products, and their trade. Such interests were intensified by the necessity felt in Europe for colonial expansion and by the fact that emigration had scattered Europeans to all parts of the world. Until recent years America has lived more within herself. A vast area containing a wide variety of resources had to be conquered and developed. America is less dependent than most European countries on foreign markets and foreign sources of foods and raw materials.

There are, however, various sorts of political and economic questions that can be handled more intelligently in the light of geographical information. For example, the proper use of land depends in part upon what the land may best produce, not immediately but over a long period. Large areas in the United States have been claimed and sold for agricultural use that had, because of one or another environmental handicap, very doubtful value for tillage. Such lands have created problems that are now pressing for solution. The creation of governmental commissions to study and correct these economic difficulties is bringing into use a vast amount of data that is essentially economic geography. Although trained geographers are among those now active in attempting to solve these problems, greater practical benefit would result from a wide and general recognition of the geographical fundamentals involved. Not only is geographical understanding important for the solution of domestic problems, but it has a place also in the realm of international affairs and military strategy. Basic to the problems of a troubled and embittered Europe is the question of resources, their distribution, and the restrictions with which they have been hedged about.

It is apparent that a large and varied body of detailed geographical facts applicable to specific problems cannot be acquired in a short time. Even a brief study of economic geography can, however, (1) open a great field for later enrichment by study and experience, (2) impart a geographic background against which public questions and business problems may be viewed, (3) provide additional basis for a broad and enjoyable outlook upon business and travel, and (4) afford a foundation upon which may be built a broad tolerance and sympathetic appreciation of the peoples and problems of the United States and other lands.

# PART I. THE UNITED STATES AND CANADA
## Regions and Industries

# Chapter II. Regional Contrasts in the United States and Canada (a preview)

Anglo-America, which includes principally the United States and the Dominion of Canada, is one of the largest subdivisions of the earth having a broad degree of physical and cultural unity. The two countries that occupy most of North America have a similar arrangement of major highlands and lowlands and share together certain of the climatic, vegetational, and soil zones of the continent. They have also, in large part, a similar cultural background and have developed many similar institutions and ways of living. By this it is not meant, of course, that all parts of Anglo-America are much alike. There are many internal differences, but parts of Canada are so much like parts of adjacent United States that it will be convenient here to survey first the general geographical features of the continent with little regard to the international boundary.

In order to arrive quickly at an understanding of this vast and complex area with its many industries, it may first be presented in terms of its major regions of contrasting geographic character. Subsequently the various agricultural, manufactural, and other industries may be considered separately and in greater detail. The present regional treatment is in some degree a preview of the topical treatments to follow. Inevitably some of the same facts here touched upon briefly in their regional associations must appear again in their topical connections. It is hoped that fuller reference to some of them under topical headings may serve to recall and emphasize the whole regional complex of which each is a part.

## The Regions of Anglo-America

There is no standard pattern by which to outline the regions of Anglo-America. So numerous are the elements involved that regions defined in terms of all of them would be very great in number. It is possible, however, to set off regions upon the basis of one or more of their elements of greatest local significance. Thus subdivided, Anglo-America may be presented in relatively simple terms. In Fig. 1 it is divided into 14 contrasting regional types. Essentially they are composite expressions of the character of the land and its resources, situation in the continent, and

11

outstanding economic activities of the people who live in them. Some of the regions are very large, and others small; some are not much changed from their primeval conditions by human activities; and others are intensively developed, densely peopled, and contain many cities. Although the land is, in general, the basic resource, the size of these regions is by

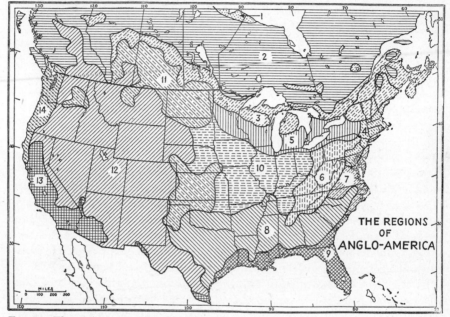

FIG. 1.—The major geographical regions here outlined are those discussed in Chap. II.

1. Tundra Pastures Region (see also Fig. 67)
2. Great Northern Forest (see also Fig. 67)
3. Forest Fringe Region
4. New England—New York Metropolitan Industrial Region
5. Lower Great Lakes Region
6. Southeastern Highland
7. Middle-Atlantic Horticultural Region
8. Cotton Region
9. Florida and the Subtropical Coast
10. Central Corn and Livestock Region
11. Cash Grain Regions
12. Region of Dry High Plains, Plateaus, and Mountains
13. Dry Subtropical Products Regions
14. Pacific Forest and Farming Region

no means the principal criterion of their relative importance. That may depend even more upon the productiveness of the land, the volume and quality of its nonagricultural resources, its commercial situation, and the number and enterprise of the people who inhabit it.

It may not be concluded either that the geographical account of a large region of relatively sparse settlement and primitive economic development is more easily or briefly made than of a smaller but more peopled region. Its very size may introduce elements of internal diversity that require comment even in a brief survey. The setting apart of such regions on a map involves, of necessity, a compromise of various considerations. Each region shown in Fig. 1 includes so many variable elements that it can be considered a unit only in a general sense, and its boundaries can seldom be located with assurance. In fact, although a map must show the boundaries drawn as lines, they seldom are truly lines but are zones of transition where the features that characterize the core of one region change more or less gradually into those which are characteristic of its neighbor.

With these facts in mind, the features of each of the major regions of Anglo-America may be sketched briefly.

## The Tundra Pastures Region

A REGION OF PRIMITIVE ECONOMIC DEVELOPMENT.    The arctic fringe of Canada and Alaska is a treeless land of meager resources, the tundra (Figs. 1, 67). Its principal inhabitants are the Eskimos, who cling mainly to the coast itself and live more upon the products of the sea than upon the resources of the land. Seal, walrus, fish, polar bear, birds, and other aquatic and semiaquatic creatures are their principal dependencies. Land hunting yields caribou flesh and skins, foxes, and an occasional musk ox but little food of vegetable origin. The total food resources of this land are not great, and the total Eskimo population probably does not much exceed 20,000. The land's poverty is explained by its climate and its geological history. It is in large part a region of hard rocks, scoured by the great continental glaciers. More important is the fact that the climate is one of long and very cold winters and short summers. The average temperature of the warmest month does not exceed 50°F. Under these conditions frost occurs every month of the year, and soils are continuously frozen to great depths. Only the surface thaws in the summer; and then the drainage is poor, and the soil acid. Agriculture is not possible under these conditions. Even the natural vegetation is greatly restricted. It is comprised principally of slow-growing lichens, sedges, grasses, flowering plants, and woody shrubs, which furnish a livelihood to herbivorous animals such as the arctic hare and the caribou. Upon such animals and the bird life of the summer marshlands live foxes, wolves, and other predatory species.

The age-long association of man and animal resources that characterized the Eskimo culture has been disturbed in recent generations. The introduction of firearms, improved animal traps, and fishing gear have enabled a more rapid exploitation of the animal resources. Organized hunting and the establishment of trading posts have made the world market for furs accessible. As a result the natural basis of livelihood has been imperiled. These changes have been counterbalanced by new elements that have appeared in the regional economy. By canoe and hydroplane mineral prospectors have penetrated remote parts of the region, and new deposits of valuable minerals have attracted small, scattered, and perhaps only temporary settlements.

PASTORAL INDUSTRY. For the Eskimo the introduction of the domesticated European reindeer (close relative of the larger wild, and apparently untamable, American caribou) has great possibilities (Fig. 2).

FIG. 2.—Alaskan reindeer feeding on the snow-covered tundra. (*Photograph by U.S. Bureau of Biological Survey.*)

Established in western Alaska at the beginning of the present century by the United States government, they have slowly increased in number. The natives have been trained to herd rather than to exploit them as game. They now number approximately 550,000 and support many Eskimo families. In the much larger and less accessible tundra region of Canada the caribou have lasted longer, and not until 1935 were reindeer finally established on its western end. They have not yet assumed any large importance even there, but without doubt they will spread eastward as the years pass and ultimately become a basic resource for the support of the native population.

It is not likely, however, that this change will bring about a very great increase in the density of human settlement. The slow-growing tundra vegetation may not be grazed frequently without severe damage, and hence a herd of reindeer must roam over a large area, and those who tend them must still maintain an essentially nomadic mode of life.

## The Great Northern Forest

From the Pacific Coast and the Yukon Basin of Alaska to Labrador and New England extends the great forest, the North American equivalent of the Russian taiga, which is the largest geographical region of the continent (Figs. 1, 67). It comprises more than one-fourth of all Anglo-America. Although the summers of this region are longer than those of the

Fig. 3.—A vast expanse of forest with many lakes in the glacier-scoured upland north of Lake Superior. (*Royal Canadian Air Force Photograph.*)

tundra, they average less than 100 days free from frost, and spells of chill weather with occasional summer frosts severely restrict the development of agriculture. In forest clearings, along highways, and near settlements hay, small grains, and root crops are raised, and pasturage and small dairy farms are established. In the main, however, this is not a region of important agricultural development. Thin and poor soils and great isolation as well as unfavorable climate work against it.

FOREST RESOURCES. The region is, however, not without important resources, although its present population, largely Indian, is thinly distributed, averaging, all told, less than one person per square mile. The forests themselves and their accompanying products, rich mineral resources, furs, and the productive salmon fisheries of the Pacific Coast are the important contributions of this region to American economy.

The taiga forests are mainly of spruce, fir, and poplar, thin and dwarfed in places and not of the highest value as sources of lumber. They constitute, however, a vast resource of wood suitable for the manufacture of paper and various products requiring woodpulp. Especially in the eastern half of this vast area, the forests are situated on the glacier-scoured crystalline rocks of the Laurentian upland whose many lakes, streams, and waterfalls furnish a means of transporting pulpwood from the forests and the power with which they may be converted into pulp and paper. The forests and their streams, lakes, and swamps also provide food and shelter to a variety of aquatic, tree-dwelling, and carnivorous animals whose furs are in great demand (Fig. 3). These same features also are attractions to the more venturesome sportsman and vacationist who wishes to get far from the requirements of urban life.

MINERAL RESOURCES. The ancient rocks, of which the larger part of this area is comprised, bear numerous deposits of the ores of valuable metals, and the rapid exploration of recent times is bringing new ones to light every year. Gold, silver, nickel, copper, cobalt, and many others are now mined in quantities that make Canada an important factor in the world production of each of them.

SETTLEMENT. The settlement of the northern forest region is of two main types. There is, first, a thinly distributed population of hunters, trappers, guides, farmers, and timber cutters whose numbers may hardly reach the average of one per 5 or 10 square miles of area. Associated with them are the people of numerous settlements, mainly small and clustered about mines, sawmills, pulp mills, water-power sites, fur-trading posts, and a few railway junctions. Of these settlements the greater number, and the larger ones, are in the eastern part of the region and near its southern margin.

## The Forest Fringe

PIONEER AND PART-TIME FARMING. The northern forest, east of the Rocky Mountains, is bordered almost continuously on the south by a region of transition that is in many respects individual (Fig. 1). Originally it was a belt of mixed coniferous and hardwood forest of a type much superior to that in the region north of it. Especially was that true of the portion from Minnesota east, which contained highly valuable stands of the eastern white pine. In large part these forests have been cut for lumber; the remaining woods have been burned over; and less valuable second growth has taken their place. This, in turn, has been cleared in part to make room for pioneer farms, which generally are scattered along roadways, avoiding the rocky and boggy districts. Often they are isolated and frequently unproductive (Fig. 4). Short summers and poor soils impose severe limits on the crops that can be raised. In the east are many older farming districts in which hay, pasture, and oats form the basis of a dominant dairy industry and the cutting of forest remnants for pulpwood and firewood gives winter employment to the farmer on land unsuited to clearing or as yet uncleared. In the west, land clearing continues, and hay, oats, and pasture provide for a small but growing dairy industry. However, wheat, for sale as grain, the principal crop of the bordering region on the south, has a much more important place on these western pioneer farms than on those of the more humid east.

This region also is one of glacial lakes and cool summers that attract the vacationist, and it has the added advantage of being much more

Fig. 4.—A pioneer farm in the cut-over lands of northern Minnesota.

accessible by road and rail and nearer the great centers of population to the south. Catering to the tourist is therefore a widespread, valuable, and highly organized phase of its economy, a supplement to agriculture, and one of its most important sources of income.

MINERAL RESOURCES. The region is also one of great mineral development, but the mining centers are older, better developed, and less widely scattered than those of the region north of it. Iron and copper mines in the Lake Superior district are world-famous, as are the asbestos mines of southern Quebec. Some of the miners are also part-time farmers.

TOWNS. Unlike the northern forest, this is a region of numerous towns and cities. Some are agricultural market centers, but the larger are commercial gateways and manufacturing towns. Winnipeg, Duluth, and other ports of Lake Superior, Sault Ste. Marie, Montreal, Quebec, Saint John, and Halifax are the larger commercial cities in this region. Through them flow grain, iron ore, pulpwood, and a great bulk of other products from their surroundings. It is not surprising that they are also centers of manufacture, but generally not on the large scale and of the great diversity found in the many cities farther south. Other towns in the forest fringe are occupied with manufacture, but mainly it is manufacture of a restricted type in which wood and its products are the leading raw materials, especially pulp and paper mills. These not only use the pulpwood of the locality but draw much also from the northern forest, and they utilize power from the streams descending from the Laurentian upland into the Great Lakes and the St. Lawrence Valley.

## The New England-New York Metropolitan Industrial Region

A REGION OF CITIES.  The relatively small Atlantic seaboard region of southern New England, New York, and southeastern Pennsylvania is the most densely peopled of any in North America (Fig. 5). The countryside is one of rocky, wooded hills and broad valleys, among which are numerous dairy and poultry farms, market gardens, country estates, suburban developments, and manufactural towns. All these focus upon the great cities of which this area has more than any other of like size in the continent—about 60 that exceed 50,000 population, nearly half of them exceeding 100,000. In the cities are concentrated industries of great variety, and through them flows a large part of the foreign commerce of the United States.

THE DEVELOPMENT OF MANUFACTURE AND COMMERCE.  Various conditions, of which only a few may be noted here, have brought about this development. Early settlement in this region and the growth of trade and fishing permitted the accumulation of capital which was available for investment in manufacturing industries at a time when other American regions were dominantly agricultural in outlook. A rapidly increasing population in a region of limited agricultural possibilities released a supply of intelligent labor which found employment in manufacture. In New England a disturbed glacial drainage provided many sites with water powers of a size suitable for the driving of small mills. Excellent harbors from Maine to Chesapeake Bay encouraged commerce. The fortunate position of Boston enabled it to become the commercial gateway of New England; Philadelphia and Baltimore served their more productive hinterlands in like manner. New York, most favored of all, not only had a superior harbor; but, via the Hudson River and the Mohawk Valley, it commanded the lowest route across the eastern highlands to the Great Lakes and the interior. After the Erie Canal was constructed along this route and the interior gradually settled, New

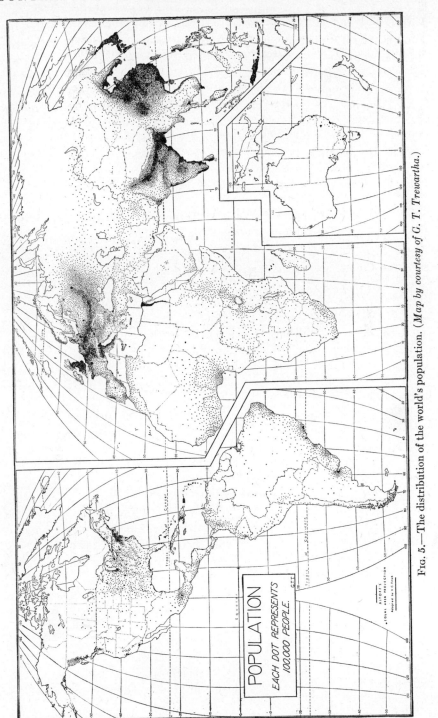

Fig. 5.—The distribution of the world's population. (*Map by courtesy of G. T. Trewartha.*)

POPULATION

EACH DOT REPRESENTS
100,000 PEOPLE.

York profited greatly from both import and export trade. With the building and improvement of railways, this natural advantage was much decreased, but the facilities for exchange already set up continued to attract trade and the industries that thrive in great commercial centers.

THE MODERN ERA reflects not only the operation of these early forces but many others of more recent application. New industries have crept in, and some of the old have disappeared, adapted themselves to new conditions, or rearranged themselves within the area. A pattern of regional contrast has emerged. Cotton-textile manufacture, originally established in southeastern New England, has spread northward along the coastal district as far as Maine but is now undergoing a contraction in the face of increasing southern competition. The manufacture of wool, once widely distributed in New England, Pennsylvania, and elsewhere, has become more specialized. The highly skilled trades related to the spinning, weaving, and finishing of wool and worsteds has now concentrated in the old textile center of eastern Massachusetts. The tanning and finishing of leather, an early industry in Boston and Philadelphia, has remained and greatly developed there and, especially near Boston, has added the related industry of shoe manufacture. Brass and copperware manufacture was established in the lower Connecticut Valley region a century ago and has now expanded until that region is a leading producer of hardware, tools, electrical supplies, and related products. New York City and its environs have industries of great diversity, but for various reasons it has come to dominate in those trades concerned with the manufacture of cloth, fur, and other materials into wearing apparel of all classes. In similar manner southeastern Pennsylvania and adjacent Delaware and Maryland have taken first rank, in the area east of the Appalachian Highland, in the smelting of iron; the manufacture of steel; the building of ships, railway equipment, heavy machines, chemicals, and many other products.

It is impossible in short space to give a comprehensive view of the great industrial development and complexity of this eastern urban region. It is important to emphasize its dominantly manufactural and commercial character and the fact that within it are districts of specialization that are distinguished from one another by the nature of their products.

## The Lower Great Lakes Region

The borderlands of the lower Great Lakes (Fig. 1) constitute an agricultural and industrial region of critical importance in Anglo-America. Its gray-brown forest soils lack the fertility of the rich prairie lands to the south and west of it. Yet it is an agricultural region of great importance. Originally it was equipped with excellent hardwood forests, but these have largely been destroyed in the process of making farms. However, the region still is one of important woodworking industries. Without any first-rank deposits of coal, petroleum, iron ore, or other metals it is, nevertheless, the principal region of iron smelting and of heavy iron- and steel-goods manufacture and turns out a vast number of secondary metal products. Although it is one of the world's newest manufactural regions, most of it having but little more than a century of white settlement, many industrial cities have sprung up within its borders. About 40 of them exceed 50,000 population, and nearly half of these exceed 100,000. The latter include Chicago, Detroit, and Cleveland, three of the very large cities of the country (Fig. 6).

Explanation of so remarkable a development lies in part, at least, in the *situation* of this region—situation in the continent; situation with

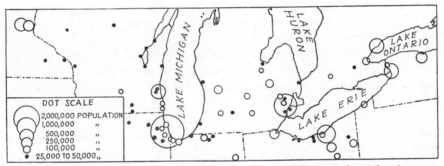

Fig. 6.—The distribution of cities in the lower Great Lakes in industrial region.

respect to great natural resources, other agricultural districts, and the eastern urban markets. Its situation is, in fact, that of a natural and necessary channel along which are gathered together streams of traffic carrying in great bulk several of the most essential classes of raw materials and manufactured goods. At meeting places and crosscurrents in this channel are centers of industry where raw materials and many kinds of manufactured goods are milled, reworked, and assembled into finished products of great variety.

AGRICULTURE.    The agriculture of the region is associated mainly with the dairy industry. From the standpoint of climate, soil, surface, and drainage much of this region is not so well adapted to grain production as are the corn and wheat regions. Corn for silage, small grains and hay for feed it can grow in great quantity, and also there is abundant pasture on rough or swampy lands. Adjacent urban markets require great quantities of fresh milk, and areas not within the market range of cities find outlet for their milk in the form of butter, condensed milk, and cheese. From western Minnesota to the glaciated highlands of southern New York the dairy farm is dominant, except in a few localities where natural or market advantages lead to specialization in fruit production or other horticultural industries.

MANUFACTURES. The manufactures of the region fall into several principal groups. First may be noted those which use the agricultural products of this or adjacent regions and transform them on their way to eastern or foreign markets. These are illustrated by flour and other cereal mills at Minneapolis, Chicago, Battle Creek, Buffalo, and many other centers; also by meat packing at St. Paul, Milwaukee, and Chicago, by the milk condensaries and numerous cheese factories of Wisconsin, and by vegetable and fruit canneries of all this region. Another group depended originally on the diverse forest products readily available. Furniture industries in western New York, southern Michigan, and northern Illinois; planning mills, door and blind factories, and wooden-implement manufactures in scores of towns are examples of this class, although many of them now are forced to draw much of their raw materials from outside sources.

Basic to most of the other manufactures are those producing raw iron and steel. These are located about the southern ends of the Great Lakes at Milwaukee, Chicago, Gary, Detroit, Cleveland, and Buffalo. There the iron ore of the Lake Superior region, transported by water, meets the coal of the Appalachian and Illinois fields and is economically smelted. Associated with these industries are many that use steel as a chief raw material. Among them are those making plates, tubes, and structural steel, lathes and steelworking machinery, heating equipment, steel furniture, agricultural implements, and, above all, the giant automobile industry, the world center of which lies in this area. These are, of course, only a few of the products turned out in hundreds of plants, large and small, from one end of the region to the other. It is the Great Lakes shipping and the several railways that must pass south of the lakes that serve to keep up the continuous flow of goods. From various sources products stream into this channel, are more or less transformed by manufacture, and flow out again east or west as their market destinations require.

## The Southeastern Highland

Stretching from Pennsylvania to Alabama (Fig. 1) is a region of wooded hills and low mountains in which small, general, and self-sufficing farms are numerous but do not constitute the regional element of greatest significance. It is rather the exploitation of natural resources, especially coal and forest products, that gives the region individuality. Once these hill lands were clothed with mixed hardwood forests, but these have in large part been harvested. Enough remains, however, especially in the more rugged areas, to support forest industries and to serve as an added attraction to the vacationist amid mountain scenery.

COAL is easily the dominant regional element, for here lie the most important coal deposits of the American continents and probably of the world. In its secluded valleys are hundreds of tiny coal-mining settlements (Fig. 7), often associated with hillside farms. In its larger valleys are great mining centers and manufacturing towns. The latter are most developed at its northeastern and southern extremities about Scranton, Pa., and Birmingham, Ala., and on its western margin near the Ohio

FIG. 7.—A small "coal camp" in one of the narrow valleys of West Virginia. Simple chutes or "tipples" leading from hillside mines are seen on both sides of the road. The valley bottom provides space for creek bed, road, railway track and a double row of cabins.

River and its tributaries. Of these cities Pittsburgh is the outstanding representative. Formerly the great center of iron smelting and steel manufacture, it remains an important figure in that business, although much of the greatly expanded industry has established itself elsewhere. In this region of cheap coal and natural gas for fuel the leading industries are such as turn out heavy iron- and steelwares, glass, and clay products, such as pottery, brick, and tile, all of which require much fuel in their manufacture. The shipping of coal and the manufacture of coke are also sources of large income to the region, for it supplies much of the fuel used in the principal regions of manufacture both north and east.

SCENIC HIGHLANDS AND TILLED VALLEYS. The eastern margin of the highland region is not, for the most part, included in the coal fields. It is comprised of a central belt of long, wooded ridges and tilled valleys and a massive eastern highland of ancient crystalline rocks. The former includes such broad and fertile strips as the Shenandoah and the valley of East Tennessee, famous for apples and other farm produce. The latter includes the Blue Ridge and the Great Smoky Mountains in which lie the highest peaks east of the Mississippi River and some of the best forests and most attractive scenery. Down their rocky slopes flow numerous streams which supply the water-power installations of the adjacent Tennessee Valley and help to run the factories of the eastern Piedmont lowland.

## The Middle-Atlantic Horticultural Region

AGRICULTURE.   The coastal lowland bordering Chesapeake Bay and the Carolina coast together with a part of the adjacent Piedmont of Virginia and North Carolina is a region of specialized farming. It lies between the cotton region on the south and the highland and industrial regions on the north. It includes the flat light-soil regions of the Coastal Plain and the rolling clay uplands of the Piedmont. Its summers are too short to grow cotton; it is unsuited by soil, climate, and location to competition for the dairy markets of the north. Its farmers have therefore turned to agricultural specialization in another direction, and the region is dominantly agricultural, although only about one-tenth to one-fifth of its area is actually in tilled crops. The remainder mainly is woodland, infertile sandy lands, or old fields that have reverted to brush or trees after the soil fertility was exhausted. The agriculture of the tilled lands is intensive: vegetable crops and tobacco on the warm light soils of the coastal peninsulas and, on the Piedmont, principally tobacco. These crops are raised at great expense for fertilizers and for labor. From villages and country stations in the coastal area trucks and trains depart throughout the spring and summer laden with vegetables for northern cities.

TOWNS.   The numerous small towns are market centers and are mainly agricultural in their interests. The cities are of two classes. Norfolk and the group about the entrance to Chesapeake Bay have commercial and marine interests. They are the port group, concerned especially with the shipment of coal and cotton, with ship repair, and with fisheries. The interior, or Piedmont, group, extending from Richmond to Winston-Salem, is concerned mainly with the manufacture of tobacco. This is the principal cigarette-making district of the United States.

## The Cotton Region

PHYSICAL CONTRASTS.   Extending from northeastern North Carolina to western Texas (Fig. 1) is a region in which a diversity of physical conditions is counterbalanced by the dominant fact that cotton is the principal agricultural crop. Here most of the elements of the regional economy are closely associated with the raising of cotton and the processing or final manufacture of its products. Physically, the region is predominantly a plain, although it includes rolling, poor-soiled uplands, rich lowlands, and swampy alluvial stream bottoms. Its original vegetation included pine forests on the sandy lands, oak and hickory woods on the uplands, swamp forests of cypress and gum, scrub oak and mesquite woods on the drier plains of central Texas, and open grass prairies in the "black belts," the Texas coastal margins, and the steppe plains of the west.

CULTURAL CONTRASTS.   In spite of the broad unity of interest imposed by cotton growing, the cotton region has many cultural contrasts within itself. The "old South" extends from Virginia to Louisiana. It is characterized by a more intensive method of cotton culture on old woodland soils in close association with woodlands. Generally, less than half the land is in tilled crops, and one-third to one-half the farmland still is wooded. Abandoned fields revert to pasture, pasture to brush, and brush to woods. These are cleared in subsequent years and returned to cultivation after a long period of rest. Cotton is produced in small fields by relatively intensive methods involving large expenditures for fertilizers and the employment of much hand labor in planting, weeding, picking, and repicking the crop. Here the farmer, tenant or owner, often a negro, tills a small farm as a unit, although it may be part of a large plantation in the hands of a white owner, bank, or corporation. The average farm unit is less than 80 acres and in some districts is less than 40 acres in size.

In central and western Texas and Oklahoma, on the other hand, methods of culture are generally more extensive. On the large cotton farms 30 to 60 per cent of the area is open prairie or thin woodland, most of which is devoted to livestock grazing. The farms generally exceed 120 and in some sections average 320 acres in size. The soils are productive, and little fertilizer is used. Production methods are designed to employ more mechanical processes than in the East and to conserve human labor. The negro is replaced to a large degree by the white farmer, who secures additional help from itinerant laborers, often Mexican.

ELEMENTS OF UNITY.   Despite the numerous contrasts in the rural scene between east and west in the cotton region, all parts of it have certain things in common. Everywhere much the same seasonal cycle of planting, tilling, and picking of cotton must be observed. Generally, corn, or its near relative grain sorghum in the west, is the next most important crop. Hay and other forage crops are much less important than in the North, since the winter feeding of livestock is not a major business on the cotton farm. For the same reason the farm buildings do not include silos or large barns with storage space for crops and shelter for many animals. In addition to the substantial house of the owner or manager, the plantation usually includes several cabins for the tenant farmers or the Mexican field hands, the cabins being almost without barns or other farm buildings.

MINERAL RESOURCES. The cotton region as a whole is not one of great mineral resources. But here again east and west are different. The portion of the region west of the Mississippi River includes a large part of the Mid-Continent petroleum field, and in several sections oil and gas wells may be seen clustered in close proximity to fields of corn and cotton.

FIG. 8.—The busy season at a cotton gin in the Alabama "black belt."

In the same region also is one of the less valuable of the great interior coal fields of the United States and one of the principal domestic sources of aluminum ore.

TOWNS AND MANUFACTURES. The villages of the cotton region mainly are market towns for the farmers, but they include also two types of processing plants that are common to most parts of the region. These are the cotton ginnery (Fig. 8), where the newly picked cotton is separated from its seed, and the sawmill, where timber cut in land-clearing operations may be sawed into lumber or small products such as box pieces, barrel staves, or lath. Other towns reflect their more central locations by the addition of cotton compresses, where the country bales are repressed for foreign shipment, or oil mills, where local supplies of cotton seed are processed for the extraction of oil.

The larger cities of the region show a greater diversity of interests, especially as between the eastern and western groups. In the former, notably the cities of the Piedmont Region from North Carolina to Alabama, cotton-textile manufacture is well established. Here water power from the "fall-line" streams and the Appalachians, together with Appalachian coal, has encouraged manufacture, and a large supply of white labor from hill farms and poor lands has enabled it to compete successfully with New England textile centers. The growth of such cities as Charlotte, Gastonia, Spartanburg, Columbia, Atlanta, and others has resulted in large part from the success of the cotton-textile industry. West of the Mississippi River, textile manufacture has but a small place in the urban economy. The principal cities, such as Oklahoma City, Dallas, Fort Worth, and San Antonio, are railway and commercial centers of great importance, and their manufactures reflect this fact. They include industries of great diversity, among which the making and repair of railway equipment, petroleum refining, meat packing, wood-products manufacture, and several others far outrank textiles in importance.

## Florida and the Subtropical Coast

FORESTS AND FARMS. Between the cotton region and the Atlantic and Gulf Coast is an area (Fig. 1) in which little cotton is grown. Light, sandy soils, large areas of coastal and interior swamp, and abundant rainfall in the cotton-picking season combine to discourage cotton planting and greatly limit the use of land for any agricultural purpose. In general, less than 20 per cent of it is even owned by farmers, and less than 10 per cent is in tilled crops. It is, nevertheless, an important agricultural region in which a long growing season and mild winters encourage the production of intensively grown horticultural crops on limited areas. Early-season and winter vegetables and fruits are grown in localities accessible to rapid transportation leading to the northern markets. Most important of these districts is the citrus fruit region of central Florida. Others include the strawberry center of eastern Louisiana and numerous vegetable districts from Texas to Florida and South Carolina. The Louisiana section and southern Florida include also the only cane-sugar-producing lands in the United States, and most of the rice grown in the United States comes also from this humid subtropical coastal margin in Louisiana and Texas.

In spite of these important crops, the larger part of the land is covered by the remnants of once extensive forests, except on the Texas coast which originally was prairie land. Southern pine, of various species, occupied the better drained sandy uplands; cypress and the gumwoods held those that were less well drained. Forest remnants, either second-growth forest or great areas of stump and brush land, occupy far more area than agriculture and, in some sections, are broken only by limited settlements where a farm, a cluster of farms, or a village has been established. In parts of the region timber cutting is still in progress, and large sawmills in operation. In others the gaunt remains of decaying mills and the sites of abandoned mill villages show the great depletion of this resource. However, a new growth of pine has come up quickly on some of the cut-over land, and in some places it already is being used for the

FIG. 9.—Second-growth pine in southern Mississippi. The young trees are being tapped, and the gum is caught in the cups.

production of pulpwood or is being tapped for its yield of turpentine (Fig. 9).

MINERAL RESOURCES also play an important part in the settlement and development of this region. In the Texas and Louisiana portion, petroleum is obtained in several localities and is in some cases closely associated with deposits of sulphur and rock salt. In west central Florida are open-pit rock-phosphate mines.

THE TOWNS and smaller cities of this subtropical region mainly are shipping centers for fruits and vegetables or are otherwise concerned with the development of agriculture and the forest industries, but the larger cities principally are commercial ports. In this capacity they reach inland for the basis of their growth far beyond the limits of the coastal strip in which they lie. New Orleans is, of course, the leading member of this port group, but others, concerned principally with exports, include Galveston, Houston, Mobile, Savannah, Charleston, and many of less importance. It is natural that manufacturing industries should be found in these port cities also, for they process wheat, cotton, and other exports and prepare fertilizers and other things required by farmers out of materials imported in raw form.

The tourist is an important source of income in this region also. Mild winters attract thousands of guests from the cold North, and even the summers bring from the cotton region some who find the Gulf coastal margin cooler than the interior and far more accessible than the distant vacation lands of the North.

## The Central Corn and Livestock Region

AGRICULTURE. North of the cotton region is the agricultural heart of the continent in which corn dominates the cropping system (Fig. 1). Undulating farm lands, rolling to rough in a few places, divided checkerboard-fashion by roads, are made productive by the fertile, dark soils of ancient prairies and forest margins. A growing season of less than 200 days is too short for cotton but ample for corn, and an average precipitation of more than 10 inches in the three summer months is a prime climatic requisite.

The agricultural system of this region may be described as livestock farming. Its primary purpose is not the production of food crops for direct human consumption but the raising of feed and forage for the maintenance of livestock. Corn and hay occupy the largest areas and are kept in rotation with the small grains—oats, wheat, and barley. In this prairie region only the stream valleys were originally wooded, and woodland now occupies less than one-tenth of the average farm; generally it covers less than 50 per cent in the rougher southern portion of the region and less than 2 per cent in the drier northwest. On the average, from 50 to 80 per cent of the total land area is under tilled crops, except in those same rougher and more wooded southern districts of the Ozark highlands and the borders of the Ohio River. So little of the land is untillable that only a small proportion of most farms is left in permanent pasture, meadows in the crop rotation and harvested hayfields serving the purpose of pasture.

The farms average large, 120 to 200 acres, and are laid out on a rectangular pattern with rectangular fields (Fig. 10). The typical farmstead includes a substantial house with a shelter belt of trees to protect it from the severe winds of winter. Its buildings include ample provision for the storage of corn and hay and shelter for the livestock raised or purchased for winter fattening. Of the abundant grain crops only a small part is sold from the farm. However, wheat is commonly associated with corn in the cropping system of the southern and eastern portion of the region, and it is sent to market as grain. Some oats and corn are sold likewise in those districts where cereal mills and corn-products factories offer a special market.

ANIMAL PRODUCTS. The greater part of the grain crops, however, together with the hay and cornstalk fodder, goes to the raising of beef cattle, swine, lambs, and poultry. Many horses and mules must be fed also. The average farm has 100 or more acres under tillage, and so much of the land is devoted to grain and feed production and so little to pasture suitable to the rearing of young cattle and sheep that only a part of the

FIG. 10.—The checkerboard pattern of corn and grain fields and the tree-sheltered farm-steads of the corn belt in Illinois. (*United Photo Shop.*)

supply of animals required for feeding is raised at home. Large numbers must be bought from the western steppe and mountain ranges. Enough cows are kept, however, so that there commonly is a small surplus of milk or cream on the corn-belt farm. Much of this goes to large butter factories in the neighboring cities, and the by-products are retained by the farmer for the rearing of young calves and pigs. Most of the large number of swine in the region are reared on the same farms from which they are finally marketed.

MINERAL INDUSTRIES. Rich land is the principal resource of the corn and livestock region, but it is not without minerals and sources of industrial power. Petroleum and gas fields lie in northern Ohio, in southern Illinois and Indiana, and in the southwestern part of the region that extends into the Mid-Continent oil field in Kansas and Oklahoma. These have long been productive districts, and yields have greatly declined except in Illinois, where they have recently been revived by deeper drilling. Of even greater importance are the coal fields of the region. The great coal basin of Illinois, Indiana, and Kentucky is the second most valuable in the United States. In parts of this area mine shafts and great piles of mine waste are located amid fields of corn and hay. Still another great coal field of somewhat lower value but great size underlies the grain fields of much of Iowa, Missouri, and eastern Kansas. Deposits of lead and zinc also are found in the southwestern part of the region.

TOWNS AND CITIES. Small towns are spaced at frequent intervals among the rich farms of the corn and livestock region. In the main they are market centers, outlets for farm produce, and sources of supply for farm needs and services. They are connected by a close network of roads and railways. In these towns there are certain to be yards for the weighing and shipping of livestock, mills for the handling and grinding of feed, implement and hardware dealers, and many supplies and services common in other American farming regions.

Of cities there are 15 that exceed 100,000 population and about as many more between 50,000 and 100,000. These are spaced at wider intervals than those in the industrial regions, but they make an impressive industrial showing of their own. The larger, St. Louis, Kansas City, Cincinnati, Indianapolis, and Omaha, include, of course, a great variety of manufacturing establishments. Much of the mechanical equipment and manufactured goods required in the region is supplied to it by the industries of the lower Lakes region and the East, but competitive plants in some lines have been established in the cities of the corn and livestock region also. Many of the leading industries reflect the economy of the region in which they lie and the fact that these cities are centers of great railway networks. Animal slaughtering and meat packing are important in all the larger and many of the smaller cities. These, together with flour and cereal mills, indicate the flow of farm produce toward the eastern markets. To supply the needs of the region there are factories making farm machinery and supplies, railway equipment, and many other classes of goods.

## The Cash Grain Regions

EXTENSIVE FARMING. The subhumid western margin of the great central agricultural region of North America is characterized by an economy in which farming is dominant, and manufacture has a smaller actual and relative part than in any region to the east of it. Primarily it is a region of extensive grain farming in which wheat is the leading crop. Broad expanses of flat or undulating plain and a wide extension of dark, fertile, prairie and steppe soils fit the region for extensive tillage. An average rainfall, generally lower than in the corn belt, decreasing toward the west and somewhat undependable, gives an advantage to such drought-tolerant crops as wheat and barley. It tends also to discourage a system of agriculture in which corn and livestock farming predominate. This is especially true in the northern part of the plains region where short summers further discourage the raising of corn. Wheat is a crop easily transported and in world demand. As such, it is too valuable to be fed to livestock, since it is hardly so well suited to that use as corn, oats, or barley. In the main, therefore, it is sold from the farm for cash and constitutes the principal source of farm income. To a smaller extent barley, oats, and, especially in southeastern Nebraska, corn also leave the farm as grain for use in regions outside.

LIVESTOCK PRODUCTION SMALL. Since little feed or forage is raised on the farms of the cash grain region, there is much less emphasis on livestock than in the regions adjacent. Horses are required to do farm work even on motorized farms. Some cattle and sheep are grazed on rough lands and patches of ill-drained land; a few beef animals are sold; and a few cows are milked on the typical wheat farm. Sometimes there is a surplus of milk to be sold to a butter factory. A few swine for home consumption are raised, and, especially in districts settled by immigrants from central and eastern Europe, swine are numerous. It is to be noted, however, that, in spite of the growing use of tractors, there are districts where the number of horses required in farm work considerably exceeds the total number of cattle, both beef and dairy. The grain region is essentially not one of livestock farming.

PARTS OF THE CASH GRAIN REGION. Wheat farming is characteristic of three distinct sections in Anglo-America (Figs. 1, 22). The southernmost, because of shorter, milder, and more humid winters, is devoted to fall-sown wheat (winter wheat). Its center is in the plains of western Kansas. That which includes North Dakota and the prairie provinces of Canada produces spring-sown wheat. The third and smallest region is the "Inland Empire" of Washington, Oregon, and Idaho. Conditions there are somewhat different, and both winter and spring varieties of wheat are raised.

In all the sections farms are large, averaging 400 to 800 acres. In the flatter and more humid sections a high proportion of the farm is tilled, exceeding 70 per cent, but the proportion decreases to 30 per cent or less on the drier margins where dry-farming methods must be practiced to insure a crop. Although the farms are large, the farm buildings are relatively few. There is little need for shelters for livestock or storage space for hay, feed grains, or even wheat, since that usually goes to market as soon as it is threshed.

TOWNS AND CITIES. Market towns are numerous in the grain regions, most of them small. They are connected by railways and a rectangular system of roads. Their most conspicuous feature is the country grain elevator, which receives the grain direct from the threshing in the field. The other features of these towns are much like those of towns in the corn and livestock region. Of great cities the grain regions have few indeed, and those mainly are on or near their eastern margins. Such are Winnipeg, Wichita, and Spokane. Of large towns there are a good number, such as Saskatoon, Sask., Fargo, N. D., and Hutchinson, Kans. These cities and towns are concentrating points in the flow of wheat from the

Fig. 11.—Wheat fields lie close by a great flour mill at Saskatoon, Sask.

country towns to the eastern markets and milling centers. They contain great terminal storage elevators and, as in Saskatoon, associated flour mills (Fig. 11). All of them have excellent railroad facilities, are wholesale supply centers, but are not centers of general manufacture.

## The Region of Dry High Plains, Plateaus, and Mountains

CLIMATIC HANDICAPS.    One of the largest regions of cultural unity in Anglo-America derives its general internal similarity from its dry climate. It is, throughout, an area of *deficient rainfall* from the viewpoint of agriculture, and those of its occupants who live from the land must resort to the grazing of livestock, dry farming, or irrigation (Fig. 1). So widespread is the grazing industry and so restricted the tilling of the soil by either irrigation or dry farming that the region might well be called one of livestock ranching, save for the fact that many of its inhabitants live by means other than agriculture or livestock raising. Aridity is a distinguishing characteristic of this region, but so is it of southern California also. It is different from California in having relatively long and cold winters. It is not remarkable that this should be true of the northern portion of this large region in Montana and British Columbia. That it is true also of most of the southern portion is due to the high altitude of the southern high plains and plateaus, from western Texas to Arizona, and their open exposure to the north winds of winter. The average frost-free season in the plateaus of Arizona and New Mexico is only a little longer than that of eastern Montana and no longer than that available in the Snake and Columbia River valleys of Washington. The crops that may be grown, even under irrigation, in this vast area are therefore

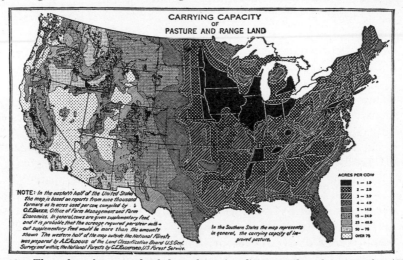

Fig. 12.—The value of pasture land depends on its climate, soil, and topography. (*U.S. Department of Agriculture.*)

restricted to those characteristic of the middle latitudes rather than of the subtropics.

GRAZING is the most widespread use of land in the region. But some of the range has deteriorated because of unwise use, and some of it, owing to aridity, never was able to support large numbers of livestock (Fig. 12). Good pasture in the high plains of eastern Montana or New Mexico will support one cow per 20 acres of land, but in the arid basins of Nevada more than 75 acres per cow generally is required. The number of persons dependent upon this resource cannot therefore be great. It takes a large ranch to carry livestock sufficient for the income from them to support a family. The average size of farms is therefore large—about 1,000 to 2,000 acres in eastern Montana and Wyoming. It is about the same in eastern Oregon, northern Nevada, northern Arizona, and most of New Mexico. In western Texas the average size reaches 4,000 to 10,000 acres. Much of the drier land of the arid plateaus and basins is hardly suitable for grazing at all, but some cattle and sheep spend the winters there, their forage supplemented by hay from irrigated land; and, in summer, they are driven up to better grass in the adjacent mountains.

DRY FARMING means the growing of crops on land that has been tilled in such a manner as to reduce evaporation and conserve moisture and to accumulate in the soil the precipitation of more than one year. This is accomplished by various means of tillage and crop management which require the investment of much more time and labor than is necessary in humid regions. In some sections it is possible by these means to get a crop every year or two crops in three years. In drier localities a crop is possible only every other year, and a large part of the arid West is too dry to make even these methods generally profitable. Agriculture of this type is adapted to a limited range of crops having relatively low water requirements, especially to wheat. The land must be as carefully culti- vated when it is not producing as in years when a crop is obtained. Dry farming can compete with the less careful agriculture of the more humid regions only by reason of the fact that it utilizes cheap land. It is most practiced on the eastern margin of the high plains where soils are excellent and the rainfall is only slightly deficient. Wherever it is used, the farms must be large, and the farming population is correspondingly sparse. It commonly is carried on in association with livestock grazing. It is in the dry farming regions that much land has been plowed up and subse- quently destroyed by wind erosion when it might better have been left in its natural grass sod.

IRRIGATION is capable of producing abundant crops on the fertile dry-land soils if only water can be had. The water is, however, generally collected from the scanty precipitation of the region surrounding the land to be irrigated or from the drainage of mountain areas. Considering this fact, it is evident that only a fraction of the total area of the dry lands ever can be irrigated. Three-fourths of the water used is obtained from streams; less than 10 per cent is pumped from wells. The utilization of these waters involves expense (1) for the construction of dams and other works to store the flood waters resulting from seasonal inequalities in stream flow and to raise the level of the water so that it may flow over the agricultural land by gravity or (2) for the installation and mainte- nance of pumping machinery for the elevation of the water. Also, the land to be irrigated must be prepared to receive the water by the digging of ditches for distributing water and providing drainage and by grading or terracing to level it. Thus, although the land in its natural state may have been nearly worthless, it is expensive land when irrigation is finally applied to it. In contrast with the great grazing ranches of this region and the large dry farms, irrigation farms generally are small.

The distribution of the irrigated land of the United States is shown in Fig. 13. To this must be added a small amount in western Canada.

It will be seen that the larger part of it lies in the region of high plains, plateaus, and mountains. In this situation it is restricted by climate as to the crops that may be grown on it. The subtropical fruits and early vegetables cannot be grown at all; and even the hardy fruits, such as apples and cherries, occupy but relatively small areas. The main crops are those which are grown without irrigation farther east—alfalfa, the small grains, sugar beets, and potatoes. The advantages of production under irrigation include (1) a closer regulation of the water supply than is possible under rainfall and (2) soils that ordinarily contain larger amounts of the soluble elements of plant food than do those of the humid regions. Crops commonly give larger yields under irrigation than they do in the eastern states.

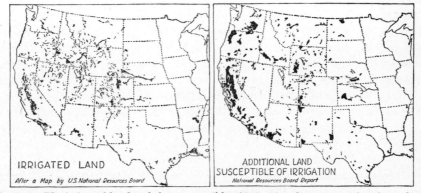

IRRIGATED LAND

After a Map by U.S. National Resources Board

ADDITIONAL LAND SUSCEPTIBLE OF IRRIGATION

National Resources Board Report

Fig. 13.—The irrigated land and that susceptible of irrigation do not comprise a very large part of the total area of the semiarid and arid West.

OTHER SOURCES OF INCOME for the people of this region include forests, minerals, and the attractive scenery of mountain and plateau, which draws an increasing number of summer visitors (Fig. 14). The mineral resources include coal and some petroleum, especially in the Rocky Mountains and the high plains border of Canada and Colorado, numerous deposits of gold, silver, copper, lead, and zinc scattered through the Rocky Mountains and the short basin ranges from British Columbia to southern Arizona. The complicated geological history of this region has included many earth disturbances and intrusions of molten rocks which have led to the formation of valuable mineral ores. The forests mainly are restricted to the mountain areas, especially to the northern mountains where there is less severe drought because of more snow and shorter summers. Generally, the forests are less valuable than those of the northern Pacific Coast or of the eastern regions. They are, however, of great importance, since they are the basis of a lumbering industry and aid in some measure in the conservation of snow and rain for use in water-power development and irrigation. They add also to the attractiveness of the mountain scenery.

SETTLEMENTS. Without doubt that part of the population dependent upon the grazing industry is the most widely dispersed of any in this large region. Isolated ranches and small market towns which supply their requirements are scattered at intervals over the entire region. Mining and lumber towns also are numerous, some of them active and others past the peak of their development or abandoned. The more stable and the larger towns are those associated with the larger bodies of irrigated

FIG. 14.—Summer pastures, woodlands, a gold mine, and attractive scenery are the resources of this U-shaped glacial valley in the Rocky Mountains of Colorado.

land. These include especially (1) the towns along the larger streams flowing east from the Rocky Mountains, (2) those at the western fringe of the Wasatch Mountains in Utah, (3) those in the Snake River Valley in Idaho, and (4) those occupying the irrigated valleys bordering the east-facing slopes of the Cascade and Sierra Nevada Mountains in Washington, Oregon, and Nevada.

Of cities exceeding 50,000 population there are only a few, and in general they command the trade of important irrigated districts and also certain routes of transportation through or around mountains. In these locations they share in the grazing, mining, timber, and tourist traffic of larger areas. East of the Rocky Mountains is Denver, the metropolis of this group. There are also El Paso, Tex., Pueblo, Colo., Great Falls,

Mont., Calgary, Alberta, and others of smaller size. Located west of the great highlands, in a somewhat similar relationship to settled farm land and mountain passes, are Salt Lake City and Ogden, Utah, and Spokane, Wash.

## The Dry Subtropical-products Regions

Although most of the land of California is devoted to irrigation, dry farming, grazing, and forestry, it is, as a region, in many respects unlike that just previously considered. Fundamental to the difference is the fact that it is predominantly Mediterranean in its type of climate. This means that it is a coastal or marine type of climate, with dry interior valleys, and that the winters are mild, almost free from frost, and moderately rainy, whereas the summers are long, warm, and almost completely rainless.

AGRICULTURE is adapted to these climatic conditions in various ways. Some of the crops grown have modest water requirements, like barley or wheat. They are grown without irrigation during the mild and relatively moist winters and mature with the beginning of summer drought. Others, including fruit and vegetable crops and some field crops such as alfalfa, are not able to endure the long summer drought without the aid of irrigation. The nonirrigated crops, such as barley, are raised under extensive farming methods, and even some irrigated crops like alfalfa and rice require only slightly more intensive methods. It is, however, the emphasis placed upon highly intensive methods that distinguishes the agriculture of California, methods that require the application of much capital and labor to relatively small amounts of land, mainly held in small farms. It is by this system that the citrus fruits are produced and likewise the grapes, peaches, prunes, nuts, sugar beets, lettuce, cantaloupes, and a score of other vegetables and fruits. But all these are grown on less than a third of the land in cultivated crops, less than 3 per cent of the total area of the state. The production and sale of such large quantities of fruits and vegetables would not be possible if it were not for a large eastern market of high purchasing power and a highly organized system of rapid transportation and of distribution.

RURAL SETTLEMENT in the dry subtropical-products region is most dense in the districts of abundant irrigation. These are not confined exclusively to California but may be made to include also the irrigated-cotton, citrus-fruit, and winter-vegetable regions of southern Arizona and the Rio Grande Valley of Texas. In California four areas of intensive agriculture may be noted: (1) the great valley, especially its eastern margin where irrigation water is available from the slopes of the Sierra Nevada Mountains; (2) the narrow irrigated valleys of the Coast Ranges; (3) the southern California piedmont slopes, spread at the base of the San

Gabriel and San Bernardino Mountains south and east of Los Angeles (Fig. 15); and (4) the Imperial Valley, which is essentially the delta fan of the Colorado River from which the irrigation water is supplied.

OTHER EARTH RESOURCES upon which the population of this region depends include forests and minerals. Forests are restricted mainly to the slopes of the Sierra Nevadas, since the natural vegetation of the valleys, coastal mountains, and eastern dry lands are grass, woody

FIG. 15.—Citrus fruit groves on the piedmont slopes which flank the San Gabriel mountains near Glendora, Calif. (*Photograph by Fairchild Aerial Surveys, Inc., L. A. Courtesy of California Fruit Growers Exchange.*)

chaparral, and desert shrubs, none of which yields timber of value. Gold in the Sierras was a prime factor in bringing American settlement to California, but it has long been surpassed in importance by petroleum. Fields of the latter occur near Los Angeles and in the southern great valley and Coast Range districts, and numerous settlements are dependent upon them.

CITIES in the dry subtropical region are strikingly numerous as compared with those in the much larger dry plateau and mountain region to the east of it. There are not less than a dozen of 50,000 or more population. However, eight of these are clustered in two close groups—one, including San Francisco and Oakland, about San Francisco Bay; and the other, including Los Angeles, Pasadena, and Long Beach, about the oil fields, orange groves, and port facilities of the southern California piedmont. In both groups, and in San Diego as well, the commercial activities associated with transpacific and Panama Canal trade have been a stimulus to growth. The manufacturing industries of this region are remarkably diverse. Great distance from eastern manufacturing centers and the high cost of transportation lead them to manufacture for their own needs many different things. Meat products, foundry and machine-shop products, airplanes, furniture, and clothing are examples. In addition there are many industries that are distinctive or grow logically from the raw materials available. Such are petroleum refining and the canning and preserving of fruits, vegetables, and fish. Other industries have sprung up through the action of various social and physical factors. The airplane industry is one of these. It is especially true also of moving-picture production, which found a particularly congenial environment in this combination of subtropical temperatures, bright sun, and complex physical settings that include sea, desert, gardens, plains, mountains, forests, highland snows, and many other features within a short radius. No small part of the great concentration of population in southern coastal California results also from the settlement of migrants from other sections of the country who find there an attractive climatic environment in which to spend their winter seasons or declining years.

## The Pacific Forest and Farming Region

The Pacific Coast of northwestern United States and southwestern Canada is a region of marine climate characterized by relatively cool and dry, but not rainless, summers and by mild, rainy winters. The area of principal settlement is a long valley included between low coastal and high interior mountain ranges. The region is in sharp contrast with most of California, since its growing season is enough shorter and its winters enough colder to exclude from its culture most of the subtropical crops that characterize the more southerly coastal region. It differs also in the fact that its copious rainfall supported an original vegetation of coniferous forest both on the mountain slopes and valley floor. The lowland has been partially cleared for agriculture, which may be carried on without irrigation. In it lie numerous towns and several cities, four of them being of 100,000 to 400,000 population. It is a region in which the principal occupations of the people are related to forestry, agriculture, commerce, and fisheries.

FORESTS are the great resource of this region. In density of stand and size of trees they exceed any other forests in the world. The giant redwoods of northern coastal California merge northward into the Douglas fir, western cedar, and hemlock forests of Oregon, Washington, and British Columbia (Fig. 70). Heavy rains and, in the mountains, heavy snows contribute an abundant moisture supply that has nourished this prodigious growth. Its exploitation, which began on the more accessible lowlands, has now progressed into the mountains, where many men are employed in, and small settlements are supported by, timber cutting. About half the timber remaining in the United States, suitable for the manufacture of lumber, stands in this region. From it is drawn the raw material that supports the most important manufacturing centers of the adjacent lowlands.

AGRICULTURE is an important aspect of the economy of the lowland, but it is not so highly developed as in the great valley of California. The

FIG. 16.—Forest clearing in the Puget Sound lowland is slow work, and pioneer farms average small in size. Much newly cleared land is used to provide pasture for dairy cows. (*Photograph by Asahel Curtis.*)

more rough and rainy coastal margin has very little tilled land, and that part of the valley bordering Puget Sound has less than the southern or Williamette Valley section in Oregon, where the land is flatter, the soils are more productive, and the original forests were somewhat less dense and more easily cleared. In this latter section the proportion of land in farms and in tilled crops reaches its highest figure for the region— about 25 per cent—and farming is of the most general type. In the region as a whole, farms are small, and a large part of the average farm remains in burned-over forest, second growth, brush, or large tree stumps (Fig. 16). Much of this is usable as pasture, and the mild winters permit its use by dairy cows the year around. The tilled land is used rather intensively. Its soil is not highly productive, but it is expensive land because of the high cost of clearing the remains of the heavy forest that once covered most of it. Hay and small grains, especially oats, are grown to supplement the pasture for dairy cows and in the feeding of large flocks of poultry. Other crops include potatoes, vegetables grown for sale, and a variety of fruit crops, such as apples, prunes, cherries, and berries in great abundance. The local markets are not sufficient, even including the numerous towns and cities, to absorb all this produce, and the eastern markets are far away. Much of the milk is, therefore, converted into butter and condensed milk, and the fruits are dried, canned, preserved, or frozen for shipment outside.

MARKET TOWNS AND MANUFACTURES. Numerous towns, more in the valley section than on the coast, serve as market towns for the rural districts and as sites for the manufactures of their produce. In them are the creameries, milk-condensing plants, numerous establishments for the manufacture of fruit products, and, on the coast, fish canneries associated with the salmon industry which this region shares with the more northern forested coastal region of British Columbia and Alaska. The largest and most numerous manufacturing establishments of this region are, however, the lumber mills of which there are more than 500. Many of them are small and isolated in the valleys and foothills amid the forests. Many more are grouped in the villages of the valley and coastal district, some of them mills of great size and sawing capacity, and still others are found in the largest cities. This region is, as a whole, poor in mineral resources, but it is not without sources of industrial power. There is in southern Vancouver Island a supply of coal, and the glaciated slopes of the Cascade Mountains combine with abundant precipitation to furnish a large amount of water power available for hydroelectric development.

CITES AND COMMERCE. The great cities of the Pacific forest and farming region are not only great centers of lumber and wood-products manufacture; they are also great commercial ports. They have much of the variety in type of manufacture that one might expect to find in connection with important ports where goods of many kinds are handled and where the local market is somewhat isolated by distance from the great manufacturing centers of the East. Lumber is, however, the dominant manufacture, even of these larger places, the other products being mainly such as supply the local markets and the shipping that enters the ports.

The growth of port cities of such size and importance as Portland, Tacoma, Seattle, Vancouver, and several of smaller size in so small and newly developed a section of the continent as this region is remarkable. That this should be possible may be attributed to a combination of circumstances. Puget Sound and the Strait of Georgia are deep waterways with numerous excellent harbors connecting with the Pacific, and the lower Columbia River also is navigable. By means of the low gateways cut by the Columbia and Fraser rivers and by mountain passes this lowland has connection with the area beyond the Cascade Mountains and with the East. The immediate region furnishes great volumes of timber, fish, and other products for export, and the farther interior furnishes grain, minerals, and other cargo. These ports are on the most favorable route from central North America to the Orient, a fact that focuses upon them much trade destined for and coming from Japan and China. They are also on the direct route to Alaska.

## Summary

The foregoing treatment has pictured in the briefest and most general terms the contrasts between the large and most strongly differentiated geographical regions of Anglo-America. It has been necessary to that end to place the emphasis upon the regional elements that are distinctive and to attempt an explanation of them in terms of their regional setting. The purpose of the discussion has not permitted the introduction of many features that are common to all the regions, features that distinguish Anglo-America as a whole and set it apart from Latin America, Europe, or Asia. Neither has it been possible to introduce the details of description and explanation concerning individual products and industries that make clear their geographical associations with the regions in which they are found, their general distribution in North America, or their relation to other parts of the world that compete with them. That will be undertaken in succeeding chapters which deal with products and industries as such and with the characteristics of other parts of the world.

SELECTED REFERENCES

"Atlas of American Agriculture," U.S. Department of Agriculture, Washington, 1936.
ATWOOD, W. W. "The Physiographic Provinces of North America," Boston, 1940.
BAKER, O. E. Agricultural Regions of North America, *Econ. Geog.*, series of articles in Vols. 2, 3, 4, 5, 6, 7, 8, and 9 (1926–1933).
BOWMAN, ISAIAH. "The Pioneer Fringe," pp. 93–142, New York, 1931.
ELLIOTT, F. F. "Types of Farming in the United States," U.S. Bureau of the Census, Washington, 1933.
HARTSHORNE, RICHARD. A New Map of the Manufacturing Belt of North America, *Econ. Geog.*, Vol. 12 (1936), pp. 45–53.
HURD, W. B., and T. W. GRINDLEY. "Agriculture, Climate, and Population of the Prairie Provinces of Canada," Dominion Bureau of Statistics, Ottawa, 1931.
HUNTER, BYRON. Dry Farming Methods and Practices in Wheat Growing in the Columbia and Snake River Basins. U.S. Dept. Agr. *Farmers' Bull.* 1545, 1927.
JONES, CLARENCE F. Areal Distribution of Manufacturing in the United States, *Econ. Geog.*, Vol. 14 (1938), pp. 217–222.
MILLER, G. J., and A. E. PARKINS. "Geography of North America," New York, 1934.
SMITH, J. R., and M. O. PHILLIPS. "North America," New York, 1940.
Soils and Men, *U.S. Dept. Agr. Yearbook*, 1938, pp. 679–722.

STRONG, HELEN M. Regions of Manufacturing Intensity in the United States, *Ann. Assoc. Am. Geographers*, Vol. 27 (1937), pp. 23–43.

TEELE, RAY P. "The Economics of Land Reclamation in the United States," Chicago, 1927.

WRIGHT, ALFRED J. Manufacturing Districts of the United States, *Econ. Geog.*, Vol. 14 (1938), pp. 195–200.

ZINK, NORAH E. Dry-farming Regions in Utah, *Econ. Geog.*, Vol. 15 (1939), pp. 421–431.

# Chapter III. Grain and Forage Crops

BASIC AGRICULTURAL CROPS. Cereal grains and the forage crops are fundamental to agriculture. Long before the commercial era made necessities of sugar, coffee, and many other foods, cereals and forage crops were the main dependence of the most populous regions of the world. The grains serve the double purpose of providing food for direct human consumption and of combining with the forage crops to feed livestock for the production of meat, milk, and eggs. In most parts of the world other products have now added great variety to the popular diet, but that has not decreased the total need of these basic agricultural crops.

The relative amounts of cereal crops grown in various world regions depend upon several conditions, such as climatic and soil environments, the standard of living in the region concerned, and the comparative world demand for a crop as expressed in terms of price. Some grains, particularly wheat, rice, and rye, are used mainly for direct human consumption; others are more largely fed to animals. If all were used, as they might be, directly by human beings, the total amount of food available would support a much larger number of people but at a lower standard of living. Tilled land used to produce feed grains and forage crops is less intensively used than that producing food directly; nevertheless it is desirable to a balanced economy.

## Wheat

THE WORLD'S PRINCIPAL BREAD GRAIN. Wheat was known to the ancients and was cultivated at the beginning of written history in China, India, southwestern Asia, and Egypt. It is believed to be native to the dry subtropical or Mediterranean climate of Asia Minor or of Mesopotamia. The world's crop of wheat exceeds (in weight) that of any other cereal except corn and rice. Of all grains, wheat is best suited to the making of light bread because of the two proteins glutenin and gliadin that are contained in the flour. When wet, the proteins, particularly the gliadin, become sticky and tenacious, giving to the dough the "strength"

45

that enables it to retain the gases produced by yeast fermentation and to expand with them.

CLIMATE AND WHEAT PRODUCTION. *Temperature* conditions are highly influential in determining the yield and character of wheat and the limits of its regions of production. Wheat is a member of the grass family, and, in common with the other small grains, all of which belong to this family, it stools, or tillers, early in its growth by sending up additional stalks from buds near the root. Thus many heads are developed by a single seed. This process of multiplying stalks is aided by cool and fairly moist weather during the period of early growth.

More than 75 per cent of the world's wheat is winter wheat, sown in the autumn. This type of wheat finds favorable conditions for its early development during the cool weather of the autumn or winter and in the spring. In regions having mild and uniform winter temperatures, as in India and Mexico, the wheat grows more or less continuously all through the winter. Where winters are more severe, as in central United States, the young plants lie dormant, often protected from excessive evaporation by a covering of snow. In north central North America and in eastern Russia, winter temperatures and winds are so severe that fall-sown wheat is seriously injured and is not a successful crop. In these regions quick-maturing varieties, sown in the spring and in this country known as "spring wheat," give larger gross returns, although they generally yield less per acre than winter wheat under favorable climatic conditions. Even the spring-sown wheats require no less than 90 days to come to maturity, and little wheat is produced where the growing season is shorter than 100 days. A cool, moist growth period followed by warm, bright summer weather permits the maturing and harvesting of the grain without damage from excessive moisture or fungus pests which cause discoloration and decrease its market value. High summer temperatures are not detrimental to maturing wheat where the atmosphere is dry; but when they are coupled with high humidity, they favor the growth of fungus diseases and other pests which often make wheat culture unprofitable.

*Relation to Rainfall.* Most of the world's wheat is grown in regions of relatively dry climate. The total annual rainfall most favorable to the growing of wheat is not easily determined because of the influence of temperature, rate of evaporation, and other factors. At present, little wheat is grown without irrigation in regions having less than 10 inches of rainfall, and most of the important wheat regions of the world have an average annual precipitation not exceeding 30 inches.

The character of the wheat grain is much influenced by the amount and seasonal distribution of rainfall. In general, the grain of humid and of irrigated regions is soft and starchy and produces a "weak" flour; that of drier land is harder and higher in protein. Many new varieties of

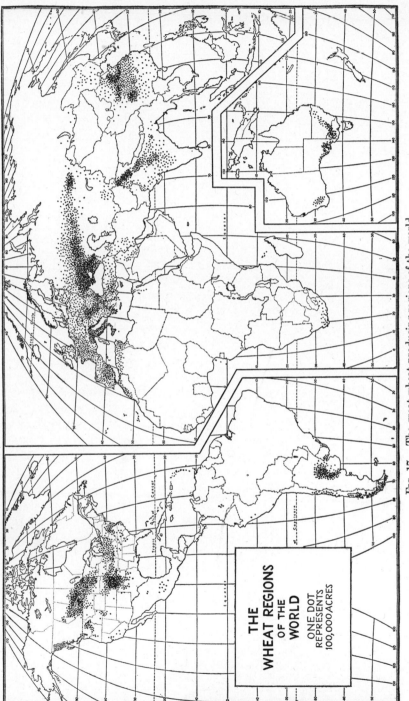

THE
WHEAT REGIONS
OF THE
WORLD

ONE DOT
REPRESENTS
100,000 ACRES

FIG. 17. — The great wheat-producing regions of the world.

drought-resistant, disease-resistant, and very hard (durum) wheat, developed by selection and breeding, are now grown in the wheat regions of central North America. Hard wheat flour is used in the manufacture of macaroni and other alimentary pastes and for mixing with that of softer wheats for bread making.

SOILS AND SURFACE CONFIGURATION have less direct effect than climate upon wheat production. In general, the best wheat soils of the world are heavy, dark in color, and of high available fertility. The black or dark-brown prairie or steppe soils (chernozems) have high lime and humus contents and yield wheats having more protein than those grown in the more leached soils of the humid forest lands. Level or undulating plains are more favorable than rough surfaces to the extensive type of farming by which much wheat is produced; they permit the use of machinery so necessary to modern wheat farming on a large scale.

ECONOMIC FACTORS in wheat production have wrought great changes in a few decades. For 40 centuries wheat had been sown, harvested, and threshed in much the same way the world over. It is little more than a century since the farmers of New York and Pennsylvania were sowing, harvesting, and threshing the principal part of the American wheat crop by hand labor. Since that time the invention of machinery has greatly reduced the human labor necessary to produce a bushel of wheat. The introduction of farm machinery and the improvement of transportation permitted the rapid expansion of wheat farming into the sparsely populated plains of central North America, South America, and Australia. An abundance of wheat not previously dreamed of followed, and prices declined so much that many of the older and less favored wheat regions were forced to turn to other forms of agriculture.

WHEAT REGIONS OF THE WORLD. Figure 17 shows the location of the world's great wheat-producing regions. It will be seen that 10 areas stand out clearly. They are (1) the central and Ohio River states of the United States, (2) the North Central States and the prairie provinces of Canada, (3) eastern Washington and Oregon, (4) northwestern Europe, (5) the Mediterranean countries, (6) the Danube Basin and southern Russia, (7) northwestern India, (8) northern China, (9) east central Argentina, and (10) southeastern Australia. The wheat production of Europe, including the Union of Socialist Soviet Republics, is normally equal to that of all the rest of the world, or more than 2 billion bushels.

WHEAT REGIONS OF NORTH AMERICA. (Fig. 18.) Although the wheat-producing areas of North America are widespread, the major regions have rather well-defined limits which are in part imposed by physical environment. The eastern and central areas are separated from the far western by the aridity of the high plains and by the Rocky Mountains. Although considerable wheat is raised in this intermediate belt on irrigated land or by dry-farming methods or by taking chances on the rainfall, the total quantity thus grown is not large. On the south, wheat production is limited (1) by the competition of the cotton crop, (2) by damage due to the freezing and thawing of open winters, and (3) by the insect and fungus pests fostered by the heat and humidity of the southern autumn, spring, and summer. The great central wheat region occupies rolling plains. Originally the larger part of these were prairie grasslands, and they are now the regions of dark-colored soils of high fertility (Fig. 19). On the

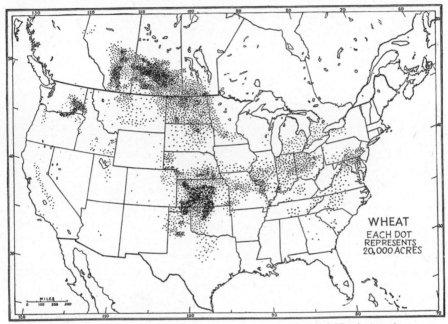

WHEAT
EACH DOT
REPRESENTS
20,000 ACRES

Fig. 18.—The three important wheat-producing regions of North America.

north the wheat region terminates at the margin of the rough land and the rocky soils of the Laurentian upland. In central Canada, level land extends far to the northward; here the limit of wheat production is not yet reached, but the crop continues to creep slowly toward the Arctic Circle, retarded, however, by the presence of forests and the shortness of the growing season (Fig. 20).

The great central wheat region is divided into spring-wheat and winter-wheat districts by a line running directly west from Chicago. Wheat culture is interrupted there by the livestock farming region in which corn, oats, and hay successfully compete with wheat for the use of the land. North of this line the dry and severe winters of Minnesota, the Dakotas, and central Canada create one of two great spring-wheat districts of the world (the other is found in eastern Russia). South of the line and east of the Great Lakes little spring wheat is grown. The winter-wheat belt extends from western Oklahoma, Kansas, and Nebraska eastward to central New York and eastern Maryland. It includes many areas where wheat is of minor importance because of the local competition of corn and other crops and because of the rough surface of the Appalachian high-

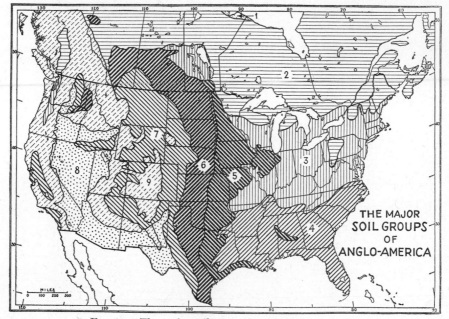

Fig. 19.—The major soil groups here distinguished are:

1. Tundra soils
2. Podzols
3. Gray-brown podzolic soils
4. Subtropical red and yellow soils
5. Prairie soils
6. Chernozems
7. Brown steppe soils
8. Gray desert soils
9. Undifferentiated mountain soils

land. In the wheat region of the Columbia Plateau (Washington, Oregon, and Idaho) both winter and spring wheats are grown.

The character of the wheats raised in various sections of North America is much influenced by climatic and soil conditions. In the drier climate and blacker soils that prevail in the plains region west of the Mississippi, both the winter and spring wheats are harder and higher in protein than those of the East. In the wheat regions of the Pacific Coast and the Columbia Plateau the grain is generally light colored and starchy, since the white varieties are better adapted to the low humus content

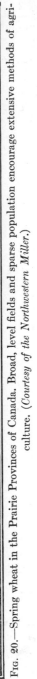

Fig. 20.—Spring wheat in the Prairie Provinces of Canada. Broad, level fields and sparse population encourage extensive methods of agriculture. (*Courtesy of the Northwestern Miller.*)

of the soils and to cool weather or moisture; this is particularly true of wheat grown under irrigation.

TRANSPORTATION OF WHEAT. In the early history of American wheat production the insufficiency of transportation made it necessary to raise most of the crop near the region where it was to be consumed. Expansion into the present wheat regions came with the development of railways and improved water transportation.

The volume of grain now produced in many counties in the wheat belts reaches into the thousands of carloads. This great traffic constitutes a problem in transportation that requires special methods of storage and handling. As a result, country elevators for primary storage have been erected along the railways, and greater elevators have been built at railways centers and terminal points between the wheat regions and the eastern markets. Such centers are found in Winnipeg, Fort William, and Port Arthur, Canada; and in Duluth, Minneapolis, Milwaukee, Chicago, Kansas City, St. Louis, and Buffalo. The service performed by the elevators is not merely that of storage awaiting a favorable market, but the grain is usually cleaned and graded while in storage, and its market value is thus increased. Although a large quantity of American wheat moves to its final destination by rail, water transportation is also an important factor. The position of the Great Lakes waterway between the spring-wheat region and the large eastern centers of population and commerce is of great economic advantage. Wheat is so easily handled in bulk with modern appliances that transportation by boat is highly efficient. A large part of the spring wheat and some winter wheat are moved by water from the ports on Lake Superior (Fig. 21) and Lake Michigan to both Canadian and United States ports on Lake Huron and Lake Erie and even to Montreal and New York. The lakes are closed by ice within from 2 to 3 months after the spring-wheat crop is ready to move, which makes it the more necessary for the ports at either end of the route to provide elevators to handle the large volume of grain suddenly poured in upon them. The storage and marketing of Columbia Plateau wheat through the northern Pacific ports are somewhat simplified by the prevalence of dry summer weather, which makes country elevators less necessary, but the ports have large storage equipment.

THE MANUFACTURE OF WHEAT FLOUR. There are approximately 2,000 flour and other grain mills in the United States and over 1,000 in Canada (Figs. 11, 22). About one-half the flour, however, is ground by a relatively few mills of large capacity. Small mills are continually being abandoned because of the competition of the larger, better situated, and more efficient establishments. These large mills are located (1) at centers of transportation near the region of wheat production or (2) in the region of consumption where efficient transportation brings wheat to their doors at low cost. The great mills of Saskatoon (Fig. 11), Winnipeg, Minneapolis, Kansas City, and Seattle illustrate the first type of location. In the case of Minneapolis the Falls of Saint Anthony furnished an original incentive to the location of this industry with which water power has long been so closely associated. The large milling interests of Buffalo, N. Y., and Port Colborne, Ont., show the influence of cheap transportation of wheat in bulk upon the Great Lakes to these eastern manufacturing centers. Intermediate in geographical position between

FIG. 21.—A few of the many grain elevators at Fort William and Port Arthur, the Lake Superior outlet for the Canadian wheat region.

these extremes are many mills of large capacity, such as those of Indianapolis and Toledo. These mills draw in part upon local supplies of wheat but also upon that of the western states. Modern milling is not the simple process that characterized the making of flour a few generations ago. This fact is due not alone to the character of the machinery used but also to the character of the grain. The widely sold patent flours must maintain uniform chemical composition and baking qualities. For bread flour, hard western wheat may be used alone or modified by blending with softer eastern or Pacific Coast wheat. Therefore, eastern mills often buy western wheat, and western mills use wheat from the more humid regions. The starchy wheats of the East and of the Pacific Coast region are used in part also for the manufacture of pastry flours and for breakfast foods.

THE BAKING INDUSTRY.  Home baking still consumes the larger part of the flour produced in the United States and Canada. There is, however, a constant increase in the use of flour in baking establishments, large and small, of which there are nearly 20,000 in the United States alone. The largest of these are found in cities where concentration of population has created a large local market for bread and other bakery products. Rapid transportation has expanded this market by enabling

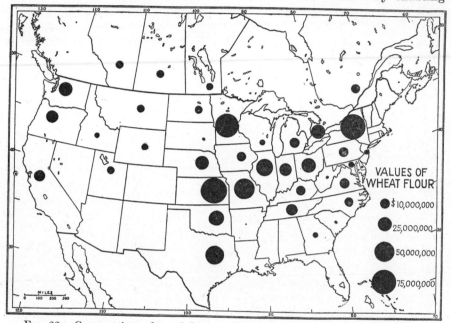

FIG. 22.—Comparative values of flour manufactured in various states and provinces. American flour-milling centers of greatest importance are situated between the wheat regions and the consuming markets.

the city bakery to send its product daily to the smaller towns of the surrounding region.

Another phase of the industry is the preparation of macaroni, noodles, breakfast foods, and other cereal products, many of which require other raw materials than wheat flour. The manufacturers are not dependent upon the local market for the sale of their products, because these are of relatively high value and are not perishable. The location of such industries, as in Battle Creek, Mich., or Niagara Falls, N. Y., is due as much to accident or some chance association as to any special advantage of situation.

AMERICAN WHEAT IN FOREIGN TRADE.  For many decades the new wheatlands of western United States provided a surplus of wheat that the industrial countries of western Europe consumed. The proportion of the crop sent from the country as wheat or flour varied, with good years and bad, from one-tenth to more than one-third of the total production. Storage and shipping facilities were developed in both Atlantic and Pacific ports to handle this large business. A tendency toward decline was halted by the stimulus to production and export brought about by the World War of 1914–1918 and the conditions in Europe immediately thereafter. Following the world financial panic of 1930, conditions were radically changed. The growth of economic nationalism, the imposition of protective tariffs by European countries, their own increased production and decreased consumption of wheat, together with serious droughts in the United States wheat regions, practically destroyed that trade. There remain certain limited markets, especially the near-by countries of tropical America, which use flour milled in the United States, but the total is only a small fraction of the exports of former years.

The situation of Canada in the wheat export trade is somewhat different. New and cheap land on the pioneer margin of the wheat belt allows wheat production at lower cost. A much smaller population in proportion to the wheat crop leaves a larger surplus for export. Empire preference enables Canadian wheat to enter the British market under more favorable tariff conditions than that from the United States. The wheat exports of Canada continue, therefore, to provide an outlet for about 70 per cent of the average annual crop.

The future trends of wheat export in America and in the world are almost unpredictable. The disturbed state of world exchange, the increasing tendency toward governmental control over wheat production and movement, and the sudden changes and reversals of policy to which these controls are subject introduce many elements unknown in the earlier conditions of the wheat trade.

## Rye

RYE AN IMPORTANT BREAD GRAIN. Rye ranks next to wheat in importance as a bread grain. It belongs to the same cereal group and has many of the same plant characteristics. It contains sufficient protein to make a flour of moderate strength and is nearly the equal of wheat in food value. Its flour is, however, darker in color and possessed of a peculiar flavor which makes it less desired. Although it is an important bread grain in Europe, it is not much used for that purpose in America where the larger part of the crop is ground with other cereals for the feeding of livestock or employed in the distilling of alcoholic beverages. The world's rye crop averages about 40 per cent that of wheat, and almost the entire crop is produced and consumed in Europe.

ADAPTATION TO CLIMATE AND SOIL. Rye is distinctly a crop belonging to cool, moist climates. It sprouts more quickly and grows more vigorously than wheat at low temperatures. It requires more water than wheat and will endure more severe winter conditions. Like wheat, it yields best on a fertile soil, but it will yield much more abundantly than wheat on poor, acid, or marshy lands. These conditions of adaptation to climate and soil have an important relation to the distribution of the crop in North America and also in Europe.

AREAS OF RYE PRODUCTION.   The rye crop of Anglo-America is less than one-twentieth as great as the wheat crop. It is grown principally

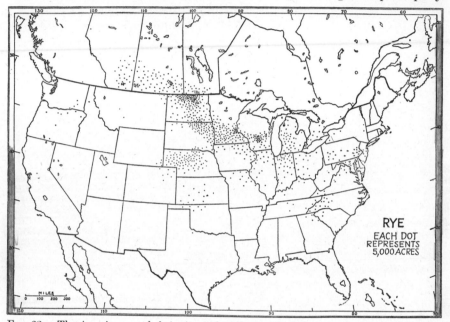

RYE
EACH DOT
REPRESENTS
5,000 ACRES

FIG. 23.—The American rye belt is situated to the north of the winter wheat belt and, in part, on poorer soils.

as a winter grain in the spring-wheat belt and in an area extending eastward through central Minnesota, Wisconsin, and Michigan into Ontario and Quebec. It is not particularly well adapted to the heavy soils of the spring-wheat region; but, because it can be sown in the autumn, it fits well into the farmer's schedule of seasonal employment. The eastern region is that of most recent glaciation in which there are large areas of poorly drained glacial swamp and marshland, with acid soils. In part, also, this region is underlain by ancient sandstones that have contributed much of their material to the glacial drift, resulting in areas of light and relatively infertile soils. It is clear from a comparison of Figs. 23 and 18 that the rye belt lies to the north of the winter-wheat belt and on its cooler and more humid margin. Much the same relationship exists between the major wheat- and rye-producing regions of Europe.

In eastern Pennsylvania, New Jersey, and adjacent parts of New York rye competes with wheat for the good soils. In this region, however, value is added to the crop by the sale of the long, tough straw that is in demand for packing purposes. In other parts of North America rye is grown but not harvested for the grain. On the Pacific Coast it is one of the grains that is grown during the winter rains and later cut for hay. In the South it is grown as a cover crop to reduce winter soil erosion, and to some

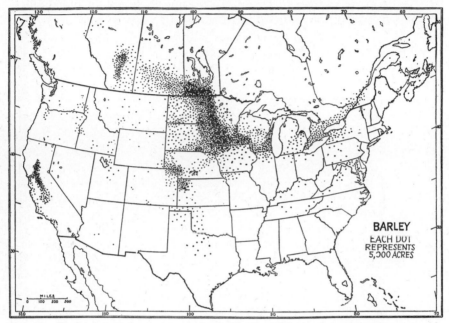

Fig. 24.—Barley is a spring-sown crop in the North and East, where the winters are cold, but a fall-sown crop on the Pacific Coast, where summers are dry.

extent the young rye is used as pasture. In New England and also in other regions, young rye is often plowed under as a green manure in the process of recovering fertility in worn-out soils.

## Barley

BARLEY A SHORT-SEASON GRAIN. Barley, like wheat and unlike rye, is believed to be native to the dry lands of southwestern Asia. Its general range of present cultivation is similar to that of wheat, except that some varieties are grown in small quantities beyond the poleward limit of wheat cultivation in the northern hemisphere, and others beyond the minimum rainfall limits of wheat culture in the dry subtropics. This great geographic range of barley is due not so much to its ability to withstand cold and drought as to the shortness of its growing season, which enables it to mature quickly and thus to escape unfavorable weather conditions, whether they be early autumn cold or summer drought. Some varieties are said to mature in as little as 60 days from the date of planting. Barley is like wheat also in that it gives satisfactory yields only on well-drained soils of relatively high fertility. It is, however, more tolerant of alkaline soils than wheat, and under equal conditions it yields nearly 50 per cent more bushels per acre. Although barley is used for food in parts of the Old World, it does not make a light bread and is cultivated mainly for animal feed, for malting, and to some extent for hay.

BARLEY IN NORTH AMERICA.   North America produces less than one-sixth of the world's crop of barley. This grain is raised in small quantity, together with spring wheat and oats, as far north as central Alaska, where it sometimes matures in 80 days. Because of its short season of growth and its resistance to soil alkali, it is used as a dry-land crop on the high plains and on the Pacific Coast, where it is an important crop both for its hay and for its bright grain, some of which is exported to European brewers. The principal barley region of North America (Fig. 24) is nearly coincident with that of spring wheat, except that it continues eastward through Minnesota and Wisconsin into Ontario. This region lies on or beyond the northern border of the corn belt, and the barley frequently enters into a rotation with wheat. Because of its rapid growth and early maturing it does not require attention at quite the same time as wheat and thus employs the time of the farmer advantageously.

# Oats

ADAPTATION TO CLIMATE AND SOIL.   Oats have many of the plant characteristics common to the other cereals. Like rye, they are most important in regions of relatively cool, moist climate. Unlike rye, however, they are not very resistant to winter conditions and are grown principally as a spring-sown crop.

The varieties of cultivated oats originated from types native to various parts of Europe, and each is adapted to the combination of moisture and soil conditions characteristic of the region of its origin. In general they require more water than wheat or barley and will give satisfactory yields on soils of low fertility. The pendant form of the head and the larger outer seed covers doubtless protect the flowers from rain and also render the matured oats somewhat less subject to damage and discoloration by moisture than are wheat and barley. Like barley, oats require only a relatively short growing season. These facts are reflected in the high relative importance of oats in the cool, humid cereal-producing regions of the world, such as Scotland, Scandinavia, and eastern Canada.

Uses of Oats.   Oats are more widely grown in North America than any other cereal. On the Gulf Coast and in the southern states they are fall-sown. On the Pacific Coast they are grown to a limited extent for hay. In New England and eastern Canada they are important because of their adaptation to poor soils and cool, moist climate. The principal region of oats production is, however, none of these. It is nearly coincident with the corn belt (Fig. 25). It will be recognized that this region has not in all respects an ideal oats climate, for it is often warm and humid

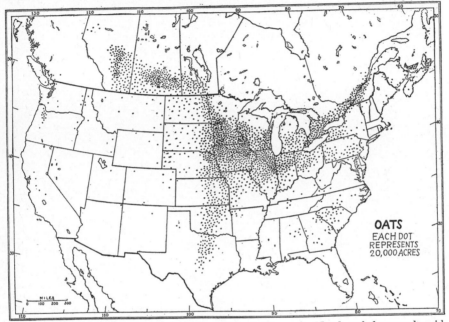

Fig. 25.—Oats are grown in the corn belt and also in the cooler North and the more humid East.

in the early summer, a condition that is conducive to fungus diseases of oats. The high fertility of the soil frequently causes a rank growth of straw, and the violent storms of early summer cause the crop to be badly blown down and lodged. Some of these environmental handicaps have been in part overcome by the introduction of new varieties derived by selection and by importation from the steppe lands of eastern Russia.

The primary reasons for the great importance of oats in the corn belt are economic.   (1) The seeding and harvesting times for oats fit well into a rotation with corn. Oats land can be prepared and the crop sown in the very early spring, long before it is warm enough to plant corn. The crop matures in midsummer, after the period of cultivating the young corn is over but well before the time of corn harvest. (2) Oats, because of their high protein content, are desired as a feed for horses and, ground with corn or barley, for feeding young meat-producing animals. (3) Oats straw is somewhat softer and more palatable and has a higher feeding value for animals than the straw of other small grains. Many oats are grown in the spring wheat region also.

The United States and Canada raise more than one-third of the oats of the world. Of this vast quantity the major part is consumed on the farms. Considerable quantities are shipped to the cities for feeding horses and to mills where rolled oats are prepared for human food. The large bulk and relatively low value of oats makes ocean shipment expensive, and only a small percentage of the crop enters into foreign commerce.

## Rice

THE PLANT AND ITS ENVIRONMENT.   Rice is a cereal that thrives in tropical and subtropical swamps and may be profitably grown only where abundant water can be provided. It is most important in southern and eastern Asia, where more than 95 per cent of the world's crop is raised. Of the small producers in other lands, most are inconspicuous, and only in Madagascar, Italy, and the United States is the amount significant. In the case of the United States it is rather the modern method by which rice is produced than the relative volume of the crop that is worthy of note.

PHYSICAL ENVIRONMENT FAVORABLE TO RICE.   The subtropical character of rice is reflected in the length of its growing season. Of the many varieties of rice some will mature in as little as 150 days, but in the principal rice regions of the United States the growing season is from 180 to 200 or more days. Temperature conditions, therefore, limit American rice culture to the region south of the Ohio River and to the Pacific Coast (Fig. 35).

More critical, however, than conditions of temperature is the requirement of rice for moisture. It demands swamp conditions, and during a considerable part of its growth it must be flooded, requiring a total of 45 to 65 inches of water during the period of growth. In the Orient this is supplied in large part by the abundant monsoon rains. In southern United States only about 20 inches of rain falls during the growth period, and from 25 to 30 inches additional must be supplied by irrigation. In the drier climate of California about 60 inches of irrigation water is required.

Level fields are essential to rice production. The flooded land must have a uniform depth of water from side to side, and at no time must it exceed 6 inches. In the Orient, hillsides are terraced to secure tiny level fields; but in America small fields are impracticable, since they are not adapted to the use of machinery, and their requirement for hand labor cannot be satisfied. The principal areas in the United States having the necessary conditions of climate and land surface are found on the borders of the Atlantic and Gulf Coastal Plains and in the valley of California. Here great areas of gently sloping land are divided into terraces by low embankments several feet wide and less than a foot high. The embankments, constructed on contour lines, enclose level areas of 1 to 100 acres and are so low that machinery is driven over them as if they did not exist (Fig. 26). Under such conditions gang plows, seeders,

Fig. 26.—A rice field on the Texas coastal plain, newly harvested and threshed. The low embankments of the terraces are clearly visible. In the background, a large herd of cattle grazes upon the volunteer rice already springing up on the moist soil.

and harvesters can be used as for wheat, and the cost of rice production is much reduced. The use of such machinery requires firm land, however, and for that reason the surface must have sufficient slope and the natural water courses must be sufficiently free to permit rapid and thorough drainage before harvest time. It is also necessary to keep the water on the fields in slow circulation to avoid stagnation during the growth of the crop.

Not all regions with proper surface and climate can compete in the rice industry, for suitable soil is also essential. If the subsoil is loose and permeable, the swamp condition cannot be maintained except by undue expense for irrigation water, which rapidly seeps away and is lost. Ideal conditions are found where a strong fertile soil is underlain by a stiff clay. Such a combination is most likely to be found on coastal plains and river alluvium where changing conditions of deposition have in the past put down in alternating layers clays, silts, and other types of material. Figure 27 shows the regions of the United States now producing rice. The coastal plain of the Carolinas was formerly most important in rice growing but has declined under the competition of the more extensive methods of the West.

American foreign trade in rice is small compared with that of Oriental countries. The American public does not consume rice in large quantities,

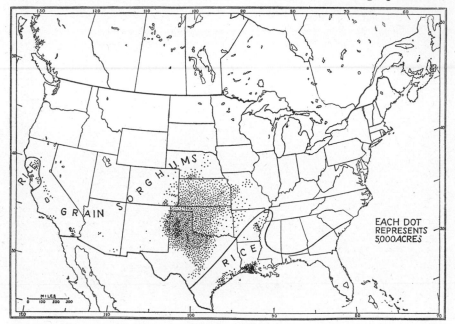

FIG. 27.—The grain sorghums are adapted to relatively dry regions while rice usually is grown on level irrigated flood-plains or delta lands.

and even the relatively small domestic crop is sufficient to provide an exportable surplus, Cuba being the largest buyer.

## Corn (Maize)

CORN DISTINCTIVELY AN AMERICAN CROP.  Corn was found under cultivation in South, Central, and North America by the European discoverers. In North America it existed in remarkable variety of forms and colors among the Indian tribes from Florida to Arizona on the south and from Maine to Montana on the north. It was introduced into Europe as "maize," the name by which it was known among the natives of the West Indies. In North America it was called "Indian corn," "corn" being the English term for grain of any sort.

Corn played an important part in the early settlement of America. In a new and forested country, cleared fields suitable for the cultivation of Old World grains were developed slowly. From the Indians the colonists learned to kill the trees by girdling, and they were able to obtain a crop of corn without further preparation of the land. With the continued development of American agriculture, corn has declined in relative importance as a direct source of human food. As a field crop it has, however, maintained first rank in quantity of grain produced and in the total value of its products. The United States grows about 50 per cent of all the corn of the world, and corn alone occupies about one-fourth of all the

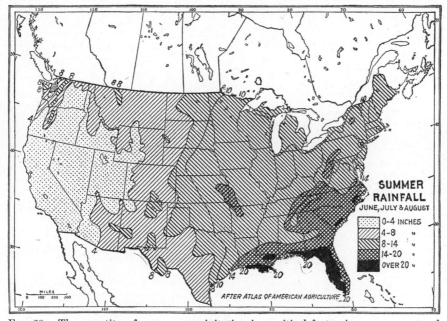

Fig. 28.—The quantity of summer precipitation is a critical factor in many aspects of agriculture.

cropped land and yields about the same proportion of the value of all crops in the country.

CORN CLIMATE. Corn is a warm-climate crop. Details regarding its origin and relationships are not known; and although it also is a grass, it is of a type different from the small grains. The corn plant is very sensitive to frost and cannot, like oats, be planted as soon as the snow has disappeared in the spring but must make its growth and reach maturity between the last frost in the spring and the first frost of the autumn. Some small varieties of corn, improved by selection, come to maturity in 80 to 90 days, and these are cultivated as far north as New England and southern Canada. Larger varieties may be grown there also for their forage and for ensilage but without assurance that the grain will mature. Toward the south, varieties of corn are grown that require increasing lengths of time for maturity with decreasing latitude. In the Gulf Coast states, 160 to 180 days is necessary. The ideal corn region must be bright and warm, warm both day and night. In this respect the slow-maturing southern varieties are more exacting than the early varieties.

Not only must the ideal corn climate be warm, but it must be relatively moist. The best corn lands have an average annual precipitation of 25 to 50 inches, of which at least 10 to 12 inches falls during the growing period of the three summer months (Fig. 28). This type of summer climate

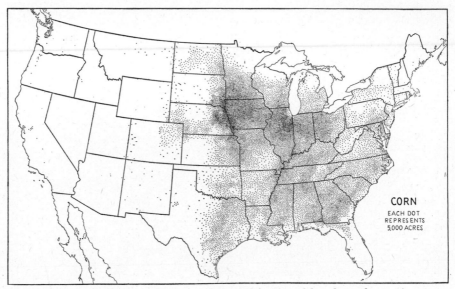

CORN

EACH DOT
REPRESENTS
5,000 ACRES

FIG. 29.—The corn belt extends from Ohio to Nebraska, although much corn is grown elsewhere.

is found in only a few localities in the intermediate zones. West-coast climates in the higher latitudes, such as those of England or the state of Washington, have not sufficiently high temperatures. Those with higher temperatures, such as Spain and California, have not, in most places, sufficient moisture.

CORN SOIL.    Corn is so widely cultivated in eastern North America that it is evident that it will grow on many different types of soil and a great diversity of surface conditions. It may not be assumed, however, that all soils are equally satisfactory when corn is grown as the main crop in an extensive farming system. The rapid growth of the plant and the great bulk of forage and grain produced require a large supply of readily available plant food, especially nitrogen. This is found in greatest perfection, together with the requisite climatic conditions, in the soils of old prairie-grass regions where generations of tall grass pushed their roots deep into a fine permeable loam, there to die and slowly decompose into humus. This provides the needed element and, together with lime, maintains in the soil a good structure and permeability to the plant roots.

THE AMERICAN CORN BELT (Fig. 29) is the most extensive region of the world having climatic and soil conditions peculiarly suited to corn. Though the winters are severely cold, the opposite extreme of summer brings almost tropical weather with rainfall of the thundershower type and plenty of sunshine. In addition the cultivation of corn in this region is favored by a gently undulating land surface and a widespread occurrence of fertile, dark-colored soils retentive of moisture and with high humus

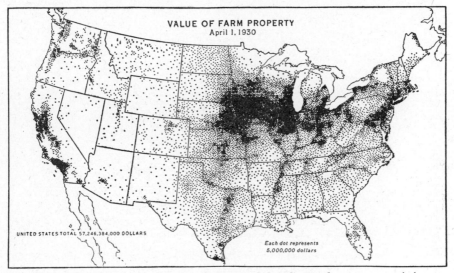

FIG. 30.—High value of farm property in the corn belt indicates the vast economic importance of that region. (*U.S. Department of Agriculture.*)

content (Fig. 19). Under such environment corn is a much more abundantly productive crop than wheat. The yield of grain per acre averages twice that of wheat, and the forage is worth at least half as much as the grain. Although it costs more per acre to produce corn than wheat, and although the farm value of wheat is more per bushel, larger gross returns enable corn to crowd out other cereals that compete with it for the use of the most suitable land and for the time of the farmer. Thus, there appears in North America a region in which corn is predominant. It includes the territory extending east and west between northeastern Nebraska and southern Ohio. Eight states included wholly or partly in this belt produce two-thirds of the American corn crop. In this region also is the largest area of highly valuable farm land in North America. It has a greater total value of farm property than any equal area of the continent and probably of the world (Fig. 30). The corn belt is bordered on the north and east by regions in which average summer temperatures lower than 68°F., and growing seasons of less than about 140 days enable the small grains and the grasses to compete more and more successfully with corn and finally to replace it altogether. On the west, decreasing summer rainfall permits wheat to compete with corn up to the line of 8 inches of summer rainfall. West of this line, corn is a minor crop. Even on the irrigated lands of the West, corn is not important. The hot, dry

Fig. 31.—Late autumn in an Iowa corn field. Hogs and cattle are used even more than sheep to harvest part of the corn crop with little human labor. (*U. S. Department of Agriculture.*)

winds of the arid lands interfere with the formation of the delicate corn silks and pollen grains; the cool nights interfere with the proper development of the stalk; and the yields obtained are generally too low to be profitable. In the humid South, corn is widely grown and of great importance. It is forced, however, to compete with cotton, which, owing to the shorter summers, cannot be grown in the corn-belt proper. Corn therefore assumes a secondary place in agriculture, although it outranks cotton in acreage in several southern states.

ECONOMIC FACTORS IN CORN PRODUCTION. The cropping system of the corn belt and the crops associated with corn have been noted previously. The reasons for these relationships are in large part economic. Corn is the dominant tilled crop, requiring much cultivation. So long as corn remains more profitable, there can be no effective competition from other crops requiring tillage at the same time, such as sugar beets or potatoes, which might be grown there. Oats, wheat, and hay do not offer that kind of competition. In the early days of corn production, as in the case of wheat, the labor involved was almost entirely manual. The invention of one machine after another has eliminated hand labor in practically every operation concerned. A large part of the total corn crop is not even harvested but is consumed in the fields by hogs, cattle, and sheep, still further reducing the labor costs (Fig. 31). Parts of the corn belt, although never densely populated, have suffered an actual decrease in rural population. Fewer men are needed because the level surface of the region makes the extensive use of machinery possible. Moreover, the substitution of tractors for horses on many corn-belt farms has had the effect of releasing a large total area of land that once produced feed for horses but is now available for the support of more cattle and swine.

THE USES OF CORN. Although corn is little used in America for direct human consumption, it is, nevertheless, a most important indirect source of human food. The protein content of corn is about two-thirds that of wheat, but it is of a type (*zëin*) that does not become sticky when wet. Corn meal and corn flour do not, therefore, produce light breads but are consumed in various other forms, most largely by the negro population of the South. It is estimated that about three-fourths of the average corn crop is fed to livestock on farms and that only near the principal industrial markets for corn is much of it sold from the county in which it is produced. The low protein content of the grain is counterbalanced by a very high starch and oil content. Corn is, therefore, an efficient fat-producing feed, and the corn belt is the greatest hog- and cattle-finishing ground in North America. The larger part of the corn crop moves to market in the concentrated form of pork and beef. A pound of pork represents the consumption of at least 5 pounds of corn, and a pound of beef represents 7 or more pounds of corn. In this concentrated form the corn, which on the western margin of the corn belt sometimes reaches the low price of 25 to 30 cents per bushel, can pay its transportation to market. The corn fodder, consisting of the stalks, leaves, and husks of the corn plant, also constitutes a valuable animal feed. In many regions a large part of the crop is chopped fine just as it comes to maturity and is preserved in silos. This furnishes a succulent feed during the winter and is especially valuable for dairy cows. The silo has somewhat extended the northward range of corn, for in case of early autumn frost the crop can be quickly placed in the silo before the value of the fodder is lost.

In central Illinois and the western part of the corn belt considerable quantities of corn are sold from the farm and find their way into industrial uses (Fig. 32). The industries that use corn as a raw material center upon the great corn markets Chicago and Omaha. In these factories the corn is treated to remove the germ, from which corn oil is extracted, and the starchy portion of the grain is made into a variety of products which include corn meal, starch, glucose, dextrin, alcohol, and numerous by-products. Supplies of superior corn, especially from Iowa, are sold in outside markets also to be used as seed for planting. The farmers of the South are large buyers. There is also some shipment of corn from North to South to be used as food, and a considerable movement of feed corn within the corn belt itself. It goes from localities or individual farmers who happen to have a surplus to others who have a temporary deficiency.

In addition to the many varieties of field corn, there is in North America an important production of popcorn and sweet corn. The latter

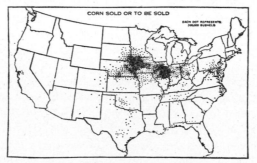

Fig. 32.—Two important regions in which a large part of the corn is sold from the farm. (*U.S. Department of Agriculture.*)

may be thought of as a vegetable and included under the head of truck farming.

FOREIGN EXPORTS OF NORTH AMERICAN CORN are very limited. The dent types of corn most cultivated have a high water content, and if closely confined in storage or shipped overseas they are subject to shrinkage and damage. The relatively low price of corn makes difficult the payment of the freight charges for long hauls. The foreign demand for American corn has in the past been small. Normal exports are less than 1 per cent of the crop.

IMPORTANT RELATIVES OF CORN. In parts of the United States are grown three main types of sorghums that yield (1) a small grain used as feed, (2) an edible molasses, and (3) a valuable brush used in the manufacture of brooms. The sorghums have much the same environmental requirements as corn except that some of them are more drought-resistant or mature in a shorter season so that they escape the disastrous effects of drought. This is particularly true of the grain sorghums, which, owing to their extensive root systems, their economical use of water, and the character of their flowers, are less harmed than corn by hot winds and low rainfall. This crop is finding an important place in the agriculture of the southern high plains beyond the moisture boundary of important corn cultivation and in the hot interior valleys of the Pacific slope (Fig. 27). The grain sorghums have been introduced from the semiarid lands of Africa and China where the seeds are eaten by native peoples.

## Hay and Forage Crops

THE DISTRIBUTION OF HAY AND FORAGE CROPS. Many crops, including grasses, legumes, and cereal grains, are (1) cut and dried for hay,

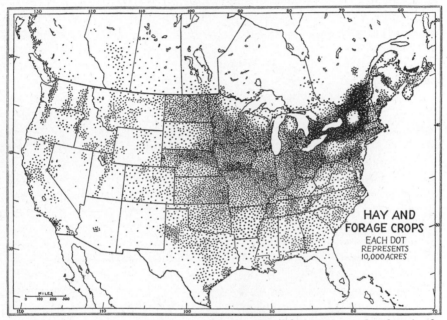

HAY AND FORAGE CROPS
EACH DOT REPRESENTS 10,000 ACRES

FIG. 33.—Hay and forage crops are widely distributed but are most abundant in the cooler and more humid northeastern regions.

(2) cut and fed green as soiling crops, (3) cut and put up as silage, or (4) used for pasture. They make up the bulk or rough feed used to balance a diet of concentrated grains. The more important in the United States are timothy, clovers, native wild prairie grasses, and alfalfa. Among them there is wide variation in adaptability to different climatic and soil conditions. It will be seen from Fig. 33 that nearly all parts of the country are provided with crops that serve some one or more of these purposes. The combined acreage of all hay crops is greater than that of the corn crop or of any other crop grown in the United States. It is equally clear that the northeastern one-fourth of the country, which includes the corn and dairy regions, is also most important in the production of hay and forage.

HAY CROPS IN THE WEST.   In the West the small acreage of hay and forage is due to the fact that only limited areas have the necessary water for the abundant production of these crops; yet in most of the West they are the leading agricultural crops. Alfalfa is a highly productive hay crop on irrigated land. In some of the irrigated districts more alfalfa hay is raised than is required for local use, and large quantities of it are baled and shipped to eastern markets. In others few if any livestock are raised, but large numbers are purchased and fed over winter on the alfalfa and supplementary irrigated crops.

On the western dry lands some hay is produced by raising quick-growing grain crops, such as barley or oats, and cutting them for drying in the green stage. Most of the winter forage on western dry ranches is, however, native grasses and other plants used as pasture. Over the larger part of the area, grasses do not grow to sufficient height or density to repay the labor of cutting for hay. On the other hand, the small winter rainfall and low humidity permit them to retain most of the nutritive value, which, in the more humid East, would be leached away. They stand practically as natural hay, cured on the ground, and yield satisfactory winter forage in spite of cold weather and occasional snows.

HAY CROPS IN THE SOUTH.   Hay is not an important crop in the South for several reasons. (1) The hay grasses of the North do not do well in the cotton belt. Active soil erosion on the better lands and light, droughty soil on the poorer make it difficult to start the crops, and high summer temperatures cause them to die out. (2) The cropping system of the South is based upon cotton and corn, and neither this system nor the type of labor employed is readily adapted to hay production. (3) The heat and humidity of the summers and the frequent rains make the curing of hay difficult. (4) The small development of the livestock industries has not in the past made a large demand for hay. A change in the last-named condition is in progress; the production of hay is increasing; and new grasses and legumes are being introduced in the hope of securing hay crops that may be more generally satisfactory under southern conditions.

HAY CROPS IN THE CORN BELT.   Next to corn and oats, hay is the most important crop of the corn region. It occupies about one-sixth of the land devoted to all harvested crops. The conditions of climate and soil in the corn belt permit the growth of several of the various crops used for hay, although the intense summer heat and short periods of drought sometimes cause serious damage. For economic reasons, however, hay is grown on practically every farm in the region. (1) Hay is needed as a bulk feed, in conjunction with corn and oats in raising and fattening cattle and sheep and in the maintenance of farm horses. It is bulky and must be grown at home. (2) Hay fits well into the crop rotations of the farmer. (3) Hay, especially clover and alfalfa, is important in keeping up the fertility of the soil.

HAY CROPS IN THE NORTH AND EAST. In the Great Lakes region and New England several factors combine to make hay an important crop. In Wisconsin it occupies nearly 40 per cent of the land that is in harvested crops, in New York nearly 60 per cent, and in Vermont more than 80 per cent. Hay also holds first rank as a crop in all of the eastern provinces of Canada. (1) The cooler summers with fairly well-distributed rainfall and frequent periods of summer sunshine are ideal for the growing and curing of the hay crops but are rather cool for corn. Heavy winter snows diminish the damage to hay crops that in other regions sometimes results from freezing and thawing and winter soil erosion. (2) This is the region of most recent glaciation, and there are areas of rough or stony glacial soils and of glacial marshlands better suited to hay than to grain crops. (3) In the eastern part of the region especially, there is much hilly land that is unsuited to tillage but from which hay can be harvested. (4) Large quantities of hay are required for the dairy industry of this region.

PASTURE LAND is in part identical with hay land, for hayfields frequently are pastured. Large total areas are, however, used for pasture alone. Many farms include stony or ill-drained areas, steep hillsides, or woodlands that are pastured continuously. The total area of farm land pastured in the United States is about 50 per cent greater than the area of lands harvested for hay. In addition there are still larger amounts of mountain, forest, and dry-land pastures that are not included in farms. Most of these are in the West. The capacity of pasture land to feed animals (shown in Fig. 12) is clearly a composite expression of the relative advantages and disadvantages of regional conditions of climate, land surface, and soil. Whether or not tillable land remains in use as pasture depends largely upon the prices of animal products compared with those of other things that the land might produce.

SELECTED REFERENCES

BAKER, O. E. The Potential Supply of Wheat, *Econ. Geog.*, Vol. 1 (1925), pp. 15–52.
———. The Agricultural Regions of the United States, *Econ. Geog.*, Vol. 3, pp. 327–339, 447–465; Vol. 4, pp. 399–433; Vol. 9, pp. 167–197.
BENNETT, M. K., and H. C. FARNSWORTH. World Wheat Acreage, Yields, and Climate. *Wheat Studies*, Food Research Institute, Stanford University, Vol. 13 (1937).
CARR, G. J. International Marketing of Surplus Wheat, *Trade Promotion Series* 130, Washington, D.C., 1932.
JASNY, N. "Competition among Grains," Stanford University, 1940.
HURD, W. B., and T. W. GRINDLEY. "Agriculture, Climate, and Population of the Prairie Provinces of Canada," Dominion Bureau of Statistics, Ottawa, 1931.
POST, L. C. The Rice Country of Southwestern Louisiana, *Geog. Rev.*, Vol. 30 (1940), pp. 574–590.
ROTERUS, VICTOR. Spring and Winter Wheat on the Columbia Plateau, *Econ. Geog.*, Vol. 10 (1934), pp. 368–373.
STRONG, HELEN M. Export Wheat Producing Regions, *Econ. Geog.*, Vol. 8 (1932), pp. 161–190.
ZIMMERMANN, ERICH W. "World Resources and Industries," pp. 228–257, New York, 1933.

# Chapter IV. Vegetable Crops

THE IMPORTANCE OF VEGETABLES AS FOOD. Under the familiar term "vegetables," custom includes a variety of items. Botanically the list includes various plant parts: roots, stems, leaves, fruits, and seeds. The vegetables most cultivated in America are, in the order of their acreage, potatoes, tomatoes, peas, sweet corn, green beans, watermelons, cabbage, lettuce, cucumbers, cantaloupes, asparagus, spinach, and onions. The land devoted to the raising of these crops ranges normally from 500,000 down to 100,000 acres each, and there are others, such as carrots and celery, that use more than 25,000 acres each.

Many millions of the world's people subsist almost entirely on a plant diet by combining cereals, legumes, and green vegetables. In some of the newer countries of the world, where meat is abundant, vegetables have occupied a relatively unimportant place in the popular diet, but the garden has always contributed a great deal to the food supply of people in the United States. A commercial vegetable industry, however, is of comparatively recent origin, for its development awaited (1) the invention of efficient methods of transporting perishable goods, (2) the growth of large city populations willing to pay for fresh vegetables at all seasons, (3) an increase in the cost of meat, and (4) the perfection of modern processes of commercial canning of vegetables for out-of-season use.

The total food available in a ton of green vegetables is not great in comparison with that in an equal weight of cereals or of meat; for example, more than 60 per cent of the substance of white potatoes is water; of cabbage, 90 per cent is water. Notwithstanding this fact, vegetables are important foodstuffs. The root, leaf, and stem crops usually contain quantities of starch or sugar together with mineral substances. In addition there is a high proportion of indigestible cellulose which serves to give bulk to the diet. Vegetables are also rich in vitamins, which are essential to health. The legumes, particularly dried peas, beans, and peanuts, contain from 20 to 25 per cent of proteins or nitrogenous materials, some of which they obtain from the air through the agency of bacteria on their roots. These seeds furnish substitutes for the more expensive proteins of a meat diet in countries where the standard of living is low.

TYPES OF VEGETABLE FARMING. The vegetable crops are so many and so different that it is impossible to state any general conditions of climate and soil that are suitable for them all. We find, rather, that economic conditions assume the place of first importance in determining the location of vegetable growing on a commercial scale and that conditions of physical environment are, in most instances, secondary.

Vegetables are raised under three systems of farming: (1) home gardening, (2) market gardening, and (3) truck farming.

THE HOME GARDEN is a form of agriculture so well known as to need little comment; its importance may not, however, be so generally appreciated. It is estimated that 80 per cent of the vegetables eaten by the farmers of the United States are raised at home, and a government survey has shown that vegetables for home use constitute nearly 12 per cent of the value of all food eaten on farms. When we add to this the unknown value of the produce from thousands of gardens in villages and cities, we see that home gardening is a very important phase of vegetable growing.

MARKET GARDENING is the growing of vegetables and small fruits for sale. From the preceding paragraph it will be realized that the great market for the sale of vegetables generally is neither on the farms nor in country villages, where kitchen gardens supply most of the need. The great market is the city; the larger the city the larger the market. Here are thousands or even millions of people with neither time nor land for gardening. In general, also, city dwellers receive larger cash incomes than farmers and hence are able to pay for the service of raising and delivering their vegetables.

Because of the city markets there is a tendency for market gardening to concentrate in the neighborhood of great cities (Fig. 34). This results from the fact that a short haul to market enables the gardener (1) to sell his produce fresh from the field and (2) to reduce transportation and packing charges on a product that is bulky in proportion to its value. Location near the city has also other advantages. Market gardening is an intensive form of agriculture, and, in proportion to the amount of land used, expenditures for labor and fertilizers usually are large. Close to a city, a fluctuating demand for labor by the market gardener is much more easily supplied than it is in rural districts. For these various reasons important centers of market gardening are found in the western end of Lond Island, in New Jersey close to New York and Philadelphia, and in the immediate surroundings of Boston, Buffalo, Pittsburgh, Cincinnati, Detroit, Chicago, and St. Louis. The smaller cities support market gardens that are, as a rule, approximately proportionate to their size. Formerly the areas from which fresh garden produce could be sold on city markets was limited to the distance of 3 or 4 hours of haul by team and wagon. Motor transport over modern highways permits a much longer haul in the same length of time. The area of urban market gardening is thus greatly increased and may include land so far beyond the city influence as to be much lower in price. In spite of this change, it is surprising to see the extent to which market gardening still flourishes on the suburban margins of great cities like Boston or Chicago.

GARDENS UNDER GLASS.    In the short-summer continental climate of northern United States, frost limits the out-of-door production of

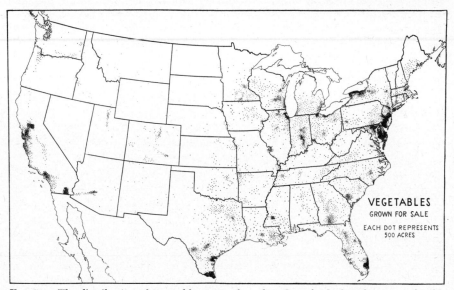

VEGETABLES
GROWN FOR SALE

EACH DOT REPRESENTS
500 ACRES

FIG. 34.—The distribution of vegetables grown for sale reflects both the advantage of mild winters in the South and West and of closeness to city markets in the Northeast.

vegetables and flowers to a season of 5 or 6 months. To overcome this climatic handicap nearly 4,000 acres of glasshouses are in use in the United States. This is a particularly intensive form of market gardening; one crop follows another in rapid succession on the highly fertilized soil. The industry requires not only the large expenditures for land, labor, and fertilizers characteristic of ordinary market gardening but large additional expense for the glasshouses and for fuel. These large expenses are offset by ability to place fresh flowers and vegetables on the winter market at high prices. Glasshouse gardening, like ordinary market gardening, tends to concentrate near the large cities that are its markets. The additional costs of the glass, steel, and fuel have, however, induced this industry to migrate somewhat to the locality where these elements are cheapest. We find, therefore, that the region south of Lake Erie has unusually large areas devoted to this type of horticulture. This is made possible only by fairly large local markets and by highly efficient railway service into the still greater market centers both east and west.

TRUCK FARMING AND MARKET GARDENING CONTRASTED. Truck farming is also the raising of vegetables for sale, and it differs from market gardening only in matters of detail. Truck crops and market gardens in the United States occupy less than 4 million acres, an area equal only to the corn acreage of Ohio, from which it differs, however, in that it is much more intensively cultivated, requires vastly more capital and labor, and yields much larger gross returns. Truck-farming regions are often located at considerable distances from their markets, with which, however, they must be connected by efficient transportation. The development of such truck-farming sections is encouraged by special advantages of climate and soil rather than by closeness to markets. Not infrequently the truck farmer is more of a specialist than the market gardener, and he may confine his efforts to a small number of the common vegetable crops, such, for example, as lettuce or spinach.

AMERICAN TRUCK-FARMING REGIONS. The primary consideration in the establishment of a truck farm is transportation to markets. Before the days of improved transportation, near-by market gardens supplied the only fresh vegetables obtainable in city markets. With the advent of improved railway facilities, several regions rose into prominence because of special advantages of climate and soil, and first among these was the Chesapeake Bay region. This part of the Atlantic Coastal Plain, extending from southern New Jersey to Norfolk, Va., is still the great vegetable garden of America. In the early days of the industry shipments were made by oyster boats, and only the nearer markets of Baltimore and Philadelphia were reached. It was not until about 1890 that the development of refrigerator cars and of forced ventilation on boats enabled the trucking industry to expand greatly both in importance and in area.

The favorable climate and soil possessed by the Chesapeake Bay region are shared in some degree by much of the Atlantic and Gulf Coastal Plain, whose great climatic advantage is earliness of season. The indented coast of the Chesapeake and Delaware region gives its climate a marine character which serves to stabilize temperatures and to lengthen the growing season. The length of the frostless season at Trenton, N. J., averages 170 days; a little farther south on the shores of Delaware Bay it is from 20 to 30 days longer. At Norfolk, Va., the season is 225 days, the same as at Augusta, Ga., which is 250 miles farther south but not so near the coast. At Wilmington, N. C., the season averages 230 days; at Charleston, S. C., 260 days; and in Florida and parts of the Gulf Coast frost occurs only a very few times during the winter (Fig. 35). Norfolk is the most northerly point at which even such hardy crops as spinach and kale can be grown in the open throughout the winter.

Some of the soils of the Coastal Plain are admirable for vegetable production. The sands and sandy loams of the Norfolk and Coxville series are of the best. These are in general light, warm, well-drained soils capable of being worked very early in the spring, but they are deficient in nitrogen. For this reason the eastern truck-growing regions purchase large quantities of commercial fertilizers (Fig. 145). The truck soils of the Atlantic Plain are widespread, and only a small part (probably less than 1 per cent) is used for vegetable growing.

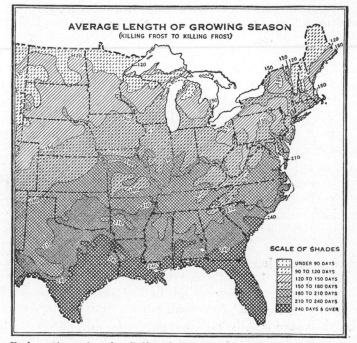

Fig. 35.—Early springs give the Gulf and Atlantic Coasts an advantage in vegetable growing. (*U.S. Department of Agriculture.*)

CLIMATE AND COMPETITION. In truck farming the early crop secures the best price, and this price may be sufficient to pay both a profit to the producer and the cost of transportation over many hundreds of miles. In North America the regions best suited to very early vegetable production are those with the least frost, such as southern Florida, the Gulf Coast, the Rio Grande Valley of Texas, and southern and central California. In these regions the hardier vegetables may be planted in the autumn and are ready for market in the early winter. Less resistant crops are planted at about the time of coldest weather and are marketed many weeks in advance of the same crops grown in the northern states. On the Atlantic Coast a complete succession of harvest dates is secured, beginning in southern Florida and continuing up the coast to New Jersey (Fig. 36). After the season of the New York crop is past, fresh vegetables are shipped south from New England and Canada. Some of them actually go to the city markets of the South. These crops continue to arrive until the approach of cold weather, and soon thereafter Florida, Texas, and California are again ready to continue the almost uninterrupted cycle.

In this competition, cost of transportation is so large a factor that crops from regions nearer the great markets replace those from the more distant regions as soon as the former are ready for market. It follows that

FIG. 36.—Celery fields in Florida, surrounded by pine woods and provided with a great icing plant and refrigeration car service to the northern markets.

any delay in marketing from the distant areas may render the crop unsalable. The business is a hazardous one at best. Competition by growers who raise vegetables under glass near the market is not restrictive because of the greater cost of this type of business. The southern truck farmer has vastly cheaper land and also cheaper labor.

THE TRANSPORTATION AND MARKETING OF TRUCK CROPS. A market for truck crops is found in every city in the country, and the system of distribution is well organized. An indication of its great volume may be had from the fact that the annual supply of lettuce alone to New York City is nearly 7,000 carloads. The United States government furnishes a crop- and market-reporting service which enables truck farmers to watch developments in competing regions. The Texas onion grower may know the amount of northern-grown onions in storage and the rate at which they are being marketed. The grower of hothouse lettuce in New York may watch the effects of a freeze on early lettuce in Florida and control his crop to take advantage of the shortage to come. This sort of information helps to prevent the oversupply of markets and aids in a steadying of prices which is to the benefit of the industry.

Although rail transportation is the main dependence of the southern truck farmers, large supplies of vegetables from the coastal districts also move north by motor truck and even by boat. Baltimore, because of its location near the head of Chesapeake Bay, is an important terminus for this traffic. In addition to the wholesale markets of the city, there is a large forwarding trade in vegetables and fruits destined for eastern and northern cities. Cincinnati and St. Louis serve in similar capacity for the markets of the Middle West. The ability of the rich eastern market to absorb early truck crops at high prices has induced the vegetable growers of the Bermuda and Bahama Islands and of the west coast of Mexico to compete with the United States growers, and for this traffic special shipping services are maintained.

VEGETABLE SUPPLY CROPS. The competition for the early northern market is the spectacular phase of the trucking industry, yet the total quantity of these early southern vegetables is not so great as that raised nearer the market, that which constitutes the main supply crop. The supply crops tend to migrate to such localities as are easily accessible to market and have, at the same time, some special advantage in quality of soil or in climate. For example, the early crop of onions is raised in Texas and Louisiana, but the later crops of New York, Ohio, Massachusetts, and other eastern states total a much greater amount. Quantities of early cabbage are shipped from Texas, Louisiana, and California, but the main crop is raised in New York, New Jersey, and Wisconsin. Florida leads in the growing of green beans as a winter crop, but New York, New Jersey, and Maryland together produce a larger quantity later in the season.

VEGETABLES FOR CANNING AND FREEZING. Certain vegetables, such as tomatoes, peas, and sweet corn, have a relatively short season of growth in the North and are perishable and expensive as out-of-season crops shipped from the South. Early tomatoes are shipped from California, Florida, the Bahama Islands, and Mexico, but at a high price, and the same is true of the winter supply of green peas which are grown mainly in California. To utilize these short-season vegetables and others a canning industry has developed in many localities, particularly in northeastern United States. The commercial canning of vegetables has several advantages. It greatly increases the quantity of these valuable foods consumed by the average person by making them available throughout the year and in regions where they could not possibly be grown. It permits these crops to be grown in climates and soils best suited to them regardless of an immediate market. It also provides a profitable outlet for what would be an unmarketable surplus in years of abundance.

The most important of all vegetable-canning regions is that adjacent to Baltimore, where tomatoes, sweet corn, peas, and asparagus are grown in large quantities. The canning of peas reaches its greatest importance, however, in Wisconsin and New York, where the cooler spring weather favors the growth of this hardy crop. Sweet corn is most abundant a little farther south, the center of its zone extending from Iowa to New Jersey. Tomatoes occupy a still more southerly latitude, the principal centers of the canning industry being southwestern Missouri, central Indiana, Maryland, and Virginia. The canning industry of California and the northern Pacific Coast region includes some vegetables as well as fruits, the most important being asparagus, which thrives in the delta region near San Francisco Bay.

In recent years the quick-freezing process has been applied to the preservation of vegetables as well as fruits, fish, and meats. By this means the same end is accomplished as in canning. Food is preserved in regions and seasons of abundance and generally with less alteration of taste and appearance than by the canning process. It is applicable to such vegetables as green peas, spinach, and broccoli but not to others, such as tomatoes. The difficulty of maintaining the low temperatures during transportation and marketing has been overcome but at considerable expense. The industry caters as yet only to the luxury trade.

## The Potato in America

POTATOES AMERICAN IN ORIGIN BUT EUROPEAN BY ADOPTION. The white potato is the most widely grown vegetable in North America. It is raised in Alaska, in every settled province of Canada, and in every state of the United States. Notwithstanding this fact, it may be said that the potato is not ideally suited to the climate of the major part of the continent. The white potato originated in the high, cool plateau lands of the Andes, where primitive varieties of the plant still are cultivated. It was introduced into North America and into Europe at about the same time but has found in Europe a habitat so much more congenial that the total crop of that continent averages more than ten times that of North America. The average yield of potatoes in the United States is about 110 bushels per acre; in Germany, 200 bushels. The average American eats about 2.5 bushels of potatoes per year. In Germany the average is more than 7 bushels. The difference in production may be attributed both to conditions of soil and climate and to contrasts in crop possibilities and general agricultural economy.

CLIMATE AND SOIL FOR POTATO CULTURE. Potatoes need cool, moist, uniform weather and are frequently injured when forced to mature in the erratic temperatures and often dry weather of American summers. For this reason, especially in the South, early and late crops are grown, the one maturing before, and the other after, the period of greatest heat. For the same reason, early planting in the corn belt is a distinct advantage. Heat-resistant varieties are known, but they are of indifferent table quality. The moisture requirement of potatoes is high, and rainfall is particularly essential when the tubers are forming. Erratic rainfall of the American summer thundershower type may be the cause of large yields one year and widespread failure the next. The influence of these conditions upon potato prices is shown in Fig. 37.

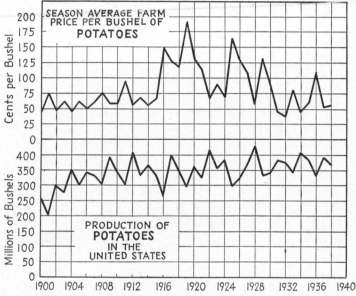

Fig. 37.—A small potato crop in the United States usually brings a high price, which, in turn, usually results in a large crop and a low price the year following.

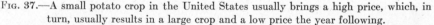

Soils best suited to commercial potato culture are loose in texture, permitting drainage, the development of strong roots, and uniform expansion of the growing tubers. These requirements are frequently met by sandy or gravelly glacial outwash deposits and by the acid peat soils of glacial marshlands. There are extensive areas of these types of land in the northeastern states, the Great Lakes region, and southern Canada. Potatoes for home use are grown in almost any type of soil.

CENTERS OF AMERICAN POTATO GROWING. The American potato crop has a general distribution somewhat like that of the human population. This is due in part to the bulkiness and usual low value of the potatoes which require that the main crop be raised near its market. The industry may, however, be divided into two types: (1) early potato raising and (2) the production of the supply crop. Like other early vegetables, early potatoes are raised in the South. In southern Florida, planting begins before Christmas, and the crop is ready to harvest by the end of March. The coast zone, from Florida to Texas, is followed in order by one zone after another until the early crop of Virginia, Kentucky, and Missouri merges with that of the northern states about July 1. Most of the early potatoes of the South are raised from vigorous seed shipped from the cooler northern states. Los Angeles and Stockton, Calif.,

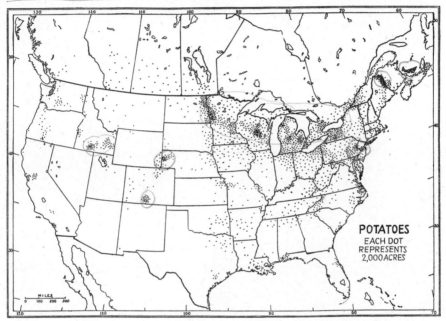

POTATOES
EACH DOT
REPRESENTS
2,000 ACRES

FIG. 38.—The principal potato-growing centers of the United States and Canada.

are also early potato-raising districts. The main supply crop shows several areas of special concentration (Fig. 38). These are (1) Prince Edward Island, Canada; (2) Aroostook County, Maine; (3) southeastern Pennsylvania, central and southern New Jersey, and the Chesapeake region; (4) a long and nearly continuous belt extending from Quebec through central New York, Ontario, and northern Ohio, lower Michigan, central Wisconsin, and Minnesota into the valley of the Red River of the North; (5) the irrigated districts of the West, among which are especially to be noted those of Nebraska, Colorado, and the Snake River Valley, Idaho. It will be observed that all these regions are on or beyond the margin of the corn belt, where they find unfavorable conditions of soil and climate and must compete with corn for the time and labor of the farmer. Several of the districts also are in regions of light, sandy, or sandy-loam soils. These soils are found particularly in Maine, New Jersey, western Michigan, central Wisconsin, and eastern Minnesota. Of all these regions northeastern Maine has the most favorable conditions, the most intensive industry, and the highest yields. About 275 bushels per acre is the average yield in Maine, whereas under the higher average summer temperature and in the heavier soils of Illinois the average is about 70 bushels per acre. Aroostook County ships annually more than 40,000 carloads of potatoes. In only a few other counties of the commercial potato regions do shipments exceed 5,000 cars, and in most of them it is less than 1,000 cars per county.

The principal crop of potatoes does not move far to its market. Maine, New York, and the New Jersey region supply the large eastern centers of population. Potatoes from the producing districts of Michigan, Wisconsin, and Minnesota move principally southward to supply the markets of the towns and cities of the lower Great Lakes industrial region and the Ohio and Missouri valleys. Conspicuous exception to this general condition may be noted in the case of potatoes from the western irrigated districts of Colorado and Idaho, which move eastward to market. This is particularly true of Idaho potatoes, which have attained a favorable reputation for quality. Although the Idaho producing district is far removed from any great urban markets, its crop about equals that of New York or Michigan. Specially graded and packed, Idaho potatoes have practically a national market.

## The Sweet Potato

Sweet potatoes are not tubers but are the fleshy roots of a tropical plant. Unlike white potatoes, they thrive in the heat and humidity of the long southern summers. They are commonly grown throughout the South and as far north as New Jersey and Iowa, but Georgia and the Gulf Coast states are the leading producers.

## Beans

The production of dry edible beans in the United States and Canada averages about 10 pounds per capita of the population of the two countries, and imports are somewhat in excess of exports. They constitute an important crop because of their high protein content and their use as a meat substitute. Although the crop includes beans of several kinds, there are still many other varieties not used for food in Anglo-America that are used for that purpose in other regions, particularly the Orient, where meat is less abundant. A much greater use of beans in the American diet is not likely so long as meat remains so plentiful that the average consumer can afford it.

Beans are, in general, adapted to mild, moderately moist climates and are troubled by insect and fungus pests in warm, humid regions. Some varieties, such as the white beans most common in America, mature in a short season and can be grown north of the corn belt, avoiding heat and humidity. The principal edible bean-growing regions include (1) central Michigan, southern Ontario and Quebec, and western New York and (2) the western irrigated bean regions, especially California, Idaho, and Colorado (Fig. 39).

Lima beans are of tropical origin and require a long season with uniform temperature and moderate rainfall. Practically the entire American commercial crop of dry lima beans is raised on the coastal margin of

## FIELD BEANS AND PEANUTS
### Principal Producing States

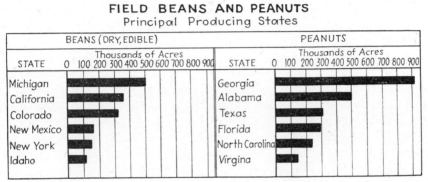

Fig. 39.—The states of the United States which specialize in beans and peanuts.

southern California, where summer rainfall is light or lacking but the air is cool and moist and there are frequent fogs.

## Soybeans

The soybean is a relatively new crop in America. It is native to the Orient, where it is used as food both directly and in a variety of other forms obtained as by-products of its processing for the extraction of oil. It is particularly adapted to the warm summers and heavy soils of the American corn and livestock regions. It was introduced primarily as a soil-improving legume and for its value as a hay and forage crop. It is still widely grown for those purposes alone. Increasingly, however, it is being raised for its crop of beans, which yield oil valuable in the manufacture of paints, soap, cooking fats, and many other products (Chap. VI). In addition, the cake resulting from the removal of the oil is a versatile raw material. It yields animal feeds, fertilizer, glue, and a variety of other products, including substances from which molded plastics, such as automobile fittings, may be made. The corn-belt states and North Carolina are the principal areas producing the beans, and the acreage devoted to that purpose has quadrupled in a decade.

## Peanuts

Another edible legume that has great industrial importance is the peanut. This is due largely to its value as a source of oil, yet the peanut is much more used as human food than formerly when it was sold only by street venders or at fruit stands. In addition to their valuable oil the seeds contain 24 per cent of protein and, in the form of peanut butter and of confections, are becoming a common food. The cakes from the oil mills are important stock feed; so also are the vines when made into hay. The whole plant is sometimes eaten by swine turned into the field to fatten.

The peanut is of tropical origin, and in America its production is confined almost entirely to the Atlantic and Gulf Coastal Plains where the light soils and long summers of the trucking regions furnish suitable conditions for the development of the underground pods (Fig. 39). Although the United States crop of peanuts increased greatly in the early decades of the present century when its value as a source of oil was appreciated, it has recently remained at a nearly uniform level. The uses to which the plant and its products may be put are not so numerous as those of the soybean, and the area to which it is adapted is much more restricted.

SELECTED REFERENCES

BAKER, O. E. Agricultural Regions of North America: Part VII, The Middle Atlantic Trucking Region, *Econ. Geog.*, Vol. 5 (1929), pp. 36–69.

CARLSON, ALBERT S., and JOHN WESTON. The Sweet Corn Industry of Maine, *Econ. Geog.*, Vol. 10 (1934), pp. 382–394.

Fruits and Vegetables. A series of articles in *U.S. Dept. Agr. Yearbook*, 1925.

HUDGINS, BERT. Bean Production in Michigan, *Econ. Geog.*, Vol. 9 (1933), pp. 265–272.

JONES, H. A., and S. L. EMSWELLER. "The Vegetable Industry," New York, 1931.

WANN, J. L. Where Florida Truck Crops Are Grown, *Econ. Geog.*, Vol. 9 (1933), pp. 85–103.

WILSON, E. M. The Aroostook Valley: A Study in Potatoes, *Geog. Rev.*, Vol. 16 (1926), pp. 196–205.

# Chapter V. Fruit Crops

GEOGRAPHIC BACKGROUND OF FRUIT CULTURE. Fruit culture, like vegetable raising, is a complicated industry, involving a wide variety of products which require unlike conditions of natural environment. The success of any phase of the fruit industry depends even more upon biologic and economic conditions than upon those of physical environment. These matters are of primary concern to the horticulturist. The student of geography, however, can find many interesting relations to land-surface features, climate, soil, and geographic position with respect to markets, in the distribution of the fruit-producing regions, their particular characteristics, and the ways in which their crops are marketed.

## Apples

AMERICA'S MOST IMPORTANT FRUIT. The apple is by far the most important fruit crop of North America in terms of land area occupied and in volume and value of products. Yet, compared with the staple field crops, its place in American agriculture is relatively small. The average apple crop of the United States and Canada is nearly 200 million bushels, of which only about one-half to two-thirds may be called the "commercial" crop. Nearly half of all the apples—the produce of scattered and often poorly tended orchards—are consumed on the farms on which they are grown and in the near-by villages or are turned into by-products or go to waste. On the contrary, the commercial crop is grown mainly in scientifically managed orchards, most of which are included in the several great orchard regions shown in Fig. 40. This specialized form of apple raising has increased greatly at the expense of the old-time farm orchard, which no longer is a very large factor in the commercial apple industry.

FAVORABLE CLIMATIC AND SOIL CONDITIONS FOR APPLE GROWING are so widespread in North America that the area of suitable land is vastly greater than is needed to supply all the apples required. Commercial apple growing has therefore prospered in districts that are in some way especially favored or for which special markets have been created by human enterprise. Among the numerous varieties of apples there are various degrees of hardiness; in general, however, the northern limit of the apple belt is determined by an average winter temperature of 13°F. This boundary includes most of the maritime provinces of Canada and southern Maine. From there the boundary crosses Quebec and Ontario to Sault Sainte Marie and continues westward through Wisconsin and Minnesota. On the west the production of apples without irrigation does

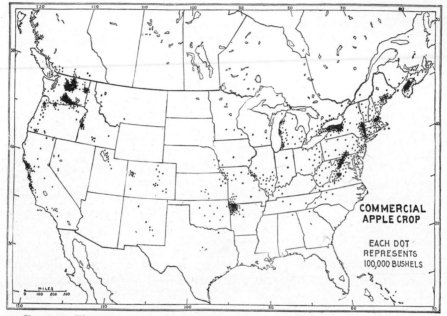

FIG. 40.—The commercial apple crop of the United States and Canada is restricted to rather well-defined regions. The noncommercial crop is much more uniformly distributed.

not extend much beyond the line of 18 inches of annual rainfall. Although the failure of apples beyond this line is due mainly to lack of rainfall, it is also due to frequent cold, dry winds in winter, unseasonable frosts, and occasional hailstorms. In the Cordilleran region of the West most of the apples are raised under irrigation. The southern margin of the apple belt is determined by summer heat and humidity and roughly coincides with the average summer temperature line of 79°F.

Apples are successfully grown on a variety of soils. They require only moderately porous soils of free underdrainage.

THE NORTHEASTERN APPLE DISTRICTS. In the maritime provinces of Canada and in New England are four or five apple-growing districts of which the more important are the Annapolis-Cornwallis Valley of Nova Scotia; the New England Baldwin belt, which extends from Maine to

Connecticut; and the Hudson River Valley. Unlike the newer commercial orchards of the West, many of these are small orchards on farms, most of which have other sources of income, such as dairying or poultry raising.

The famous orchards of the Annapolis-Cornwallis Valley occupy a particularly favored spot. The peninsular character of the province affords the protection of a marine climate. The valley is broad and open, about 80 miles long and 4 to 12 miles in width. The orchards lie on the well-drained slopes of the valley, protected by a low mountain range from

Fig. 41.—The scattered apple orchards and intermingled hay and oats fields typical of the Annapolis-Cornwallis Valley of Nova Scotia. View taken from the crest of North Mountain, the sheltering ridge, near Wolfville, N. S. Compare with Fig. 42 for contrast in intensity of apple culture.

the continental winds that may sweep across the Bay of Fundy (Fig. 41). Since the valley usually markets a large part of its apples in England, its location, although somewhat isolated from the rest of North America, brings it, in fact, nearer its market. The New England orchards occupy, in part, rough lands and relatively thin granitic soils or stony glacial deposits and are not so productive as some of the larger and better situated orchards of the West. The predominance of the hardy Baldwin apples in this region gives the name to the largest district. The crop is marketed principally in New England and New York.

THE ORCHARDS OF THE APPALACHIANS extend from Pennsylvania to northeastern Georgia. This belt includes several adjacent districts, such as (1) the Shenandoah-Cumberland Valley region and (2) the Piedmont Region, which extends along the eastern front of the Blue Ridge of Virginia and more or less continuously through the Carolinas into Georgia. Although there are many old orchards in the Appalachian region, others are newer and more productive than those of New England. In addition to the hardy varieties of the North, these southern orchards grow some varieties less resistant to cold. Nearly one-half the apples produced in this region come from its northern portion, the Shenandoah-Cumberland valleys of Virginia and Maryland.

ORCHARDS NEAR THE GREAT LAKES. The Great Lakes serve in some degree as regulators of temperature and moisture on their leeward shores. In the spring, cold winds from the lakes slightly retard the blooming of the fruit until the season is sufficiently advanced so that disastrous frost is not so likely to occur; in the autumn the heat radiated from the lakes tends to delay the occurrence of frost. In the winter the lake influence somewhat moderates both the temperature and the dryness of the westerly winds. These conditions permit fruit to be grown in a latitude that is generally unsuitable in the central plains states. Two principal centers of commercial apple culture have been established in this region. They are (1) western New York, the Niagara Peninsula of Ontario, and the north shore of Lake Ontario and (2) the fruit belt of western Michigan.

Western New York was once the most important United States apple region. The commercial orchards of this district are mainly on the glacial lake plain, and they border the lake in a more or less continuous belt about 10 miles wide for a distance of 125 miles eastward from Niagara Falls. The apple industry of this section of New York is interesting on account of its early start and the fact that it has always been conducted as an adjunct to general farming. Few farms in this belt have more than 10 per cent of their areas in apples. This region is geographically continuous with that of Ontario. From the New York and Ontario districts apples are shipped both east and west, and some Ontario apples compete with the Nova Scotia product in the English market. The apple industry of the Michigan fruit belt resembles that of New York in many geographic respects. The markets of this district lie mainly to the west, including Chicago and Wisconsin.

THE CENTRAL PLAINS APPLE REGION consists of isolated districts in southern and western Illinois, in the Ozark highland, and in the Missouri and Arkansas River valleys. These areas lie far enough south in the central plains, so that, although damage from severe winters and unseasonable springs is frequent, it does not occur every year. Cold weather during the budding period is the usual cause of damage. The probability of loss is somewhat decreased by the placing of orchards on hill slopes in southern

Illinois and the Ozarks and on the rough lands bordering the rivers. There the heavy cold air in time of frost tends to settle in the valleys, leaving the orchard sites less likely to have freezing temperatures. Nevertheless, the output of this region is subject to rather wide variation from year to year.

IRRIGATED ORCHARDS are located in various parts of the West from the Pecos Valley in New Mexico to the Okanagan Valley of British Columbia. This vast territory includes more than a dozen orchard districts. The best known among them are the grand valley of Colorado; the Wenatchee and Yakima valleys of Washington; Watsonville, Calif.;

FIG. 42.—Irrigated apple orchards in the Wenatchee Valley, Washington. The close spacing of the homes and the intensive cultivation of this valley indicate small holdings of expensive land. (*U.S. Department of Agriculture.*)

and the Hood River Valley of Oregon. In general, these regions have dry, sunny climates and require irrigation, though, in the districts nearest the Pacific Coast, irrigation is not universally practiced (Fig. 42).

In the irrigated orchards of the West, apple culture is of a highly specialized character. As compared with the less intensively cultivated orchards of the East they have many disadvantages: (1) The land is high in price; (2) there is constant heavy expense for irrigation; and (3) their principal market is hundreds or even thousands of miles distant. Offsetting these difficulties are several important advantages: (1) In some of the regions frost damage is not common; (2) fungus diseases are more easily controlled than in the humid East; (3) control of the water supply induces heavy yields; and (4) the high proportion of sunny weather produces a highly colored fruit of dessert character. These apples are carefully graded, wrapped, and packed in boxes, rather than shipped in barrels or in bulk. Much of the marketing of apples from the irrigated districts is handled by cooperative organizations. So are many other phases of the business also, for cooperation is more easily developed in these restricted areas than it is among the more general farmers of the eastern apple regions. Here cooperative effort is often necessary to secure irrigation water, and practically all the farmers have identical interests and problems. Owing to the high cost of shipping to eastern markets, the western apple growers do not get high prices for their apples as compared with eastern growers. This difference they must make up by more efficient production methods.

The combined crop of the orchards of the Cordilleran section of the continent averages about 40 per cent of the commercial apples of North America. Nearly one-half the western apples are shipped from the Wenatchee and Yakima valleys, which lie on the dry and sunny eastern slopes of the Cascade Mountains in Washington. Only a small part of this fruit can be consumed in the sparsely populated West. Apples from British Columbia move eastward to compete with those of Ontario in the markets of the central provinces. In the same way, the fruit of Washington or of Colorado competes in the East with that of the eastern orchards. From the Pacific ports of Canada apples are shipped through the Panama Canal mainly to Great Britain. More than one-half the Canadian commercial crop is exported. United States exports of apples, also mainly to Great Britain, have not been large in recent years, seldom exceeding 15 per cent of the commercial crop, but now they have further declined as a result of tariff restrictions and disturbed conditions in Europe.

## Pears

THE AMERICAN PEAR CROP. The growing of pears is much less important in North America than is the growing of apples. The total average crop of about 27 million bushels is only one-seventh as great as the apple crop. This is to be attributed in part to the poorer shipping and keeping quality of pears. Some varieties of pears must be consumed quickly after they ripen or must be preserved by canning. The pear tree is not quite so hardy as the apple, and its range is somewhat farther south.

WESTWARD MIGRATION OF PEAR GROWING. The raising of pears as a commercial enterprise has migrated to the Pacific Coast. Nearly two-thirds of the pear crop of the United States now grows in the three Pacific Coast states, mainly in the Sacramento, Rogue River, and Yakima valleys. The very rapid migration of this industry has been encouraged by the spread of pear diseases which have very nearly exterminated some of the more prized varieties in the East. Vigorous methods of disease control and drier climate in the West have retained such pears as the

Bartlett, which now hold the eastern market for dessert pears. The West also has the advantage of ample fruit-canning facilities which provide an outlet for the unmarketable surplus of abundant crop years. The Great Lakes fruit regions of New York and Michigan produce most of the eastern crop.

## Peaches and Apricots

CLIMATE AND SOIL INFLUENCES IN PEACH CULTURE. The distribution of peach growing in North America shows a general response to climatic influences very similar to that already described for pears. In districts such as the central plains, where winter temperatures frequently

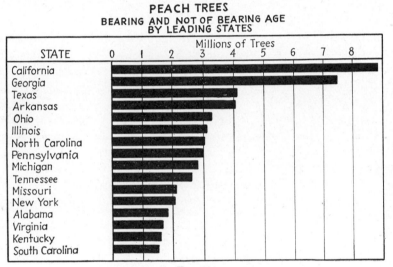

**PEACH TREES**
BEARING AND NOT OF BEARING AGE
BY LEADING STATES

FIG. 43.

fall to −15°F., the peach buds are likely to freeze, and the risk of crop failure under such conditions is so great as to discourage commercial peach culture. The influence of bodies of water in controlling temperatures has been described; it is not surprising, therefore, to find that the most northerly peach districts in North America are on the Pacific Coast and in the fruit belts of the Great Lakes region in Michigan, Ontario, and New York. This crop is almost entirely absent from the central plains north of central Iowa (Fig. 43). The earlier blooming habit and tender foliage of peaches, as compared with apples, makes security from late spring and early autumn frosts even more important. For this reason, rolling hill regions, where peach orchards may occupy intermediate slopes, permit the drainage of cold air to lower levels, where frost may occur while the orchard sites remain unaffected. The susceptibility of peach trees, buds, and blossoms to cold and frost leads to frequent losses in practically all peach regions. For example, in Massachusetts and in the Great Lakes districts not only the buds but the trees have on several occasions been killed by long-continued winter cold, and thousands of acres of orchards destroyed. Notwithstanding their sensitiveness to cold, peaches do not fruit abundantly in regions of continuously warm temperatures.

AMERICAN PEACH REGIONS.    The total American peach crop averages more than 50 million bushels, one-fourth as much as the total apple crop.

FIG. 44.—Trays of split apricots exposed to the dry heat of one of the interior valleys of California. Dry air, abundant sunshine, and irrigation water enable the adjacent trees to produce a crop particularly suited to drying.

The commercial crop, which is more than half the total, is grown in more than 30 states and provinces. A few centers of special importance, however, market a large portion of the peaches. In the East the most important areas are in Georgia (noted for its early crop), Texas, Arkansas, and the Great Lakes districts. From the hill slopes of Georgia alone comes nearly 10 per cent of the total crop.

Peach growing has also migrated to the favorable conditions found on the irrigated lands of western Colorado and of the Pacific Coast, whence fast refrigerator trains take fresh fruit to eastern markets. In California, dry air and rainless summers produce solid fruits of high sugar content particularly suited for drying and canning. The same weather conditions encourage inexpensive evaporation of the fruit in the open. Drying and facilities for canning provide an outlet for a large part of the crop. The average peach crop of California is 40 per cent of the crop of the continent.

APRICOTS are closely related to peaches but differ from them in hardiness. So sensitive to cold is the apricot tree that it reaches commercial importance only in California and in certain select localities in Oregon and Washington. The market for fresh fruit is limited, and the crop mainly is dried or canned (Fig. 44).

## Cherries, Plums, and Prunes

Cherries and plums exhibit many of the characteristics of distribution previously noted for the other tree fruits. Both are widely grown in the East but also show an increasing importance in the great fruit garden of the continent, the Pacific Coast. Of the two fruits, cherries are more restricted in distribution, the eastern sour-cherry belt being practically coincident with the corn belt. Notable extensions of this hardy crop are found in the fruit region of New York, western Michigan, and the Door County Peninsula of Wisconsin. Sweet cherries, for canning or the fruit-stand trade, are grown in limited sections of the East but mainly in the Pacific Coast regions, which produce about one-third of the total cherry crop of the United States.

Plums show a much more general distribution within the northern limit of apple culture and even beyond it into North Dakota. In the East the crop is produced mainly for local markets, for the fruit is soft and easily damaged in transit. The dry subtropical summers of the Pacific Coast and freedom from diseases make possible the growing of large, solid varieties which reach the eastern market through a long summer season. The most important plum crop of the West consists, however, of those varieties which are grown in the Pacific Coast states for drying. They are called "prunes," but not all western plums are prunes, for only certain varieties have the proper firmness and sweetness to cure into a satisfactory product. Prune growing has become an important industry in Oregon and particularly in Santa Clara County, California. American-grown prunes are now able to supply the home demand and yield an annual surplus for export which exceeds 175,000,000 pounds.

The growing of small fruits (mainly berries) is an industry similar in many respects to truck farming, with which it is often allied. The bush fruits are, for the most part, hardy. Some of them have long blossoming seasons, and late frosts can destroy only a part of the crop. In general, their fruits do not stand transportation well and are grown for local markets. As a result of these conditions the bush fruits are produced in abundance in the area of large population north of the Ohio River and east of the Missouri. The mild moist climate of the Pacific Northwest is, however, particularly favorable to the raising of these fruits. Lacking a large local market, this region, and especially the Puget Sound district, sends much of its large and varied crop to market canned, frozen, or otherwise preserved.

Strawberry growing resembles, in some respects, the potato industry, there being an early crop from the South, followed by crops from a succession of regions ending with a main supply crop in the North. The centers of intensive strawberry culture are so distributed that part of them coincide with centers of fruit growing and part of them with well-known truck-farming districts. Among the former are the Niagara Peninsula of Ontario, western Michigan, the Ozark Mountains, and the San Francisco and Los Angeles regions. Among the trucking centers that also ship strawberries are western Florida, Hammond, La., Norfolk, Va., and the Delaware River region. The industry is influenced by economic conditions quite as much as by those of natural environment. The demand for early berries, coupled with the fact that they stand shipment well, has shifted the main crop out of the northern consuming region to the South, which now produces more than half the total crop of nearly 10,000,000 bushels a year.

## The Canning and Drying of Fruits

THE FRUIT-CANNING INDUSTRY. Before the development of modern transportation, the canning and drying of fruit was a general household practice. A great deal of fruit is still canned in the home, though the home drying of apples and berries has almost disappeared. The importance of California and the Pacific Northwest as fruit-canning centers has already been mentioned. In spite of admirable conditions for fruit production, the handicap of distance is keenly felt in the Far West, particularly when good crops occur in the East. It is the canning industry that averts disaster at such a time. Gradually the domestic and foreign market for canned and preserved fruits has grown until the canneries regularly consume a large part of the output of Pacific Coast orchards and gardens. The eastern fruit growers have not been slow to see the economy of this practice, and fruit canneries have sprung up in many eastern districts, first to act as absorbers of the surplus in years of overproduction and later to develop into a stable business.

Fruit drying is practiced mainly in California. Most of the common fruits of the East are too soft and pulpy and too low in sugar to be valuable when dried, and the cost of mechanical evaporation is too high to permit them to compete with fruit raised under California conditions and dried in the open air. Therein is clearly an industrial adaptation to climate. The low rainfall and dry heat of the California summer produce fruits suitable for drying and make possible their out-of-door drying on a vast scale. The industry is located in the interior valleys where the temperatures are higher and the atmospheric humidity much lower than near the coast. The prune industry of Santa Clara County, the raisin drying of Fresno County, and the peach drying of Kings County are conspicuous examples. The favorable climatic conditions that exist in these districts may be seen in a comparison of relative humidity, cloudiness, and rainfall records of these and other fruit-growing regions of the United States.

AVERAGE WEATHER CONDITIONS AFFECTING FRUIT DRYING, FOR THE THREE MONTHS JUNE TO AUGUST, INCLUSIVE

| Station | Average Temperature, °F. | Rainfall, Inches | Relative Humidity, Per Cent | Sunshine, Per Cent of Total Possible |
|---|---|---|---|---|
| Rochester, N. Y. | 69 | 9.0 | 64 | 67 |
| Tampa, Fla. | 81 | 24.5 | 74 | 64 |
| San Jose, Calif. | 66 | 0.1 | 58 | 84 |
| Fresno, Calif. | 79 | 0.1 | 32 | 95 |

## Grapes and Raisins

TWO TYPES OF GRAPES IN AMERICA. A study of the natural conditions affecting grape growing in North America involves two problems, for there are two kinds of grapes, with different environmental requirements. California grows principally the viniferous or European types of grapes. In the eastern part of the continent the many varieties of grapes are mainly of native origin. In colonial times attempts were made to introduce European grapes into English colonies but without success, although wild grapes were found in abundance from Nova Scotia to Florida. Many years later it was discovered that, in addition to the unsuitable climate for south-European grapes, failure resulted from their susceptibility to fungus diseases induced by summer humidity and to the work of a root parasite (Phylloxera) to which native grapes were immune. Successful grape culture was finally assured for the East by the selection and improvement of types of native wild grapes rather than by introduction of types from Europe. Yet the Spanish were immediately successful in transplanting the Mediterranean vine to southern California. Thus two types of grape industries were established in North America.

GRAPE DISTRICTS OF THE EAST. Although the vines of eastern grapes are hardy and seldom winterkill, the late frosts of the northern spring or cold rains at blossom time may ruin a crop, or a short season may not permit the fruit to mature. Therefore, most of the commercial crop of the East is limited to five districts, the climates of which are tempered by lake or other moderating influence and which have at the same time a good location with respect to the great urban centers of consumption. These are (1) southwestern Michigan; (2) the southern shore of Lake

Erie, including the Chautauqua district of western New York which lies on the glacial lake plain north of the Allegheny Plateau escarpment; (3) the shore of Lake Ontario north of the Niagara escarpment from Hamilton, Ont., eastward into New York; (4) the steep bluffs bordering the Finger Lakes of New York; and (5) a less concentrated region in the hill lands of the Ozarks where lower latitude enables the maturing of a slightly earlier crop (Fig. 45). In the first three named, the Concord grape is the leading variety and is a table grape only. It does not keep well,

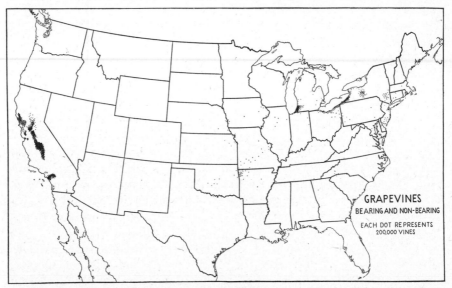

GRAPEVINES
BEARING AND NON-BEARING
EACH DOT REPRESENTS
200,000 VINES

FIG. 45.—The principal grape-growing regions of the United States. California produces about 90 per cent of the total grape supply. The raisin grape area in the San Joaquin Valley has the largest number of vines.

and the bulk of the crop must be consumed as soon as it is ripe; easy access to large markets is therefore essential. The market for Michigan grapes in Chicago and adjacent territory may be reached by rail or by motor truck in a few hours. The Chautauqua grapes supply the eastern cities and sometimes reach the middle-western markets. In these regions grape-juice factories have been established to provide a market for a surplus crop. None of the varieties of native grapes has sufficiently solid pulp and high sugar content to make satisfactory raisins, but some, especially in the Finger Lakes region, are used in the making of wine.

CALIFORNIA VINEYARDS.    Grapes are grown in the Pacific states from Mexico to British Columbia. The bulk of the crop, however, and indeed about 90 per cent of all the grapes grown in the United States, is produced in California. The principal commercial vineyards are in central California, back from the coast with its fogs and humidity. Varieties of grapes are grown that are particularly suited to the (1) manufacture of wines, (2) curing for raisins, and (3) shipment for use as table grapes. All are of

FIG. 46.—Trays of drying raisins in a California vineyard. The trays are tilted toward the south in east-west rows to get more direct sunlight. They must remain here from one to two weeks, a time when rain brings ruin. (*Courtesy of Sun-Maid Raisin Growers Assn.*)

the viniferous type which originated in southern Europe and are by their deep-penetrating root systems well suited to withstand the long dry summers of Mediterranean climate. However, the summer rainfall of the

interior valleys of California is considerably less than it is even in the
drier portions of Italy and Spain. For that reason most of the California
vineyards require irrigation.

In general, the wine and table grapes are grown in the somewhat
less dry Sacramento Valley, north of San Francisco, or in the more open
coastal valleys of the southern part of the state. Sometimes the varieties
of grapes used for wine and some of the leading raisin varieties are shipped
east as fresh table grapes. Most of the viniferous grapes are solid, are of
high sugar content, and stand shipment and storage much better than
eastern grapes. This fact, coupled with great improvements in methods
of packing and distribution, has so encouraged the sale of fresh California
grapes that now they may be had, in season, in almost every eastern city
and village. Formerly most of the viniferous table grapes used in the
markets of northern Europe and eastern United States and Canada came
from the vineyards of Almeria in southern Spain, where the production
of table grapes was a special business. The American market was captured
by California years ago; and when the late war in Spain ruined production
there, many California grapes were taken by the British market. The
total California exports of grapes have reached 40,000 tons.

RAISINS are viniferous grapes, of high sugar content, dried. This use
consumes about one-third of the California grape crop. They are produced
mainly on irrigated alluvial plains bordering the Sierra Nevada mountains
in the hot and dry San Joaquin Valley. Dry air and intense sunlight
during the growing season produce solid grapes containing about 25 per
cent sugar. The same conditions enable the grapes to be cured as raisins
in the open air (Fig. 46). Several varieties of raisins are produced. Some
are large and contain seeds, but the variety in greatest demand is made
from the small white seedless grapes familiar on eastern fruit stands in
the late summer. They are in demand because the raisins are seedless,
and they are convenient for the grower because they mature early and
dry quickly, thus avoiding the danger of early autumn rains. The present
crop of raisins averages about 200,000 tons (over 3 pounds per person in
the United States). California is more than able to supply the normal
demand of the United States market, and about one-fourth of the crop
is exported.

## Citrus Fruits

THE ORIGIN OF CITRUS FRUITS.   The principal citrus fruits of commercial importance are the orange, lemon, lime, and pomelo, or grapefruit.
All these fruits originated in the humid subtropics of southeastern Asia
and have been cultivated elsewhere for a few centuries only. From
southern Asia citrus fruits were introduced into Palestine and southern
Europe. From Spain they were carried to the New World, including the

United States, which now leads the world in quantity of fruit grown and in scientific methods of culture and marketing.

THE RELATION OF TEMPERATURE TO CITRICULTURE. The tropical origin of citrus trees is plainly manifested in their inability to withstand temperatures below freezing for more than a very few hours at a time, without serious damage to the crop or to the tree. The various citrus fruit trees differ somewhat in hardiness, the orange being the most resistant, followed in order by pomelo, lemon, and lime trees. In spite of the constant danger from frost, citrus fruits grown beyond the margin

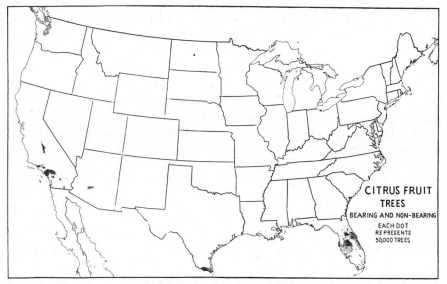

CITRUS FRUIT
TREES
BEARING AND NON-BEARING
EACH DOT
REPRESENTS
50,000 TREES

FIG. 47.—The citrus crops of California, Arizona, and Texas are irrigated, but those of Florida and the Gulf Coast are not.

of the tropics generally are considered superior in flavor to those of the tropics. Citrus growers in America are often put to great expense and labor to protect their groves from frosts during cold spells in winter. The principal means of protection is the use of heaters among the trees on frosty nights. Conditions of temperature, therefore, limit sharply the possible citrus regions of the United States. Each of the leading regions has, on occasions, been visited by severely destructive freezes.

MOISTURE INFLUENCES. It is worthy of note that the citrus fruits have several times been subjected to a change in their moisture environment. In their original removal from southeastern Asia to the Mediterranean region the change was from a region of abundant summer rainfall to one of summer drought, where irrigation was necessary to keep the trees alive. The transplanting of these fruits from Spain to Florida, the West Indies, and eastern South America brought them back to a moisture environment similar to the original. When the navel orange of Brazil was established in California, this influence was again reversed. Adaptability in this respect does not mean that citrus trees are entirely at home in the Mediterranean climate. They cannot grow there wild and unirrigated, as they do in the West Indies and even in Florida.

AMERICAN CITRUS REGIONS.    The districts of greatest importance in American citrus growing are shown in Fig. 47. Among them are considerable differences in types of fruit grown and in market relations. In part, these are differences resulting from situation and features of physical environment.

The Florida citrus region occupies flat lowlands, on both the eastern and western coasts, and a rolling central upland. The general situation of the region in central Florida affords some protection against cold waves from the northwest, such as once destroyed the industry in northern Florida, since these winds may be tempered to some degree by the warmth of the Gulf of Mexico. Location in southern Florida might be still safer, but it is not feasible because of the great swamps that occupy the larger part of that area. In the central upland some local protection is afforded by planting on sloping land where air drainage is effective, and numerous lakes add to the protection at critical times. Abundant rainfall makes irrigation unnecessary, and high humidity develops fruits of a high juice and lower solid content and of comparatively poor keeping quality. Oranges and grapefruit are satisfactory crops under these conditions, but not lemons. Florida produces about 35 per cent of American oranges and over 60 per cent of the grapefruit. Florida is much closer than the other producing regions to the great eastern city markets to which the fruit moves quickly, some of it by automobile truck.

The Texas citrus region is situated far south on the irrigated delta of the Rio Grande, out of reach of most of the cold winds that make citrus culture a minor feature of the agriculture on the Gulf Coast between there and central Florida. This region produces only about 2 per cent of the oranges but over 20 per cent of the grapefruit crop.

In California there are two major citrus districts, both requiring irrigation (Fig. 48). The northern, and less extensive, occupies foothill sites at the base of the Sierra Nevada Mountains, where good air drainage serves as some protection from frost. The more extensive district lies on the piedmont plain bordering the San Bernardino and San Gabriel Mountains in southern California (Fig. 15). It has two sections. An eastern area of drier atmosphere produces mainly the winter and spring crop of seedless navel oranges. A section nearer the coast, with more humid atmosphere, produces the larger part of the summer and early autumn crop of Valencia oranges. The output of the latter variety is now more than half the California total, since the winter crop must compete in eastern markets with Florida and Texas oranges, whereas summer oranges have no citrus competitors.

The dry air and warm winters of California are satisfactory for the growing of solid, disease-free lemons of good keeping quality, and the entire commercial crop of the United States is grown there. The market for lemons is during hot weather in the East, but they mature most abundantly in the winter and spring and are largely picked green, cured,

Fig. 48.—In southern California the irrigation water is conserved by pumping it through underground pipes. Here it is welling up from below and pouring out through small openings in the vertical tile. Each little stream irrigates a small furrow. The large tile in foreground houses the control valve for the entire row.

and held in storage for later market demand. The same dry conditions do not produce the mild-flavored, juicy grapefruit favored by eastern consumers. The irrigated districts of California and Arizona combined produce less than one-sixth of that crop.

THE CITRUS GROWER DEPENDENT ON EFFICIENT MARKETING. It is obvious that the growers of citrus fruit are dependent upon the large city markets of the northeastern states from which they are 1,200 to 3,000 miles distant. Although the citrus fruits, protected by thick, oily skins, were imported from Mediterranean Europe and the West Indies a century ago, losses were large, and prices high, and the fruits were hardly sold outside a few port towns. The development of a great domestic industry awaited the perfection of rapid transportation and of methods of protection against unfavorable weather and other damage in transit. The average time for the movement of cars of oranges between California and New York is about 2 weeks. In warm weather the cars require refrigeration, and in very cold weather protection from frost. Shipments of California fruit are also being marketed in the East by way of the Panama Canal.

The average citrus-fruit grower has a small farm but a large invest-ment, because fruit land is valuable, and in California and Texas addi-tional expenditures for irrigation are required. At best the margin of profit is small, and there are many failures. Under these conditions the small growers have sought protection from the disadvantages of their relation to market by highly scientific methods, by demanding a protec-tive tariff, and by combining in organizations such as the California Fruit Growers' Exchange and the Citrus Protective League. The latter is an organization that deals with legal and political matters and with policies relating to the industry as a whole. Similar organizations have also been developed in Texas and Florida. The former is designed to promote efficiency in the grading and packing of fruit and to act as a clearinghouse through which fruit may be effectively marketed. The supervision of this organization does not end with the shipment of the fruit, but through its agents it guides each car to a profitable market and handles its sale for the grower. Under the direction of these organizations, citrus by-products industries have been established which, as has been noted for other fruits, help to absorb surplus or inferior fruit and to steady the market.

## Minor Fruit and Nut Crops

Some crops of great value, originally wild, are now cultivated to a considerable extent in America. Such a crop is the pecan, grown in the South. Many other foreign crops have been introduced. Only a few, however, are of much significance or are so concentrated in area as to be recognized as industries. Those crops which have become important in these respects are not mainly the new and untried plants of the tropics but are the fruits and nuts to which the European taste is accustomed and of which large quantities have been imported into North America. They have been introduced, mainly into California, since the develop-ment of efficient transportation which enables them to compete with similar goods from overseas. Figs, olives, walnuts, and almonds, all grown in the dry climate of the West, compete with those of the Mediter-ranean countries. Dates grown on the hot, irrigated desert of the Imperial Valley yield fruits no less valuable than those of Mesopotamia but as yet in small quantities.

The plant explorers of the U. S. Department of Agriculture have searched the world for new plants and for new varieties of old plants that may be well adapted to American environmental conditions. Doubtless a few decades will add many other valuable items to this already long list of American fruit and nut crops.

SELECTED REFERENCES

ACKERMAN, E. A. Influences of Climate on the Cultivation of Citrus Fruits, *Geog. Rev.*, Vol. 28 (1938), pp. 289–302.

BAKER, O. E. Agricultural Regions of North America, Part VIII, The Pacific Subtropical Crops Region, *Econ. Geog.*, Vol. 6 (1930), pp. 166–191, 278–309.

CALDWELL, J. S. Evaporation of Fruits, *U.S. Dept. Agr., Bull.* 1141.

FREEMAN, OTIS W. Apple Industry of the Wenatchee Area, *Econ. Geog.*, Vol. 10 (1934), pp. 160–171.

HODGSON, ROBERT W. The California Fruit Industry, *Econ. Geog.*, Vol. 9 (1933), pp. 337–355.

ZIERER, CLIFFORD M. The Citrus Fruit Industry of the Los Angeles Basin, *Econ. Geog.*, Vol. 10 (1934), pp. 53–73.

# Chapter VI. Sugar, Vegetable Oils, and Tobacco

## Sugar

THE SUGAR SUPPLY OF NORTH AMERICA.   The use of a large quantity of sugar by a people, like the use of white bread, reflects general wealth and a high standard of living. Some of the new countries and most of the industrial countries of the world rank high in this respect, among them the United States and Canada (Fig. 49). In 1900 the average per capita

PER CAPITA SUGAR CONSUMPTION IN THE UNITED STATES
AND CERTAIN OTHER COUNTRIES
Average, 1936–1937

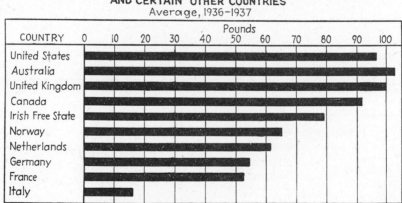

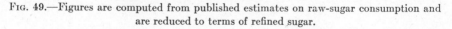

FIG. 49.—Figures are computed from published estimates on raw-sugar consumption and are reduced to terms of refined sugar.

consumption of sugar in the United States was about 70 pounds. The rate of consumption has risen with increasing national wealth, and now the average American uses about 100 pounds of sugar per year. In Canada also the rate of consumption is high. It is obvious that the total quantity of sugar required for the two countries is very large; it has amounted in recent years to about 14 billions of pounds. Of the 6½ million tons consumed in the United States about 27 per cent is grown at home; about 40 per cent is obtained from Hawaii, Puerto Rico, and the Philippine

Islands; and the remaining 33 per cent is imported from foreign countries, mainly from Cuba (Fig. 50).

THE AMERICAN CANE-SUGAR CROP.   Sugar cane is a tropical plant, and many varieties require nearly a year of warm weather to reach full maturity. Cane requires also a fertile soil, abundant sunlight, and 50 inches or more of rainfall each year. Nowhere in the United States or Canada are these environmental conditions combined except in parts of the Gulf Coastal Plain (Fig. 51). The principal cane-growing district is located on the fertile alluvial soils of the Mississippi delta of Louisiana,

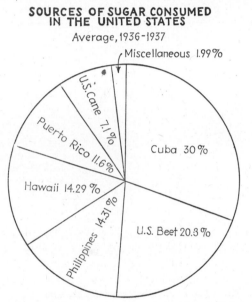

SOURCES OF SUGAR CONSUMED
IN THE UNITED STATES
Average, 1936–1937

FIG. 50.—Nearly one-third of the sugar supply of the United States comes from Cuba.

where cheap negro labor helps to make possible an unequal sort of competition with tropical cane growers who are more favored by climatic conditions and by much lower labor costs. A second United States region is located on the drained swamplands of southern Florida where sugar production is increasing. In Louisiana frosts occur annually; and although early varieties of cane are grown which may be harvested in 8 months, the pieces of cane to be used for replanting must be protected from frost, and much new planting done each spring. These precautions and American labor both are more expensive than the cropping methods employed in Cuba, for example. Yields of sugar in Louisiana are commonly decreased by the fact that weather conditions force the cutting of immature cane, from which a full yield of crystallizable sugar cannot be obtained. The average amount of sugar produced per acre is less than half that obtained in Cuba or Hawaii. As a result of these economic and natural handicaps

United States sugar planters are generally insistent upon a sugar tariff that will offset the disadvantages of their position. The cane sugar grown in the United States is but a small part of the total quantity of sugar used in the country, averaging about 5 per cent.

SUGAR MANUFACTURE.   The extraction of the sugar from American cane is done in local mills. As the cane comes from the fields, it is bulky and easily damaged and may not be transported far. Unlike beet-sugar factories, cane-sugar mills generally do not make refined sugar but a soft, brown or yellow product called "raw sugar." The raw sugar of Louisiana, like most imported sugar, requires refining before it is marketed (Fig. 52).

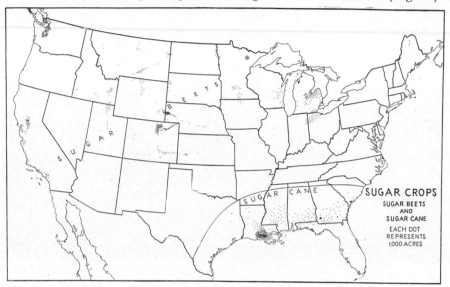

FIG. 51.—The zoning of sugar crops in North America is due in part to climatic influences.

SUGAR REFINING.   The process of sugar refining consists of dissolving the raw sugar, clarifying it by the use of bone charcoal, and the filtering and recrystallizing of the sugar from the solution. Refining is done on a vast scale and so cheaply that the process adds but little to the final cost of the sugar. The great refineries run night and day, and one of the largest has a daily capacity of more than 4 million pounds of sugar. So vast a business may not be profitably located in the sugar-growing districts. Rather, the refinery must stand at a great commercial gateway to a large consuming region. Here raw sugar from any of the producing regions of the world may be concentrated every month of the year in a never ending stream, and in the most modern plants it is discharged from the ship's hold directly into the melting pans of the refinery. The great refineries of America are found in or near Boston, Brooklyn, Philadelphia, Baltimore, New Orleans, and San Francisco. The prompt distribution of the sugar from these refineries to the inland markets calls for the superior railway service obtainable at these great commercial gateways, and the packing of the sugar requires many millions of bags and barrels.

BEET SUGAR.    Sugar beets are grown under a wide variety of climatic and soil conditions. In general, the most suitable conditions of natural environment for sugar-beet growing are found where the soil is deep, friable, and well drained; where, except in irrigated regions, there is a moderate and well-distributed summer rainfall; and where the summer temperatures are somewhat lower than those required for corn. Young

FIG. 52.—Sugar cane and a "sugar house" or mill in Louisiana.

beets are easily frosted; but since they grow rapidly, planting may be delayed until danger of frost is past. Mature beets are very hardy, and cool autumn nights alternating with warm bright days increase their sugar content. Shallow soils and excessive moisture cause ill-shaped roots and decreased yields.

The sugar-beet regions of North America stretch westward from Ontario through Michigan, Wisconsin, northern Iowa, Nebraska, Colorado, Utah, Idaho, and California (Fig. 51). West of the Great Plains margin in this long belt the beets are grown under irrigation. Because of the western farmer's ability to control moisture conditions more closely and because of their larger factories, the western regions can produce sugar more cheaply than the eastern, but the latter has the advantage of a nearer market. It will be noted that the sugar-beet belt extends along the cool northern margin of the corn belt and beyond its dry western side but does not include it. The heat of the corn belt is partly responsible for this, but the competition of beets and corn for the time and labor of the farmer is also an important factor. Beets require a great deal of handwork. It is not often that there is enough resident labor in an important beet region to tend the crop. Outside laborers, often foreign-born, are drawn from other employment, to which they return in the winter. Many of these people emigrated from the beet-growing districts of Europe and are already familiar with the care of the crop. Central Europeans in the East and Mexicans in the western districts contribute a large part of the labor. An entire family usually works as a unit and undertakes to care for a certain area of beets. Sometimes the laborer rents or buys land and

Fig. 53.—A sugar-beet field and factory in Utah. Raw material for this factory is close at hand. (*U.S. Department of Agriculture.*)

becomes a permanent resident in the community. American wages, even for this low-paid labor, are high, and the beet-sugar manufacturers are quite as interested in a protective tariff as are the cane-sugar producers.

An average acre of beet land yields from 9 to 11 tons of roots of which 13 to 18 per cent by weight is recovered in the form of sugar. It is clear that so large a bulk of unproductive water and cellulose will increase the cost of the sugar greatly if the beets are shipped more than a few score of miles. For that reason beet-sugar factories are located at various points in the regions of beet growing (Fig. 53). They draw their raw materials from the immediate region by motor truck and by rail from outlying sections up to 100 or 200 miles distant.

MINOR SUGAR CROPS.   In the broad zone between the sugar-beet belt and the commercial cane-sugar region of North America, sugar cane and sorghum cane are raised locally on a small scale, and their juices are reduced to sirup and molasses in rural mills. These crops are mainly for home supply, although their products are expanding their markets and may now be obtained in convenient canned form. More than 30 million gallons is made annually in the United States, the equivalent of about 2 pounds more of sugar per capita of the total population.

In northeastern United States and adjacent provinces of Canada, maple trees yield a considerable addition to the sugar supply of the continent. In the United States about 1 million pounds of maple sugar and 3 million gallons of maple sirup are made annually, mainly on the hilly farms of Vermont and New York, but the quantity is only about one-half what it was in the middle of the past century. Canada, mainly Quebec, produces about five times as much maple sugar as the United States and about one-half as much sirup.

## Vegetable Oils

VEGETABLE OILS OF INCREASING IMPORTANCE.    Fat is an important part of the human diet. Pure fat has a fuel value of about 4,000 calories per pound, whereas the cereals possess less than 2,000 calories per pound. As a heat-producing food, therefore, fat, in moderate quantities, is necessary. It is essential in cold climates, but it is a common element of diet also among people of the tropics.

Edible fats are obtained from both animal and vegetable sources. In some parts of the world vegetable fats have been in common use for many centuries. Yet among the races of northwestern Europe and their American descendants the fats in common use have until recently been of animal origin, principally lard, tallow, and butter. That is due, no doubt, to the lack of any important oilseed crop in the agriculture of northwestern Europe. In the densely peopled Oriental lands, especially where religion forbids the use of flesh, and in the Mediterranean countries, the oils of the olive, the soybean, and many other seeds have supplied the principal edible fats. As long as western Europe and the New World were dominantly agricultural in occupation, the supplies of animal fats remained sufficient. But the growth of industrial populations in the last quarter of the past century brought that era to a close. The wide commercial interests of Britain brought cheap meats to her cities and caused her to feel the pinch of a fat shortage less quickly than did France and Germany. It was therefore the latter countries that took active steps to develop great vegetable-oil industries. Gradually the shortage made itself felt in Britain; and as the cost of lard and butter advanced, cheaper fats of vegetable origin grew in popularity. In America the same transition gradually came about. Even while American exports of lard were mounting to enormous totals, vegetable cooking fats began to appear; and while butter was being made in greater quantity and of better quality than ever before, substitutes for butter found a market.

CLASSES OF VEGETABLE OILS. There are now in common use more than a dozen vegetable oils, some of them subdivided into numerous market classes and grades. Some are considered edible; others, inedible. In fact, edibility is largely a matter of price and degree of refinement, and these grades are to some extent interchangeable. An industrial classification of oils is commonly made on a basis of their drying qualities. Some, such as linseed and tung oils, when exposed to the air, absorb oxygen rapidly and form a tough, rubbery film. These are known as the "drying oils" and are used mainly in the manufacture of paint and varnish. Other oils, such as cottonseed oil and olive oil, oxidize very slowly and are called "nondrying oils." There is nearly complete gradation between these two extremes; soybean oil, for example, called "semi-drying," is of intermediate character.

COTTONSEED OIL. About two-thirds of the weight of unginned cotton consists of seeds which yield 16 per cent of their weight in oil. For decades this vast and growing resource was little used. Some of the seed was returned to the land as fertilizer, and a little was fed to animals, but a much greater quantity was burned or permitted to decay. Before the Civil War a little cottonseed oil was made in the United States, but as late as 1875 only about 5 per cent of the 2 million tons of seed ginned annually was treated in the crushing mills. About 75 per cent of the annual crop of cotton seed, or nearly 5 million tons, now goes to the mills. The total annual yield is more than 10 pounds of valuable oil for every person in the United States, besides more than 2 million tons of cottonseed cake and other important by-products. Since the seed is bulky, the crushing mills are most advantageously located close to the supply of raw material. More than 450 such mills are scattered throughout the cotton belt.

As the oil comes from the presses, it is not suitable for human consumption but requires clarifying and refining, processes that separate it into a number of products suited to different uses. Cottonseed oil is nondrying; its light, clear products are used directly as salad oil or, in solid form, as lard substitutes. The latter are mixtures of liquid cottonseed oil with solid animal fats, or they are made by treating the light oil with hydrogen, which turns it into a solid fat. The inedible products of the refinery serve as raw materials in the manufacture of soaps and chemicals. Refining is most economically done on a large scale; the crude oil from the small crushing mills is, therefore, commonly shipped in tank cars to refineries that are located in large southern cities or in the industrial centers of the North. Much of the cottonseed cake is used for animal feeding in the South; but, since it is rendered compact by pressure, it also is shipped in large quantities to distant consumers.

LINSEED OIL is obtained from the seed of the flax plant. In North America the crop is grown almost entirely for its seed. It is treated as a spring-sown cereal, drilled, harvested, and threshed by machinery the same as that used for wheat. The region of American flax growing is practically that of the spring-wheat belt of the central plains (Fig. 54). The largest areas are found in the Dakotas, Minnesota, and Saskatchewan. Flax starts its growth slowly and is easily crowded out by weeds. Also it is subject to disease when grown continuously on the same land. For these reasons it does best on newly turned prairie sod or in a crop rotation. It was formerly a common pioneer crop in the Northwest, followed by the cereals. As the supply of new land in the United States has decreased, and

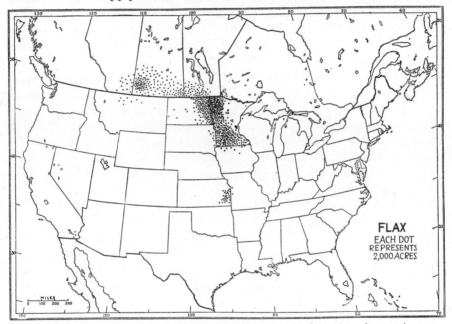

FLAX
EACH DOT
REPRESENTS
2,000 ACRES

Fig. 54.—Flax for seed is one of the alternative crops in the spring-wheat region.

as cheaper substitutes have replaced it in industrial uses, the flaxseed crop has decreased also. The present average crop of 6 million bushels is much less than that of 25 years ago. The Canadian crop is much smaller than that of the United States and is decreasing also.

Flaxseed is valuable, compact, and easily handled and is crushed for the extraction of its oil in large mills, often far distant from the flax fields. In this respect also the flaxseed resembles wheat rather than cotton-seed. The principal mills are found in Minneapolis, Toledo, and Buffalo. Instead of the large number of mills required to handle the cottonseed crop, the entire flaxseed crop is handled in a few establishments. The method of milling is similar to that employed for other oilseeds, and the cake from the presses has likewise a high value as a concentrated feed for livestock.

Although linseed oil is used to some extent for food in Russia and India, its sole use in America is industrial. Its drying property makes it a convenient binder in many preparations, such as paint, varnish, linoleum, oilcloth, patent-leather finish, and printers' ink. The high cost of other items entering these industrial wares in which linseed oil is a binding substance permits their manufacture in localities quite unrelated to the centers of oil production.

America is the world's largest user of linseed oil. Owing to the abundance of our forest resources and a high standard of living, frame buildings are more numerous, and the use of paint is more common than in any other country. In recent years the combined linseed crops of the United States and Canada have not been sufficient for domestic needs, and twice as much more has been imported, mainly from Argentina. Importation into the United States is in part counterbalanced by large exports of linseed oil and mixed paints.

OILS FROM IMPORTED SEEDS.  Rapid growth in the sale of vegetable-oil substitutes for lard and butter and their use in the manufacture of soap and other industrial processes have encouraged the use of domestic seeds, such as corn, peanuts, and the soybean, for oil production. It has also led to the importation of these and other oilseeds, including copra (dried coconut meats), from many parts of the world. Of all classes, such imports total nearly a half million tons. Fortunately, these raw materials require treatment but little different from the seeds of cotton or flax. The mills dealing with them seldom are fully employed throughout the year, and by slight modification of their equipment they can crush and press peanuts, beans, or copra. The best peanut oil is used directly as salad oil, but the other oils are made edible only by refining or are used industrially.

In addition to the oilseeds that are imported, economy of ship space has encouraged the importation of oils pressed from these seeds in foreign lands—for example, soybean oil from Japan and coconut oil from the Philippines. The total import of these also reaches a half million tons. The production of them may be considered more fully in their appropriate regional connections.

## Tobacco

ORIGIN AND USES OF TOBACCO.  Tobacco is an American plant. When America was discovered, the use of the leaf was an immemorial custom among the natives of both continents. Tobacco cultivation was introduced into Europe by the Spanish, but the practice of smoking was introduced through England and spread rapidly to the rest of the continent. This created a great market for tobacco, which at that time was supplied mainly from the plantations of the Virginia colony. The first exported crop of tobacco in 1618 amounted to 20,000 pounds; in 1695 it was 20 million pounds. The crop was of such importance in Virginia that bundles of tobacco leaves served as currency, and the shipments to England served to provide necessities and luxuries for the growing colony.

The tobaccos grown in North America may be grouped into two general classes: cigar leaf and manufacturing types. Three types of leaf tobacco are used in the manufacture of cigars, *viz.*, fillers, wrappers, and binders. Manufacturing types are those used in making smoking mixtures, cigarettes, chewing tobaccos, and snuff. Some quantities of the latter enter the export trade also.

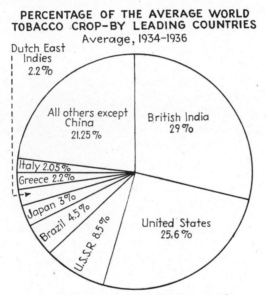

PERCENTAGE OF THE AVERAGE WORLD
TOBACCO CROP—BY LEADING COUNTRIES
Average, 1934–1936

FIG. 55.—India and the United States are the world's largest tobacco-producing countries.

TOBACCO AND PHYSICAL ENVIRONMENT. Few plants are more sensitive to conditions of climate and soil than is tobacco. Nevertheless, few crops are less restricted in world distribution by these same conditions. It is grown in all latitudes from Canada to the tropics and the southern hemisphere. It is probably native to the humid subtropics and requires considerable moisture, but it can be grown under irrigation. Tobacco is highly sensitive to frost but has a short growing season; and, especially since it usually is started in hotbeds and transplanted, it can mature in regions of short summers. It is the quality of the leaf that is most influenced by soil and climate. Cool, moist summers and light, porous soils tend to produce leaves of fine texture and weak aroma. Heavier soils and higher temperatures tend to produce smaller, thicker leaves of stronger aroma. Various combinations of temperature, moisture, and soil character result in a great variety of qualities of thickness, elasticity, aroma, absorptiveness, and burning quality due to chemical content. These inherent qualities are further accentuated by differences due to various methods of harvesting, curing, and handling the crops. The result is a large number of classes and grades destined for different markets and uses.

AMERICAN TOBACCO REGIONS. The United States is the world's largest source of tobacco (Fig. 55). The average crop of 1 to 1½ billion pounds is about 25 per cent of the world's supply. A small quantity is raised in Canada also, mainly in Ontario and Quebec. Most of the United

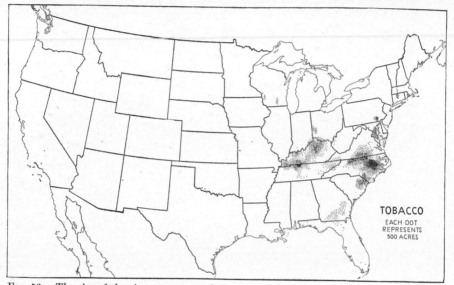

TOBACCO
EACH DOT
REPRESENTS
500 ACRES

FIG. 56.—The rise of the cigarette to popularity has caused a great increase in the tobacco crop of the Carolina Coastal Plain and Piedmont region.

States crop is raised in several districts of the eastern states (Fig. 56). The larger of these lie in the area between the cotton belt on the south and the corn and winter-wheat region on the north. Of these districts each has demonstrated its ability to grow a type of leaf that, when cured according to the prevailing method of the region, is superior for a specific use. The light Coastal Plain soils of Virginia and the Carolinas, for example, yield mainly the light-colored leaves used in cigarette manufacture. The Piedmont region (Fig. 57) and western Kentucky yield dark leaves much used in pipe tobaccos and for export. Northern Kentucky produces the light spongy leaf largely used in the manufacture of chewing tobacco. Pennsylvania and Ohio tobacco is employed largely as cigar fillers. Varieties from Wisconsin and Connecticut make the inner coverings, or "binders," of cigars; and the thin, elastic leaves, grown under artificial shade (Fig. 58) in Connecticut, Georgia, and Florida make the outer coverings, or "wrappers," of cigars. Most tobacco products are blended by combining two or more specific types or grades of leaf according to the formula of the particular manufacturer.

FIG. 57.—A field of tobacco on the rolling surface of the Piedmont in North Carolina. (*U.S. Department of Agriculture.*)

FIG. 58.—This tobacco is growing in the Connecticut Valley under the shade of a coarse cloth. The lower leaves have been harvested.

TOBACCO MANUFACTURE. The manufacture of cigarettes and of smoking and chewing tobaccos consists largely of mechanical processes that lend themselves to large-scale factory management. In cigar manufacture principally the cheaper grades are machine-made. Expensive cigars are made almost entirely by hand. In the past this industry has been widely distributed; the number of cigar factories is, however, rapidly decreasing. The small factory is giving way to larger shops which can (1) standardize their cigars by being large buyers and by getting the select leaf tobacco, (2) effect savings in labor by introducing division of labor and supplementary machinery, and (3) do more effective advertising. Large shops of this sort are located in large cities, principally Philadelphia, to take advantage of the labor supply; or in Florida, where Cuban labor can be induced to settle. The number of cigars made annually in the United States is about 4 or 5 billions.

The American cigarette industry has increased greatly in recent decades. The present average annual output of about 140 billions of cigarettes is about thirty times that of the first years of the present century. It consumes more than half of all the tobacco used in American manufacture. Cigarette manufacture is a machine process and requires mainly cheap labor. On this account the factories are fewer in number and larger in size than cigar factories. About 80 per cent of the total cigarette output is made in the Piedmont district, of which Richmond, Va., and Winston-Salem and Durham, N. C., are the principal manufacturing centers. Other important centers are in Kentucky, New Jersey, and Pennsylvania.

Smoking and chewing tobaccos and snuff also are manufactured near the centers of tobacco production. Although some imported tobaccos are used for blending in these products, the bulk of the raw material is of domestic origin. Three centers, St. Louis, Louisville, and Winston-Salem and Durham, handle more than half the total business. The necessity for large capital in the establishment of a tobacco manufactory has led to the formation of powerful corporations. In the United States, as in most countries, the production and manufacture of tobacco is a business conducted under close governmental supervision. Much of this is for purposes of taxation, but in part also it is for the protection of the grower and the prevention of monopoly.

FOREIGN TRADE IN TOBACCO. Exports of American tobacco are large. The principal item of export is leaf tobacco of which normally about 425 million pounds is shipped to all parts of the world. The largest buyers are the United Kingdom and other west-European countries. However, the United States is not the only source of export tobacco, as was clearly shown in 1939–1940, when Britain shifted her purchases of cigarette tobacco to Turkey in partial payment for Turkish political support in the Near East. This leaves the American grower in an unfortunate situation. In many countries the manufacture of tobacco is a government monopoly, and imports of manufactured tobaccos are restricted. There are, however, some exports of cigarettes, cigars, and other tobacco from the United States, the principal purchasers being Canada and the west-European countries. American imports of tobacco are comparatively small, special grades of cigarette leaf from Greece and Turkey being the principal item and amounting to only about one-tenth the exports.

SELECTED REFERENCES

BROWNE, W. A. Dark-fired Tobacco Region of the North Highland Rim, *Econ. Geog.*, Vol. 14 (1938), pp. 55–67.

FOSCUE, EDWIN J., and ELIZABETH TROTH. Sugar Plantations of the Irish Bend District, Louisiana, *Econ. Geog.*, Vol. 12 (1936), pp. 373–380.

GAGE, C. E. American Tobacco Types, Uses, and Markets, *U.S. Dept. Agr., Circ.* 249, 1933.

GUTIERREZ, V. "The World Sugar Problem, 1926–1935," London, 1935.

HUDGINS, BERT. Tobacco Growing in Southwestern Ontario, *Econ. Geog.*, Vol. 14 (1938), pp. 223–232.

LANDON, C. E. The Tobacco Growing Industry of North Carolina, *Econ. Geog.*, Vol. 10 (1934), pp. 239–253.

LYNSKY, MEYER. "Sugar Economics, Statistics, and Documents," New York, 1938.

ROBERTSON, C. J. Geographical Trends in Sugar Production, *Geog. Rev.*, Vol. 22 (1932), pp. 120–130.

STILGENBAUER, F. A. The Michigan Sugar Beet Industry, *Econ. Geog.*, Vol. 3 (1927), pp. 486–506.

———. The Sugar Supply of the United States, *Jour. Geog.*, Vol. 27 (1928), pp. 287–310.

Sugar, *U.S. Tariff Comm., Rept.* 73, 2d Series, 1934.

ZIMMERMANN, ERICH W. "World Resources and Industries," pp. 258–302, New York, 1933.

# Chapter VII. Vegetable Fibers
# and Textiles

## Cotton Growing

COTTON A COMMERCIAL STAPLE.   The spinning of cotton fiber and the weaving of cotton cloth is a very ancient industry. Plants closely related to modern American cotton grow in many parts of the Old World, and their fibers have been spun and woven in the Orient for many centuries. Yet before cotton could attain world significance, it was necessary to wait upon inventive genius. The Oriental hand method of removing the seeds from cotton was too expensive in the western world. Machines were required to replace hand labor in ginning. The use of the cotton gin and the application of mechanical power to spinning and weaving began in the latter part of the eighteenth century.

Cotton growing in America had its origin with the colonial settlers of the South Atlantic states. Its use was, however, limited mainly to the making of homespun cloth until the close of the American Revolution. At that time a regular foreign trade in cotton began, and it was greatly increased following the invention of the cotton gin in 1793. The influence of this machine upon cotton growing is seen in the fact that the total American cotton crop of 1791 was only about 4,000 bales, but 19 years later it had increased to 100,000 bales. The present United States cotton crop averages nearly 13 million bales, which is about half the total cotton crop of the world (Fig. 59).

The preeminence of the United States in cotton growing is due to a combination of favorable conditions. The world has for many years been searched, particularly by British interests, for other possible cotton-growing regions which would make the British spinners less dependent upon the American cotton supply. Their search has slowly been rewarded, and the United States share of the world's production has declined from about 80 per cent 50 years ago to about 50 per cent now. However, the total world consumption of cotton has increased greatly in the meantime, and the actual average crop in the United States now is more than one-third larger than it was at the earlier date. The conditions that

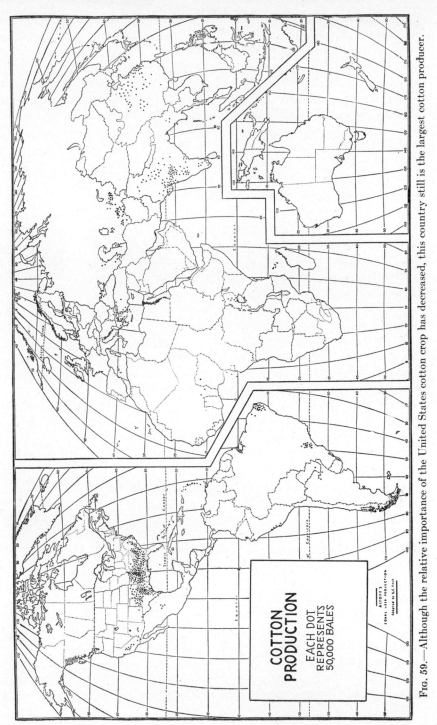

COTTON
PRODUCTION

EACH DOT
REPRESENTS
50,000 BALES

FIG. 59.—Although the relative importance of the United States cotton crop has decreased, this country still is the largest cotton producer.

enable the United States to retain its leading position are both physical and economic.

CLIMATE AND COTTON.    The cotton plant is a woody shrub of tropical origin. Some varieties still growing in the tropics are perennial and attain treelike forms. In the American cotton belt, however, the occurrence of freezing winter weather makes it necessary to treat the crop as an annual. The slow-growing, woody plant does not come to maturity so quickly as the cereals and does not prove profitable where the frostless season averages much less than 200 days in length. Not only must the growing season for cotton be long, but it must be warm and moist. In nearly all of the cotton belt the summer temperature averages at least 77°F. The western margin of the cotton-growing section, except where the crop is irrigated, nearly coincides with the annual rainfall of 20 inches and has a warm-season (April to September) rainfall of 15 inches or more. Farther east the annual rainfall is as much as 50 to 55 inches in parts of the cotton belt. In general, the rainfall is of the thundershower type, interspersed with abundant sunshine. It is usually more abundant in the spring and summer months than in the autumn. This condition is particularly favorable to cotton growing, since frequent rains in the autumn discolor the cotton of the opening bolls and interfere with picking. In Florida and on the entire coastal margin of the southern states east of Texas, autumn rains are more abundant than farther inland, reaching 10 to 20 inches as compared with 6 to 10 inches in the cotton belt. This is one reason why very little cotton is grown in the coastal strip.

IMPORTANT DISTRICTS IN THE AMERICAN COTTON BELT.    Within the temperature and rainfall boundaries stated above, cotton is as generally grown as is wheat between Colorado and Maryland. Figure 60 shows, however, that there are several districts in which the proportion of the total area planted to cotton is greater than the average. These areas reflect especially suitable conditions of soil, surface, and drainage and freedom from cotton pests. Several among these districts should be particularly noted: (1) The inner portion of the Atlantic and Gulf Coastal Plain from North Carolina to Mississippi. This is characterized by a gently rolling surface and by well-drained and comparatively light soils that resulted from the clearing of original forests. The soils generally are not of high fertility, have been depleted by long-continued cotton cropping, and some of them are badly eroded. Heavy applications of fertilizer are used, and the actual yields of cotton generally are superior to those obtained from some of the more fertile soils of the drier western districts. Within this area is the crescent-shaped district known as the "Alabama black belt," extending from eastern central Alabama to northeastern Mississippi. It is a region of original prairie, which had heavy dark soils and was one of the most productive parts of the cotton belt. Soil depletion, erosion, and the ravages of cotton pests have caused farmers to diversify their crops by the introduction of forage crops and the livestock industry. It is still an important cotton-producing area but no longer outstanding. (2) The Piedmont belt of the Carolinas and Georgia. This is separated from the Coastal Plain district by a less productive area of sandy land. The Piedmont is more hilly than the Coastal Plain. Its red clay and clay loam soils are derived from crystalline rocks; were originally forested; and, because of their steeper slopes and long cultivation in

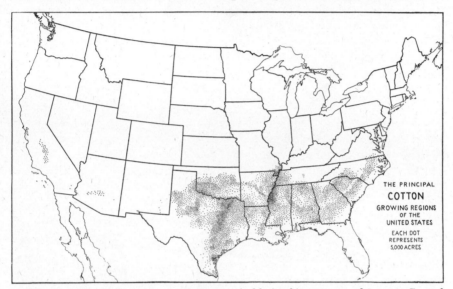

THE PRINCIPAL
**COTTON**
GROWING REGIONS
OF THE
UNITED STATES
EACH DOT
REPRESENTS
5,000 ACRES

FIG. 60.—Five major cotton regions recognizable in this map are: the upper Coastal Plain, the Piedmont, the Yazoo bottoms, the Texas black prairies, and the prairies of Oklahoma and western Texas.

cotton, are badly eroded. Heavy fertilization and intensive tillage practices, such as terrace cultivation, tend to keep up a high cotton yield in this area also. (3) The Mississippi River bluffs and bottomlands. The bluff lands have fine, deep, productive soils of loessial origin but are much dissected by streams and severely eroded. The bottomlands are the alluvial flood plains of the Mississippi and are extremely fertile but in part poorly drained and subject to floods. The tilled portions, which in parts of the district reach 60 per cent of the total area, are among the most productive cotton lands in the country. (4) The "black-waxy" prairies of east central Texas. These are old grassland soils derived from soft limestones. They are like the Alabama black belt but have been tilled a shorter time and, being somewhat drier, are less subject to cotton pests. (5) The red prairies and high plains districts of western Oklahoma and Texas. These are flat to undulating lands with prairie soils of high lime and humus content. They are deep and fertile, and the drier climate of this region gives greater freedom from cotton pests and water erosion but increases the damage resulting from wind erosion. This is the newest section of the cotton belt and is characterized by the most extensive methods of cotton production. It is separated from the productive cotton lands of eastern Texas by a partially wooded region of rougher surface and of more shallow and less fertile soils.

Several other districts where cotton growing is important are to be seen in Fig. 60. Some of these are the valleys of the Tennessee and

Fig. 61.—Good short-staple upland cotton growing in the Texas black prairies.

Arkansas rivers, the uplands of northeastern Texas and adjacent parts of Arkansas and Louisiana, and the irrigated cotton lands of the Rio Grande Valley and also those of Arizona and California.

CLASSES OF COTTON.   Many classes and grades of cotton are produced in the United States. They differ in length of staple, color, and fineness. The principal part of the crop is medium- to short-staple cotton, having fiber from ⅞ to 1 inch long (Fig. 61). It is suited to the manufacture of many classes of ordinary cotton cloth. Variations exist, however, within this type that are the result of differences in the producing districts, especially in conditions of moisture. The more fertile soils generally produce the longer staples, especially the Mississippi alluvial bottomlands and the irrigated cotton lands of the western districts. The most superior staple ever grown in the United States, known as "Sea Island," was formerly produced in the Southeast, especially in Georgia and northern

Florida. This variety never constituted more than 1 per cent of all American cotton, and its production has practically ceased owing to destruction by the boll weevil. The longest and finest staples now grown are of the Egyptian types raised mainly in Arizona, but the quantity is small.

ECONOMIC FACTORS IN COTTON GROWING. Cotton is a peculiarly important crop in southern United States. There is no other equally large area of the world where cotton can be grown so well, a fact that has led to intense specialization. In parts of the cotton belt one-half, and in some localities as much as three-fourths, of the cultivated land is planted annually to this one crop. Cotton, like wheat, is a cash crop. Little of it is retained for use on the farm. Like that of wheat, its price fluctuates greatly from year to year with variations in world supply and demand. During the prosperous war years 1916–1920 the average farm price of cotton reached nearly 25 cents per pound. During the depression year of 1931 it averaged less than 6 cents. Increasing competition from foreign producers, unsettled conditions of world economy, and large domestic crops have combined with other factors to produce a condition of general economic distress among the cotton growers.

So specialized a form of agriculture gives rise to economic conditions very different from those found in regions of general farming. (1) Crops other than cotton are not intensively cultivated. Corn is the crop of next importance, and other cereals as well as many fruits and vegetables are grown, yet the total amount of food produced is often insufficient for the needs of the people of the intensive cotton districts. The deficiency is made up by importing goods from the northern states. (2) The scarcity of hay and grain crops causes the animal industries to be less important than in the North. The absence of animal manures makes it necessary for the planters to spend large sums of money for commercial fertilizers in order to maintain the fertility of the poorer cotton soils (Fig. 145). (3) The abolition of slavery left many plantations without sufficient labor; some of them have been broken up into small farms, but many still remain under the management of a single owner. The small farms are generally cultivated by white or negro tenants who share the crop with the owner or pay cash rent for the land. (4) The nature of the cotton plant and the irregular way in which its bolls ripen have, so far, made picking by machinery difficult. For cotton picking, cheap labor is necessary. The 500 pounds of ginned cotton in one bale represents about 10 days' work for an average cotton picker. Often it requires the entire family of a tenant to pick the cotton that he has been able to plant and tend. Where extra labor at picking time is hard to get, the quantity of cotton per farm may be limited to the amount the family can pick, perhaps 10 or 12 acres. The labor requirement of cotton was the principal reason for the maintenance of slavery in the southern states, and cotton growing is now the principal occupation of the negro population (Fig. 62). (5) Since cotton can be neither eaten nor worn by the farmer, he must sell it for cash with which to buy food and clothing. Even a partial failure of the cotton crop or an unexpected decline in price may necessitate mortgaging next year's crop for funds. In general, the cotton growers operate upon a basis of credit to a greater extent than do most other American farmers. This condition has, in the past, led banks to discourage the introduction of other crops or of forms of animal industry that would not be likely to yield an

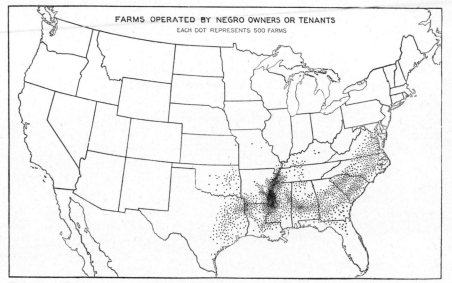

FARMS OPERATED BY NEGRO OWNERS OR TENANTS
EACH DOT REPRESENTS 500 FARMS

FIG. 62.—The importance of negro labor in the eastern part of the cotton belt is shown by comparing this map with Fig. 60.

immediate cash return with which debts could be paid. The unwisdom of this policy is now widely recognized, and banks are foremost in the encouragement of diversified agriculture in the cotton belt.

THE INFLUENCE OF COTTON PESTS.    Cotton is subject to the ravages of several diseases and pests. The most important and destructive of these pests is the boll weevil, which entered southern Texas from Mexico in 1892 (Fig. 63). The weevil is the larva of a beetle. The eggs of the insect are laid through perforations made in the covering of the young cotton boll, and the growing larvae feed upon the immature fiber. Year after year the pest spread north and east until, in 1921, it reached North Carolina, and all of the principal cotton districts were then affected. The first appearance of the weevil often brought crop failure and financial disaster. Fortunately, not all districts are equally afflicted, nor is the damage in all years uniformly great. Cold winters and dry springs are harmful to the weevil. For that reason the western cotton fields of Texas suffer less than others, and in some years other sections of the cotton belt are comparatively free from damage. It is also true that familiarity with the ways of the pest has taught means of control by the introduction of more careful and varied methods of agriculture and by the selection of quick-maturing varieties of cotton. Although the weevil takes a large annual toll from the cotton planters, it is not so large as to be generally

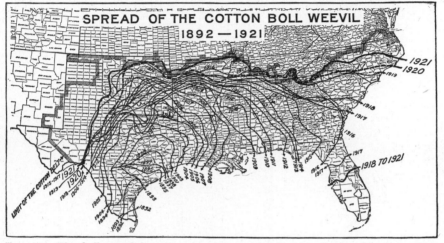

Fig. 63.—The boll-weevil has now spread to nearly all parts of the cotton belt. (*U.S. Department of Agriculture.*)

disastrous. Indeed, by some, the weevil has been pronounced a blessing in disguise, since it has enforced more careful farming and the partial abandonment of the one-crop system in favor of a more diversified type of agriculture in the cotton belt.

## Cotton Marketing

PREPARATION FOR MARKET. About two-thirds of the weight of freshly picked cotton is in the seeds. The preparation of cotton for market begins with the removal of the seeds at a local ginnery (Fig. 8). There the fiber is pressed into rather loose burlap-covered bales which average about 500 pounds in weight. The farmer pays for the service and removes his cotton and its seed to await a favorable opportunity to sell.

THE COTTON WAREHOUSE. The baled cotton is commonly stored in public warehouses where it is protected from damage. The warehouse receipt delivered to the owner is good security for a bank loan which may carry him until the cotton is sold. The warehouse also serves as a convenient place for grading cotton into lots of uniform quality. The grading is done largely upon a basis of standards determined by the U. S. Department of Agriculture.

COTTON MARKETS.    Cotton is sold by the grower to a buyer who may be a local merchant, or he may represent a middleman or even a distant mill. Farmers having only one or two bales of cotton commonly sell immediately after the cotton is ginned, usually to local merchants. Yet, whether the bale is a part of a large or of a small lot, it eventually finds its way with many others from the primary market into a central market. (1) The central market may be one of the larger cities of the cotton belt

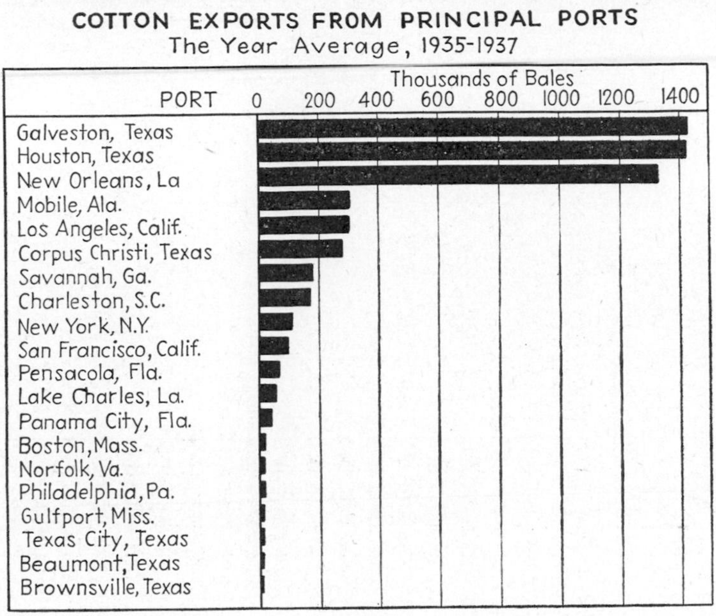

### COTTON EXPORTS FROM PRINCIPAL PORTS
The Year Average, 1935-1937

| PORT | Thousands of Bales |
|------|--------------------|
| | 0   200   400   600   800   1000   1200   1400 |
| Galveston, Texas | |
| Houston, Texas | |
| New Orleans, La | |
| Mobile, Ala. | |
| Los Angeles, Calif. | |
| Corpus Christi, Texas | |
| Savannah, Ga. | |
| Charleston, S.C. | |
| New York, N.Y. | |
| San Francisco, Calif. | |
| Pensacola, Fla. | |
| Lake Charles, La. | |
| Panama City, Fla. | |
| Boston, Mass. | |
| Norfolk, Va. | |
| Philadelphia, Pa. | |
| Gulfport, Miss. | |
| Texas City, Texas | |
| Beaumont, Texas | |
| Brownsville, Texas | |

FIG. 64.

where the grading is completed; and if the cotton is destined for export, the bale is further compressed to save shipping space. (2) It may be an export market in a coast city, such as Galveston, New Orleans, or Savannah, where the bale may be sold for overseas shipment (Fig. 64). Or (3) it may be a consuming market in which is located the cotton mill that will manufacture the bale of raw cotton into a fabric. The cotton markets known as "future" markets are important because of their cotton-exchange dealings and their influence upon cotton prices rather than because of the number of bales of cotton actually handled in them. New York and New Orleans are the cotton "future" markets of the United States, but Liverpool, England, is the principal cotton-exchange center of the world.

AMERICAN FOREIGN TRADE IN COTTON.    Before the World War of 1914–1918 more than two-thirds of the average United States cotton crop was shipped to foreign markets. This was true of no other important farm product. Since that time various conditions have combined to decrease both the proportion of the crop exported and the actual quantity (Fig. 65). Foreign competition in the growing of cotton has become more keen. European buying countries have attempted, so far as possible, to supply their needs from colonial possessions. The disturbed state of world exchange, growing out of a contagious spirit of economic nationalism, has made foreign purchasers less than normally able to buy in the United

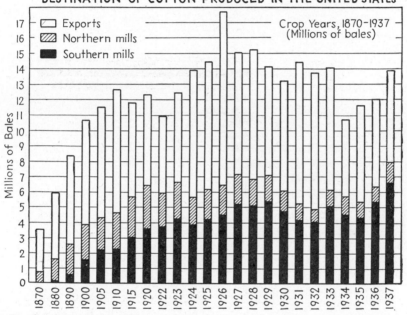

Fig. 65.—Southern cotton mills use an increasing proportion of the American cotton crop.

States market. American mills have increased their consumption of domestic cotton by about 10 per cent of the crop during the 25-year period. The average crop of the present, 13 million bales, is about the same as it was at the beginning of the second decade of the century, but American exports of raw cotton have declined from more than two-thirds to less than half the production, and exports of cotton manufactures have declined also. In consequence, the unmarketable surplus which has to be carried over has increased and recently has averaged nearly one-half the normal crop. This is a further cause of depression among the cotton planters, and no satisfactory market outlet is in sight.

The normal cotton movements and exports constitute a large part of the business of the railways of the cotton region and of the ports along its margin. Texas has the most important ports of export, yet New

Orleans and Savannah also have large shares in the trade that is directed mainly toward the ports of northwestern Europe. A large quantity moves from the Gulf ports via the Panama Canal to Japan and China, and some even moves by rail to the Pacific ports en route to the same countries.

## Cotton Manufacturing

THE IMPORTANCE OF COTTON TEXTILES.    The manufacture of cotton cloth is not native to America or even to Europe. The exhaustless patience

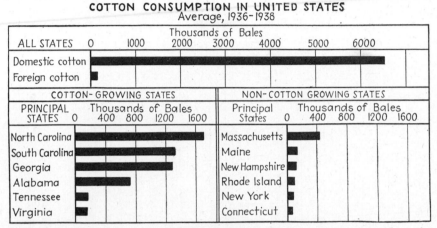

FIG. 66.—The mills of the cotton states use more cotton than those of the North, but the latter use a larger proportion of fine cotton, including much of that imported from Egypt.

and cheap labor of the Orient enabled the people of China and India to separate the fiber from the seed of native cotton and to spin and weave cotton fabrics, all by the simplest of hand apparatus, long before such an industry was thought of in the western world. The Coromandel Coast of India was particularly famed for the fineness of its fabrics. Although little of the best was ever exported, cotton cloths obtained by European and American traders from the Indian port of Calicut were in great demand. They were known to the trade as "calicoes."

Cotton cloth has been abundant and in general use in Europe and America for little more than a century. Cheap cotton in America was followed by the development of factory spinning and weaving in England and subsequently in the United States and many other countries. Cotton fabrics became so inexpensive that in many parts of the world the household manufacture of linen and woolen cloth was given up and the arts of home spinning and weaving were forgotten. Cotton now enters not only into clothing but also into an infinite variety of other essential commodities.

TYPES OF COTTON MILLS. The most important type of cotton-manufacturing establishment is the mill, which spins and weaves raw cotton into piece goods. Such cloths are of great variety, ranging from canvas or blankets to the finest lawns and organdies. Other types of establishments turn out knit goods, chiefly hosiery and underwear; cotton small wares, from laces to lampwicks; bags, yarns, threads, and twine.

THE DISTRIBUTION OF AMERICAN COTTON MILLS. Cotton manufacture in America clings to the Atlantic seaboard states (Fig. 66). Some mills have sprung up in the middle western states and some in the cotton-growing districts west of the Mississippi River. Relatively, however, they are few in number, and the total value of their products is small.

The mills of eastern North America are distributed from Quebec to Alabama and may conveniently be divided into three important groups: (1) New England, (2) the Middle Atlantic states, and (3) the South. The cotton industries of the three differ in many important respects.

COTTON MANUFACTURING IN NEW ENGLAND. The manufacture of cotton began in New England at the close of the American Revolution. For some years the industry made little progress, owing to scarcity of labor and of capital and to the strength of British competition. The first quarter of the nineteenth century saw (1) the accumulation of considerable capital in New England through the shipping and fishing industries, (2) a greatly increased supply of raw cotton available in the South, and (3) the introduction of the power loom and other mechanical improvements in spinning and weaving. These inventions permitted the utilization of some of the abundant water powers of New England in cotton manufacture and thereby reduced the cost of human labor, an important factor in the competition with goods made in England. The impetus furnished by these new conditions caused cotton mills to spring up in many parts of New England but especially on water-power sites along streams near the coast. This region included the lower Merrimack River in northeastern Massachusetts and the district close to Narragansett Bay in Rhode Island and southeastern Massachusetts. When the capacities of the principal power sites were outgrown, the latter region had the advantage because of the greater ease with which it could get coal by boat from the Middle Atlantic ports.

Increasing competition from southern mills and the fact that the once great markets of India and the Orient are manufacturing cotton goods for their own use have wrought a great change in the New England cotton-textile industry. The major change has been a decrease in its size. The number of spindles active in 1938 was barely one-third the number in 1920–1923. This great shrinkage has caused the abandonment of mills, some of them of the largest size, and their idleness or conversion to other uses. That, in consequence, created unemployment in the mill towns. The most important centers are now principally those near the coast and especially in the southeast of New England, where cities such as Fall River and New Bedford, Mass., continue to hold high rank. A second change is in the character of the cotton goods produced. The northern mills have been forced to utilize their more experienced labor, higher organization, and better climatic conditions to produce finer goods, such as require more skill and less cotton than those manufactured in the South. Evidence of this trend is seen in the fact that, although New England has still nearly one-fourth of the active cotton spindles in the United States, its mills consume only one-eighth of the raw cotton spun. This indicates an emphasis on fine rather than coarse yarns and on the manufacture of fine cloth. The great domestic markets for cloth, particularly New York, are close at hand also, and the New England manufacturers pay close attention to the demands of these markets as the clothing manufacturers anticipate or create changes in style.

Cotton Manufacturing in the Middle Atlantic States is of less importance and of a different type from the industries of New England and the South. Its mills are smaller and are characterized much more by the knitting industries than by the weaving of cloth. Although wool, silk, and rayon as well as cotton are used in the knitting industries, separately or in combinations, cotton constitutes more than half the bulk of the raw materials consumed.

Knitting mills were established at Germantown, near Philadelphia, at an early date, and Pennsylvania still is the leading state in the industry, which is concentrated mainly in its southeastern portion and also in adjacent New Jersey and New York. This phase of the textile industry is, however, much more widely distributed in the country than cotton-cloth manufacture, since it does not require highly skilled labor. Knitting mills are particularly numerous in the cities of the Mohawk Valley of New York. There are many also in parts of the South (North Carolina and Tennessee) and even the Middle West, especially Wisconsin and Indiana. Some of the widely distributed mills were established long ago and have continued to prosper because of their reputation for excellent products and because they had access to abundant supplies of cheap labor.

Cotton Manufacturing in the South.   Cotton manufacturing has developed rapidly in the southern states. More than six times as much raw cotton is used in the southern mills as in those of New England. This development may be attributed to several factors. (1) Cheap water power developed at the "fall line" and in the southern Appalachians is an attraction to cotton manufacturers. This industry is one that finds hydro-electric power particularly adaptable to its needs, and recent years have seen a large increase in the available supply of cheap electricity in the southern Appalachian region. For such mills as still require coal, supplies are as conveniently available from the southern Appalachian fields as any source of supply is to New England mills. (2) The greatest attraction for cotton mills in the South has been the large supply of white labor available at lower wages than are prevalent in New England. The labor was, and to a large degree still is, less skilled than that in New England. However, the labor laws of southern states are less restrictive, and hours of labor are longer. There are other minor savings for the southern manufacturer also, such as lower taxes and lower costs for housing and heating.

As a result of these and other factors, the type of cotton manufacturing in the South differs in several ways from that found in New England. (1) The mills are numerous; and though most of them are modern and well equipped, they average smaller than those of New England. (2) The goods manufactured, though of great variety, are generally heavier than those made in New England mills, requiring more cotton and less skill. The annual quantity of raw cotton spun in Massachusetts is about 24 pounds per 1,000 spindle hours; in North Carolina it is more than 40; and in Georgia, more than 50 pounds per 1,000 spindle hours.

Although cotton manufacture was established in the South almost as early as in New England, it did not develop rapidly until the last two decades of the past century, and its great increase has taken place within the present century. The spinning capacity of southern mills first exceeded that of New England mills in 1923. The region of greatest first growth was the Piedmont section of the Carolinas (Fig. 66). Subsequently mills were established farther south, and now Alabama has half as many spindles as Massachusetts and consumes considerably more cotton. This south and westward movement is aided by the large amounts of hydroelectric power recently made available in the Tennessee Valley region.

THE DYEING AND FINISHING OF TEXTILES. Newly spun cotton yarn is gray or tan in color and contains impurities. Before it can be marketed as cloth, it must pass through many processes designed to cleanse, bleach, dye, or otherwise improve or change its appearance. The processes are technical and require skilled labor and abundant pure water. Many large New England mills dye and finish at least a part of their own cloths; but, in general, dyeing and finishing comprise a separate industry which deals also with rayon, silk, wool, and mixed yarns or fabrics. Because of its close association with spinning and weaving the dyeing and finishing industry was first established in the textile region between Boston and Philadelphia. This region still conducts more than two-thirds of the total business, for in addition to an early start it has other advantages, such as an abundance of pure water and nearness to the great cloth markets where styles in color and design are set. The great increase in southern weaving has, however, attracted the same processes to that producing region, and nearly one-third of the value of dyeing and finishing may now be credited to the southern states.

THE MANUFACTURE OF COTTON CLOTHING. The manufacture of clothing from cotton cloth is an essential part of the general clothing industry. The cotton piece goods are obtained from many sources, and the market is widespread. The principal influence affecting the location of the industry is the supply of inexpensive labor, and, like other clothing industries, this one is found principally in the great cities, especially New York, Philadelphia, and Chicago. In the manufacture of collars, cuffs, and shirts, New York and Pennsylvania predominate. The industry is particularly concentrated in the city of Troy, N. Y., largely as a result of its early start. These industries employ linen, silk, and other fabrics as well as cotton cloth.

AMERICAN FOREIGN TRADE IN COTTON MANUFACTURES. The same restrictive influences that have reduced the exports of raw cotton have affected the exports of cotton wares made in American mills and clothing factories. The principal exports are cotton cloth of all grades, especially the heavier, such as sheetings, ducks, drills, and other plain cloths, both dyed and uncolored. Smaller quantities of finer goods and cotton clothing of great variety are included also. But the total value of the entire list has recently declined to about one-third that of only a decade ago. At the same time the value of United States imports of cotton manufactures has declined also but not to so great a degree. The volume of imports of the cheaper grades of plain cloth and semimanufactured wares has actually more than doubled. They are produced at low cost by the cheap labor of Asia, especially Japan. The improved quality of American cotton manufactures makes it less necessary to import fine goods from Europe, and tariff restrictions make it more difficult for European manufacturers to sell in the United States market. However, some quantities still are purchased, especially from England and Switzerland.

## The Plant-stalk Fibers and Rayon

HOME-GROWN FIBERS UNIMPORTANT. Many other plant fibers are used in manufacture, but only a few of them compete with cotton in the manufacture of textiles. Most of the others are coarse and are used in making rope, twine, and similar products but not cloth. Among those of greatest use in textiles are flax, hemp, and jute. None of these is grown in important quantity in Anglo-America. Jute can be grown only in the tropics. Flax and hemp are well adapted to American conditions of soil and climate and have been successfully grown here—flax in the Great Lakes region; hemp, in the Ohio Valley. Both crops, however, require so much human labor in their harvesting and preparation for spinning that it is impossible for the American-grown crop to compete in price with foreign fibers, raised where labor is cheap, especially in Russia and the Baltic Plain of Europe. The fiber of the flax plants grown for seed in the American spring-wheat region is harsh and brittle and has no value for the manufacture of textiles.

THE MANUFACTURE OF PLANT-STALK FIBERS. The products of flax fiber, hemp, jute, and other fibers of plant origin are required in America in great quantity. They include linen piece goods, linen thread, hempen rope, twine and coarse cloth, jute twine, bagging and burlap of all grades, from art burlap to grain sacks and the coarse material used to cover cotton bales. Linens are purchased largely in manufactured form, although some 5,000 or 6,000 tons of raw or unmanufactured flax fiber are purchased for use in American spinning and weaving. Jute also is imported, mainly in the manufactured form of burlap. Large amounts of jute and other coarse fibers are imported in the raw state for manufacture into twines and cordage, especially binder twines for use in harvesting grain crops.

RAYON is both a vegetable fiber and a chemical product. It is made from cellulose, principally woodpulp, which has been digested chemically and forced through a group of minute openings and then hardened. This is essentially what silk is also, although the digestion and expulsion are performed by the silkworm. It is with silk that rayon principally competes.

Although the raw materials used in rayon manufacture are woodpulp and cotton linters, the industry generally is not located with particular regard to the sources from which they come. The rayon mills are located rather in those areas having a high degree of industrial organization and particularly those having well-established chemical industries. Such are the manufacturing regions of the United States, Japan, Germany, and England, which are the principal rayon producers. In the United States the leading centers of manufacture are the industrial districts of southeastern Pennsylvania, Maryland, and Virginia; the Lake Erie industrial belt; and that of the middle Appalachian region of Tennessee and West Virginia. Within these areas the principal localizing condition is the availability of a large supply of clean, soft water. Good rail connections, cheap power, and abundant labor are also essential.

The world output of rayon fiber has increased tenfold within a decade, and further rapid increases may be expected as well as changes in the raw materials used and improvements in the quality of the product. The yarn made in rayon factories is raw material for many weaving and knitting mills. Its further manufacture is closely associated with that of silk and may be discussed in that connection.

SELECTED REFERENCES

BAKER, O. E. Agricultural Regions of North America, Part II, The South, *Econ. Geog.*, Vol. 3 (1927), pp. 50–86.

BURGY, J. H. "The New England Cotton Textile Industry," Baltimore, 1932.

LEMERT, B. F. "The Cotton Textile Industry of the Southern Appalachian Piedmont," Chapel Hill, 1933.

STINE, O. C., and O. E. BAKER. "Cotton," U.S. Department of Agriculture, Office of Farm Management, 1918.

VANCE, R. B. "Human Geography of the South," pp. 177–204, 275–315, Chapel Hill, 1935.

"World Cotton Production and Trade," International Institute of Agriculture, Rome, 1936.

ZIMMERMANN, ERICH W. "World Resources and Industries," pp. 325–378, New York, 1933.

# Chapter VIII. Forests and Forest-product Industries

FOREST PRODUCTS ESSENTIAL. Among primitive peoples wood and other forest products serve a wide range of economic needs and are indispensable in their modes of life. The industrial and commercial nations of the world have developed numberless substitutes for wood but have not thereby decreased their consumption of it or become less dependent upon forests. New demands have arisen that utilize the products of the forest in a multitude of ways unknown to primitive men. Directly or indirectly every aspect of modern life would be handicapped if the woods, resins, and chemical products of forest trees became scarce or unduly expensive. One can easily think of some of the numerous ways in which these products are involved in the growing and packing of foods; the manufacture of plastics, clothing, and paper; the erection of shelters; the construction of means of transportation and communication; and the making of a wide array of items of less essential nature.

North America is a new land. Most of it is well supplied with rainfall, and it originally supported vast forests of a quality unequaled in any other continent. This heritage has been freely used; much of it has been wasted; but fortunately a good part of it still remains. Intelligent consideration of the wise use, conservation, and perpetuation of these essential materials is the duty of every person.

PRIMEVAL FOREST REGIONS. The original forests of North America consisted of a broad, northern, transcontinental belt with three unequal southward projections (Fig. 67). The boundaries of these forests were determined mainly by conditions of climate, surface relief, and soil.

The northern margin of the forested region extends from central Labrador westward to Hudson Bay, on the west side of which it inclines northward to the mouth of the Mackenzie River and across Alaska. North of this irregular line is the tundra where the average temperature of the warmest month is less than 50°F., and soil moisture is so permanently locked up by frost that valuable trees cannot grow. The transcontinental northern forest belt is most valuable on its southern margin, north of the Great Lakes region. Its three southward projections are (1)

135

the forests of the Pacific slope, (2) the Rocky Mountain forests, and (3) the broad eastern forest region extending from Lake Superior and the Gulf of St. Lawrence southward to the Gulf of Mexico. These three unequal forest regions are separated from one another by (1) the broad dry stretches of the cordilleran plateaus and (2) the grassy expanses of the central plains.

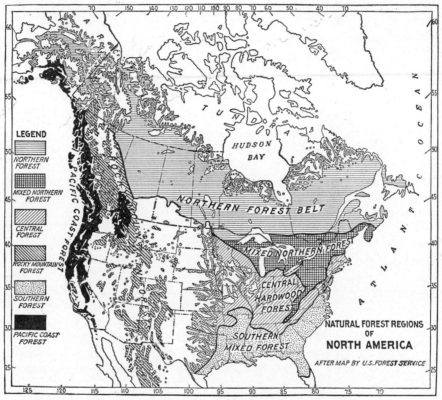

FIG. 67.—The original forest regions of North America.

TYPES OF ORIGINAL FOREST.   The forests of North America contain a greater variety of valuable trees than are to be found in the forests of Europe or any other middle-latitude region. Although many of the species are, by conditions of temperature and rainfall, limited to small parts of the continent, so great is the number of species that nearly every locality has a considerable variety. Yet each of the principal forest regions is characterized by a group of species that have determined the main uses to which the wood is put. The northern forest belt of Canada is predominantly a region of spruce, fir, birch, and poplar. The eastern forests [(3) above] include three dissimilar subdivisions: (a) A mixed northern forest, originally dominated by the white pine, the hemlock, and such valuable hardwoods as the maples, birch, and beech. A peninsular projection of this section follows the Appalachian Mountains southward. (*b*) A central hardwood forest region in which various kinds of oaks and hickory are only a few of the abundant and valuable species. (*c*) A southern mixed forest section in which different kinds of pine occupy most of the sandy lands (Fig. 9) and cypress is dominant in the extensive swamps (Fig. 68). Except on the prairie margin, these forests were originally dense and in places almost impenetrable.

Fig. 68.—Cypress, gum trees, and red maple growing in a Louisiana swamp forest. (*Photograph by U.S. Forest Service.*)

The western mountain forests are made up almost wholly of coniferous trees of many kinds, of which the Douglas fir is one of the most valuable. Except where the rainfall is heavy, as on the northern Pacific Coast, the mountain forests are much more open and scattered than were those of the East (Fig. 69). The splendid forests of Douglas fir, redwoods, and pine found in northern California and in western Oregon, Washington, and British Columbia are among the most valuable in the world (Fig. 70).

THE PRESENT FOREST SITUATION. The original forests of the United States covered about 820 million acres, or more than 40 per cent of the total area of the country. The destruction of these proceeded with great

FIG. 69.—The open timber of the Rocky Mountain forests. The mountain valleys and intermediate slopes furnish grazing for cattle and sheep. (*Photograph by U.S. Forest Service.*)

rapidity. Settlement in the forested states involved the clearing of timber to make room for agriculture. Moreover, competitive conditions in the lumbering industry and the very abundance and cheapness of wood encouraged the practice of destructive lumbering and the use of only the best timber. Such conditions were not particularly to be deplored, except where land unsuited to agriculture was stripped of its forest, for the rate

Fig. 70.—The dense stand of Douglas fir and cedar in a forest on the rainy Pacific Coast. Contrast with Fig. 69. (*Photograph by U.S. Forest Service.*)

of growth was, for several decades, even more rapid than the rate of consumption. That happy state has, however, passed, and of the original area of virgin forest only about 12 per cent now remains, and much of that in the least accessible places (Fig. 71). About one-fourth of the area of the United States is still classed as timberland, but less than 40 per cent of that land bears saw timber, either old forest or second growth; about 45 per cent of it is burned-over and cut-over land which now bears an irregular growth, often of undesirable species, some of which is suitable for firewood or ultimately may become saw timber. Nearly one-sixth of the total carries only poor young growth or is idle land, entirely devoid of timber. Unfortunately, many of these lands, naturally unsuited to agriculture, have been so damaged by fire and soil erosion that forests will

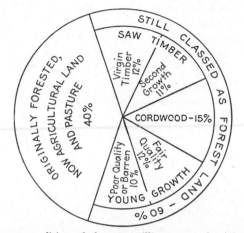

Fig. 71.—The present condition of the 820 million acres of original forest land in the United States.

Fig. 72.—The desolation that has followed lumbering and fire in northern Minnesota. Much of this kind of land is included in the land classified as forest. (*Photograph by U.S. Forest Service.*)

again find footing slowly if at all (Fig. 72). So great is the present forest depletion that the annual rate of cutting for lumber, firewood, and the many other uses, together with destruction by forest fires and other losses, is more than twice as great as the quantity added by the annual growth of new timber. At that rate of destruction the small remnant of this vast heritage cannot last long unless conservative methods are brought into operation quickly.

AMERICAN FOREST CONSERVATION. The problem of ensuring adequate forest resources for the future has long been urged upon the people of America by the advocates of conservation. The problem is very complex; and although it is being approached in many ways by Federal and state authorities, a generally satisfactory solution is not assured. In spite of a widespread appreciation of the approaching timber shortage, destructive methods of lumbering, devastating fires, and destruction of young growth by grazing livestock continue to deplete the forests. Various factors contribute to this condition, but perhaps the most important is a serious and long-standing conflict between public and private interests. It is obviously to the public interest that economical and selective methods of lumbering should be practiced, that cut-over lands not valuable for agriculture should be reforested, that efficient patrols should be established in all forest regions to reduce losses from fire, and that the young growth on potential forest lands should be protected from damage by excessive grazing. On the other hand, lumbering has always been intensively competitive, a condition that, together with high freight charges, has kept the lumberman's margin of profit low. He has, therefore, not generally been able to practice economical lumbering or to establish fire patrols. Customary methods of taxation upon timberlands have also made the cost of holding them so great that the lumberman could not afford the slow practices of selective cutting of timber but has had to strip his land as quickly as possible. He does not set about reforesting his cut-over lands, because his business judgment tells him that, in consideration of the long wait for returns and the many risks involved, the investment is a poor one. It is clear that, in this conflict of interests, public welfare demands that government shall plan for the future, when private enterprise finds it unprofitable to do so.

NATIONAL FORESTS. Proceeding upon this basis the United States government began in 1891 to acquire permanent forest lands, and nearly one-third of the forest lands of the United States, or about 150 million acres, is now federally owned. Location of these national forests is shown in Fig. 73. It will be observed that the larger part of them is in the western highlands. Mainly they are mountain forests that had not yet passed into private ownership at the time when it was realized that they should be held under Federal control. They had merely to be set aside. In the East the smaller national forests have been much more difficult to establish, since large parts of them had, by one means or another, to be acquired from private owners.

There is much deforested land, especially in New England and the Upper Great Lakes region, that has been farmed for a time and then abandoned because of infertility or other causes. Such lands and others upon which unpaid taxes have accumulated are being taken over, in some cases by the states, in others by the counties and even the towns. They are to be operated as perpetual forests for the benefit of the public owners, for the protection of water-supply districts, or as recreation areas. A total of about 5 million acres of forest land is now owned by the several states. The area in county, town, and city forests already is more than a

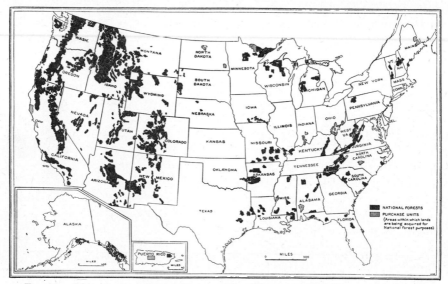

Fig. 73.—The extent of United States national forests in 1939. The eastern forests are increasing in number and extent by government purchase. States, counties, and even towns have forests in addition to these.

million acres and is increasing rapidly. Much of the scientific forestry of the United States, including selective cutting of timber and replanting of cut-over forest, is practiced on these publicly owned lands.

The wisdom of holding forest lands in public ownership has been recognized in Canada at a much earlier stage in forest exploitation than in the United States. Only about one-tenth of the whole forest area of the Dominion has passed into private ownership. Some 13 per cent more is licensed to private timber cutters, but they do not own the land. Some national and provincial forest reserves have been established, but, in fact, about 90 per cent of the total forest area is in public ownership.

FOREST DEPLETION AND MIGRATION OF THE LUMBER SUPPLY. In New England, lumbering was an early industry, and the forests were the basis of an important shipbuilding industry and also provided the colonists with a commodity for export to Europe. In 1850 New York was the leading state in the cutting of timber and the manufacture of lumber. So rapid was the depletion of her forests that 10 years later the lead had passed to Pennsylvania. The northern white pine forests continued, however, to furnish the most desirable lumber, and the center of the industry moved westward through Michigan, Wisconsin, and Minnesota. For many years thereafter the main source of building timbers was the pine forests of the South. Now only a small remnant of the original supply of southern pine remains, and the rate of cutting is diminishing. Six-tenths of the saw timber remaining in continental United States is in the three Pacific Coast states, and 78 per cent of the total lies west

## SAW TIMBER IN THE UNITED STATES

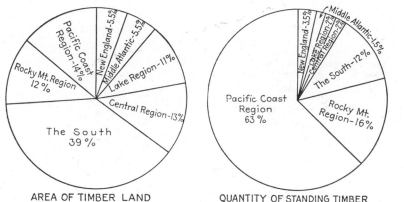

Fig. 74.—The distribution in the United States of the remaining stand of saw timber.

of the Great Plains (Fig. 74). Lumber from the West now predominates in the markets of the Great Lakes region and is an important factor in those of the East and South. Washington is the leading state in timber production.

THE TIMBER SUPPLY OF CANADA AND ALASKA.   The rapidly growing shortage of lumber in the United States may not be materially relieved by importation. Only in Canada and to a moderate degree in Alaska do large areas of accessible timberland remain untouched. The original forests of Canada are estimated at about 725 million acres, or nearly 90 per cent as great as the original forests of the United States. Much of this land is, however, near the northern limit of tree growth, and not more than one-third of the area contains timber of much value for lumber. It is obvious that the United States can expect only temporary relief from her timber shortage by importations from Canada.

The heavily timbered areas of Alaska are confined to the rainy sections of the Pacific slope (Fig. 164) and to narrow belts in the river bottoms of the interior, the uplands of the interior having little or no merchantable timber. The principal species of trees in Alaskan forests, like those of much of Canada, indicate that their future importance will be in the production of pulpwood rather than of lumber.

TRANSPORTATION AND LUMBER COSTS.   The shifting of the lumber supply of North America to the South and then to the West has had important consequences, since the principal market has not shifted with the supply but has remained in the North and the East. One important consequence is the greater freight charges imposed by the longer rail hauls to market. In 1893 the cost for shipping lumber from the Michigan forests to the Chicago market was from $1.50 to $2 per 1,000 feet, board measure. In 1905 the cost for shipment from Alabama and Mississippi to Chicago was $5.50 to $6.50. In 1918 to 1920 the cost of shipment from Portland, Ore., to Chicago was $15 per 1,000 feet. After 1915 other items in the cost of lumber increased more rapidly in proportion to the selling price than did the freight charges.

THE MANUFACTURE OF LUMBER.   The annual consumption of timber in America includes 38 billion board feet of lumber, nearly 5⅓ million cords of pulpwood, 50 million railway ties, and 60 million cords of fuel, besides many millions of poles, posts, and mine timbers. Only the lumber and its products and the pulpwood require manufacture to bring them into usable form.

The first step in lumber manufacture is timber cutting. The nature of this operation is considerably influenced by the physical situation of the forest. In the period during which the northeastern forests were exploited it was carried on principally in the winter. Logs were taken by sled to the most accessible waterway, where they were piled on the ice to await the spring freshets which would float them to a sawmill. In the southern forests climate did not permit of such methods, and logs had to be hauled by teams and woodland railways. In the swamp forests of the Mississippi delta, streams, bayous, or even canals dug for the purpose aided in collecting the timber. The high mountain forests of the West presented other problems. Railways, located in the valleys, were often considerable distances from the scene of timber cutting, which could not easily be reached by roads. Logs were skidded down the slopes or washed down in flumes constructed for the purpose out of timber. The progress of road construction in nearly all parts of the United States has, in recent years, permitted continually larger parts of the logs cut to be assembled at the sawmill by motor trucks.

The most widely distributed form of wood manufactory is the sawmill. Because logs are heavy and bulky and because a considerable part of their volume remains as mill waste (Fig. 75), they are sawed into the more easily handled and more concentrated form of lumber close to the region of timber production. It follows, therefore, that sawmills will be found in every part of the United States and Canada where there are lumbering operations (Fig. 76). The number of sawmills varies greatly from year to year. The census of 1937 records about 7,500 such mills in the United States alone. It is to be noted, however, that most of them are small and that many are portable mills which are readily set up on new sites for the sawing of small amounts of timber, or they may cease operation entirely. A large part of the lumber sawed is the produce of a

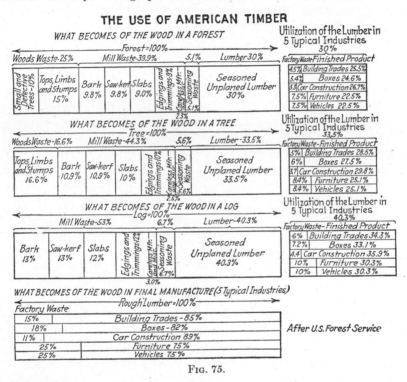

FIG. 75.

relatively small number of large mills, of which the majority are in the states bordering on the Pacific Ocean and the Gulf of Mexico.

The relative importance of the various kinds of lumber manufactured is shown in Fig. 77. Other important sawmill products are shingles, lath, veneers, and cooperage stock for the making of barrels, tubs, and similar containers.

MANUFACTURING INDUSTRIES THAT USE LUMBER AS A RAW MATERIAL. More than one-third of the lumber cut in sawmills is used in a rough form for construction and similar purposes. Nearly two-thirds of the total, however, serves as raw material in factories that make a great variety of wares in which wood is used alone or in conjunction with metals or other materials. More than half the total lumber used for manufacturing is consumed by planing mills which make flooring, siding, window sash, moldings, doors, and other house-finishing woodwork. Many of these products are bulky or fragile, and their manufacture requires considerable power and labor. The establishments are therefore usually located as near as possible to the great centers of population, yet some of this type of manufacturing is done in conjunction with the large sawmills. Planing-mill products are the principal forms of lumber manufacture in nearly all

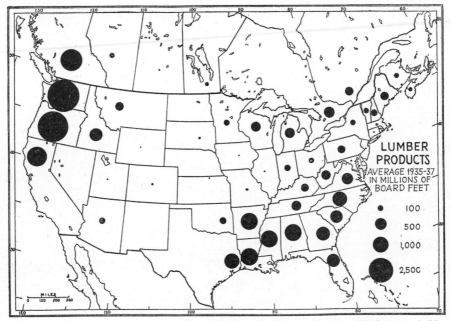

FIG. 76.—The rank of the states and provinces in lumber production. Washington holds first place.

parts of the United States but particularly in the states that still have, or in the past have had, large timber resources.

The second most important use of lumber is in the manufacture of boxes, crates, standard packages for fruits, and other forms of containers. This industry is also widespread, and in some states it consumes more lumber than the planing mills. The principal centers for the manufacture of such containers are near the industries that they serve. California and Florida require a large output of them for the shipment of fruits and vegetables. Illinois and New England also are large producers, since their factories ship much general merchandise in wooden cases.

THE MANUFACTURE OF FURNITURE requires many kinds of woods, hard and soft, native and imported. The principal native hardwoods used in this industry in the United States are oak, walnut, red gum, maple, and birch; the principal imported wood is mahogany. Large quantities of softwoods are necessary also for the interior parts of furniture and for crating furniture for shipment. Not infrequently as much wood is used in crating a piece of furniture as goes into its construction. These conditions, together with the presence of the principal market and cheap power, are reflected in the distribution of furniture factories through the northern part of the hardwood belt. About half of all American wood furniture is made in the lower Great Lakes industrial region, and much of the metal furniture as well. This region had an original advantage in a growing

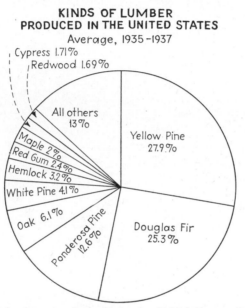

### KINDS OF LUMBER
### PRODUCED IN THE UNITED STATES
Average, 1935-1937

Cypress 1.71%
Redwood 1.69%
All others 13%
Maple 2%
Red Gum 2.4%
Hemlock 3.2%
White Pine 4.1%
Oak 6.1%
Ponderosa Pine 12.6%
Yellow Pine 27.9%
Douglas Fir 25.3%

FIG. 77.—Kinds of lumber manufactured in the United States, showing the relative importance of the principal tree species used.

market and an abundance and variety of raw materials. In the hardwood forests of the region were supplies of oak, maple, and walnut, and in the area immediately northward were birch and white pine. A large part of the forests are now gone, but the industry remains. Most of the necessary cabinet woods are imported. The leading states of the region in furniture output are New York, Indiana, Illinois, and Michigan. Grand Rapids, Mich., early gained a reputation for its fine furniture; and although it is now outranked in production, it continues to be a great exhibition and sales center for these wares.

A second important manufacturing district is the Piedmont of North Carolina and Virginia. There the highlands to the westward furnished both water power and coal and also a variety of hardwoods. The lowlands to the east provided pine, cypress, and gumwoods. The industry, like that of the North, has now to depend to a large degree on wood from other parts of the country. The principal manufactures are the less expensive types of furniture.

The great distance between eastern furniture centers and the Pacific Coast centers of population has encouraged the manufacture of this bulky commodity there also, mainly furniture of the cheaper grades. California ranks eighth among the states in the value of its furniture products.

AMERICAN FOREIGN TRADE IN TIMBER.   The United States is both an exporter and an importer of timber and its semimanufactured products, as well as its more complete manufactures, such as furniture and paper. As might be anticipated, the region of greatest timber abundance, the Pacific Northwest, is the region of largest export both of unsawed logs and of lumber. Plain sawed timbers and lumber are the most valuable of the major classes of timber exports; and a variety of manufactured wood products, including furniture, takes second rank. Logs, poles, and other unmanufactured forest products are least exported.

Imports of these same classes of wares are about half as great as the exports, and the principal imports are softwood lumber, mainly from Canada. The same type of product is the principal export. Cabinet woods, such as mahogany, do not, on the average, make up much more than one-tenth the total imports.

WOOD THE PRINCIPAL SOURCE OF PAPER.   Paper is a felted mass of plant fibers. Former generations made limited quantities of paper in single sheets by slow hand processes from grass, flax, straw, and other vegetable fibers. Much high-grade paper still is made from rags and other relatively expensive materials. Cheap and abundant newsprint and wrapping papers are, however, the result of processes that turn logs of wood into endless strips of paper in the form of rolls having any desired width and weight. One type of machine manufactures newsprint paper 18 feet in width at the astounding rate of 1,200 feet per minute.

In recent years the United States has used, on an average, about 7½ million cords of pulpwood per year in the manufacture of woodpulp and paper, and Canada has used over 4 million cords. The average annual output of manufactured and remanufactured woodpulp products in the United States is about 150 pounds per person.

NORTHERN FORESTS THE PRINCIPAL SOURCE OF PULPWOOD.   Many kinds of wood are used in the manufacture of pulp for paper. The most important are spruce, hemlock, fir, pine, and poplar. Spruce constitutes more than a third of the total used for pulp in the United States and Canada. Four important methods are employed in the manufacture of woodpulp. They are called the "mechanical," "sulphite," "soda," and "sulphate" processes. The three last named break down the structure of the wood by digestion with chemicals. The mechanical process accomplishes the same end by pressing the bolts of wood, from which the bark has been stripped, against large, power-driven grindstones. This is the oldest method and requires the most power; but although it is cheaper, it does not produce so strong a paper, and its products are suited principally for use in newspapers. These conditions have helped to locate the pulp mills near the spruce and fir forests and in regions of abundant supplies of pure water and of cheap water power. Figure 78 shows the

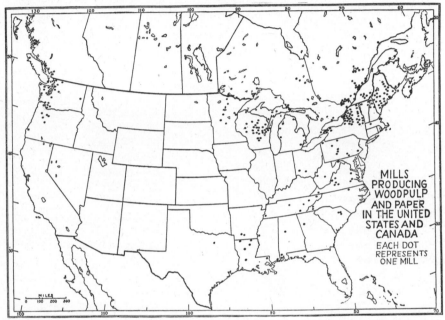

MILLS PRODUCING WOODPULP AND PAPER IN THE UNITED STATES AND CANADA

EACH DOT REPRESENTS ONE MILL

Fig. 78.—A large part of the pulp and paper mills of Anglo-America are concentrated in the northeastern region, where they have access to the water powers of the glaciated Laurentian border, the wood of the northern forests, and the markets of the great cities.

distribution of North American pulp and paper mills and reflects the factors mentioned. The smaller number of mills on the Pacific Coast and in the South is due also to the greater distance of their forest areas from the large eastern paper markets. The East has not until recently felt any shortage of pulpwood (Fig. 79). Under the stimulus of a growing western market the manufacture of pulp and paper on the Pacific Coast has notably increased. During recent years also the perfection of the sulphate process has made possible the profitable utilization of hemlock and southern pine for pulp. This has opened the door to new and possibly more permanent sources of pulpwood, for under the mild climatic conditions of the South some species of pine can be grown to pulpwood size in 20 years or even less.

MANUFACTURES OF AND FOREIGN TRADE IN PULPWOOD AND ITS PRODUCTS. The products manufactured from pulpwood include pulp, papers, cellulose, pulpboards of several classes, and innumerable small wares. The total United States output of woodpulp is nearly 5 million tons, and that of Canada is about 3 million. However, the quantity of products manufactured each year from pulp is considerably greater, especially in the United States, because of a large volume of remanufactures from waste paper. More than 4 million tons of wallboards, carton boards, and similar products, largely of reworked paper, make the largest

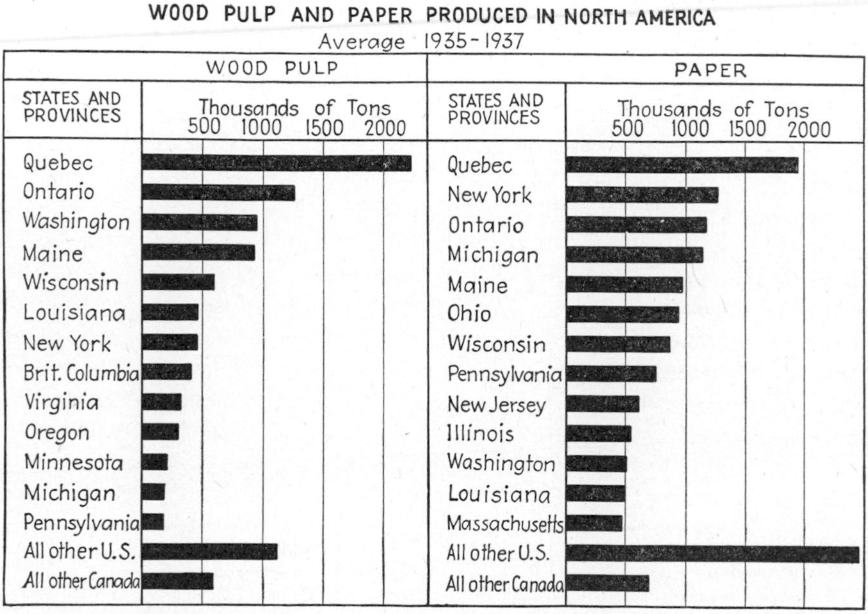

WOOD PULP AND PAPER PRODUCED IN NORTH AMERICA
Average 1935-1937

FIG. 79.—The leading states and provinces in woodpulp and paper manufacture.

item in the list of United States woodpulp manufactures. Next most important is the manufacture of high-grade book and writing papers, more than 1½ million tons. These include some fibers other than woodpulp. Another large item, of about the same quantity, is wrapping paper. Only one-fifth of the United States pulp output is used in the manufacture of newsprint paper. In Canada the situation is quite different. There, four-fifths is so employed, and newsprint is by far the largest item of Canadian paper manufacture. This reflects the predominance of spruce and fir in the Canadian pulpwood supply, the abundance of suitable water and water power on the northern forest margin, and the large United States market for newsprint resulting from the decreased supplies of pulpwood in the northeastern states and the large demand in that area.

United States imports of paper and its materials include many items, but the larger part is composed of newsprint paper and woodpulp. The paper is obtained mainly from Canada, but some of the pulp comes from northwestern Europe. Doubtless more Canadian pulp would be imported for manufacture into paper in United States mills were it not for a Canadian law requiring that all wood cut on crown lands be manufactured in that country. United States imports of newsprint from that source, more than 1½ million tons, far exceed the domestic production of that type of paper.

United States exports of paper and its materials are only about one-fourth the value of the imports, but they include many items. Most valuable is woodpulp, rags, and other paper stock, about one-sixth as much as is imported. Other large items include the higher grades of writing and book papers, wrapping paper and paper bags, and paper-boards. Newsprint is not a large export, being far exceeded by old newspapers for remanufacture in other countries.

WOOD PRODUCTS AND THE CHEMICAL INDUSTRIES. The chemical industries draw some of their raw materials from the forests. Wood is an important source of cellulose, one of the basic requirements of a large group of chemical products now coming into prominence. They include rayon, Celluloid and allied plastics, and nitrocellulose, the principal ingredient of certain explosives. From the distillation of waste hardwoods are obtained alcohol, acetate of lime, and charcoal. The first two are important in many chemical processes. The resinous softwoods under similar treatment yield wood turpentine, tar oils, tar, and charcoal.

AMERICAN NAVAL STORES. Early in American history the wooden shipbuilding industry of New England required quantities of tar, rosin, and turpentine. These substances came to be known as "naval stores." They are now used principally in a variety of industrial products including paint and varnish, papermaking, polishes, roofing, and electrical supplies, most of which are not particularly related to shipping. The naval stores are obtained from various species of resinous pines. The trees are tapped for a yield of gum from which turpentine is distilled, leaving rosin as a residue. The average annual yield of these items in recent years has been about 32 million gallons of turpentine and more than 1 billion pounds of rosin. The tapping methods formerly employed in America were very destructive, and the average life of the tree after tapping began was only about 5 years, after which it was cut for lumber. Owing to these methods, the turpentine industry, like lumbering, migrated to new districts. In the early days New England was the important center of the industry, which later migrated to the forests of resinous pine in the South. Production in the Carolinas rose and fell and moved to the Gulf Coast states. However, new methods have been introduced, and second-growth forests on the sandy Coastal Plain lands have reached productive age (Fig. 9). Georgia, Florida, and Alabama now lead in output, and with careful management the permanence of the industry there seems assured.

SELECTED REFERENCES

BROWN, N. C. "A General Introduction to Forestry in the United States," New York, 1935.

DuPuy, W. A. "The Nation's Forests," New York, 1938.

GREELEY, W. B., *et al.* Timber, Mine or Crop, *U.S. Dept. Agr. Yearbook*, 1922.

HUDSON, GEORGE M. A Study of a Permanent Alabama Lumber Town, *Jour. Geog.*, Vol. 36 (1937), pp. 308–314.

LEMERT, B. F. Furniture Industry of the Southern Appalachian Piedmont, *Econ. Geog.*, Vol. 10 (1934), pp. 183–199.

PARKINS, A. E., and J. R. WHITAKER. "Our Natural Resources and Their Conservation," pp. 229–274, New York, 1939.

A National Plan for American Forestry, 2 vols., *Senate Doc.* 12, 73d Cong., 1st Sess., Washington, 1933.

SMITH, J. R. "Tree Crops, a Permanent Agriculture," New York, 1935.

ZIMMERMANN, ERICH W. "World Resources and Industries," pp. 379–425, New York, 1933.

ZON, R., and W. N. SPARHAWK. "Forest Resources of the World," New York, 1923.

# Chapter IX. Animal Foodstuffs

## The Meat Supply

ECONOMIC ASPECTS OF THE USE OF MEAT  The abundant use of meat in a national diet reflects in that country either a primitive state of economic development or a comparatively high standard of wealth. Meat is, in general, an expensive form of food, a form that requires the use of a large area of land which possibly might be devoted to crops destined for direct human consumption. The making of 1 pound of edible pork, for example, requires about 5 pounds of corn, and a pound of beef represents at least 7 pounds of corn besides other plant products. It is obvious that meat production is not the most intensive possible use of agricultural land. Yet meat and meat products are now regarded as essentials in the food supply of nearly all modern nations. In only a few countries, such as China and Japan, has the pressure of population upon the land become so great that strict economy does not permit of the relatively extravagant use of land for the raising of numerous meat animals.

In spite of a very general use of meat in many parts of the world the total quantity consumed is small in proportion to that of some of the food cereals. The world's annual production of meat, outside China, for which data are not obtainable, is estimated at about 50 billions of pounds.[1] It may easily be computed that, on the basis of calories of fuel value for human consumption, this is the equivalent of no more than about 15 per cent of the fuel value of the world's wheat crop alone. It is obvious that factors other than the fuel value of the meat must be taken into account in estimating the real importance of the meat-producing industries. It is probable that the wholesale market value of the meat consumed in all countries is nearly, if not quite, equal to the value of the flour made from the world's wheat crop. This statement lends emphasis to the expensiveness of meat as a food. Livestock are much more numerous in proportion to the human population in some parts of the world than in

---

[1] *U.S. Dept. Agr., Rept.* 109, p. 15, Office of the Secretary.

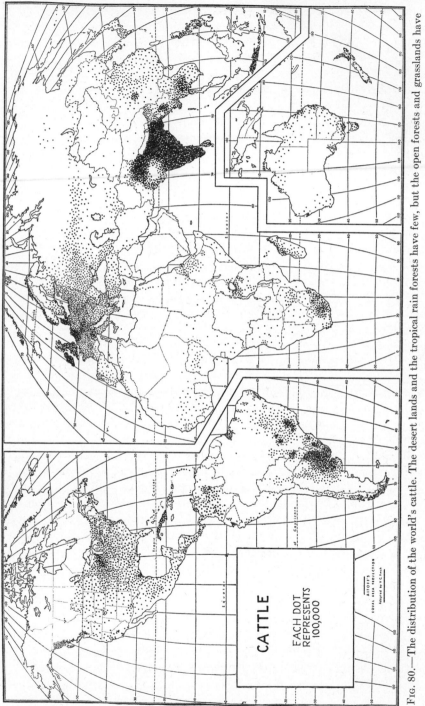

FIG. 80.—The distribution of the world's cattle. The desert lands and the tropical rain forests have few, but the open forests and grasslands have many.

others. In this respect there is striking contrast between the forested mountain land of Japan, with dense population, and the new and sparsely peopled grazing lands of the Southern Hemisphere, such as Argentina, Australia, or New Zealand. In Japan, for example, there are approximately 40 persons for every cow, 90 persons for every hog, and practically no sheep at all. The per capita allowance of meat from these sources must obviously be very small. It is even smaller than the figures alone show, because most of the cattle are work animals. In New Zealand there are, in contrast, about 2½ cows (many of them dairy cows) for every person, 19 sheep per person, and about 1 hog for every 3 people. The position of the United States in this respect is intermediate—about 2 persons for every cow, a like number for every hog, and 2 sheep for every 5 persons.

THE WORLD'S MEAT ANIMALS AND PHYSICAL ENVIRONMENT. The origin and development of the domesticated breeds of cattle, sheep, and swine have much to do with their present geographic distribution and therefore with the character of the meat industry.

Domestic cattle have been derived from types of wild cattle that inhabited the forests and grassy plains of Europe and Asia. In that type of environment they developed characteristics that adapted them to range conditions and to the pioneer life of the new and sparsely settled lands of the New World, as well as to the denselyp eopled lands where greater care and more concentrated feeds (the products of settled agriculture) can be provided for them (Fig. 80).

The ancestors of domestic sheep were mountain animals, native to the rough, dry upland pastures of southern Europe and central Asia, where neither food nor water is abundant. The present world distribution of sheep (Fig. 81), which are particularly important in many rough or subhumid regions of sparse human population, is doubtless a consequence of the ability of the sheep to be at home in such surroundings. Sheep have attained great importance in some humid lowlands, particularly in England, but under the constant menace of certain diseases from which in other environments they are comparatively free.

Swine, on the other hand, are the descendants of forest-dwelling animals whose life habits were adapted to a rich and concentrated diet of nuts and roots dug from the forest floor. They are not range animals, nor do they promptly attain industrial or commercial importance in new lands. Rather, as a rule, they follow settled agriculture and live from its products under the daily care of the farmer (Fig. 82). They show in every way adaptation to an intensive form of meat production.

DEPENDENCE OF MODERN MEAT INDUSTRY UPON TRANSPORTATION. Before the era of modern transportation, the growing, slaughtering, and marketing of meat was almost entirely a local industry. So perishable a substance as meat had to be prepared near the consuming market.

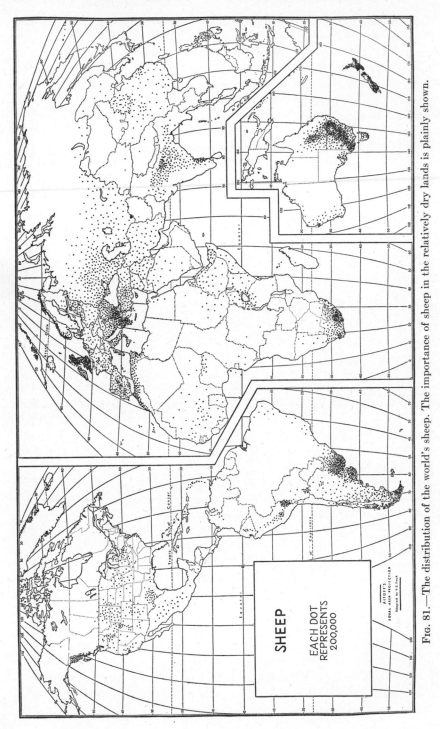

Fig. 81.—The distribution of the world's sheep. The importance of sheep in the relatively dry lands is plainly shown.

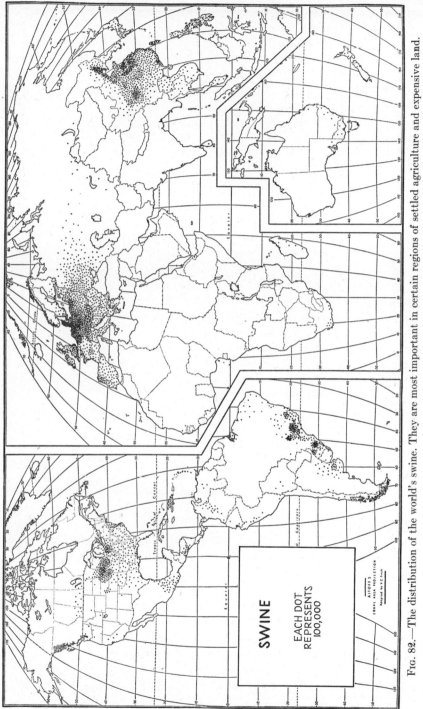

SWINE

EACH DOT
REPRESENTS
100,000

Fig. 82.—The distribution of the world's swine. They are most important in certain regions of settled agriculture and expensive land.

Under these conditions most countries were necessarily self-sufficing with respect to their meat supplies. In the densely peopled lands the rural communities supplied themselves and sent their surplus to adjacent cities, and each city had its own slaughtering establishments. If the animal industries of a country could not provide a sufficient supply of meat, prices increased, and the shortage had merely to be endured. In the sparsely peopled grazing lands of the world, meat was at the same time often almost worthless, and mature animals were slaughtered by the millions merely for the value of their hides and their tallow, as they were in Argentina, for example.

The advent of railways and steamships, and particularly of refrigerator boats and refrigerator cars, has changed the character of the world's meat industry to a remarkable degree and nowhere more than in North America. People in the meat-producing regions have not been slow in adjusting their activities to this new condition in their environment.

THE EARLY DEVELOPMENT OF THE AMERICAN BEEF INDUSTRY. Cattle raising in America began in two widely separated geographic regions and under very different economic circumstances. French and English types of cattle were introduced by the colonists who settled upon the Atlantic seaboard from Quebec to Georgia. The cattle were used as draft animals and as dairy animals and were slaughtered for local meat supply, but they were always the adjuncts of settled agriculture. At an early date cattle of the Spanish type were introduced from Mexico to the ranges of Texas and California. They were reared in the open at a low cost by Mexican ranchers; and since there was but a limited local market for meat, the animals were worth very little. Many were slaughtered for their hides and tallow, products that could be stored and shipped when a favorable opportunity occurred.

Early in the nineteenth century settlers advanced from east of the Appalachian Mountains into the Ohio River Valley. Upon the abundant hay and corn crops of their newly cleared farms they could raise cheap beef, but the local market was small. In 1805 cattle were first driven eastward across the mountains to a profitable market in Baltimore. Therewith began a custom that for many years provided New York, Philadelphia, and Baltimore with cheap beef and the new West with a market. The territory drawn upon for these drives gradually included not only Ohio and Kentucky but Indiana and even Illinois. This phase of the American beef industry increased in importance up to 1850 and was terminated by the completion of through railways to the East. The cheaper cattle of Illinois and Iowa could then reach the eastern markets without the handicap of the excessively long drive.

The advent of the railways was also a cause for a rapid increase in settlement of the land and the growth of cities in the region between the

Ohio River and the Great Lakes. The farmers of the region turned their attention to wheat growing, and the eastern markets drew additional supplies of beef from farther west. Then, for the first time, the ranchers of Texas saw an opportunity to get their cattle to a large and profitable market (Fig. 83). The first attempts were made by driving cattle from Texas to Chicago, but the distance was great, and there were many discouragements. However, the rapidly growing tentacles of the railway system were pushing westward and had shortly reached into Iowa, Missouri, Kansas, and Texas itself. Cattle could profitably be driven to the ends of the newly built railways and then be transported quickly to the Chicago market. Many of the cattle received in Chicago during this period were killed to supply the local market; some were converted into salted

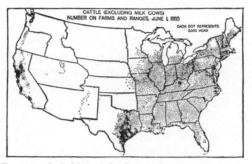

Fig. 83.—In 1860 Texas and California had many cattle, but very restricted markets. (*U.S. Department of Agriculture.*)

and cured beef products which could be shipped east. However, the majority of the cattle were shipped alive to the eastern consuming markets. Under the stimulation of new markets the range-cattle industry expanded rapidly northward as the herds of buffalo disappeared, and by 1880 the grazing ranges were stocked nearly to the Canadian border. During the succeeding decade the multiplication of branch railways in the cattle country had so far progressed that long drives were no longer necessary, and this picturesque phase of the American cattle industry practically disappeared.

THE PROGRESS OF AGRICULTURAL SETTLEMENT IN RELATION TO THE SHEEP INDUSTRY. The early history of the production of mutton and pork in America is closely related to the occupation of the land. In the colonies both sheep and swine were the adjuncts of nearly every farm home. The sheep were raised primarily for their wool, but they also supplied meat.

Early in the nineteenth century the demand for fine wool caused the American farmer to turn from the unimproved coarse-wooled English types of sheep, which they had used for more than a century, to imported Merinos and other fine-wooled breeds. The industry attained great importance in New England and spread through New York and Pennsylvania into the Ohio River settlements and eventually westward to the Mississippi River. Wool could be shipped eastward by the slow lake and canal transportation of the time, but the mutton of the fine-wooled sheep was inferior and had only local value. Under the competition of cheap wool from the Middle West, wool growing in the East gradually declined.

The westward spread of the railways which marked such great changes in the beef industry had a no less notable influence upon sheep raising. Prior to the coming of the railways, sheep were few in the dry lands of the high plains and the Rocky Mountains because cattle could more readily be marketed. Distances over which it was feasible to drive cattle were too great for the profitable transportation of wool. The penetration of this territory by the railways inaugurated a sheep industry of a new type in America, a range industry, independent of any settled agriculture. Its establishment was attended by a long and bitter struggle between "sheepmen" and "cattlemen." That the industry was successfully established is abundantly evidenced by the fact that the 7 million sheep of the Far West in 1871 had increased to nearly four times that number in 1885. Cheap wool from the range sheep then came into competition with the wool of Illinois and Ohio. The farmers of the Middle West, therefore, followed the example of the East. Many went out of sheep raising, and the total number of sheep decreased, but the breeding of the mutton types of sheep increased.

THE DEVELOPMENT OF THE AMERICAN SWINE INDUSTRY. Swine raising in the United States, like cattle raising, was put upon a commercial basis as soon as agricultural settlers took up the rich corn lands of the Ohio Valley. Swine could not be driven to the eastern market so easily as cattle, nor had they the transportable fleece of the sheep; yet pork products, smoked or preserved, became one of the principal exports of the Ohio country at an early date. Cincinnati became a great pork-packing center, and pork products moved to market by boat down the Ohio and Mississippi rivers. The forest-fed hog of the East became a corn-fed hog, and interest was manifested in the improvement of breeds. Hog raising followed the agricultural settlers westward across the prairie lands of the corn belt but never, as in the case of cattle and sheep, outstripped them. The packing of pork products also followed, and before 1870 it was well established in Chicago, St. Louis, and other middle-western towns. Live hogs suffered greater loss in transportation by rail than did cattle and sheep; and pork, pickled in brine or in the form of ham, bacon, or lard, was more readily marketable than was cured or pickled beef or mutton.

THE SITUATION OF THE AMERICAN MEAT INDUSTRY AT THE INTRODUCTION OF REFRIGERATION. During the period of great railway expansion pork packing was common in the Middle West, and large numbers of cattle and sheep also were slaughtered to supply the growing markets of the region. The great eastern markets, however, were supplied with beef and mutton by the local slaughtering of animals shipped from far and near. In 1869 the receipts of cattle at New York City totaled more than 325,000 head. They came from an area that included Canada, Florida,

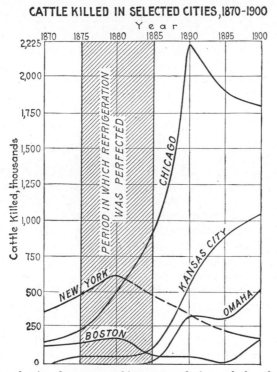

CATTLE KILLED IN SELECTED CITIES, 1870-1900

FIG. 84.—Showing the rise of western packing centers during and after the period in which processes of refrigeration were perfected.

Nebraska, and Texas, though the largest numbers came from Illinois, Ohio, Texas, and the state of New York. In the same year the total receipts of cattle at Chicago were 400,000 head, of which only one-fourth were slaughtered in that city and three-fourths were shipped on to the eastern markets. The rate of slaughtering and packing of all types of meat for shipment was closely related to the seasonal variations of weather. Principally it was a winter industry and dwindled or ceased altogether with the approach of warm weather.

The general conditions described above would doubtless be characteristic of the American meat industry of the present, except for the perfection of mechanical refrigeration and the introduction of the refrigerator car. These improvements brought about a change in the meat industry no less revolutionary than that wrought in the vegetable and fruit industries during the same period.

THE INFLUENCE OF REFRIGERATION ON THE AMERICAN MEAT INDUSTRY. The direct result of the application of refrigeration to the meat industry was the removal of slaughtering and meat packing from the great consuming markets of the East westward to the regions of animal raising. The economies that dictated this change are easily understood. The quantity of merchantable beef obtainable from ordinary cattle averages only about 50 per cent of their live weight. As soon as it was possible to dress beef near the place where it was grown, transportation was saved on the inedible products. Moreover, when stock is shipped alive over great distances, unavoidable loss and damage to the animals

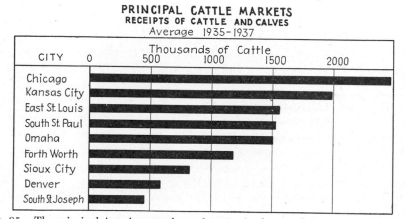

### PRINCIPAL CATTLE MARKETS
#### RECEIPTS OF CATTLE AND CALVES
##### Average 1935–1937

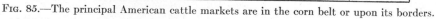

FIG. 85.—The principal American cattle markets are in the corn belt or upon its borders.

occur in transit. As an adjustment to the new conditions, there occurred a relative decline in the number of cattle killed in eastern markets; a rapid increase of slaughtering in Chicago; and the rise of new packing centers still farther to the west, such, for example, as Kansas City and Omaha (Figs. 84, 85).

The economies in transportation made possible by refrigeration were accompanied by other economies in the preparation of meat for market. Particularly noteworthy are those which resulted from the centralization of the slaughtering industry and from a large scale of operation. These economies were favorable to the development of the great meat-packing plants and the powerful financial interests that now control the industry in America. The use of refrigeration in the transportation and storage of meats tended also to stabilize the market for meat animals and to free it from wide seasonal fluctuations. Animals may now be killed at any season of the year, and there are only minor seasonal variations in the slaughtering of any meat animals except hogs. About 25 per cent of the total American pork supply still is killed on the farms, mainly in the early winter.

MODERN BEEF PRODUCTION. The introduction of refrigerator transportation did not influence the meat-packing industry alone. The broadening of the accessible market for meat brought about changes in methods of meat production and in types of meat animals as well. Cattle that formerly moved to market directly from the western grazing ranges were shipped in increasing numbers to the farms of the corn belt to be put in prime condition and then passed on to the market. The cattle-marketing centers that are located between the grazing ranges and the corn belt handle most of the young cattle for fattening, and to them the farmers of the corn belt come to buy. In 1937 about 15 per cent of all the cattle received at public stockyards were not slaughtered there but were shipped out again to farmers to be fattened for later marketing. In general, the western stockyards, as at Kansas City and Omaha on the western margin of the corn belt, resell a larger part of the cattle that they receive than do those, such as Chicago, near the eastern margin. Many cattle are sold direct from western ranges also to the corn-belt farmers without passing through the great stockyard markets.

When dry-farming methods were introduced in the region of the high plains, settlers took up for cultivation much of the best of the open range, restricting the area for cattle grazing. Moreover, competition in the range-cattle business had been keen. Ranchmen, each bent upon getting his share of the free pasture, had greatly overstocked much of the range, and its productive capacity declined. In response to this relative decrease, farmers in the corn belt have greatly increased their own production of young cattle and have made of the corn belt the most intensive and most important cattle-breeding and cattle-feeding center of North America.

Rapid increase in the cost of land and labor also enforced changes in methods of cattle raising. In the period of cheap land it was common to fatten three-, four-, and even five-year-old cattle for 6 months or more before they were marketed. High-priced feeds have made such methods unprofitable, and recent decades have seen a rapid improvement in the character of American cattle and an increasing economy in methods of feeding. These changes have been brought about by the introduction of improved breeds of beef cattle noted for their excellence of form, for their thriftiness, and for their early maturity. Cattle in the corn belt are now put on a fattening ration at an average age of 18 or 20 months. How long they are fattened thereafter depends on several factors, such as their weight and condition when purchased, the season of the year, and the price of corn in relation to the price of beef. Older cattle fatten more quickly than young animals that are still growing but less economically, considering the cost of raising them to the fattening age. Many three-year-old cattle still are fed in America, yet there is a constant tendency to reduce the age of market cattle. This is evidenced by numerous campaigns for development of interest in the growing of "baby beef," which means early-maturing cattle finished and ready for market at eighteen months of age or less. This type of beef has several advantages. (1) Although young cattle do not fatten so rapidly, they make greater total

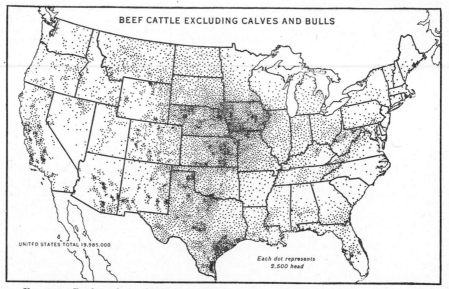

BEEF CATTLE EXCLUDING CALVES AND BULLS

UNITED STATES TOTAL 19,985,000

Each dot represents
2,500 head

FIG. 86.—Beef cattle in the United States are most numerous in the corn belt and the Texas coastal prairies. The dry pastures of the western states have many cattle, but they are not able to support as many in proportion to their area as are the more humid grasslands and agricultural regions such as the corn belt. See Fig. 12. (*U.S. Department of Agriculture.*)

gains in weight on the same quantity of feed than do older animals. (2) The capital invested in the herd is turned over more rapidly. (3) The size and quality of the cuts of beef from yearling animals are preferred by the ordinary consumer to those from more mature cattle. Raising baby beef requires experience, however, and an abundance of certain types of feed, and not all regions are adapted to it.

AMERICAN BEEF-PRODUCING REGIONS. The distribution of beef cattle in the United States is shown in Fig. 86, in which the importance of the corn belt is easily seen. Corn and clover or alfalfa hay are the most common fattening feeds for cattle in America. The cornstalks are used as rough feed, and in recent years corn silage has been added to the beef ration by the majority of cattle feeders, particularly in the eastern half of the corn belt.

From the foregoing it will appear that there are two contrasting systems of beef production in the United States. These have been touched upon previously in dealing with the geographical regions of the country (Chap. II). The first may be called "livestock ranching." It is characteristic of the subhumid plains, plateaus, and mountain ranges of the West and of the Texas coast. There young cattle are raised, and some are finished as fat cattle ready for market where the pastures are good or where irrigated land provides alfalfa and grain for supplementary feeding. The larger part of them are shipped to corn-belt farmers, who prepare them for market. The second system is that of the corn belt, and it may be called "livestock farming." There many calves are raised on dairy by-products, ground grain, and the available pastures, but the supply of grain is so much greater than they require that many more animals are purchased each year from the western ranches and, with those raised at home, are fed for market.

Outside these regions are others that also contribute something to the beef supply of the continent. In practically all farming districts, either general or specialized, there is normally a surplus of beef which moves to adjacent markets or to the great packing centers. This is particularly true of the spring-wheat belt of the United States and Canada and of the dairy belt of the Great Lakes region. It is rapidly becoming true of the cotton belt of the South.

AMERICAN SHEEP REGIONS. Figure 87 shows the distribution of sheep in North America and clearly indicates the importance of the sheep in the dry-land and mountain pastures of the West. There they range, often in bands of several hundred, under the care of a herder who moves them from one pasture to another, guided by the condition of the forage and the season of the year. In the mountain regions this frequently involves a progressive movement up the foothill and mountain slopes during the summer. In the autumn the sheep are returned to lower elevations; lambs are sold to feeders; and the breeding stock is wintered in the basins or deserts where there is less snow or some supplementary feed from irrigated farm lands. The extended market for fresh lamb, which came with the introduction of refrigeration, influenced the character of American sheep just as it did that of cattle. Fine-wooled sheep have decreased in number, and the western ranges carry crossbred lambs of higher mutton-producing quality.

The mutton industry has two aspects, just as the beef industry has. There is (1) the range industry where lambs are raised but where there is little grain to fatten them for market; and (2) the lamb-finishing industry in the hay and grain belt of the East and in the irrigated sections of the West. Many lambs are raised also in the eastern regions, but the proportion is much smaller than in the cattle industry. One section of the

East, the rough lands of the upper Ohio River Valley, has maintained importance in sheep raising since its earliest settlement. There the sheep are kept as relatively small farm flocks in a region of general and diversified farming. In addition to those raised there, many hundreds of carloads of western range lambs are fattened every winter in Ohio and southern Michigan as well as in parts of the corn belt.

AMERICAN SWINE REGIONS.    The similarity in the present distribution of swine and of corn in America (Figs. 88, 29) is obvious, and the reason for the similarity is clear. Corn produces in hogs a desirable type of solid white fat for making lard. The American corn-belt farmer, having

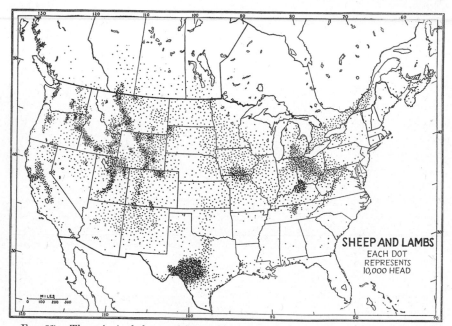

FIG. 87.—The principal sheep-raising and sheep-feeding regions of the United States.

an abundance of corn, has improved types of swine that are the most efficient lard producers known. There are indications, however, that the day of the lard hog is passing, for cheap vegetable oils from cotton seed and tropical sources are cutting into the world market for lard. This may eventually transform the American hog into a specialized producer of ham and bacon instead of fat and require new methods of feeding, although corn may well continue to be the basic element in the ration.

THE PACKING AND MARKETING OF MEAT.    The conditions that led to the westward movement of meat packing and to its centralization led also to great economy and high efficiency in the disposal of the products of the packing industry. These conditions are (1) rapid transportation and (2) refrigeration. By these means the handicap of geographical distance is overcome, and the most perishable of substances can be marketed in perfect condition in distant places (Fig. 89).

The degree to which the centralization of slaughtering is carried on in America and the giant corporations that dominate the packing industry are unknown in European countries. In a highly favorable environment of cheaply grown meat animals and of a well-to-do meat-eating population the packing industries have had a remarkable growth. They have pushed their influence into every corner of America and into many foreign coun-

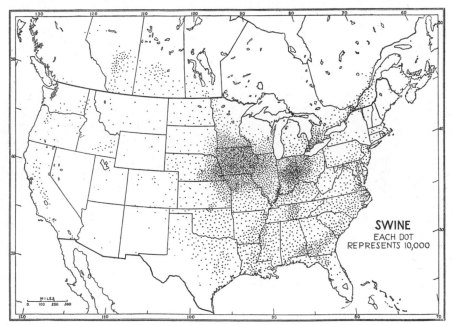

SWINE
EACH DOT
REPRESENTS 10,000

Fig. 88.—The corn belt is the principal swine-raising region of the United States.

tries. They have nearly done away with inefficient and unsanitary local slaughtering, and they have found economic uses for the offal of animals which, under earlier conditions, was wasted. They have organized many branch distributing houses and refrigerator-car routes by which distant cities and villages may be supplied with meat at regular and frequent intervals. The volume of this business and the delicacy of its balance is indicated by the following facts. The average person in the United States eats about 125 pounds of meat per year, not including poultry and other minor items. Of this, beef makes up about 55 pounds, pork 55 pounds, lamb and mutton 7 pounds, and veal 8 pounds. The relative proportions of these differ considerably, however, in the several major parts of the country. Some sections, for example, use a great deal of lamb and mutton, and others little or none. It is the business of the packing industry to judge these requirements and to have the necessary quantity of this perishable produce ready for the consumer when it is wanted.

AMERICAN FOREIGN TRADE IN MEAT.    Throughout the past century the opening of new lands in America suitable for animal raising caused a more rapid growth in the numbers of meat animals than in the human population. This increasing surplus of meat went in various forms to supply the deficiencies of the industrial nations of Europe and of tropical

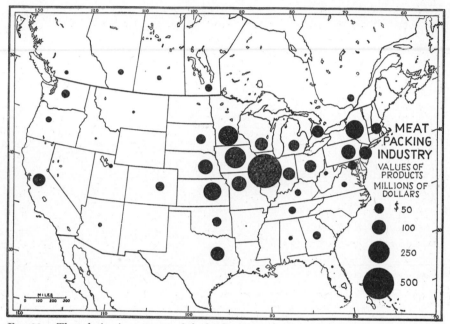

FIG. 89.—The relative importance of the leading states and provinces in the meat-packing industry.

lands that do not produce much meat. Before refrigeration was possible, American exports of meat were mainly in the form of salt, smoked, and pickled beef and pork; hams, bacon, lard, and tallow. Live cattle were exported only to Canada and the West Indies prior to 1874, when the first important shipment was carried across the Atlantic by steamship. Thereafter the foreign trade in live cattle grew considerably, but it was not an economical way of shipment. Cattle were injured or killed in transit, and losses were high. Live shipment exceeded one-half million head per year for several years about 1904–1907, but they declined rapidly and are now unimportant.

Fresh meat, under refrigeration, figured in American exports first in 1876. The trade grew steadily until the early years of the present century, when a decline set in. This was because of increasing competition in European markets by foreign competitors, especially Argentina and the British colonies, and because of large home consumption by a growing urban population. The first World War increased United States meat exports again but only temporarily. Foreign competition and trade restrictions have caused the current downward trend to reach new low levels. If European nations are prevented from selling their manufactures in the United States, they have no way of getting exchange with which to buy American meat or other foodstuffs. However, not only is the general trend of American meat exports downward, but so also is the

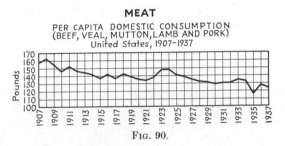

**MEAT**
PER CAPITA DOMESTIC CONSUMPTION
(BEEF, VEAL, MUTTON, LAMB AND PORK)
United States, 1907–1937

FIG. 90.

trend of domestic per capita consumption (Fig. 90). The number of meat-producing animals on farms and ranches has decreased considerably since the beginning of the century. Nevertheless, increasingly efficient meat animals, a more rapid turnover on the farms, and an increasing population in the country have enabled the production and domestic consumption of somewhat more meat than was produced in earlier decades.

## The Dairy Industry

DAIRY ANIMALS.   The milk of many types of domesticated animals is used as human food in various parts of the world. Those most commonly employed for milk production are cattle, buffaloes, goats, and sheep. Of these, cattle are much the most important. Until within the last two centuries, there was little attempt to differentiate between breeds of cattle used for milk production and those used for meat or for draft. Indeed, it is only in the countries of greatest economic advancement that any particular difference is to be noted at present.

The breeds of world-famous dairy cattle all were developed by painstaking selection in the countries of northwestern Europe. In fact, each of the breeds well known in America represents a district in the British Isles or northwestern Europe, such as Jersey, Guernsey, Ayrshire, Holland, and Switzerland. Others, less well known in America, such as the Dairy Shorthorn, the Red Polled, the Dexter, and the Kerry, have also been developed in the British Isles.

Fancy breeding animals have been shipped to America from their native regions for many years. In America selection by breeders has further improved the milk production of these cattle, and the demand for dairy products has resulted in a great increase in their numbers. American herds now contain some of the world's most famous dairy animals.

THE ECONOMY OF DAIRYING. Not only is milk a good human food, but it is an economical form of food. This is especially true if its food value and its cost of production are compared with those of beef.

"Ordinary market beef has about 5 times as much food value per pound as average cow's milk. A choice 2-year-old beef steer will yield, including all edible portions, as high as 65 per cent of its live weight in meat, or about 650 pounds. It would therefore require approximately 3,250 pounds (650 × 5) of milk to yield an amount of human food equivalent to that which required 2 years to grow in the form of beef. Data compiled by the United States Department of Agriculture show that the average annual yield of milk per cow in the principal American dairy states is about 5,000 pounds. In some European countries the average is higher: Denmark 5,666 pounds and Netherlands 7,585 pounds, while a world's champion cow has a record of 37,000 pounds of milk in one year. Other figures compiled by the Department of Agriculture show that an acre of land will produce about 4 times as much digestible protein and about 5½ times as many calories of fuel if it is devoted to milk production as it would if devoted to the growing of beef. (U.S. Department of Agriculture, Farmers' Bulletin, 877.) Another authority says, 'It is a very conservative statement to assert that, under the very best possible conditions of production with both classes of animals, the cow is more than twice as economical in her use of food energy, when we consider the output for human uses, than is the steer or sheep.'"[1]

THE IDEAL DAIRY REGION. Dairy cows need a different type of feed from that required for fattening beef. Much of the heavy ration of grains and other concentrated feeds is replaced by hay, rough forage, and succulent plant products. Pasture is particularly essential. For these crops and also for the preservation of dairy produce, long cool summers with rainfall uniformly distributed are desirable. One writer described the typical dairy region as follows:

"The characteristics of a naturally good dairy region will generally be found to be a rolling, undulating, somewhat hilly surface, a soil not too heavy and damp, but deep, loamy, and retentive of moisture; a sweet and nutritious herbage of natural grasses that springs up early and tends to grow vigorously late in the season, a somewhat low average temperature with frequent showers in the summer, and a never failing supply of good springs."[2]

Modern invention has done much for the spread of dairying by devising substitutes for various of these geographical aspects of the ideal

[1] Jordan, W. H. The Importance of Milk as a Food, *Am. Acad. Pol. Soc. Sci.*, Vol. 74 (November, 1917), p. 188.

[2] Sheldon, J. P. "Dairying," p. 17, London, 1912.

dairy region. Thus, the silo and soiling crops are used to provide succulent feed for the cows during summer drought and to extend the use of such feed throughout the year. Refrigeration is used to protect the dairy produce from the effects of high temperatures; deep wells and mechanical pumps make a supply of spring water unessential. It is to be noted, therefore, that many important dairy regions of the present have none of these ideal characteristics and that very few regions are ideal in all respects.

AMERICAN DAIRY REGIONS. Dairying is an industry of some importance in every settled region of North America. Yet 60 per cent of the

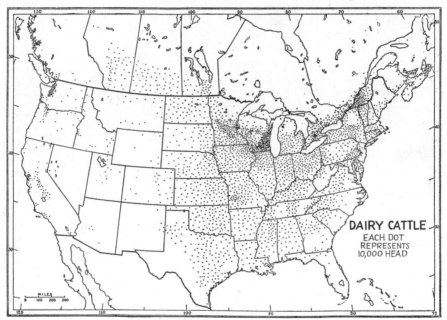

FIG. 91.—The major concentration of dairy cattle is in the region extending from central Minnesota to the lower St. Lawrence Valley.

milk in the United States is produced in that quarter of the country which includes the states north of the Potomac and Ohio rivers and east of the Missouri, and 70 per cent of the milk of Canada is produced in the provinces east of the Great Lakes (Fig. 91). This is partially explained by the fact that more than 50 per cent of the people of the United States and about 70 per cent of the people of Canada live in this same region. Dairying is a relatively intensive form of animal industry and requires more labor than meat raising. Moreover, the primary products are perishable and must be produced, like the principal vetegable crops, fairly close to the great city markets (Fig. 92). Yet in addition to these economic influences upon the distribution of dairying there is also a

Fig. 92.—An American dairy scene. Grass and field crops are transformed by means of the silo and the cow into milk for the near-by city market. (*U.S. Department of Agriculture.*)

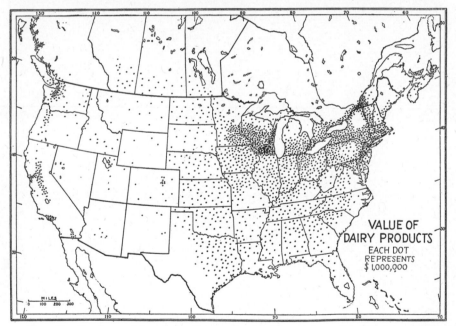

Fig. 93.—In the outlying dairy districts local milk supply and butter manufacture consume most of the milk produced. In the northeastern dairy region milk for the great cities, condensaries and cheese factories consume additional quantities.

climatic factor. The summer rainfall of the American dairy region is greater and more uniformly distributed than in the western half of the continent, and the summer temperatures are notably lower than those of the South. These climatic conditions are favorable to the production of grass and hay. Abundant summer pasture reduces the labor of summer dairying, and the hay provides a part of the winter feed for cows. More than 50 per cent of the hay crop of the United States is raised within the boundaries above described. It will also be noted from a comparison of Figs. 93 and 29 that the principal dairy centers within this general dairy region lie along the northern border of the corn belt, where the growing season for corn is sometimes cut short by early autumn frosts

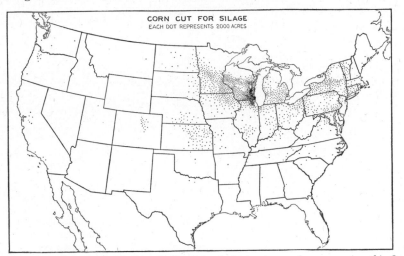

CORN CUT FOR SILAGE
EACH DOT REPRESENTS 2000 ACRES

FIG. 94.—The importance of silage in the dairy industry is seen by comparing this figure with the preceding one.

In this region the silo (Fig. 94) and the dairy industry provide a profitable means of caring for a part of the corn crop, especially that which must be harvested in an immature condition.

FORMS OF DAIRY PRODUCE. Most dairy regions market all the primary dairy products, yet modern dairy regions tend, because of geographic conditions and economic relationship to markets, to specialize in milk, butter, or cheese. The fresh-milk trade, because of the perishability of the product, centers about the great city markets or in such localities as have rapid transportation to the great cities. This industry is particularly important in New England, eastern and southern New York, parts of New Jersey, and eastern Pennsylvania. It is important also in a considerable area immediately tributary to Chicago and other large cities. In order that a large volume of milk may be collected within an economical shipping radius it is necessary that there be productive farm land devoted mainly to dairying and having a large number of cows per square mile. Modern milk transportation in huge insulated tanks on trucks and trains has extended the radius considerably, but the larger part of the supplies for New York and Chicago still comes from distances less than 150 to 200 miles.

In regions less advantageously situated with respect to large markets, milk is more profitably employed in the manufacture of condensed milk, cheese, and butter. These products are easily handled, and the elements of time and cost are not large factors in their marketing because of their high value and relative imperishability. The manufacture of cheese is concentrated in the cooler parts of the intensive dairy belt and in districts

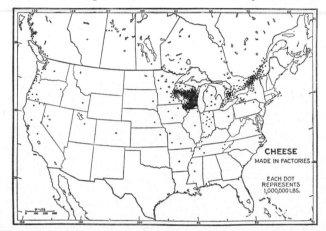

FIG. 95.—Wisconsin and the St. Lawrence Valley are the leading cheese-producing regions of North America.

less accessible than the market milk areas to rapid transportation (Fig. 95) but where there are quite as many cows and an equally large volume of milk per unit of area. Cooler summer temperatures and short hauls make it possible for farmers to deliver milk at cheese factories in more uniformly good condition, a factor of greatest importance in the manufacture of cheese of high quality. Wisconsin, northern New York, and Ontario are particularly noted for their cheese. Butter manufacture is much more widespread (Fig. 96) and is common in regions of fewer dairy cows in proportion to the area, where a more general type of farming is practiced, and to regions of higher summer temperature. The condition of the milk or cream on arrival at a butter factory is not so critical a matter as it is at the cheese factory. Some of the largest butter factories are in the corn belt, where cream in small amounts is assembled in large total quantity by trucks and trains from areas many miles in radius. By contrast, the Wisconsin cheese factory is a small establishment. Its radius of collection is seldom more than 4 or 5 miles.

The growth of city populations in the United States requires ever larger supplies of fresh milk; about 45 per cent of the total milk produced is now consumed in that form. About 35 per cent is made into butter on the farms or in factories. Condensed, evaporated, and dried milk requires about 5 per cent of the total; ice cream, about 3 per cent; and cheese manufacture, about 6 per cent. Some is fed to livestock or wasted. In Canada, where the local milk market is relatively smaller, the proportions are somewhat different. Butter and cheese employ about 50 and 7 per cent, respectively, of the milk produced.

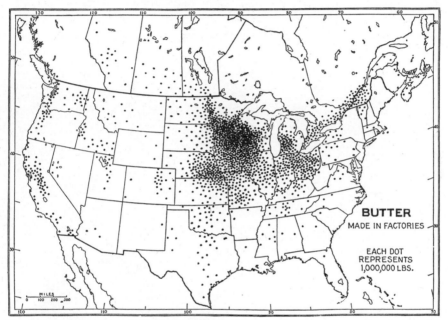

**BUTTER**
MADE IN FACTORIES

EACH DOT
REPRESENTS
1,000,000 LBS.

Fig. 96.—A comparison of this figure with Fig. 93 shows that butter is not the most profitable form of dairy product near New York, Chicago, and other large cities.

DAIRYING AN IMPORTANT PHASE OF AMERICAN AGRICULTURE. The importance of the dairy industry to America may be appreciated when it is realized that the farm value of all the milk and its products in the United States is greater than the farm value of the corn crop and that for these products the average American family pays more than $100 per year. It is not, however, its large value only that gives it great importance. Dairy products are ordinarily subject to much less violent fluctuations of price than are the cereal crops. For that reason there is a noticeably stability in the economic welfare of the principal dairy regions.

FOREIGN TRADE IN DAIRY PRODUCTS. As may be supposed, little fresh milk enters into either the import or the export trade of the United States and Canada. Fresh milk from the St. Lawrence Valley could easily reach the urban markets of New England and New York; and, were it not for a tariff barrier, it would undoubtedly do so. Tariff restrictions are tending, however, to reduce not only the imports of milk and its products into the United States but also all its dairy exports. The former customers were principally the European industrial regions, but they can no longer buy when they are not permitted to send manufactured wares in exchange. United States exports of dairy products have declined in value to one-third that of a decade past. The principal export items are various forms of condensed and evaporated milk for which there is a market in tropical America. The principal United States dairy imports are luxury items, especially the noted types of cheese obtained from Italy, Switzerland, Denmark, the Netherlands, and France. Canadian exports of dairy products are more than twice the United States total. Nine-tenths of them go to the British market, the largest items being cheese and canned milk.

SELECTED REFERENCES

CASSELS, J. M. "A Study of Fluid Milk Prices," Cambridge, 1937.
CLEMEN, R. A. "The American Livestock and Meat Industry," New York, 1933.
DURAND, L. Cheese Region of Southeastern Wisconsin, *Econ. Geog.*, Vol. 15 (1939), pp. 283–292.
HARTSHORNE, R. A. New Map of the Dairy Areas of the United States, *Econ. Geog.*, Vol. 11 (1935), pp. 347–355.
SHAW, EARL. Swine Production in the Corn Belt of the United States, *Econ. Geog.*, Vol. 12 (1936), pp. 359–372.
WHITAKER, J. R. Distribution of Dairy Farming in Peninsular Ontario, *Econ. Geog.*, Vol. 16 (1940), pp. 69–78.
ZIMMERMANN, ERICH W. "World Resources and Industries," pp. 303–324, New York, 1933.

# Chapter X. Fisheries

RESOURCES OF THE SEA. Water covers about three-fourths of the earth's surface; yet in spite of this great expanse of water, the total value of the world's fishery products is small when it is compared with that of even a single crop like corn. Some of the reasons for this are apparent when it is remembered that all sea life is dependent ultimately upon microscopic organisms which in turn subsist upon materials dissolved in the ocean waters and upon materials derived directly or indirectly from the land. These sources are clearly not comparable with the soil in productivity.

TYPES OF FISHING INDUSTRIES. The location of the world's important fisheries is influenced (1) by the habits of the principal fishes of economic value and (2) by the distribution of the food supply of the various species. Classified according to location, three general types of fisheries are deep-sea fisheries, shore fisheries, and fresh-water fisheries. The more abundant sea fish may be distinguished, according to their habits and the method of taking them, into the following groups: (1) those which live and feed near the bottom and are taken by trawls or by hook and line, and (2) those which feed on minute organisms at the surface and are taken by nets. Cod belong to the first group, and mackerel to the second.

THE VALUE OF AMERICAN FISHERIES. Among the attractions that first drew European adventurers to the shores of North America were its fish, of which English, French, and Portuguese fishermen gathered a harvest for the European markets. They were prepared for these distant markets by curing with salt. Fishing was one of the principal occupations of the New England colonists, and the fishing fleets have continued to be a training school for American seamen.

In comparison with other great industries, however, the money value of the fishing industries is small (Fig. 97). The total income received by United States fishermen for their products probably does not exceed 80 to 100 millions of dollars a year; that received by Canadian fishermen probably does not usually exceed 25 to 30 millions. All the fishery products in North America do not, therefore, return to the producers more than about 125 millions of dollars a year, an amount less than one-fourth the average value of the eggs produced on the farms of the United States alone. The consumers of the dressed, prepared, and canned products of the fisheries, however, pay much more than that sum for them. The total value of American fisheries is perhaps not so significant as the fact that the quantity of fish available seems to be declining. Several species formerly caught in great abundance are now rare, and most of the commercial fish show declines over the last half century. The contribution

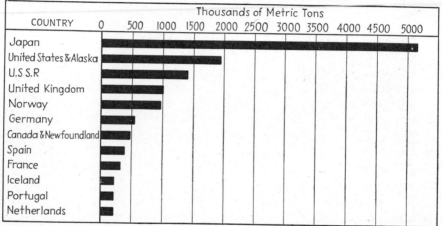

FISHERY PRODUCTS—LEADING COUNTRIES

Fig. 97.—In Japan the food supply is more largely supplemented by fish than in any other country.

of fisheries to the American income and food supply seems destined to become even smaller than it is unless some more general measures of conservation are brought into operation.

## The American Atlantic Fisheries

THE WHALING INDUSTRY. Under the term "fisheries" is commonly included the capture of marine mammals such as the seal and whale. Whaling was, in 1845, the leading fishing industry of the United States. It was centered in New England, but the fishermen pursued these huge mammals into every ocean for their oil and bone. Their numbers greatly depleted, they were probably saved from extinction by the substitution of petroleum products for whale oil in illumination. Whaling is now a minor aspect of American fishing and is carried on most extensively by the fishermen of the northwest European countries.

THE BANKS FISHERIES. On the margin of the broad continental shelf which lies off the northeastern coast of North America is a chain of shallows known as the "banks" (Fig. 98). The largest and outermost, the Grand Bank, lies southeast of Newfoundland. The southernmost, George's Bank, lies 100 miles southeast of Cape Cod. Some parts of these banks are covered by relatively shallow waters (25 to 200 feet). They extend for a total length of more than 1,100 miles and have a combined area of some 70,000 square miles, equal to that of all New England or the state of Washington. Here are the feeding and breeding places of certain ground fish such as cod, haddock, and halibut. These formerly were taken largely on hand lines or by long trawls, lines with hooks attached at intervals. The lines were operated by men in small boats put out by the fishing schooner on reaching the fishing grounds. More recently these methods have largely been replaced by the steam trawler operating a

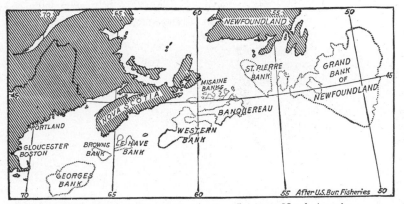

FIG. 98.—The principal fishing banks off eastern North America.

large bag net which is towed along the bottom by cables. This is a much more rapid method of fishing, and it requires fewer men but a larger capital outlay for equipment. Such a boat may often take 150 tons of fish on a single trip to the banks. On the banks and in the Gulf of Maine surface fish such as mackerel and herring are taken in gill nets or by surrounding schools of fish with long purse nets.

NORTH ATLANTIC SHORE FISHERIES. The shallow waters that border the Atlantic coasts of maritime Canada and New England yield a large supplement to the banks fisheries. In part the shore catch is of haddock, cod, herring, and others that are taken in the deeper waters also. But large quantities of lobsters and clams add to the total value. The shore fish are caught by lines, nets, traps, and weirs operated from the shore or by men in small craft who are seldom more than a few miles from their homes.

MARKETING THE NORTH ATLANTIC FISH. Formerly, when most of the banks fisheries were conducted by hand lines, the number of fishing craft was very great, and their owners were distributed in villages along the entire coast from Long Island Sound to the Gulf of St. Lawrence. Many of the settlements were so isolated that they had little opportunity to market fresh fish beyond their own limited requirements. The surplus fish, cod especially, were salted and dried on open racks for shipment to distant markets (Fig. 99); and some, such as halibut, herring, and mackerel, were smoked or pickled. Many fish still are preserved in canneries which dot the shores of New England and maritime Canada, especially the small herring which are canned as sardines. However, the introduction of the steam trawler and methods of icing and quick freezing

FIG. 99.—Split and salted cod drying on the "flakes." This was formerly a common sight in all the fishing centers of New England and maritime Canada. Now one may see it principally in the smaller villages, where there is not quick transportation to the great markets for fresh fish. (*U.S. Bureau of Fisheries.*)

have brought great changes in the marketing of fish. Now great cargoes of edible fish may be caught and brought to central markets in a few hours. There they are dressed and frozen for shipment to any interior point. This change has decreased the importance of the isolated fishing village and increased that of such centers as Boston, Mass., and Halifax, N. S. Here are located great fish wharves with canning, freezing, and icing plants capable of caring for many tons of fish quickly. Smaller centers such as Gloucester, Mass., and Portland, Maine, have been forced to provide similar equipment to keep their fishing business. Fast boats bring live lobsters from Nova Scotia to the Boston and New York markets, whence they are shipped even to interior cities. Vestiges of the former fishing business and the old-fashioned drying of salt cod cling mainly to less accessible villages, where the shore catch still is cured in the open air. The same changes have greatly affected the fishermen also. Many fewer are needed than formerly, and the man of small capital is at a disadvantage in competing with the companies owning fleets of trawlers.

OTHER ATLANTIC AND GULF FISHERIES. The value of the fisheries of New England and eastern Canada is greater than that of all the other Atlantic fisheries of the United States combined. Yet these others have variety and importance. They include fisheries both off- and onshore in the Middle Atlantic and Gulf states. The more important of them take oysters, shrimp, sponges, and at least a dozen important species of food fish. Of the latter the Florida mullet is taken in largest quantity. Certain other species, such as the menhaden, are caught largely for their oil and fertilizer value.

The shallow waters of embayments in the Atlantic and Gulf coasts from Long Island Sound to Mexico are the home of oysters of excellent quality. Suitable conditions are found where salt or brackish water under 130 feet in depth has gravelly bottom to which the larval oysters can attach themselves. Sufficient current is desirable to sweep away stifling deposits of silt and to bring fresh supplies of the microscopic organisms upon which the oysters feed. The principal oyster fisheries are those of the Middle Atlantic states, particularly of Chesapeake Bay. So constantly are these beds fished that the continuation of the supply is secured only by artificial planting and close attention to prevent destruction of the industry, such as has already occurred in most of New England. Scientific methods of oyster propagation have recently enabled the establishment of new varieties and the growth of an industry in the waters of the northern Pacific Coast district of the United States where formerly oysters had little importance. Excellent oysters are produced also in the shallow waters bordering the Mississippi delta.

Shrimp fisheries likewise are characteristic of the shallow bays and bayous of the Gulf of Mexico Coast. The shrimp are netted from shallow-draught vessels. Some are marketed fresh, and small quantities are dried, but the larger part is canned in factories located at intervals along the coast. Sponges are taken mainly by divers operating on grounds, the most productive of which lie off the west coast of Florida. The food fish of the Gulf region are caught both alongshore and in the open water, the larger part from small sailing craft by hand lines and nets of various types. The steam trawler and the expensive gear so characteristic of the northeastern banks fisheries have, as yet, no great part in the southern fisheries.

PACIFIC COAST FISHERIES. The Pacific Coast fisheries of the United States are nearly as valuable as those of the Atlantic. If the value of the Pacific fishery products of the United States, British Columbia, and

Alaska are combined, the total is about equal to the Atlantic fisheries of both Canada and the United States. This is due most largely to the catch of salmon, although many halibut are taken also in the northern waters, and tuna and some lesser fish off southern California.

The streams that enter the Pacific Ocean between northern California and Alaska are the spawning grounds of five principal species of salmon which spend most of their lives in the adjacent salt water. During the spawning season, which, for the different species and different sections of the coast, includes the spring, summer, and autumn months, they approach the streams in great numbers. There they are easily taken by nets and traps, and some are caught at all seasons by trolling in open water. Small quantities of the fish are marketed fresh, frozen, or smoked,

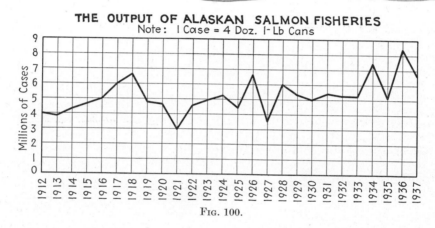

THE OUTPUT OF ALASKAN SALMON FISHERIES
Note: 1 Case = 4 Doz. 1-Lb Cans

Fig. 100.

but much the larger part are processed in adjacent canneries (Fig. 164). Of such canning establishments the United States has about 60, British Columbia about 50, and Alaska more than 100. Their combined output exceeds 60 million dollars in value and is the largest single phase of the North American fishing industry.

More than half a century of continuous salmon fishing for the canning industry has affected the supply of this resource. Although the total output has remained at about the same level for many years, it is only by means of greatly increased production in Alaska that it does so (Fig. 100). In Washington and Oregon, where the industry started, there has been a general decrease in the quantity of salmon caught over the last two decades, and in northern California the industry has all but disappeared. To offset the depletion several score fish hatcheries are maintained in the United States and Canada by both private and public agencies, but it seems unlikely that they alone can maintain the supply at its present level.

# Fresh-water Fisheries

The commercial fisheries in the lakes and rivers of North America are of small importance compared with the sea fisheries. Most extensive are those of the Great Lakes which are shared by the United States and Canada. The industry provides the markets of the Great Lakes region with fresh fish, of which cisco, lake trout, and whitefish are the most valuable.

The fresh-water clams of the interior streams, especially the Mississippi River, have been made the basis of a pearl-hunting industry, and their shells furnish the raw material for the manufacture of pearl buttons and similar products.

SELECTED REFERENCES

ACKERMAN, E. A. Depletion of New England Fisheries, *Econ. Geog.*, Vol. 14 (1938), pp. 233–238.

ADAMS, J. The Pacific Coast Halibut Fishery, *Econ. Geog.*, Vol. 11 (1935), pp. 247–257.

BIGELOW, H. B. "Oceanography: Its Scope, Problems, and Economic Importance," Boston, 1931.

FREEMAN, O. W. Salmon Industry of the Pacific Coast, *Econ. Geog.*, Vol. 11 (1935), pp. 109–129.

HJORT, JOHN. The Story of Whaling: A Parable of Sociology, *Sci. Monthly*, Vol. 45 (1937), pp. 19–34.

MATHEWS, J. H. Fisheries of the North Atlantic, *Econ. Geog.*, Vol. 3 (1927), pp. 1–22.

———. Fisheries of the South Atlantic and Gulf States, *Econ. Geog.*, Vol. 4 (1928), pp. 323–348.

PARKINS, A. E., and J. R. WHITAKER. "Our Natural Resources and Their Conservation," pp. 511–532, New York, 1939.

RADCLIFFE, L. Fishery Industries of the United States, *U.S. Bur. Fisheries. Doc.* 932, 1921.

# Chapter XI. Animal Fibers, Furs, and Skins

## Animal Fibers

WOOL THE MOST IMPORTANT ANIMAL FIBER. Nature has endowed many animals with two types of hairy coverings: one a coarse outer hair and the other a fine wavy undercoating of wool. The beaver, the seal, and the wild sheep are examples of animals so equipped. In the domestic sheep, selection and breeding have almost eliminated the coarse outer coat, leaving only the wool as a protection. Yet there are in existence, particularly in tropical countries, breeds of domestic sheep on which the hairy coat, like that of the goat, still predominates and in which the undercoat of wool is of no commercial value.

If a fiber of wool is compared under the microscope with strands of cotton, linen, or silk, it will be noted that the wool is covered with minute overlapping scales not unlike those of a young pine cone. When wool is properly treated, lapped, and beaten or twisted, these scales cling to one another and give to the woolen fabric its felted quality. For example, the nomads of the Arabian desert have for centuries made their tents of felt from the wool of their flocks. It is primarily these properties of fineness, waviness, and serrate surface to which are due the warmth, wearing qualities, and distinctive spinning and weaving characteristics of wool.

DEPENDENCE OF TYPES OF THE WOOLEN INDUSTRY ON CLASSES OF WOOL. The selection and breeding of sheep in various parts of the world have produced fleeces of widely different character. Extremes in this variation are found in the fine silky wool of the pure Spanish or Australian Merino, the long coarse wool of the English Lowland breeds, and the coarse short staple from the unkempt fleeces of the nomadic sheep native to the highlands of central Asia. Altogether, more than 300 varieties of wool are used in American mills. Yet from the industrial viewpoint they may be grouped, according to three general uses to which they are put, into (1) clothing wools, the finer, shorter stapled wools used in the manufacture of woolen cloth; (2) combing wools, the longer stapled and coarser wools used in worsted manufacture; and (3) carpet wool, short, coarse wool of poor grade used in carpet and rug manufacture.

"The essential difference between woolens and worsteds lies in the fact that in the manufacture of worsted, the fibers are combed before spinning. The combing process takes out the short fibers (noils) and leaves the long fibers parallel, when they are sent, in the form of 'tops,' to the spinning room. In the manufacture of woolen yarns, on the other hand, the fibers are merely 'carded'; and the 'roving' which is sent to the spinning department is a frail strand made up of fibers of varying lengths which are interlaced in every direction. While this is the essential difference between woolens and worsteds it is not the only one. This combing process in the worsted industry involves so many special problems in respect to raw materials, production methods, and character of the product, that the two industries are quite distinct.

"While the two products, woolens and worsteds, are distinct and the industries which produce them are separate, the idea should not be gathered that the two industries are always operated separately. Much of the machinery is interchangeable with slight modifications, and many mills make both types of product.[1] Furthermore, woolen and worsted yarns are often combined in the same fabric."[1]

THE DOMESTIC WOOL SUPPLY. The average annual consumption of new wool in the United States is about 650 million pounds, of which normally one-half to three-fourths is of domestic origin. The domestic wool is grown in every part of the country; yet three-fourths of the total is obtained from the dry-plains region and the western plateaus and mountains, especially from the northern Rocky Mountain region, Texas, Oregon, and California (Fig. 87). Wool, because it is nonperishable and easily stored and transported, is produced in keen competition with the product of other world sheep regions (Fig. 81). The principal American production being from areas of dry and rough land, it is also relatively cheap land. But even there the wool is grown under hazardous conditions of weather and under the menace of predatory animals and sheep diseases. The output tends to fluctuate greatly. Moreover, American land and labor both are expensive as compared with those of some other world regions of wool production. Only by a high tariff on wool is domestic production kept at its present level.

Formerly, nearly all American wool was fine wool; but following the introduction of English coarse-wooled sheep and the growing of crossbred lambs for mutton, the quantity of domestic coarse wool has increased. More than one-half the western crossbred wool is, however, sufficiently fine to be classed as clothing wool. Much of it can be used either for carding or for combing. The introduction of coarse-wooled sheep has had a notable effect also upon the quantity of wool. Early in the past century the average fleece in America probably did not weigh more than 3 pounds. The introduction of Merino sheep raised that average by a pound. Still later the increase of English blood in American flocks gradually raised the weight of the fleece to the present average of 8 pounds. Thus, although

[1] Cherington, P. T. "The Wool Industry," p. 1, Chicago, 1916.

there has been a decrease of 15 per cent in the number of sheep in the United States since 1900, there has been an increase of nearly 50 per cent in the production of wool.

The total number of sheep in Canada, less than 4 million, is little more than half the number in Texas, and the average wool production is hardly 5 per cent that of the United States. Although wool and its manufactures are exported from Canada in the equivalent of more than a third of the domestic production, the country has in fact a deficiency. It imports more raw wool than it produces and an even larger quantity of

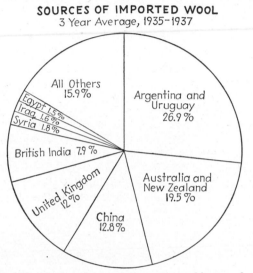

**SOURCES OF IMPORTED WOOL**
3 Year Average, 1935–1937

All Others 15.9%
Egypt 1.5%
Iraq 1.6%
Syria 1.8%
British India 7.9%
United Kingdom 12%
China 12.8%
Argentina and Uruguay 26.9%
Australia and New Zealand 19.5%

FIG. 101.—The United Kingdom exports some domestic wool but much also that originated in her colonies.

woolen and worsted yarns and fabrics. Unlike the distribution in the United States, most of the Canadian wool is the produce of small farm flocks pastured on rough and semiwooded lands in the humid eastern provinces.

AMERICA REQUIRES IMPORTED WOOL. About one-third of the wool manufactured in America is imported. It comes from nearly every part of the world (Fig. 101). The proportion of the total imports of wool made up of each of the principal classes has varied greatly. In recent years, however, fully two-thirds of the total has been carpet wool from many sources. Next most important is combing wool, the long coarse fiber of which the United States flocks produce least. Its source is largely Great Britain and the British colonies.

WOOLEN MANUFACTURE AN OLD INDUSTRY IN AMERICA. The spinning and weaving of wool began as a household industry soon after the first European settlements in America. In spite of British restriction upon colonial manufacture, the American farmer continued to clothe his family against the rigorous winters with the produce of his flocks. It was not until after the American Revolution that a factory system of woolen manufacture became established. The factory industry was particularly prosperous following 1821, and before the time of the Civil War home manufacture of woolen cloth had nearly ceased.

"The decline of the household manufacture was followed, particularly in the West, where the wool supply was rapidly increasing in the 40's, by the rise of a large number of small factories. Here we see the industry in its process of evolution from a household basis to a town or small community basis. The introduction of the carding and fulling mills was the first step in the woolen industry away from the self-sufficing economy of the household. Then came the gradual addition of other machinery and processes, till finally the completed woolen mill or factory emerged. This was a small concern, the number of sets of condensing cards per factory in 1845 averaging about one and three-quarters, and few of the establishments supplied more than a local market.

"The woolen mill, together with the grist mill, the lumber mill, and the various establishments of similar mill type, all supplying simply a local market or a small community, were a part of that town economy which appeared in this country in the East and the Middle West for a brief period in its industrial history; in the South the scattered population, the absence of towns, and the dominance of the plantation gave the household or the plantation economy a much longer life."[1]

MODERN WOOLEN MANUFACTURE MORE CENTRALIZED.    Most of the numerous small woolen mills of the early period were located primarily with respect to a neighborhood supply of wool and a local market and secondarily with respect to a local source of power, usually water power. The census of 1870 records 2,891 mills scattered through the territory east of the Mississippi River, although about one-fifth of them were in New England. The products of these mills were mainly plain woolen fabrics for dress goods and suits. In recent decades the growing popularity of worsted goods for men's wear and the substitution of cotton and silk for wool in dress goods have greatly curtailed the business of these country woolen mills. A demand for fancy goods gave advantage to the larger mills with expensive machinery. Many of the small mills have been abandoned. The census of 1937 records only about 500 mills both large and small, 330 of them manufacturing woolens and about 170 worsteds. In addition, there were more than 100 others spinning woolen and worsted yarns but weaving no fabrics. Such of the small country mills as continue in operation manufacture mainly blankets and flannels. The newer and larger mills are concentrated principally in the textile district of Massa-

[1] Wright, C. W. "Wool-growing and the Tariff," pp. 113–114, Harvard University Press, 1910.

chusetts and Rhode Island and near Philadelphia. Massachusetts alone
has about one-fifth of all the woolen mills of the country and one-fifth of
the wage earners employed in that industry. Of worsted mills it has also
one-fifth; but of the wage earners in worsted manufacture, four-fifths,
indicating the much larger average size of worsted mills and the high
concentration of the worsted industry in that state.

WORSTED MANUFACTURES OUTSTRIP WOOLENS IN VALUE. Although
the recent census shows only one-half as many worsted as woolen mills,

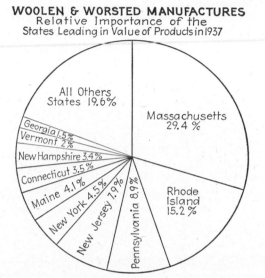

WOOLEN & WORSTED MANUFACTURES
Relative Importance of the
States Leading in Value of Products in 1937

FIG. 102.—Nearly 80 per cent of the woolen manufactures of the United States are produced
in the Atlantic Coast states from Maine to Pennsylvania.

the number of persons employed in worsted manufacture and the value
of worsted products are nearly twice as great as those of the woolen
industry. That also implies a much greater concentration of the worsted
industry in large establishments than characterizes the manufacture of
woolens.

"The chief characteristics of the worsted industry as it is at present constituted are: (1) the relatively large size of the plants, (2) the high degree of specialization, and (3) the high degree of centralization in a few states, and more specifically in the cities of Lawrence, Mass., Providence, R. I., and Philadelphia, Pa.
These three cities together produce the greater part of the country's output."[1]
(Fig. 102.)

As a result of so great a concentration of woolen and worsted manufacturing in the East and particularly in New England, Boston has
become the leading raw-wool market of North America.

[1] Cherington. *Op. cit.*, pp. 8, 9.

THE MANUFACTURE OF WOOLEN AND WORSTED CLOTHING. One of the important causes for the reduced number of woolen mills now in operation in America and for the concentration of both the woolen and worsted industries in large mills is to be found in a change in the character and location of the market for the cloth. Formerly the market was widely distributed. The plain cloth woven by country mills was made into clothing by local tailors and dressmakers. The rise of ready-made clothing into popularity has transferred a large part of the primary market for cloth to the great cities which are the centers of clothing manufacture. It is in these centers that the changing fashions in type, weave, and color of fabrics are set. Mills must be in close contact with the changing requirements, and a few large mills with highly skilled labor can more quickly be organized to meet them than many mills that are small and widely scattered.

As in the case of cotton clothing, the centers of manufacture for woolen and worsted clothing are located in the great cities owing to (1) the abundant supply of adaptable labor, largely Russian Jews, and (2) the large local markets and good marketing facilities. New York City has more than one-half the establishments devoted to the manufacture of ready-to-wear clothing. Boston, Philadelphia, Baltimore, Cleveland, and Chicago are also conspicuous centers in this trade. By reason of its relation to the clothing trades, as well as its nearness to the great centers of cloth manufacture, New York City has become the great market for woolen and worsted cloth. Not only are there to be found here the samples of cloths and clothing, but here exist all the necessary agencies for trading in these wares. To New York, therefore, come the buyers for firms of various classes in all parts of the country.

OTHER USERS OF WOOL are the carpet and rug, shoddy, knit-goods, and felt industries. Of these none is more geographically concentrated than the manufacture of carpets and rugs. Nearly two-thirds of all American wool-rug and carpet mills are located in or near Philadelphia and New York. This fact is due more largely to historical than to environmental factors, though the use of imported raw materials in rug manufacture continues to give a port some advantage over any interior location. Philadelphia is also an important center for the knit-goods and felt industries. The latter, which includes hat manufacture as its principal phase, uses cut fur as a raw material to a greater extent even than wool. Nearly three-fourths of the felt-hat manufactories of the United States are located in Connecticut, New York, New Jersey, and eastern Pennsylvania.

AMERICAN FOREIGN TRADE IN WOOL MANUFACTURES. In spite of the great development of American woolen and worsted manufacture, there has continued to be in the country until recently a large market for the finer grades of cloth and clothing which come mainly from European mills with their cheaper and more specialized labor. Great Britain was the source of most of these imports. However, the same restrictive forces that have been noted with respect to United States foreign trade in other commodities affect these also. Woolen and worsted goods, knit goods, and wearing apparel are both imported and exported, the imports being about ten times greater in value than the exports. But, in both cases, the present trade is less than half that of a decade ago.

In recent years, however, the products of American looms have been exported in considerable values but not nearly equal to the value of the imported goods. The principal export is cloth, although manufactured wearing apparel is also an item of some importance. The markets for

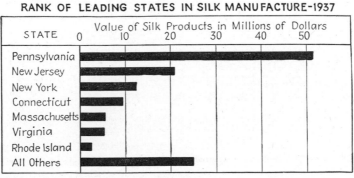

RANK OF LEADING STATES IN SILK MANUFACTURE-1937

Fig. 103.

American exports are widely scattered, though the near-by customers Canada and Cuba are among the largest buyers.

AMERICA A LARGE USER OF SILK. The expensive agricultural labor of America does not permit silk production in competition with the Orient, especially Japan. Yet, owing to high per capita wealth and large population, America buys more silk than any other nation. Of all the silk imported into the United States, about nine-tenths, in value, is in unmanufactured form. This silk furnishes the raw material used in more than 600 mills scattered through the eastern industrial districts. Many of them produce only silk yarns and thread. Some of these are used with wool and other fibers in mixed goods, woven or knitted. More than two-thirds of the mills, however, produce woven silk goods; and of these, nine-tenths are located in Pennsylvania, New Jersey, and New York. Associated with them are nearly as many mills employing rayon yarns in similar and competing products. The rayon mills are located principally in the same area but have been established also in the textile districts of New England and the Carolina Piedmont (Fig. 103).

In this eastern industrial district is available a large supply of the type of labor needed in silk and rayon manufacture—deft-fingered women and girls whose husbands or fathers may be employed in the iron and steel or other mills of this region. There is, then, some justification for the statement sometimes made that silk manufacture is a "parasitic industry." It is an industry that moves to the labor supply. The weight of the silk is so small and its value so high that the cost of transportation either of the raw material or of the finished product is a very minor item of expense. The raw silk moves from Japan and China as high-class freight. In fact, it would be possible to load an entire year's imports into two or three good-sized ships. From American Pacific ports the silk is carried across the continent in express trains to the principal region of manufacture.

The rapid growth of the rayon industry is indicated by the fact that the amount of rayon produced in the United States is more than four times the quantity of silk imported. The rise of rayon and its substitution for silk have had the effect of decreasing the imports of silk by about 25 per cent. But the substitution is not complete, and much silk still is required. Rayon has had a striking affect on the price of silk, which has decreased to about one-third its former level.

## The American Fur Industry

FURS AN INCENTIVE TO EARLY EXPLORATION IN NORTH AMERICA. Few of the natural resources of North America exerted greater influence upon its early history than did the fur-bearing animals with which its forests and streams abounded. From the early settlements on the lower Hudson to those of a later day on the lower Columbia River are many North American cities and towns that owe their locations to the establishment of fur-trading posts. If all were named, the list would be a long and interesting one. To the settlers of New England and of eastern Canada, particularly, the trade in furs, along with forests and fisheries, offered prospects of immediate income, where the ice-scoured rocks and boulder-strewn soils promised but little room for the expansion of agriculture. Furs furnished the incentive for some of the earliest exploration and soon replaced the search for the "Northwest Passage" as a reason for penetrating the interior of the continent.

PHYSICAL ENVIRONMENT FAVORABLE TO FUR PRODUCTION IN NORTH AMERICA. For nearly 300 years the fur trade has flourished in North America. Some of the fur-bearing animals have been greatly reduced in number, and it has been necessary to protect most if not all of them by legislative restrictions. Yet this continent remains unexcelled in the volume, variety, and beauty of the furs that it is able to produce. This fact is attributable in large measure to climatic and other environmental conditions favorable to the growth of furs of high quality and to the organization of the fur-collecting industry. (1) The long, cold winters of northern North America put the coats of the fur bearers into prime condition and give a long season in which they may be captured before the fur begins to suffer from the approach of warm weather; (2) the physiographic and climatic conditions of the western mountains and the Laurentian upland and its outliers have rendered them unattractive for agricultural settlement, and much of them has therefore remained forested and a great retreat for fur-bearing animals; (3) the numerous streams, lakes, and marshes of North America constitute the homes of some of the most abundant and valuable fur-bearing animals, such as the beaver, muskrat, otter, and mink; (4) these same waterways furnished the original means of access through the forests to the northernmost fur regions, a means that, except for the growing use of the airplane, still remains the only one available in nearly half the continent.

FUR FARMING.  Furs are luxury goods, go in and out of style, and are subject to great fluctuations in price. In good times high prices are paid for choice peltries, and the trapper is well rewarded for his work; but in bad times he may have almost no market at all. Always the larger part of the demand is supplied by cheaper products, such as sheep- and lambskins and rabbit fur. These are the produce of farms, not forests. Of the wild-fur resources of the United States and Canada no inventory has ever been possible. It is known that some of the fur bearers have been greatly depleted, but whether or not the total supply is dwindling is not certain. The market for superior furs has, however, been generally good enough to suggest raising them on farms also. The problem is a very different one from the handling of ordinary domestic animals, and many mistakes have been made. Procedures are now pretty well standardized, however, and a fur-farming industry exists on a large scale. Although many of the common fur-bearing animals are raised in captivity to some extent, the silver fox is much the most important.

Fur farming is practiced in every Canadian province and most of the states of the Union. It reaches its greatest development, however, in the cooler, wooded farm-land region of the northeast. Minnesota, Wisconsin, Michigan, Ontario, Quebec, and Prince Edward Island form a belt in which the industry is common. In Canada the value of the fur-farm products is nearly half that of the wild furs taken, and it has tripled in a decade.

AMERICA A GREAT FUR MARKET AND MANUFACTURER OF FURS. In 1764 a fur-trading post was established on the present site of St. Louis, Mo. By its location it was able to command a large part of the fur trade that came down the Missouri River from the far Northwest and also that which came from the North down the Mississippi. The post became in subsequent years an outfitting point for fur traders and a central market and distributing point for furs. This ancient interest the city has maintained and expanded in spite of a vast growth in other forms of enterprise, and St. Louis now holds rank as one of the principal raw-fur collecting points of the world. Formerly most of the world's raw furs were sent to London or Leipzig for sale to dressing and dyeing establishments where they were made into wearing apparel. During the First World War a change was necessary, and New York now performs both the marketing and the manufacturing functions. To its salesrooms come the furs of all parts of the United States and many foreign countries. In one section of the city also is a district given over almost entirely to the dyeing and finishing of furs and their manufacture into garments. Of the dressing and dyeing establishments in the United States, New York and the neighboring city of Newark, N. J., have more than three-fourths. A similar proportion of all the persons in the United States engaged in fur-goods manufacture are in New York alone. A considerable quantity of Canadian furs are dressed and manufactured in Montreal.

## American Leather Manufactures

IMPORTANCE OF LEATHER MANUFACTURE.  Few peoples have had a civilization so primitive that they did not possess methods of tanning leather, and some processes perfected long ago have never been excelled by modern industrial art. In every civilized nation, even those which support but few domestic animals, leather is made to serve many essential purposes. The United States is the world's largest manufacturer and user of leather.

EARLY LEATHER MANUFACTURE IN THE UNITED STATES.  The raw materials used in leather manufacture include (1) hides and skins, (2) tanning materials, and (3) numerous minor materials used in giving pliability, finish, and color to the leather. In the early history of American tanning, all these materials could be obtained in almost any community. The local slaughterhouses and farms furnished hides and skins, and the local forests yielded oak and hemlock bark. Small tanneries were then scattered throughout the settled portions of the country, and the leather was used mainly by local shoemakers and harness makers.

As the clearing of the forests progressed, local supplies of tanbark dwindled. In fact, great quantities of timber, especially hemlock, were cut merely to get the bark. It began to appear also that hides and skins from various parts of the country yielded classes of leather not all of which could be used locally, and improving transportation facilities made it possible to assemble materials from many sources at reasonable cost. Tanneries that were favorably located with respect to raw materials and markets expanded their operations; those less well-established went out of business. In 1870 there were more than 7,000 tanneries in the United States, most of them small, for they employed an average of only four

men each. Consolidation has progressed, and the census of 1937 shows
only 331 tanneries. However, they employ an average of 150 men each,
and have much more mechanical equipment than those of the earlier date.

In the development of the tanning industry it was the source of tanbark and the location of the principal markets, more than the source
of the hides and skins, that determined the growth of the large American
tanning centers. In the manufacture of hemlock-tanned sole leather, one
ton (2,240 pounds) of bark will tan about two average cowhides (115

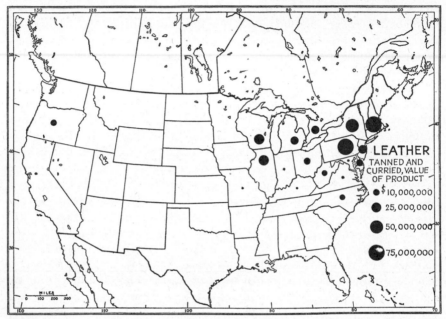

Fig. 104.—The relative importance of the leading states and provinces in leather
manufacture.

pounds) and, together with minor ingredients, will make of them about
190 pounds of sole leather. In the tanning of light upper leather only
about one-half as much bark is required.[1] It is obvious that the relatively
small quantity of compactly baled hides could stand the cost of transportation better than the large quantity of loosely corded bark and
perhaps even better than the finished leather. Tanneries tended, therefore, to grow in number and importance in regions where bark was
available and near the centers of population. The oak and chestnut
forests of the Appalachians and the forests of New England met these
requirements early, and somewhat later the forests of Wisconsin and
Minnesota served in like manner to the population center near Chicago.
It is not surprising, therefore, that in 1870 the old and well-established

[1] Watt, Alexander. "Leather Manufacture," pp. 272–275.

tanning centers near Philadelphia, New York, and Boston were out-standing, having together about one-third of all the tanneries of the country.

THE MODERN TANNERY NOT DEPENDENT UPON TANBARK. The leaching of tannin from the tanbark was formerly carried on in the tanyard, but it is just as satisfactorily done in the bark-producing district. The obvious economy in the latter practice appeared as the sources of bark gradually receded from the established tanneries as the result of timber depletion. The shipment and use of large quantities of tanning extracts instead of the bark made the necessary adjustment to growing distance. Still later the importation of foreign extracts and tanning materials and the increase in chemical tanning, particularly of the chrome processes, have rendered the location of the modern tannery quite independent of the supply of domestic tanbark. Yet, owing to the influence of the location of leather markets and to the persistence of a rooted industry, there has been comparatively little shifting in the location of tanning centers as a result of this emancipation (Fig. 104). The eastern district, including the Philadelphia, New York, and Boston areas, now does more than half the leather tanning of the United States. In fact Massachusetts is the leading leather-making state. It has considerably more tanneries and more persons employed in the tanning, currying, and finishing of leather than Pennsylvania, its nearest rival. There is only one important tanning region in the interior of the country. It is most highly developed in the lower Lake Michigan district, especially in Chicago and Milwaukee, where hides from the packing houses were conveniently tanned with the bark and tanning extracts obtained from the northern forests early in the industrial history of the region, and where it continues to operate. The combined industries of Illinois and Wisconsin are approximately equal to that of Pennsylvania.

PORTS INFLUENCE THE LOCATION OF TANNERIES. America is so large a user and exporter of leather and its products that even the large domestic supplies of hides and skins are wholly inadequate. Approximately three-fourths of all the hides and skins used in American tanneries are imported. The imports include large numbers of cattle hides, mainly from South America; calfskins and sheepskins, of which Europe is the principal source; and millions of goatskins, practically the entire American supply of which is imported, mainly from Asia. The principal trade is through the Atlantic ports Boston, New York, and Philadelphia. It is therefore fully as important that the modern tannery be located near these ports as that it be convenient to the great packing houses of the Middle West. Not only are hides and skins imported, but many of the tanning agents now used are obtained from foreign sources through these same commercial gateways.

AMERICA THE WORLD'S GREATEST SHOEMAKER.   The largest use for tannery products is in the manufacture of shoes. So varied are the aspects of the shoemaking industry that it includes in its raw materials rubber, felt, fiber, and wood as well as many classes and grades of leather. Until about 1850, shoes were made in small shops by hand. In the 35 years subsequent to that date there were invented in America the principal machines that revolutionized the manufacture of shoes. Over 450 million pairs of leather boots and shoes are made annually in the factories of the United States. Made cheaply by machinery, these products supply the

**RANK OF THE LEADING STATES IN BOOT AND SHOE MANUFACTURE - 1937**

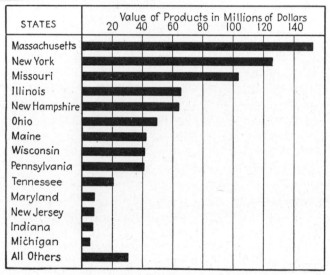

FIG. 105.

very large domestic market and until recently enabled some 2 per cent of the output to be sold abroad, some even in Europe. Trade restrictions have now reduced exports to a fraction of 1 per cent of the number manufactured, and the larger part of these are sold in the near-by Caribbean countries.

SHOE MANUFACTURE LOCATED NEAR THE LEATHER SUPPLY.   Since the great tanneries have located principally in the eastern industrial region of the United States, it follows that the shoe-manufacturing industry when located in the same region has the double advantage of proximity to both raw material and markets. In 1939 there were about 1,100 boot and shoe factories in the country, of which six-tenths were in the region between southern Maine and the city of Philadelphia. A like proportion of all the shoes were made in these factories, and nearly one-fourth the total industry was centered in the factories of eastern Massachusetts alone, especially in the closely grouped cities of Boston, Brockton, Lynn, and Haverhill (Fig. 105).

There has, however, been a considerable development of shoe manufacture in the Middle West. Shoes are high class and rather bulky freight and take a high freight rate. With the development of a large market in the central and western states it became profitable to assemble leather and to make shoes near this market. St. Louis is the principal shoe-manufacturing center of this region and one of the most important in the country, but many shoes are produced in the secondary tanning region including Chicago and Milwaukee.

OTHER MANUFACTURES OF LEATHER. Next to the manufacture of shoes, the harness and saddlery industry uses the most leather and yields products of the greatest total value. This is, by comparison, a typically decentralized industry. The majority of the harness shops are small. No complicated or expensive machinery is required; the products are bulky and are sold principally in the rural districts; and the industry tends to remain close to the markets. At least two-thirds of the 48 states have one or more such factories, and the leading state, Illinois, accounts for only about 6 per cent of the total industry.

The leather-glove and -mitten industry, on the other hand, is remarkably concentrated, 60 per cent of all the factories being in New York State, mainly in the neighboring cities of Gloversville and Johnstown, where it was established by a settlement of Scotch glovemakers and where craftsmen skilled in this trade are now concentrated.

SELECTED REFERENCES

COLE, A. H. "The American Wool Manufacture," Cambridge, 1926.
HOOVER, E. M. "Location Theory and the Shoe and Leather Industries," Cambridge, 1937.
SCHNITZER, J. G. International Trade in Leather, *U.S. Dept. Commerce, Trade Promotion Series* 103, 1930.
———. Leather: World Production and International Trade, *U.S. Dept. Commerce, Trade Promotion Series* 157, pp. 36–50, 1935.

# Chapter XII. Fuel and Power

FUEL AND POWER VITAL TO MODERN INDUSTRY. It is impossible to picture the paralysis of industry and the suffering that would afflict the industrial nations of the world if the abundant supplies of fuel and power, to which their national economies are adjusted, were to be cut off. Several modern industrial nations have from two to four times as many people as could be well supported from the land of those countries by agriculture alone. Large parts of these excess populations live by working in factories, on railways and ships, or at other nonagricultural pursuits. Yet most of the occupations that they follow could not exist if it were not for mechanical energy. Not only would those who work in factories suffer, but all others as well. So much of our clothing and food and so many of our utensils are made in factories by the use of power that it is as if we had many servants in our employ to do these things for us. So long has this been true that the majority of people do not know the arts of spinning, weaving, tanning, shoemaking, cabinetmaking, blacksmithing, and other crafts by means of which each small community formerly supplied its own needs. It may be said, therefore, that industrial nations exist in large measure upon a basis of coal, petroleum, natural gas, and water power, the chief sources of mechanical energy—the vital element in modern industry.

THE CONSUMPTION OF ENERGY IN THE UNITED STATES is enormous, proportionately far more than in any other nation. It has been estimated that, per capita, it is 50 per cent higher than that of Great Britain, twice that of Germany, 10 times that of Japan, and 150 times that of China. Heat for buildings and industrial processes; light indoors and on the public streets; power for transportation by land, water, and air; power for all mechanical processes on farms and in factories and from every source— all such needs for energy in 1937 represented for each family in the country the equivalent of the work of 120 theoretical horses working 8 hours a day 6 days a week for the entire year.[1]

[1] Energy Resources and National Policy, p. 8, National Resources Committee, Washington, 1939.

198

SOURCES OF ENERGY IN THE UNITED STATES. In the provision of so large a quantity of energy all the important sources of it are drawn upon. It is estimated, by the National Resources Board, that of the total energy output bituminous coal supplied, in 1937, about 48 per cent, anthracite coal 7 per cent, petroleum 32 per cent, natural gas nearly 10 per cent, and water power less than 4 per cent. Although coal is most used, it has shown a relative decrease in recent years due largely to a much increased use of petroleum and natural gas (Fig. 106). Whether or not there are adequate supplies of these critical natural resources for a reasonable future is clearly a matter of great concern. In this connection it may be noted that of this group water power alone is a renewable resource. The others have required the geologic ages for their formation, and once they are used they cannot be replaced. The conservative use of these resources involves many questions that cannot be touched upon here. It is important, however, that the principal facts be known concerning their abundance, qualities, and distribution. On those facts rest many of the features of present American industrial life and perhaps its future.

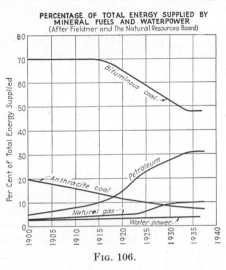

PERCENTAGE OF TOTAL ENERGY SUPPLIED BY MINERAL FUELS AND WATERPOWER
(After Fieldner and The Natural Resources Board)

FIG. 106.

## The Coal of North America

THE DISTRIBUTION OF COAL RELATED TO ITS GEOLOGIC ORIGIN. Coal is preserved vegetation. It is known that there are many rock formations in North America of an age earlier than the appearance upon earth of abundant vegetation capable of forming coal. Consequently there are large areas in which it cannot be expected that coal ever will be found. Such are the rocks of the Laurentian upland and some of the older Paleozoic sediments.

When abundant vegetation did appear upon the earth, it did not collect uniformly for the formation of future coal deposits. Certain favorable conditions of physical geography, in addition to abundant vegetation, seem to have been necessary, one of which was the existence of large areas of swampland created by the encroachment of shallow seas upon the continent. The location of these ancient swamps determined the position of the great coal fields, and the recurrence of such conditions in geologic history has given coals of differing age and characteristics

(Fig. 107). There are in North America deposits representative of nearly every stage in the process of coal formation—peat, brown coal or lignite, bituminous coals from low to high grade, and anthracite. The character of coal has been much influenced also by subsequent events in its geologic history.

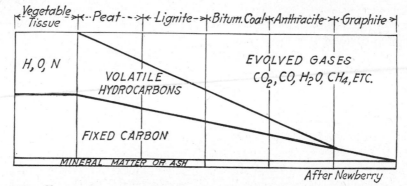

FIG. 107.—Changes that occur in the composition of vegetable tissue in its transformation through various stages in coal formation.

ANTHRACITE COAL REGIONS.   The series of geologic events required to transform the accumulations of ancient swamps and bogs into anthracite coal was not completed in most of the American coal regions. The anthracite districts are therefore of limited extent. The total quantity of anthracite coal mined in North America averages less than one-ninth of the total coal production of the continent. The only important anthracite field lies in the highly folded rocks of northeastern Pennsylvania, where

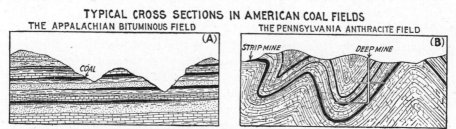

FIG. 108.—A. Nearly horizontal coal beds in the dissected Allegheny plateau. B. Highly folded coal beds in the Appalachian region.

areas totaling only 480 square miles contain practically all the known reserves of this excellent coal. Because of the complicated structure of the rocks, deep mining is in large part necessary, involving heavy expenditures for labor and machinery (Fig. 108B).

Most of the commercial output of anthracite is used in the northeastern states. Formerly it was the leading industrial fuel and in 1860 accounted for more than half the coal mined in the United States. It is now too expensive for that purpose and is used mainly for the heating of buildings. Even for this use it is being largely replaced by cheaper coal and petroleum. Some quantity moves westward by rail or to the Great Lakes ports and is carried by boats to the upper Great Lakes region where it is used as domestic fuel. About two-thirds of the original supply of anthracite still remain underground, but it is the part most difficult to mine. Since it is expensive fuel, its use is declining, and the reserve may actually last a long time.

VAST RESERVES OF BITUMINOUS AND LOWER GRADE COALS. North America, and particularly the United States, is fortunate in its possession of vast reserves of coal for the future. The total quantity of readily minable bituminous coal in North America is estimated at about $1\frac{1}{2}$ trillion tons, of which more than nine-tenths is in the United States. This is so vast a quantity that, if all of it could be utilized, it would supply the entire world, at its present rate of consumption, for more than a thousand years. No other continent except Asia has reserves of bituminous coal estimated at half this amount.

In addition, North America has even larger reserves of low-grade coal and lignite, estimated at more than 2 trillion tons, of which more than a fourth is in Canada. The low-grade coals and lignite have lower heating value than bituminous coal, crumble rapidly when exposed to the air, cannot be shipped far, and are now used only near the place of mining. They constitute, however, a source of potential energy for a future time when they may be more needed than they are now and when means for their economical utilization shall be better developed. Although the total coal resources of the world are not completely known, it appears possible that North America has as much as 60 per cent and that the United States alone may have 45 per cent of the world's supply.

Estimates such as these are only approximations, although most of the coal fields have been explored by deep drilling, and the number, extent, and thickness of most of the beds are known. Many of the beds are so thin and others so deep underground that they may not prove profitable to mine in the future. To put the matter in more concrete terms, the known coal reserve of the United States would last this country, at the present rate of consumption, for about 5,000 years. However, there is no assurance that the present rate of use will continue to be sufficient or that all the coal known to exist could be mined profitably if ever it were needed.

THE APPALACHIAN COAL FIELD. The location, extent, and general character of the North American coal regions are shown in Fig. 109. Of these various regions that which is known as the "Appalachian field" is most important, not only because of its great extent and present output but also because of the high quality of its coal. The region extends from northern Pennsylvania to Alabama, mainly through the dissected

Allegheny-Cumberland Highland, and from it is obtained more than two-thirds of all the bituminous coal mined in the United States. Its

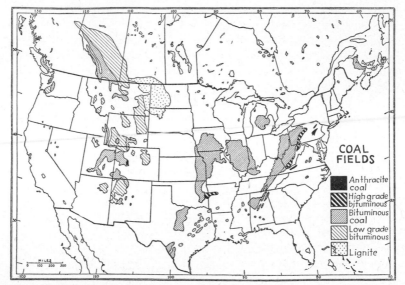

COAL
FIELDS

Anthracite
coal

High grade
bituminous

Bituminous
coal

Low grade
bituminous

Lignite

Fig. 109.—The principal coal fields of the United States and Canada distinguished as to location, extent, and principal types of coal.

Fig. 110.—A representative valley in the Appalachian coal field. The mine mouth is on the valley side at the right. Coal is conveyed in mine cars over the trestle and is discharged through the tipple into railway cars. (*Photograph by U.S. Bureau of Mines*).

favorable geographic location and the ease with which the coal can be mined have contributed much to its importance. The process of uplift that formed the plateau deformed the strata but little, and the alternating beds of coal and of rock deposited in the ancient swamps still lie in nearly horizontal position. In more recent geologic ages streams have carved their valleys deeply into these layers, exposing the edges of the coal beds along the valley sides. Incidentally, it is probable that this long-continued stream erosion has removed much more of the original coal than remains (Fig. 108A).

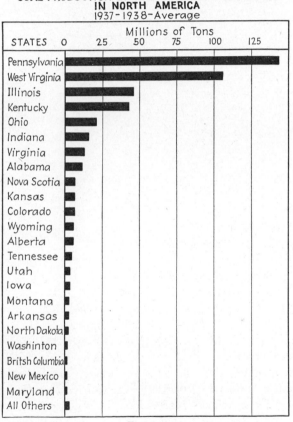

COAL PRODUCTION BY LEADING STATES AND PROVINCES
IN NORTH AMERICA
1937-1938-Average

Fig. 111.

It is obvious that horizontal beds of coal exposed on hillsides present a comparatively simple mining problem. New mines can be opened easily. Coal brought to the mine mouth can be dumped into railway cars in the valley below (Fig. 110). So advantageous is this situation that, with the aid of modern mining devices, even the expensive labor of America can produce coal very cheaply. This remarkable ease of mining coal has, however, led to at least one serious misfortune, namely, the opening of too many small mines, and to competition that frequently results in over-production followed by depression of prices, congestion of transportation, enforced idleness of workmen, and labor difficulties.

The geographical location of the Appalachian coal region also is highly fortunate from the commercial viewpoint. Its northern and most productive section (Fig. 111) lies within easy reach of Great Lakes transportation; and throughout its length, rivers and valley roadways opening east and west form routes of transportation. Coal moves by rail eastward to Norfolk, Va., and New York and thence by boat to New England consumers or into export trade or is used as ship fuel. Coal from Ohio, Pennsylvania, and West Virginia constitutes the principal return cargo for the Great Lakes freight boats that move iron ore eastward. The coal is stored at the upper lake ports during the summer for use during the winter when the lakes are closed by ice. The central and northern part of the Appalachian coal region is the principal source of high-grade bituminous coal required in the manufacture of coke, essential in iron smelting.

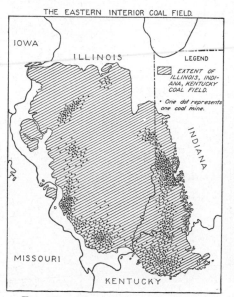

FIG. 112.—Most of the coal mines in the broad basin of the eastern interior field are located upon its shallower margins.

INTERIOR COAL FIELDS. Four bituminous coal fields of great importance are situated in the interior plains of North America. In the order of their present importance they are (1) the eastern interior field, in Illinois, Indiana, and Kentucky; (2) the western interior field, in Iowa, Missouri, Kansas, and Oklahoma; (3) the southwestern interior field, in Texas; and (4) the northern interior field, in Michigan. The eastern field produces the most and the best coal of the interior region. It competes with Appalachian coal for the industrial markets of the Great Lakes region. The coal beds of this eastern interior field lie in the form of a broad and shallow basin beneath the nearly level plains of the region. They are deeply buried near the center but lie near the surface about the upturned margins of the basin. For that reason most of the present mines are near the margins of the field (Fig. 112). In southern Illinois much coal is recovered by removing a few feet of overlying earth by giant steam shovels and working out the exposed layer of coal at the bottom of the furrow before turning another (Fig. 113). The coals of the western and southwestern fields are deeply buried except along their eastern margins, where they are mined. They are of lower grade and are used principally as railway fuel and for local needs. Only a small quantity of this coal moves far from the place of its production. Very little of the Michigan coal is being mined because better grades of coal are readily secured from other fields.

ROCKY MOUNTAIN AND PACIFIC COAST FIELDS. At various points in the Rocky Mountains, in the Puget Sound region of the United States

FIG. 113.—Giant furrows turned by power shovels in the process of strip mining in southern Illinois. The 4-foot bed of coal exposed in the bottom of the trench is mined out before the next furrow is turned.

and Canada, and in Alaska are scattered fields of bituminous coal. The total output of these fields is relatively small, but the coal has a great local importance because of the distance that separates these regions from the eastern coal fields. The Puget Sound fields, especially those on Vancouver Island, constitute the only important source of steamship coal on the Pacific Coast.

COAL AN INDUSTRIAL RAW MATERIAL. The principal use of coal in America is as a source of power. The power producers include steam locomotives, which consume more coal than any other single type of use, stationary power plants in factories, and the plants that generate electricity by steam. The next class of use includes those in which coal is used as fuel for heating homes and in certain industrial processes that require heat. Coal is also an important raw material in some widely distributed industries, particularly the manufacture of coke and illuminating gas.

In the Appalachian coal region, where coke is made in large quantities for blast-furnace use, the by-products of coke manufacture are of great value. When properly treated, a ton (2,000 pounds) of coal will yield 1,425 pounds of coke, 10,500 cubic feet of gas, 7.1 gallons of tar, 2.4 gallons of crude oil, and 19 pounds of sulphate of ammonia.[1] Tar and sulphate of ammonia are raw materials of importance in the chemical industries. In the past, crude methods of coke manufacture have wasted nearly all these valuable by-products, and much still is being wasted (Fig. 114). Con-

Fig. 114.—Beehive coke ovens in the Connellsville region. The fumes from these ovens carry away the many valuable by-products recoverable by modern processes. (*U.S. Bureau of Mines*).

nellsville, Pa., is the center of coke making in America, and the presence there of superior coking coal was the chief reason for the early growth of the iron and steel industries in the Pittsburgh district.

THE USE AND CONSERVATION OF AMERICAN COAL. The abundance of American coal and the relative ease with which it is obtained have invited wasteful methods in its exploitation and use. Figure 115 shows the rapid rate of increase in the production of coal in the United States, which now mines about 35 per cent of the annual coal supply of the world. Coal constitutes over a third of the carload freight of railroads in the United States,[2] and the problems involved in the distribution of so large

[1] "World Atlas of Commercial Geology," Part I, p. 9, U.S. Geological Survey.

[2] Energy Resources and National Policy, p. 78, Natural Resources Committee, Washington, 1939.

a quantity to its markets are extremely difficult to solve. In coal mining it is possible, by proper methods, to secure about four-fifths of the coal, yet the abundance of coal and the highly competitive mining conditions in the United States encourage the mining of the best and most accessible coal, often rendering thinner layers unavailable for the future. Actually, on the average, about a third of the coal is left in the ground. The movement for the conservation of coal in America should be directed toward the correction of wasteful practices and particularly toward ensuring a proper distribution and use of coal. The vast reserves available make

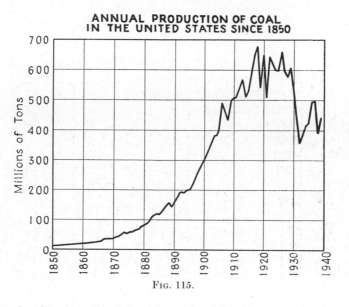

ANNUAL PRODUCTION OF COAL
IN THE UNITED STATES SINCE 1850

FIG. 115.

reduction in the quantity of coal consumed unnecessary and probably undesirable, if so large a quantity can be used efficiently. It may be assumed with reasonable safety that the future will see more effective methods of coal utilization and probably also new means of fuel and power production as outgrowths of existing industries dependent upon coal. Such a hope is, however, not an excuse for the waste of a necessary and exhaustible resource.

FOREIGN TRADE IN AMERICAN COAL. A large part of the world has not coal enough to run its necessary industries and move its trains (Fig. 116), and these regions depend on imported coal. America has not had a large share in this foreign trade in coal. Relatively small amounts (less than 2 per cent of the average annual production) constitute the normal coal exports of the United States, and they are less than those of a decade past. Great Britain, the principal source of export coal, may find it necessary to husband her fuel, and the coal of America may be, in the not far distant future, the principal available supply. There can be no question about the abundance of American coal, yet the United States is not well situated to engage in this trade. The total export trade of the country is already more bulky and requires more ship space than all the commodities imported. Many ships must now return to American ports empty. If coal is added to the export trade, still more ships will be required, and the freight rates charged on coal must help to pay for empty space in returning ships. American coal in most foreign regions will,

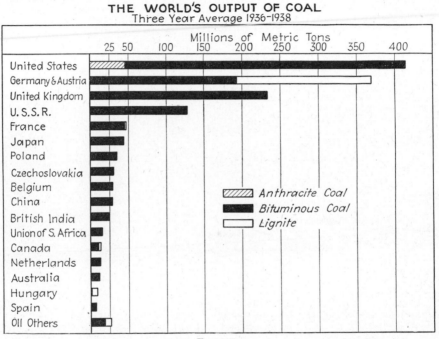

THE WORLD'S OUTPUT OF COAL
Three Year Average 1936–1938

Fig. 116.

therefore, be expensive. At present, most of the United States export trade in coal is from the Appalachian field into the coalless industrial section of Ontario, Canada, to which it can move by rail and lake steamer.

## Petroleum in North America

NATURE AND USES OF PETROLEUM.    Crude petroleum is a complex substance of varying chemical and physical properties. As recently as 1850 petroleum had few known uses and little commercial importance. Since that time it has sprung into a place of importance second only to that of coal as a source of power, and its possession is now a matter of greater international concern than is the possession of coal.

The importance of petroleum lies in its compactness, the ease with which it is handled, the directness with which it can be converted into mechanical power, and also the many other uses to which the crude oil or its distillates may be put. Along with the other sources of fuel and power, petroleum has in a few decades contributed wonderfully to man's effectiveness and to the overcoming of his environmental handicaps. As a source of illumination it lengthens his day; and as a source of airplane, automobile, railway, and ship fuel it shortens his geographic distances. Above all, as a source of lubricants it is indispensable to the operation of

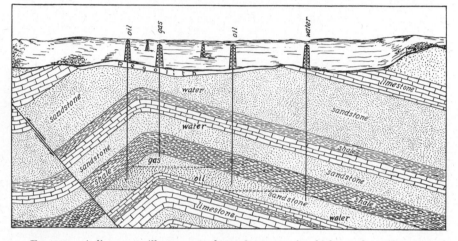

FIG. 117.—A diagram to illustrate one form of structure in which petroleum is entrapped and the relation between the locations of several wells and the nature of their respective products.

all types of modern machinery which lighten the labor and increase the efficiency of human hands.

THE ORIGIN AND OCCURRENCE OF PETROLEUM. Petroleum is believed to be the greatly altered product of minute forms of plant and animal life trapped in some of the sediments laid down in ancient seas. In the process of its formation, the oil and its associated products moved sideward or upward under pressure, and much of it escaped. However, where geologic conditions were favorable, oil and gas were imprisoned in porous rock underneath subterranean domes or other favorable structures of impervious rock (Fig. 117). From these buried pockets or reservoirs of differing size, petroleum is obtained by drilling through the impervious capping rock beneath which the oil is confined. Ordinarily gas is encountered in the upper part of the dome; then oil, underlain by water. Under the pressure of ground water or of the gas, some oil wells "gush" or flow continuously for a time and then require pumping. Others require pumping from the first. Eventually the oil-bearing rock is drained, and further

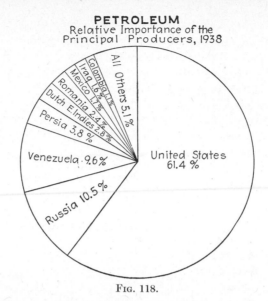

### PETROLEUM
#### Relative Importance of the Principal Producers, 1938

FIG. 118.

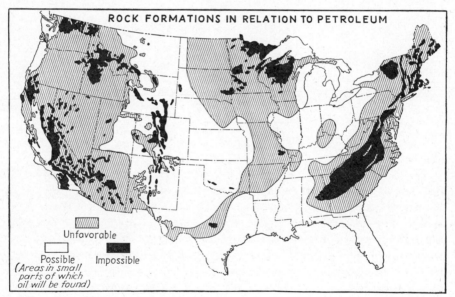

## ROCK FORMATIONS IN RELATION TO PETROLEUM

Unfavorable

Possible
(Areas in small parts of which oil will be found)

Impossible

FIG. 119.—This map distinguishes those areas in the United States in which the geological formations are such that petroleum (1) has been or may be found, (2) is not likely to be found, and (3) cannot possibly occur. (*Redrawn from a map by the National Resources Committee.*)

pumping yields only water or so little oil as to be unprofitable. It is believed that from half to two-thirds of the oil in the average "pool" remains in the rock and is not recovered. This is largely because films of oil cling to the particles of the rock in which it lies and only that in the larger pore spaces of the rock is able to move freely into the wells under force of gravity or the pressure of overlying gases or water. Improved methods of recovery may in the future make some of this oil in the depleted fields available. They are already increasing the average proportion of oil recovered, which, in some of the older wells, did not exceed

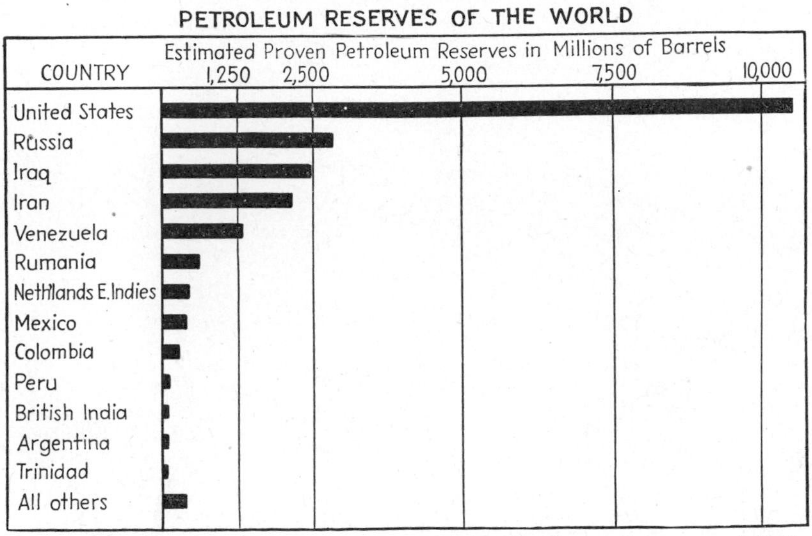

## PETROLEUM RESERVES OF THE WORLD

Fig. 120.—Data for the above estimates are published in *Energy Resources and National Policy*, National Resources Committee, Washington, 1939, p. 287.

one-tenth of the total. Under the best of conditions it is not likely that more than two-thirds of the oil in the ground can be got out.

AMERICA THE GREAT SOURCE OF OIL. The United States is the source of about 60 per cent of the world's output of petroleum (Fig. 118), but unfortunately this dominance does not appear to be guaranteed for the future. The reserves of petroleum are much less perfectly known than those of coal. By the very nature of the structural relations of petroleum occurrence they cannot be well estimated even though the promising and some of the unpromising areas of the United States have been probed by nearly a million deep wells in the search for oil. Estimates can be made of what are called "proved reserves," and these indicate a known supply sufficient only for 12 years at the current rate of production, which is in excess of a billion barrels per year. By deeper drilling and new methods for exploring the conditions underground, new supplies will surely be discovered in the large areas in which they may possibly exist. How much more may be discovered it is impossible to say. In more than half the country the occurrence of oil is either geologically impossible or very unlikely (Fig. 119). In the remainder, discoveries are possible in small localities but are probable in only very limited sections, most of which already are well explored. It seems certain that petroleum in its present abundance cannot last for many years. However, the United States still appears to have almost half the proved oil reserves of the world. Estimates on the distribution of the world's principal reserves are

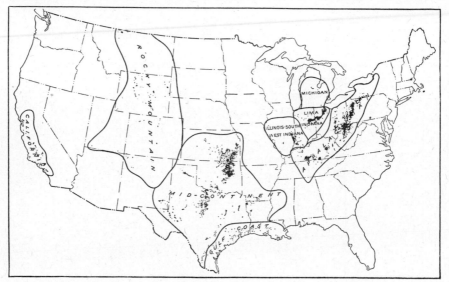

Fig. 121.—The distribution of producing districts in each of the several great oil fields of the United States. (*Map from National Resources Board report.*)

shown in Fig. 120. The oil of the United States has come from a large number of localities which may, however, be grouped into eight main producing regions, shown in Fig. 121.

THE UNITED STATES OIL-PRODUCING REGIONS are known as the Appalachian, Lima-Indiana, Michigan, Illinois-Indiana, Mid-Continent, Gulf Coast, Rocky Mountain, and California regions. The Rocky Mountain field extends slightly into the province of Alberta, but otherwise the oil regions are confined to the United States. The first of the regions to be exploited was the easternmost. It continues to produce oil, and new wells are drilled every year. However, many of its wells have been abandoned, and other regions have so far surpassed it in production that it has long since ceased to be a large factor in the domestic petroleum output. The newest region is that of Michigan, but it has not attained large production and gives little indication of taking high rank. The most productive region is the Mid-Continent, first from the fields of Kansas and later from those of Oklahoma and Texas, the last-named state being now much the largest producer. The present relative importance of these several regions is indicated by Fig. 122.

The rise and decline of individual pools in the oil fields is rapid, and figures as to their relative importance are of temporary value only. Some fields having passed the peaks of their production and declined to relative

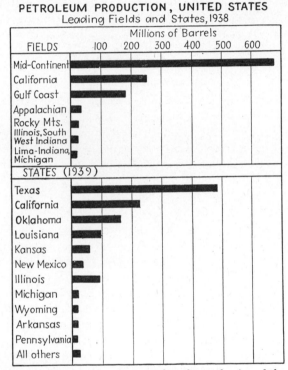

FIG. 122.—It is obvious from this diagram that the production of the several great oil fields is not in proportion to their areas or to the areas of the blackened districts shown in Fig. 121.

unimportance are revived by deeper drilling which taps previously unknown reserves. Such was the case in the East Texas field in 1931. Once practically abandoned, it is now the most productive field in the country. The same revival occurred in the southern Illinois field in 1937. In the succeeding months scores of new and deeper wells were drilled; and in October, 1939, the produce of new wells was thirty-five times greater than that from all the old wells still being operated.

Because deeper drilling has discovered new reservoirs of oil in these fields, it does not follow that it will necessarily do so in others. Some Texas wells are exploring at depths of 2 miles, and in California a well has reached a depth of nearly 3 miles. In any case there are limits beyond which the cost of drilling would be prohibitive or the deeper and older rocks would offer no possibility of petroleum content.

Total quantity of oil produced is not the sole measure of the relative importance of an oil field; the quality is also a factor. In general, the oils of the eastern fields, particularly the Appalachian, yield a higher proportion of gasoline and light oils and have a lower sulphur content than do those of Texas and California. The former also yield paraffin as the end product of their distillation, whereas those of California yield asphalt. Mid-Continent oils contain varying amounts of paraffin and the more volatile oils.

TRANSPORTATION AND REFINING OF PETROLEUM. Some crude petroleum is burned in the form in which it comes from the well for the production of power and for other purposes. Much the larger part of the total, however, is refined or broken up by distillation and treated for the removal of sulphur and other impurities. The exact nature of this process depends in part upon the character of the oil and in part upon the market demand. The total number of petroleum refineries in the United States is large (350 to 400), and, measured in terms of the value of its products, petroleum refining is one of the half-dozen largest industries in the country. Many of the refineries are small establishments of 1,000 to 10,000 barrels daily capacity. They distill off the gasoline and kerosene, mainly for local markets, and sell the residue as fuel oil. Such plants commonly are found in or near the oil fields. They spring up as new pools are opened and close down where the older wells have ceased to produce. The plants that practice complete refining generally are larger in size (average daily capacity over 20,000 barrels, the larger having capacities of 150,000 barrels). Such plants are permanent in character and are located at points to which oil from large fields or producing regions may easily be piped or are located close to large consuming markets or exporting points. Great refineries of this type are found at Bayonne, N. J., and at other points adjacent to New York City, Philadelphia, Chicago, Los Angeles, San Francisco, and the Gulf Coast and Mid-Continent cities.

The crude oil used by the refineries frequently requires transportation over hundreds of miles. It is more economical to move a large part of it in bulk near to the consuming centers before breaking it down into its several products, each of which must then be transported separately. Formerly this was done by tank cars, but the liquid nature of the material has aided greatly in the solution of the transportation problem. Pipe lines, with numerous pumping stations along the route, tap the storage tanks near the oil wells and convey the products of many wells to refining centers at a very low cost as compared with transportation by rail. Some

Gulf Coast oil moves to eastern refineries by tank ship also. The main lines of the vast network of pipes are shown in Fig. 123. Their combined length totals approximately 120,000 miles.[1]

In recent years also the volume of natural and distilled gasoline to be shipped has required the construction of more than 8,000 miles of pipe line to carry that product from wells to blending plants and from refineries to consuming centers. The trunk lines extend from the Mid-Continent region to Minneapolis, Chicago, and Detroit and from the eastern refineries inland toward the Great Lakes cities.

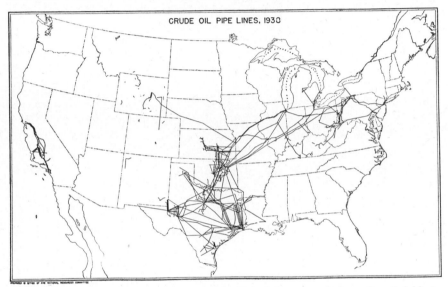

CRUDE OIL PIPE LINES, 1930

Fig. 123.—The crude-oil pipe lines of the United States reach from the oil fields to interior refining centers and to eastern, southern, and western ports. (*Map from Energy Resources and National Policy, National Resources Committee.*)

AMERICAN FOREIGN TRADE IN PETROLEUM. Although 60 per cent of the world's petroleum is produced in the United States, the amount is not enough for home and export requirements. The United States has about 70 per cent of the automobiles and motor trucks in the world, and in no other country is so much petroleum used in ships, locomotives, engines, and heating plants of all types. Imported petroleum, mainly from Colombia and Venezuela, now constitutes about 1 per cent of the total American supply. Exports of petroleum and its products from the United States consist mainly of the heavy oils, ship's fuel, and gasoline, and they total about three times the quantity imported. They have an average value of one-fourth billion to half a billion dollars a year and are important items in the export trade of the United States to nearly every

[1] *Oil and Gas Journal*, Sept. 19, 1940, p. 78.

corner of the world. The exports of crude oil are mainly from Texas and California.

NATURAL GAS is found in many oil-producing regions and to some extent in closely adjacent districts that do not produce oil. It is comprised of the more volatile constituents of the original petroleum substance which have separated from the liquids underground. The expansion of imprisoned gas causes some oil wells to flow without pumping; but in some cases the gas reservoirs are reached before the petroleum, the gas pressure is lost, and great quantities of the gas itself are wasted. However, natural gas is the preferred fuel in many regions because of its cleanliness and

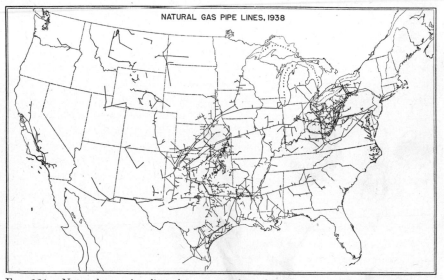

NATURAL GAS PIPE LINES, 1938

FIG. 124.—Natural-gas pipe lines have many branches to serve many city and town markets. (*Map from Energy Resources and National Policy, National Resources Committee.*)

convenience. It has household use, is used for the production of industrial heat and power, and is the source of the thousands of tons of carbon-black powder (commercial soot) used in the rubber, paint, printing-ink, and other industries. Moreover, the less volatile constituents of the gas are liquefied and blended with gasoline in the refineries, adding considerably to the supply of high-grade gasolines. Its relative importance as a source of energy is indicated by Fig. 106.

Natural gas is not stored, but when produced it must be used at once or wasted. Large quantities produced in the Appalachian region find ready market in a thickly populated industrial region. Even larger quantities produced in Oklahoma, western Texas, and coastal Louisiana are not so readily marketed, and much has been wasted. In recent years a larger outlet for gas has been provided by the construction of nearly

200,000 miles of pipe line, separate from the petroleum lines and reaching from the gas-producing districts toward the larger consuming centers, mainly east and north (Fig. 124). From a half to three-fourths of the natural-gas reserves are believed to be in the Mid-Continent and Gulf Coast regions. If the reserve can be recovered without great loss, it should last, at the present rate of consumption, for something like 25 years. Consumption is increasing, but some new sources of gas are likely to be discovered also.

OIL SHALES. Even with improved methods and greater economy in the production and use of American petroleum, the estimated reserves cannot last many decades. A supplementary source of oil is known to exist in extensive beds of oil-bearing shale rock that have been discovered in the Rocky Mountain region of both the United States and Canada, as well as in other parts of the world. These rocks are too fine-grained and compact to permit the oil that they contain to flow into wells. They must first be quarried or mined, then crushed and roasted to drive off the crude oil, which is then refined in the usual way. Methods for recovering oil from such shales are practiced somewhat in Europe, Japan, and Australia, but they are too expensive to compete with petroleum at its present price in America. The oil shales are therefore a potential source of oil for future use, the amount of which may greatly exceed the original American petroleum supply, but it will be far more expensive also.

PETROLEUM SUBSTITUTES. The use of petroleum and its products has brought into existence and made a vital necessity of the internal-combustion engine which requires a liquid or gaseous fuel. The principal petroleum-using nations are manifesting anxiety regarding the future, and many minds are busy with the problem of substitutes. Already experiments have proved the feasibility of using as fuel the by-products of coal distillation and alcohol, if only they can be produced cheaply and in sufficient quantities. Processes using bituminous coal, lignite, and the by-products of coke manufacture for the production of gasoline substitutes are now employed, especially in Germany and Japan. However, they require not only coal as a raw material but hydrogen and other ingredients, together with more coal to produce the high temperatures at which the transformation into liquid fuel is accomplished. This makes their products more costly than those derived from crude oil, and it is not likely that such fuels will be used on a large scale in the United States until oil is less abundant than now. Alcohol could be obtained from the products of temperate and tropical agriculture and probably without serious restriction of the world's present food-producing areas. Since, however, it is the product of agriculture and requires expensive manufacture afterward, it is not likely that alcohol can be produced for prices that will allow it to compete with petroleum products.

Up to the present no means has been devised for turning vegetable oils into satisfactory substitutes for petroleum products in the lubrication of high-speed machinery. That problem may perhaps be left with some confidence to the ingenuity of the future chemist. At all events the uncertainty of the future in regard to supplies of both liquid fuels and lubricants is ample reason for the practice of economy and of the most improved methods in the production of petroleum and also in the manufacture and use of its products.

## The Water Powers of North America

NATURAL ENVIRONMENT IN RELATION TO THE DEVELOPMENT OF WATER POWER.   Water power is a natural resource of large present value and of even greater possibilities for the future. Unlike coal and petroleum, it is not a wasting resource but is constantly renewed by nature. Fortunately, the water-power resources of the world are better distributed than either its coal or its petroleum, for most countries have some water power capable of development (Fig. 125). Yet great potential water powers depend on favorable conditions of environment which include (1) abundant precipitation; (2) fairly uniform discharge of water through streams, resulting from (a) uniformly distributed precipitation or (b) regulation of stream flow through natural lakes, forested watersheds, or artificial storage behind dams; and (3) a slope or gradient that permits the water of a stream to be used and reused for power development. An ideal physical situation for a great water power is found at such a place as Niagara Falls, where a large river, the drainage of a large region of abundant and fairly well-distributed rainfall, has its volume regulated by natural storage in great forests, numberless glacial lakes and marshes, and a series of Great Lakes. Then it plunges abruptly over a vertical cliff of great height. Few water-power sites are so ideal in all their physical aspects; many require expensive improvements by man to make up for their natural shortcomings. Valuable though they are, there are not in the United States water powers, capable of development, that would meet the present total power requirements of the country even if they could all be utilized. Their present importance as compared with the other principal sources of energy is shown in Fig. 106.

GEOGRAPHIC LIMITATIONS OF WATER POWER.   Before the day of steam, water power was the principal source of industrial energy. Many industrial cities of America, such as Minneapolis, Minn., and Lawrence, Mass., owe their locations to the influence of water-power sites on their early industries. But as industries multiplied, the water powers of these localities were outgrown. New industries used steam power because the advantages of central location often outweighed those to be gained by

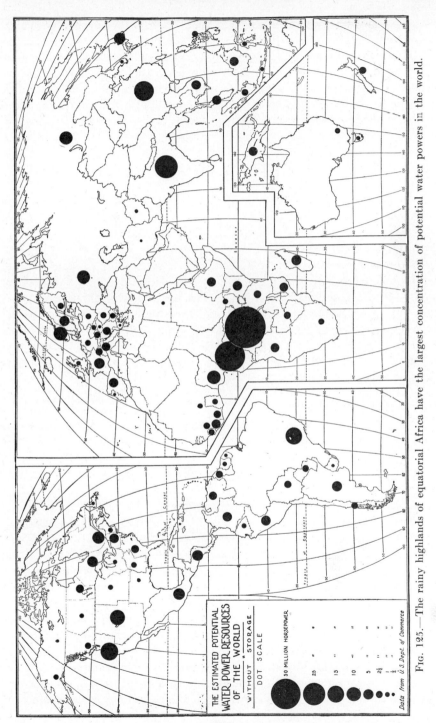

THE ESTIMATED POTENTIAL
WATER POWER RESOURCES
OF THE WORLD
WITHOUT STORAGE

DOT SCALE

50 MILLION HORSEPOWER
25    "    "
15    "    "
10    "    "
5    "    "
2½    "    "
1    "    "
½    "    "

Data from U. S. Dept. of Commerce

Fig. 125.—The rainy highlands of equatorial Africa have the largest concentration of potential water powers in the world.

seeking new water-power sites elsewhere. The water power could not be moved.

The development and improvement of hydroelectric power has introduced a large measure of elasticity into the utilization of water power. The factory that desires to use it need no longer be located on the site of the power plant. Yet even the most modern improvements have failed to free water powers entirely from this disadvantage of fixed location. Mechanical appliances now make possible the transportation

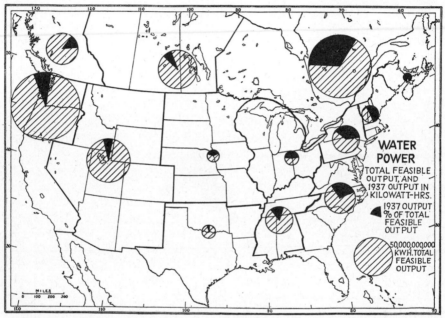

Fig. 126.—The largest water powers of the United States and Canada are in eastern Canada and western United States; regions with small resources of coal. Circles represent total output of electricity that it would be feasible to develop in the districts within the heavy lines. The data for Canada and the United States are not strictly comparable. (*Data from National Resources Committee report, and Canada Year Book, 1939.*)

of electric power over long distances, although transmission losses mount rapidly. However, the financial investments in long transmission lines are large, and the cost of line maintenance is high. The rates that must therefore be charged for electric power increase rapidly with distance, and it cannot now compete with cheap coal where the length of the transmission line exceeds 250 to 300 miles. Many of the best water-power sites of North America are much more than that distance from any place at which raw materials and labor can now be assembled for the economical utilization of the power. The distribution that is now a handicap to the development of water power may someday be an advantage, for it will be noted from a comparison of Figs. 126 and 109 that some of the great potential water powers are in regions not well provided with coal.

THE DEVELOPED WATER POWER OF NORTH AMERICA. In the competition between cheap coal and water power in America the lower cost of installing steam plants has given coal the advantage. It is, therefore, principally the best, the most accessible, and the most cheaply developed water powers that have been utilized. It will be observed from Fig. 126 that each of the principal regions of developed water power in the United States is to be explained in terms of both its physical setting and its market outlets for power. In the Northeast the industrial markets of New England and New York have encouraged the high degree of development of the powers potentially available in the streams descending from (1) the glaciated crystalline hills of New England, (2) the Adirondack Mountains, and (3) Niagara Falls. Other regions of large development include (4) the growing textile and other industrial region about the southern Appalachians, (5) the fringes of the crystalline upland adjacent to Lake Superior, (6) the Ozark highland region, (7) the northern Rocky Mountain area, (8) the Cascade Mountains and the Sierra Nevada Mountains in California. In some instances single streams are the sources of great powers. Notable are the Niagara River, the Susquehanna, the Tennessee, the Mississippi in southeastern Iowa, and the Colorado at the Boulder Dam in southern Nevada. A map for Canada would show a large concentration of developed power in Ontario and Quebec where the numerous lake-regulated streams flowing southward from the glaciated, forest-covered upland descend abruptly into the St. Lawrence Valley.

Some areas of large potential powers have been relatively little developed. In the hilly region of the upper Ohio Valley, for example, there is much potential power near great industrial markets, but it must compete with local coal and natural-gas energy. In the northern Rocky Mountain region the glaciated mountains and fairly abundant precipitation provide favorable power sites, but small population and small industrial development do not offer large markets for power.

UNDEVELOPED WATER POWERS OF NORTH AMERICA. It is estimated that the water-power resources of the United States are, on the basis of the amount available 75 per cent of the time, about 50 million horsepower and those of Canada about 25 millions of horsepower. These figures total more than three times the amount of water power now developed. It is believed, moreover, that, if reservoirs were constructed and other means were used to store and completely utilize the surface waters, the water powers of the United States might reach 80 million horsepower or more.

# The Power Problem in America

WASTE CHARACTERIZES THE USE OF POWER IN AMERICA. Nature has endowed North America, and particularly the United States, with abundant fuel and power resources, yet an acute problem exists with respect to this wealth. Its very abundance has led to production at a rapid rate and by careless methods. Means of transportation and proper utilization have not kept pace with production. The result is waste of material and waste of effort: *waste of material*, (1) in production, through failure to recover all the coal and oil that might be obtained and through fire and loss of vast quantities of gas into the air, (2) in transportation, through inefficient storage and careless handling, (3) in manufacture, through failure to recover valuable by-products in coke manufacture and in certain types of oil refining, and (4) in use, through inefficient firing of boilers, the use of inefficient engines, and the use of unrefined petroleum and of natural gas for purposes better served by other things; *waste of effort*, (1) through the effects of unrestricted competition and (2) through unnecessary transportation of materials.

A SOLUTION OF THE POWER PROBLEM MUST BE FOUND. The conditions upon which the solution of the American power problem rests are principally governmental and economic. Yet physical conditions, including the location of the principal sources of power with respect to raw materials and markets, are of vital importance. The problem is extremely complicated, and even the direction in which the solution is to be sought can hardly be foretold. Suggestions have been made for bringing together vast amounts of coal and water power in the form of electric energy to be distributed over the great industrial region of northeastern United States. This proposal for a "superpower zone" has many advantages, particularly those of saving in transportation on coal turned into electric energy at the mine mouth and in the greater cleanliness of industrial centers. The inertia of established methods of power production and the necessity for revised legislation will, however, retard these desirable reforms, even though they might result in a saving to the nation of many millions of dollars per year.

SELECTED REFERENCES

ARNOLD, R., and W. J. KEMNITZER.: "Petroleum in the United States and Possessions," New York, 1932.

BRADLEY, VIRGINIA. The Petroleum Industry of the Gulf Coast Salt Dome Area, *Econ. Geog.*, Vol. 15 (1939), pp. 395–407.

EMMONS, W. H. "Geology of Petroleum," New York, 1931.

HARTSHORNE, RICHARD. Coal and Iron Mining Districts of the United States and Western Europe, *Jour. Geog.*, Vol. 34 (1935), pp. 1–11.

HOAR, H. M. The Coal Industry of the World, *U.S. Dept. Commerce, Trade Promotion Series* 105, 1930.

LEITH, C. K., *et al*: "Elements of a National Mineral Policy," New York, 1933.

Mineral Raw Materials, prepared by staff of Foreign Minerals Division, U.S. Bureau of Mines, New York, 1937.

MURPHY, RAYMOND E., and MARION MURPHY. Anthracite Region of Pennsylvania, *Econ. Geog.*, Vol. 14 (1938), pp. 338–348.

PARKINS, A. E., and J. R. WHITAKER. "Our Natural Resources and Their Conservation," pp. 297–326, 423–462, New York, 1939.

TROM, W. T. "Petroleum and Coal," Princeton, 1929.

VER WIEBE, W. A. "Oil Fields in the United States," New York, 1930.

VOSKUIL, W. H. "Economics of Water Power Development," New York, 1928.

ZIMMERMAN, ERICH W. "World Resources and Industries," pp. 448–583, New York, 1933.

# Chapter XIII. The Iron and Steel Industries

---

THE MODERN IMPORTANCE OF IRON AND STEEL. The maintenance of modern industrial economy depends upon large quantities of iron and steel. The need for iron has grown rapidly in recent decades. Only one century ago the average quantity of it produced in the United States was barely 50 pounds per person per year. Now it is about 650 pounds per person for a vastly greater total population (Fig. 127). Similar changes have taken place in Europe; but in some parts of the world little iron is

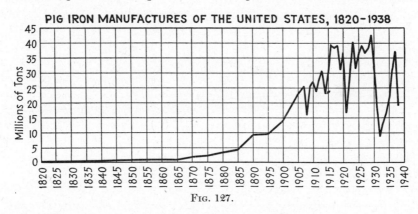

**PIG IRON MANUFACTURES OF THE UNITED STATES, 1820-1938**

FIG. 127.

manufactured, and relatively little is required. For good or for ill, those countries which can produce iron and steel abundantly have come to dominate in both the industrial arts of peace and the destruction of war, and the economy of an iron age has settled upon the world.

The unique position of iron among the metals lies in its great abundance in the earth and in the wide range of properties that can be imparted to it by various treatments and by alloying it with various amounts of other metals. The great strength, rigidity, and hardness that may be given to steel; the ductility, elasticity, magnetism, and keen edge that may be imparted; the special properties of temper and cutting power, even when red-hot, by alloying it with other elements, all combine to qualify it for an endless variety of purposes. It is well understood that

224

the development of machinery, by which human efficiency has been greatly multiplied, depends mainly upon iron and sources of energy in the hands of mechanically inventive people. Both the manufacture of iron and the use of machines built of it require coal and other sources of power. It is not surprising, therefore, that the great centers of iron production are those regions having access to the ores of iron and abundant supplies of coal.

IRON IN NATURE. Iron is one of the most abundant elements of the earth's crust, but it is very rarely found in a pure state in nature. Only three elements—oxygen, silicon, and aluminum—are more abundant. On an average, iron forms about $4\frac{1}{2}$ per cent of the earth's surface rocks. It occurs in upward of 100 different minerals, but four of these supply practically all the iron that is used; they are hematite, magnetite, limonite, and siderite. Hematite, one of the oxides of iron, is by far the most important, both because some of the richest and most abundant deposits of iron ore in the world are hematite and because the metallic iron is more easily separated from this ore than from the others. The percentage of iron in the pure forms of these four ores ranges from about 48 in siderite to 70 in hematite and 72 in magnetite. However, the ores as they occur in nature are almost never pure. In the United States not much iron ore yielding less than 50 per cent of its weight in iron is being smelted, but in Europe lower grade ores are commonly used. Iron, in the form of oxides, is found almost everywhere in the crust of the earth, giving the yellow, brown, and red colors to soils and to weathering rocks; but only here and there has the iron been sufficiently concentrated to make an ore worth mining and smelting. Ores frequently contain sulphur or phosphorus or both sufficient to injure the steel produced from them, but special processes of treating such ores have been devised and are successful in removing these injurious substances.

LOCATION OF THE PRINCIPAL IRON ORES OF NORTH AMERICA. The leading iron-ore region of the United States is near Lake Superior, with the principal mines in Minnesota and in the northern peninsula of Michigan (Fig. 128). About 100 miles north of Duluth is the Mesabi iron range from which the ore is mined by powerful steam shovels working in open pits (Fig. 129). Here high-grade hematite ore lies near the surface, covered only by glacial drift. In Minnesota also are two other ranges of less importance than the Mesabi. In the northern peninsula of Michigan are several ranges, two of which extend into Wisconsin. The Mesabi range is the greatest producer of iron ore in existence, yielding annually about 55 per cent of all that is mined in the United States. (1) The great abundance of ore in the Mesabi range, (2) its high proportion of metallic iron, (3) the remarkable cheapness with which it is mined, and (4) the cheapness with which the Lake Superior ores are transported on the Great

Lakes all combine to make the Mesabi range of paramount importance in our iron and steel industries. The Lake Superior region supplies about 80 per cent of the iron ore mined annually in the United States; Alabama (Birmingham district) supplies about 10 per cent; and New York, Pennsylvania, Colorado, and several other states supply small amounts (Fig. 130).

The Dominion of Canada is lacking in accessible iron ores of high grade. In western Ontario, north of the Mesabi range, there is a relatively small but rich deposit. Unfortunately it is so situated as to be difficult to

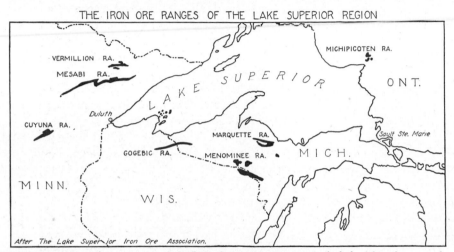

THE IRON ORE RANGES OF THE LAKE SUPERIOR REGION

FIG. 128.—The iron-ore ranges of the Lake Superior region are included within the area of ancient crystalline rocks.

mine, and at present Canada produces a mere fraction of its own needs. Newfoundland, however, has iron-ore reserves among the largest in the world, although the present production is not large. The lack of iron ore and coal in the provinces of Ontario and Quebec, which contain the greater part of the population and manufacturing industries of Canada, is a serious handicap which is met in part by importation from the United States.

IRON SMELTING AND STEEL MANUFACTURE. Modern iron smelting is conducted on a large scale. The various ingredients are required in great quantities, and the products are so heavy that the location of the industry must be made with due consideration of the sources from which the raw materials and power are obtained and the accessibility of markets. Centers of iron manufacture in the United States, which produces about one-third of all the iron of the world, have, since the early days of the industry, grown and shifted their locations with respect to these factors, particularly that of the market.

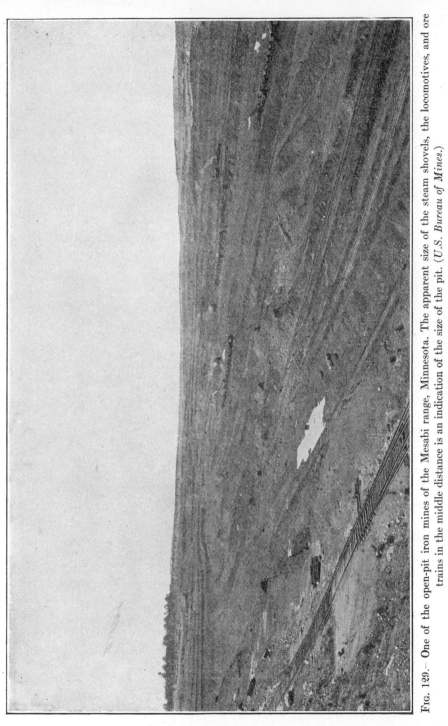

FIG. 129.— One of the open-pit iron mines of the Mesabi range, Minnesota. The apparent size of the steam shovels, the locomotives, and ore trains in the middle distance is an indication of the size of the pit. (*U.S. Bureau of Mines.*)

The iron in iron ores is chemically combined with oxygen and physically associated with various earthy materials called "gangue," from which it is separated by the process of smelting. The modern blast furnace is essentially a tower into the top of which coke, iron ore, and limestone are dumped (Fig. 131). The limestone serves as a flux, fusing with the gangue. Carbon from the coke combines with the oxygen of the ore, releasing the metallic iron which, in liquid form, flows from the bottom of the furnace. The intense heat necessary is provided by the combustion of the coke which burns in a blast of heated air forced into the bottom of the furnace.

In the production of 1,000 tons of iron about 2,000 tons of ore, 500 to 1,000 tons of coal (in the form of coke), and some 700 tons of limestone are required. Additional fuel is required for the power needed in the associ-

### PRODUCTION OF IRON ORE BY STATES
#### 4 Year Average 1935–1938

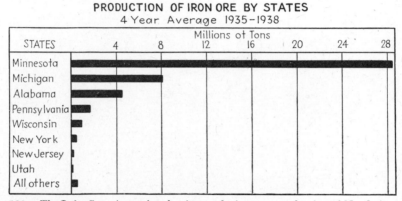

FIG. 130.—The Lake Superior region dominates the iron-ore production of North America.

ated industrial processes. The economical assembling of the materials for the smelting of the 30 million tons of iron produced annually in the United States is of itself a large task.

The output of steel in the United States averages more than 40 million tons, or one-third greater than the production of iron. This is largely because of the quantity of scrap iron and steel that each year is melted down and reworked. A part of the blast-furnace iron is cast into "pigs" and moves to distant plants where it is manufactured into cast-iron wares or is transformed into steel. A larger part, however, is made into steel in the same plant where it was smelted and is rolled into sheets, plates, bars, or structural shapes before it is allowed to cool. The processes by which it is transformed require large additional quantities of power and heat in the form of coal and natural gas; great volumes of water; supplies of the alloy metals to give special qualities to the steel; plant space; machinery; and labor.

The manufacture of steel from iron was originally a slow hand process. It was greatly speeded up about the middle of the past century by the

FIG. 131.—A modern iron-smelting plant. The stock pile of ore may be seen at the left, and above it the traveling crane used in loading the small cars, which move up the inclines to charge the furnaces. (*Courtesy of the Iron Trade Review, Cleveland, Ohio.*)

invention of the Bessemer process. In this process tons of molten iron are poured into a great converter, and a blast of air is forced through it, burning out certain undesirable elements. The necessary alloy metals are added, and the steel is ready to cast or mold into ingots suitable for rolling into shapes. The entire process takes only a few minutes. The Bessemer process requires, however, that the ore be free from phosphorus and some other impurities that this treatment cannot remove. The high-grade Bessemer ores are not so abundant as formerly, and less than 7 per cent of the United States steel output is now made in this way. Better steel for most purposes can be made by the basic open-hearth process, in which jets of flame are played upon the surface of a pool of molten iron and the impurities are burned out more slowly. About 90 per cent of the United States steel output is now made by this process. Certain alloy steels for particular uses are made in electric furnaces, but these products are expensive and make up less than 2 per cent of the average annual production.

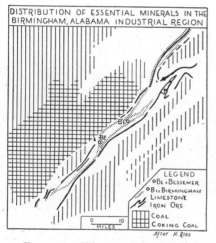

FIG. 132.—The iron ore, limestone, and various grades of coal are closely grouped in the Alabama industrial region.

CENTERS OF AMERICAN IRON AND STEEL MANUFACTURE. An ideal location for a blast-furnace and steel-mill industry would include in one district all the essential elements— iron ore; coking coal; power coal; limestone; alloys; water; labor; transport facilities; and, above all, markets. No region actually has all the elements, yet some of these, such as the alloy metals, are not required in large quantity; and others, such as capital and labor, are mobile and can be permanently assembled at the chosen site. The critical items are iron ore, coal, and markets.

Among the American smelting centers the most nearly complete is that of the Birmingham, Ala., region. There the iron ore, limestone, and various grades of coal are found in close proximity (Fig. 132). Transportation has been provided, and the South furnishes a market. However, it is not the greatest market, and the total iron output of this region is less than 10 per cent of the United States total.

Abundant iron and steel were first produced in the Pittsburgh, Pa., district. That region provided the best grade of coking coal in abundance, with other cheap coal and natural gas as fuels. It included the valleys of the Mahoning, Monongahela, Allegheny, Ohio, and lesser streams which furnished routes through this hilly country and led both east and west into the great manufacturing districts of the Middle Atlantic states and the Middle West. The region was not far distant from the Lake Erie ports, where specially constructed ore boats discharged the ore brought cheaply from the mines of the Lake Superior region.

Later, new blast furnaces and steel mills were established to meet the demands of a growing western market created by the building of new railroads and pipe lines and by the growth of other steel-using industries.

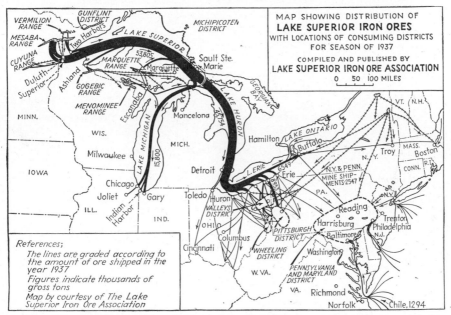

FIG. 133.—The iron-smelting districts of the United States are fed with ore mainly by Great Lakes transportation, but the eastern centers get ore from the Adirondack Mountains and foreign sources also.

The more important of these are found in two groups. One includes several great mill centers in the cities and towns on or near the south shore of Lake Erie. These include Buffalo, Cleveland, Detroit, and smaller lake ports. There the Pennsylvania coke meets the Lake Superior ores at the point of unloading (Fig. 133). Numerous sites are available on the spacious flat lands of the shore belt, and harbors are developed in the mouths of tributary streams. Power is available from Appalachian coal brought from Ohio, Pennsylvania, and West Virginia. Limestone is obtained near by, and the lake furnishes the large volumes of water required. Another group similar to this has grown up about the southern end of Lake Michigan where the steel mills of Gary, Ind., Chicago, and Milwaukee are located. These draw upon the Illinois coal fields for fuel and have a still closer proximity to the western markets. The more distant markets of the Northwest and the Far West have encouraged the location of smelteries and steel mills at Duluth, where coal can be brought cheaply by the returning ore boats, also in Colorado, where both local coal and

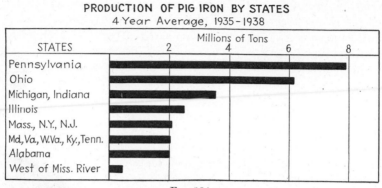

PRODUCTION OF PIG IRON BY STATES
4 Year Average, 1935 – 1938

Fig. 134.

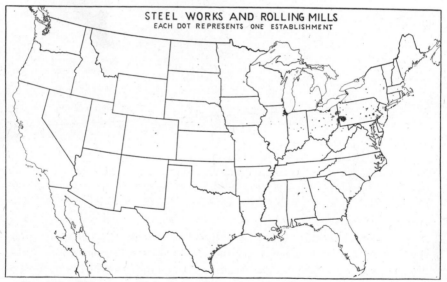

STEEL WORKS AND ROLLING MILLS
EACH DOT REPRESENTS ONE ESTABLISHMENT

Fig. 135.—This map, which shows the number of steelworks and rolling mills, does not indicate the volume or value of their output. On another basis western Pennsylvania and the districts bordering Lakes Erie and Michigan would show an even greater concentration.

ore can be employed. But these more distant markets are not large, and the Duluth and Colorado steel industries remain small by comparison with those previously mentioned.

The great industrial markets of the East attracted the steel industry in that direction also. The Bethlehem center in eastern Pennsylvania and that at Sparrows Point, Md., are examples of this development. The latter is located on Chesapeake Bay and receives ore imported from Chile, Sweden, Cuba, and other foreign sources.

In the production of both iron and finished steel the state of Pennsylvania, with its several centers of production, ranks first (Fig. 134). The Lake Erie region takes second rank, followed by the Lake Michigan and Alabama regions. The distribution of the steelworks and rolling mills is indicated in Fig. 135.

In Canada there is nowhere any close grouping of the prime essentials of iron and steel manufacture. The closest approach to such a combination is found in the coal fields of northeastern Nova Scotia, to which Newfoundland ores are readily brought. This region, unfortunately, is a long distance from the leading industrial district of Ontario, which has the largest requirement for steel. More than four-fifths of the primary iron and steel manufactures of Canada are located in Ontario, but the plants are supplied with imported coal and ore, principally from the United States.

## Iron and Steel Products Manufacture in the United States

MAGNITUDE OF THE INDUSTRIES.   When the many branches of industry that use iron and steel as their principal raw materials are taken together, they make an imposing array. The products included are as diverse as locomotives and needles, as essential as cookstoves or nails. It is almost impossible to group for discussion any large part of this great number of things, and only a few will be mentioned. No branch of manufacturing better illustrates the American industrial tendency to integrate its various phases and to substitute mechanical for manual labor. In America as nowhere else have the conditions for large-scale production been favorable, because (1) the supplies of iron and steel are abundant; (2) transportation facilities are excellent; (3) the rapidly growing home market, unequaled in any other country, has been able to absorb the greater part of the products at good prices; (4) the natural wealth of the country has made possible the accumulation of capital with great rapidity; (5) unprecedented opportunities have stimulated energy, inventiveness, and daring.

REGIONAL SPECIALIZATION IN THE MANUFACTURE OF STEEL PRODUCTS. The products of the blast furnace and the steel mill are in some cases completely manufactured before they leave the original mill to move toward distant markets. These, mainly, are the heavy products requiring simple manufacture, such as railroad rails, steel pipe, and structural steel. In other cases the finished product requires additional operations such as casting, welding, drawing, machining, or stamping. Many of the finished products are both more bulky and more fragile than the pig iron, steel shapes, bars, plates, or sheets from which they are made. Some have national or world-wide markets; others are designed for highly special uses and have only local sale. Because of these facts there are some regions of great diversity in metal manufactures and others of considerable specialization. The regions of diversity are likely to be the great industrial centers adjacent to the sources of iron and steel; the regions of specialization are more commonly located close to the final markets or to the industries that consume their products. Illustrations of the first type are found in the manufacture of stoves and furnaces, road-building machinery, electrical and metalworking machinery. These have widespread and general use and are at the same time heavy. In the making of them the states of important iron smelting and steel production are the leading centers, especially Ohio, Pennsylvania, Michigan, Indiana, and Illinois. The class of special machines is illustrated by manufactures of textile machinery and shoe machines. Of the former more than one-third is produced in or near the spinning and weaving districts of Massachusetts and Rhode Island alone.

For reasons that are as much historical as economic some metal products having wide markets are manufactured in restricted areas. There being nothing in particular in the physical and economic surroundings to oppose the success of the industry, once established and well managed, it continues, aided by its favorable reputation. Such products are carpenter's and machinist's hand tools, a large part of which are made in western Massachusetts and Connecticut; or household washing machines, one-third of which happen to be made in Iowa.

Some sections of the American industrial region have great diversity in metal manufactures. The state of Ohio is outstanding in this respect. Itself a great center of iron and steel production, it has abundant power resources, and it lies across the main thoroughfares of traffic between East and Middle West, between the Lake Erie steel mills and the South. It has also its own requirements for machines, such as those necessary to mining, agriculture, and diverse manufacture.

Some manufactures of iron and steel are of such great value or importance that their localization may receive separate comment.

SHIPBUILDING is, of course, controlled by a different set of conditions, for ships must be built near deep water. The Middle Atlantic states include the chief shipbuilding centers, for these states are nearest the coal and iron region; their coastal waters—especially Delaware River and Bay and Chesapeake Bay—are well protected, and the winter climate permits outdoor labor the year round. These advantages have caused the relative decline of shipbuilding on the New England Coast, which was the foremost American shipbuilding section in the days of wooden ships.

AGRICULTURAL MACHINERY includes a variety of implements required in plowing, tilling, harvesting, and the transporting of farm products. The great need for these things arose particularly with the opening of the vast farm lands of the Middle West. Originally most of them were partly or wholly made of wood, and both the raw materials and the markets were in the region of the lower Great Lakes. Subsequently the markets expanded to national and international proportions, and the implements were made largely of steel. But the area of principal manufacture has remained the same. It is the Chicago district, including southeastern Wisconsin, southern Michigan, and northern Illinois, Indiana, and Ohio. Illinois and Wisconsin alone produce two-thirds of the total.

Certain other large steel-using industries that depend on the farm market are found in the same region. One of them, for example, is the manufacture of barbed-wire and woven-wire fence. The basic inventions for these were largely made in northern Illinois and southern Michigan under the stimulus of a growing need for fencing on the treeless farms of the western prairies and plains. These states remain the principal centers of manufacture, although the industry has spread eastward into the other steel-producing districts, whereas the market has spread to all parts of the United States and to many foreign countries.

AUTOMOBILE MANUFACTURE. The making of automobiles, their bodies and parts, is the greatest of all American manufacturing industries. The only other that approaches its magnitude is the entire textile group which is concerned with several different raw materials and kinds of products. Automobile manufacture began as an offshoot of wagon and carriage manufacture, industries closely related to the agricultural implement industry, using much the same kinds of raw materials and catering to similar markets. Many of the early automobiles were made in wagon and carriage factories and employed the same craftsmen, such as wheelwrights, blacksmiths, painters, and upholsterers. The region of the lower Great Lakes was outstanding in wagon and carriage manufacture at the beginning of the present century and quickly took first place in the making of automobiles. It was not without other advantages. It already was a center of steelmaking; and at a later date when steel became the principal material employed, it shared in the advantages possessed by the steel industry and itself became that industry's largest customer.

The original automobile factories were small, and some of the more modern are not large. They are, in fact, little more than assembling plants where parts manufactured in many outlying specialty plants are put together into a finished machine. The parts factories are found in many of the cities and villages of the region. Gears, springs, wheels, rims, trimming hardware, and lighting and ignition units are only a few of their products. Some of the greater automobile manufacturers produce practically everything that they require but not in one establishment. However, the high development of this industry has given examples that are without parallel of the large-scale organization of complex manufacture and its integration on favorable sites.

The principal region of motor-vehicle production includes southern Michigan and northern Indiana and Ohio. Within it are concentrated the establishments, large and small, that turn out more than two-thirds the value of all products of this class. The larger part of the total is credited to southern Michigan, and nearly one-fourth the national total is produced in the city of Detroit alone. This city has in high degree all the advantages characteristic of the region—ease of assemblage by water and rail of the ore, fuel, manufactured steel, and other component materials; and excellent railway, road, and water routes for the distribution of vehicles in both partially and completely assembled forms. In it have grown also the financial and trade institutions willing to support and designed to promote the industry.

THE MANUFACTURE OF LOCOMOTIVES AND CARS. This branch of the steel-using industry is closely localized in the steelmaking states, especially in Pennsylvania, Illinois, Indiana, and Ohio, states that manufacture about three-fourths of the value-product of railway cars. The manufacture of locomotives remains largely in the Middle Atlantic district where the older companies with established reputations have long been located. These are notably eastern Pennsylvania, New York, and New Jersey. It is an interesting fact that the value of the automobiles manufactured annually in the United States is many times as great as that of all the locomotives and railway cars that are made.

IRON AND STEEL PRODUCTS IN THE FOREIGN TRADE OF THE UNITED STATES. Down to the year 1892 the United States imported more iron and steel manufactures than it exported. Since that time exports have grown to large proportions. The largest values exported are in the complex forms of machinery and vehicles which include many kinds of material other than iron or steel. Their value reaches from a quarter-billion dollars in poor years to nearly a billion in good years. Of the more strictly iron and steel products there is great variation in exports also. The United States being a great source of these products, it is drawn upon heavily in emergencies, especially for war needs. Exports rose from $1\frac{1}{2}$ million tons in 1910 to $5\frac{1}{2}$ million in the war year 1916 and after the war declined again. They rose from the depression level of $1\frac{1}{3}$ million tons in 1933 to $7\frac{1}{2}$ million in 1937 but declined to 5 million in 1938, apparently owing to financial stringencies. The principal increase in exports was in the crude forms from which munitions are made. In 1937 more than 90 per cent of the exports by value were in the form of scrap iron, pig iron, steel plates and sheets. The principal buyers were Japan, Italy, Great Britain, and

Germany where war or the prospect of war created a sudden demand. United States imports of iron and steel, such as machinery and vehicles, do not total 10 per cent of the value of the exports of such goods.

SELECTED REFERENCES

CARLSON, A. S., and C. B. Gow. Scrap Iron and Steel Industry, *Econ. Geog.*, Vol. 12 (1936), pp. 175–184.

DAUGHERTY, C. R., M. G. DE CHAZEAU, and S. S. STRATTON. "The Economics of the Iron and Steel Industry," 2 vols., New York, 1937.

HARTSHORNE, RICHARD. The Iron and Steel Industry of the United States, *Jour. Geog.*, Vol. 28 (1929), pp. 133–152.

———. Location Factors in the Iron and Steel Industry, *Econ. Geog.*, Vol. 4 (1928), pp. 241–252.

LEITH, C. K. "World Minerals and World Politics," New York, 1931.

PRIMMER, G. H. Future of Lake Superior Iron Ore Supply, *Econ. Geog.*, Vol. 10 (1934), pp. 395–401.

WHITE, LANGDON. The Iron and Steel Industry of the Pittsburgh District, *Econ. Geog.*, Vol. 4 (1928), pp. 115–139.

———. The Iron and Steel Industry of the Birmingham District, Alabama, *Econ. Geog.*, Vol. 4 (1928), pp. 349–365.

ZIMMERMANN, E. W. "World Resources and Industries," pp. 584–665, New York, 1933.

# Chapter XIV. Mineral Industries

A Variety of Minerals Necessary to Modern Industry and Trade.  Iron and steel occupy the foreground in any picture of modern industry, but their use would be very much limited if it were not for other minerals used in conjunction with them. The other essential minerals are of two fundamental classes: (1) metallic and (2) nonmetallic. The former includes many semiprecious and precious metals, and the latter the rocks, earthy materials, and natural salts of industrial or chemical value.

A complete list of the minerals that are of importance to modern industry would be a long one. Only a few of the more important may be chosen as examples to show the situations in which such resources are placed by nature and their associations with the manufacturing industries that use them. North America is favored in the possession of valuable deposits of many of these minerals. Their exploitation and manufacture have developed as logical accompaniments of the iron and steel trades and of other industries, most of which result indirectly from the possession of large resources of fuel and power.

## Metallic Minerals

Geologic Factors Influence Geographic Distribution.  The principal metallic minerals to be surveyed in this connection and the ores from which they are obtained are, most of them, directly or indirectly traceable to the results of igneous activity. Although the valuable minerals often are found not in the igneous rocks but within other rocks adjacent to areas of igneous activity, they are believed to result from hot solutions and gases associated with the origin of igneous rocks. It is, therefore, not remarkable that the principal deposits of the valuable metals and their ores are found in regions where igneous activity has been an important factor in geologic history rather than in the great regions of undisturbed sedimentary rocks. This rule is, however, not without exceptions.

In general, regions of igneous activity have been regions of mountain building, either ancient or geologically modern. This fact has also a relation to the distribution of mining industries. Associated with the mountain-building forces are the formation of veins and of other types of ore bodies redeposited from underground solutions. Moreover, the mountain-building forces have frequently elevated mineral deposits, and the rapid stream erosion of mountains has served to expose them, whereas in level lowland regions the minerals would have remained deeply buried had they been formed under such conditions. The ranks of the states in gold, silver, and copper production indicate to what extent the mining of precious and semiprecious metals of importance in North

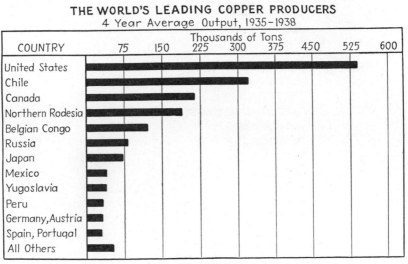

THE WORLD'S LEADING COPPER PRODUCERS
4 Year Average Output, 1935–1938

FIG. 136.

America is located in the mountainous sections of the continent (Figs. 137, 142, 143).

COPPER IMPORTANT IN ANCIENT AND MODERN INDUSTRIES. The use of copper preceded the use of iron in the development of civilization. Combined with tin it made the bronze implements of ancient peoples, and some copper is still employed for bronze manufacture, although brass, an alloy of copper and zinc, is of larger importance to modern industry. The use of pure copper has been greatly increased by the development of electrical machinery and electric transmission, and the electrical industries are now the largest consumers of copper. In the United States about 45 per cent of the copper produced is used for these purposes, and the total quantity used for all purposes amounts to about 10 pounds per person per year.

SOURCES OF AMERICAN COPPER. The United States and Canada together produce about 40 per cent of the world's copper, and the United States alone produces nearly 30 per cent (Fig. 136). The ores of copper are of various classes. In the Keweenaw Peninsula of Michigan, ores containing native or metallic copper are obtained, mainly by deep and expensive mining, and these ores commonly yield 5 to 7 per cent of their weight in metal. The greater part of the American copper supply is now obtained, however, from the ores of Arizona, Utah, and Montana. In these western mines the copper is found in chemical combination, mainly in the form of sulphides. They are principally ores of low grade and contain only about 1½ per cent of their weight in metal. They can be profitably used only because they occur in large quantity, and some of

**COPPER PRODUCTION IN THE UNITED STATES AND CANADA**
Average Output, 1935–1938

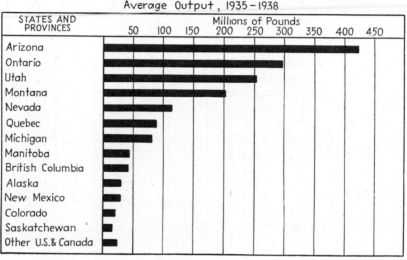

FIG. 137.

them are near the surface where they can be mined cheaply. The ores of Canada are found in several localities in the ancient rocks of the Laurentian upland. More than half the total, however, is recovered as a by-product from the nickel mines of the Sudbury, Ont., district. Figure 137 shows the rank of the leading states and provinces in copper output, and the preeminence of the West is easily seen.

COPPER SMELTING AND REFINING. The preparation of metallic copper from the Lake Superior ores requires only mechanical concentration and melting. The greater part of the American ores, however, must be concentrated and reduced from their chemical combinations by smelting. Since the average yield of copper in the United States is less than 40 pounds per ton of ore (1.8 per cent), it is clear that the concentration and smelting of the ores is most economically done near the mine in order to avoid transportation charges on a great bulk of worthless rock material. Many large mines have their own smelting plants (Fig. 138).

Fig. 138.—A copper smelter in the mining district of Utah. It is established in this region to be near the mines. (*U.S. Bureau of Mines.*)

The product of this first step in smelting, called "copper matte," contains only 35 to 50 per cent of copper but is sufficiently concentrated to bear the cost of transportation considerable distances for the completion of the process. Further smelting produces a copper (called "blister copper") of more than 95 per cent purity, which frequently contains valuable amounts of silver and gold. This copper is refined by electrolysis, and the precious metals are recovered. Most Lake Superior copper also is now refined to increase its purity and to recover silver. Electrolytic refining requires a large and expensive plant, and the average American refinery can handle the output of as many as ten large mines. Most of the refining of copper in America is done at Atlantic seaboard points from Baltimore to New York. These refineries are near the principal market for copper and have the added advantage of port facilities for handling South American and other foreign copper imported for refining and for the exportation of refined copper to Europe, which is the principal foreign market. Refineries have been established in Montana and on Puget Sound in response to a growing market for copper in the western half of the continent and to an export market in Japan.

Copper, like iron, is a vital necessity to the prosecution of war, and war or the prospect of war causes it to move in quantity from the United States to prospective belligerents who do not have large resources of their own. In this connection it is significant to note a rapid rise in United States exports to Japan after 1936 and to Germany after 1937, in spite of the fact that Japan is one of the world's important copper producers.

The manufacture of copper into wire, sheets, brass, and miscellaneous articles is concentrated principally in the North Atlantic states near the large markets for these wares.

LEAD AND ZINC are commonly associated metals, and both have wide industrial applications. Zinc, in the form of a galvanized coating, protects iron and steel from oxidation. It is used also in the manufacture of brass and as a substitute for lead in various appliances and in paint manufacture. Lead is used principally in the manufacture of paint; in type metal, solder, and other alloys; in electrical and plumbing supplies; and in shot. In most mines the ores of the two metals are found together, sometimes in conjunction with silver. Yet they are unlike in general properties and uses.

The lead and zinc mined in North America constitute about one-third of the world's supply of each of these valuable metals. Unlike most other metals, a considerable fraction of the total supply of these is mined in the great interior plains of the continent. The ores of this region are somewhat different in origin from those of the West, which are generally associated with igneous intrusions (Fig. 139).

It is of importance to note that tin, a metal of somewhat similar properties and associated uses with lead and zinc, is produced hardly at all in North America. It is vital to the tin-plate and solder industries, both of which are required in food canning as well as for many other purposes. It is mined principally in southeastern Asia and Bolivia, sources upon which the United States is completely dependent.

THE FERRO-ALLOY MINERALS. It has been stated previously that the manufacture of steel requires the admixture of at least small quantities of other elements with molten iron. There are several metals used in this way, and they are known as the "ferro-alloy minerals." Some of them have other and independent uses also. The more important members of the group are manganese, chromium, nickel, tungsten, molybdenum,

**LEAD AND ZINC PRODUCTION IN THE UNITED STATES AND CANADA**
3 Year Average, 1936-1938

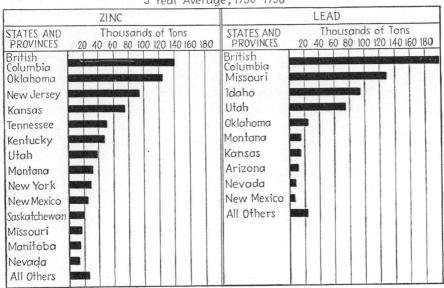

FIG. 139.

vanadium, cobalt, and silica. One or more of these in proper amount give steel the qualities of hardness, toughness, tensile strength, resistance to corrosion, and other properties necessary to particular uses. Lathe tools to cut steel rapidly at high temperature, edge tools, automobile gears, springs and axles, and scores of other uses require alloy steels. It is necessary for as great a steel-using country as the United States to have them available in large quantity. The domestic production of some of these is large; of others, little or none at all.

*Manganese* is required in largest amounts because it enters into railway rails and many other crude-steel products. There are manganese ores in the United States, but they are not much used, since they are difficult to extract, and it is cheaper to import supplies from Russia, Africa, Cuba and other sources.

*Nickel and chromium* are commonly used in making hard, tough steels such as armor plate and for many other alloys. Each is used as a plating metal also to protect brass or iron from corrosion. Neither is produced in the United States, but Canada is the source of about 85 per cent of the world's output of nickel. It is mined in the Sudbury district of Ontario, north of Lake Huron. The ores of chromium are produced especially in Africa, Russia, Turkey, and Cuba. Some are known in the United States, but it is cheaper to import than to mine them.

The United States produces its entire requirements of some of the ferro-alloy minerals, such as molybdenum and silica; must import part of its requirements of others, such as tungsten and vanadium; and is completely dependent on foreign sources for a few, such as cobalt. The urgent need for all these metals in industry and the fact that the United States has little if any of some of them is one of the fatal weaknesses in the arguments of those who still cling to the belief that this country should be made economically self-sufficient.

ALUMINUM is the most abundant of the metallic elements of the earth, exceeding even iron. It is a constituent of ordinary clays and shales. Unfortunately no methods have been devised for the profitable reduction of material of such low metal content. The principal ore of aluminum (bauxite) is an altered claylike substance of high aluminum oxide content derived from the ancient weathering of certain rocks. Deposits of bauxite are known in several southern states, but central Arkansas produces most of the domestic supply, which is only about half the quantity needed. The balance is imported from various sources, especially the British and Dutch Guianas. Other great sources, especially for the European consumers, are several of the countries of southern Europe and the East India Islands.

The ores contain silica and other impurities that are removed by concentration processes, usually near the mines. In the United States, East St. Louis is a concentration center for much Arkansas ore, and some of the Guiana ore is brought there also by ship to New Orleans and then by Mississippi River barges. From the concentrators it goes as nearly pure oxide of aluminum to the smeltery. The smelting is best done by electric furnaces and is most economically done where cheap electric power is available. In the United States it is centered principally at points on the North Carolina Piedmont and in eastern Tennessee that share the great water-power resources of the southern Appalachians. Some is smelted also with electricity from Niagara Falls and the Adirondack Mountains. Only Germany exceeds the United States in output of aluminum, and that has been true only in the recent period of rapid building of military airplanes (Fig. 140). Aluminum and its alloys already play a large part in the making of transportation equipment that is strong but so light that it increases the efficiency and thus reduces the cost of transportation on land and in the air. In this connection it is important to note the great abundance of this metal if only effective means can be found for recovering it from low-grade ores.

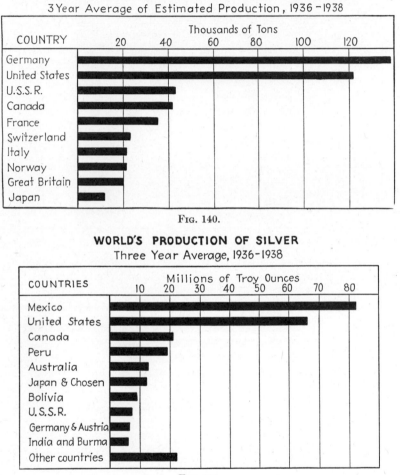

THE WORLD'S LEADING ALUMINUM PRODUCERS
3 Year Average of Estimated Production, 1936-1938

Fig. 140.

WORLD'S PRODUCTION OF SILVER
Three Year Average, 1936-1938

Fig. 141.

GOLD AND SILVER. We are accustomed to think of the world's production of the precious metals as a very important and vital industry, and so it is, for they have many essential uses. Yet the combined value of all the gold and silver annually produced in the world would be hardly one-fourth enough to buy the average corn crop of the United States. North America is relatively a much more important figure in the production of silver than in the production of gold (Figs. 141, 305). The United

States, Alaska, and Canada yield only about one-fourth of the world's gold but one-third (and if the quantity produced in Mexico is added, about two-thirds) of the world's silver. Figures 142 and 143 show the general distribution of the gold- and silver-mining industry in the United

FIG. 142.

FIG. 143.

States and Canada. The great importance of the western mountain regions will be seen. The two metals are commonly associated in the mines, and both are obtained in part as by-products in the mining of copper, nickel, lead, and zinc. They occur both as metallic gold and silver and in various chemical combinations. Mining methods and methods of concentration and smelting depend upon the nature of the ores. The product of the smelter must be further purified in a refinery.

## Nonmetallic Minerals

STONE AND EARTH MATERIALS WIDELY DISTRIBUTED. Rocks, gravel, sands, and clays commonly used in construction are found in many regions and are used locally for many different purposes. In some regions stones of exceptional beauty or quality are found, and these enter into commerce and may be transported great distances. However, the majority of this class of nonmetallic mineral substances are so heavy and so low in value that their commercial movements are limited. The total value of these materials used annually in the United States exceeds the value of the gold and silver produced.

STONE. The principal stones of economic value in the United States are limestone and granite. Marble, sandstone, and others are quarried in smaller values. The largest quantities of stone used are (1) crushed stone for concrete construction, road building, and railway ballast; (2) limestone for blast-furnace flux, other industrial and agricultural uses; and (3) building stone. Limestones are widely distributed, and local supplies usually are drawn upon to provide crushed stone and flux. The most commonly used limestone for building purposes is the widely known gray stone of the Bedford-Bloomington district of Indiana. It is valuable for its uniform texture and because it is easily carved and shaped when fresh from the quarry but hardens on exposure to the air. For this reason it is much used not only for the walls of buildings but for turned and fluted columns and ornamental trimmings. Granite is a more common building material in the East than in the Middle West. The principal granite quarries of New England lie not far from the coast. Granite for use in the Middle West is supplied from quarries in central Wisconsin, from the southern Appalachian Mountains, and from the famous quarries near Barre, Vt.

GRAVEL AND SAND constitute a resource of large importance, particularly since the coming of the era of extensive road improvement and of concentrate construction. They commonly are the sorted products of stream deposition and are found in many localities. The most widespread supplies of them are in the regions of most recent glaciation in the northern states. The water-sorted products of glacial crushing are found in local moraines, eskers, and outwash plains and are so well distributed over the area that improved roads of great length have been constructed where the maximum haul of gravel was but a few miles. This is a geographical advantage that may be measured in terms of millions of dollars per year. The cost of local stone crushed for road construction in Wisconsin is about 50 per cent more per cubic yard than is that of local gravel screened and washed for similar use. This difference represents in a rough way the value of glacial crushing. The service of a geologist trained to recognize and locate such deposits is a preliminary to extensive road-improvement projects in several northern states.

SAND AND THE GLASS INDUSTRY.    Sand is the principal raw material of the glass industry. Glass sand is obtained by crushing pure sandstones and from water-laid deposits, the latter mainly for cheap glass. Glass sands are widespread and are produced commercially in a score of American states of which the leading are Illinois, Pennsylvania, and West Virginia.

The cost of the sand is, however, but a relatively small item of expense in glassmaking. A satisfactory fuel is more important, and the glass sand generally moves to a region of cheap fuel for manufacture. Natural gas, which is a particularly desirable fuel, and the coal of the upper Ohio Valley have attracted this industry, and more than half the glass of the United States is made in western Pennsylvania, West Virginia, and eastern Ohio. The central location of this region with respect to the glass-consuming market is also an important consideration, since only one-fourth the glass manufactured, measured in terms of value, is in the compact form of window glass, whereas three-fourths is pressed and blown glass—bottles, jars, and other hollow wares, which are both bulky and fragile and take high freight rates.

CLAY AND ITS PRODUCTS.    Clay, of various grades and degrees of purity, enters into the manufacture of a large number of things, among which the more important are brick, tile, terra cotta, cement, pottery, graniteware, and paper.

*Brick and tile* are heavy clay products which may be made of a variety of clays, and some are made in nearly every inhabited portion of North America. Yet improvement in transportation and the increasing cost of fuel have had a notable influence in concentrating this industry also in the upper Ohio Valley. Pennsylvania and Ohio make about one-third of all of the brick and tile manufactured in the United States (Fig. 144). The principal markets for common brick are the great cities, notably New York and Chicago, and the marketing phase of the clay-working industry is particularly important in the parts of Illinois and New York State near these cities.

*Pottery and porcelain* manufacture is an aspect of the clayworking industry upon the location of which the source of the clay has little influence. The quantities of the high-grade clays used are relatively small; and if other conditions are favorable, they can profitably be imported. The critical conditions affecting distribution are fuel and skilled labor and location with respect to markets. The manufacture of low-grade pottery products is established in many parts of the United States. Two large centers of high-grade pottery manufacture are (1) Trenton, N. J., established in pre-Revolutionary days but surpassed in importance in recent years by (2) a small district in the upper Ohio Valley, comprising Columbiana and Mahoning counties, Ohio, and Hancock County, West Virginia. East Liverpool, Ohio, is the principal center. The great advantage of this region is its high-grade coal and natural-gas fuels and its central location with respect to the eastern and middle western markets. The clay used in both the Ohio and the New Jersey potteries is largely shipped in from the southern states and even from Europe.

Fig. 144.—The products and the smoking kilns of a sewer-tile factory in southeastern Ohio.

CEMENT. Without Portland cement, cheap and durable structures such as modern highways, bridges, and buildings would be impossible. Its manufacture is a vital industry. It is a combination of clay and limestone which has been burned to drive off water and then pulverized. The raw materials used in its manufacture in various mills include clay, shale, limestone, marl, and blast-furnace slag. Some combination of these materials suitable for cement manufacture is of relatively common occurrence. The ingredients are burned in a rotary kiln requiring a highly combustible fuel, and a source of fuel is likely to be of greater influence than the raw material in determining the location of cement manufacture. Although some cement is burned with crude oil or natural gas, more is produced with powdered coal as a fuel. Location with respect to market is also a factor of great importance; for cement is heavy and relatively low in price, and transportation charges add much to its final cost. In such localities, therefore, as combine good limestone, clay or shale, abundant coal, and accessibility to a large market, cement manufacture is likely to prosper. Such a location is the Lehigh district of eastern Pennsylvania. In 1900 this region made nearly three-fourths of the cement output of the United States. With the westward expansion of cement markets, new regions, such as the Ohio Valley, the Chicago district, Michigan, and Missouri, have become important cement producers, but Pennsylvania still makes nearly a fifth of the national output and is the leading state. The large use of cement on the Pacific Coast and the long haul from the eastern mills has resulted in the development of cement manufacture in California, which holds second rank among the producing states.

ASBESTOS is composed of the fibrous crystals of certain igneous rock minerals. The better grades of it may be crushed into cottonlike fiber sufficiently long to be spun into yarn and woven into coarse fireproof fabrics. Much larger quantities are used in brake linings; in insulating and valve-packing compounds; and as a binding material in fireproofed composition boards, shingles, and similar products. The most productive asbestos mines in the world are located in southeastern Quebec. In recent years great quantities of mineral wool, a sort of substitute for asbestos in certain of its uses, have been produced. It is made by blowing a jet of air or steam through molten rock, blast-furnace slag, or glass. As fireproofing and heat and sound insulation this material has come into common use. It is manufactured in many places but particularly in Indiana, Ohio, Illinois, and the Pennsylvania-New Jersey industrial region.

SULPHUR is an essential material in many industries. In the mineral form it enters into the manufacture of rubber and into the composition of orchard sprays and of explosives. In the form of sulphuric and sulphurous acids it is the basis of many chemical industries—the preparation of phosphate fertilizer, the refining of petroleum, and the manufacture of woodpulp. The United States possesses large resources in sulphur and produces more than three-fourths of the world's supply, some of which is exported. In the Gulf Coast region of Louisiana and Texas, pockets or domes are found in which sulphur fills the pores and crevices in a form of limestone, and it often is in association with salt and petroleum. Its situation is such that it cannot profitably be recovered by mining. A very cheap method of obtaining it has been devised, however, in which the sulphur is melted by forcing superheated water down through pipes. It is then brought to the surface by compressed air. Much sulphur is used in the manufacture of sulphuric acid, but larger quantities of acid are made from iron sulphide (pyrite). Vast amounts of valuable sulphurous gases are wasted in smelters where metals are extracted from the sulphur compounds in which they occur. In some countries pyrite and smelter gases are the only sources of domestic sulphur.

SALT is a mineral of such common occurrence in America that it is difficult to realize that in some parts of the world it is not easily obtained. In the early history of eastern North America local sources of salt were the occasion for the establishment of several settlements.

For half a century, underground deposits of salt have been worked in various parts of the continent, and the total product amounts now to about 9 million tons annually, or more than 125 pounds per person. Large quantities of the salt are used in the chemical industries, but much is required also in the preservation of meat and fish and for domestic consumption. Most of the North American salt supply is obtained (1) from the artificial brines made by conducting water down to buried salt deposits and pumping it again to the surface, (2) by mining rock salt, or (3) by evaporating the natural brines of salt lakes or springs. The principal salt-producing regions are (1) Michigan, Ohio, Ontario, and western New York, where beds of rock salt are encountered at variable depths; (2) Kansas; (3) the Gulf Coast; (4) California. The northeastern industrial region is the largest salt producer. Most of it is recovered by underground solution and the evaporation of the brines. It is a basic raw material for many chemical industries, and the manufacture of soda ash (a form of sodium carbonate) is the first step in many of these processes. It consumes salt in large quantities. The Gulf Coast salt is largely rock salt mined from thick deposits beneath domelike rock structures similar to those mentioned in connection with sulphur. In humid regions surface salt is scarce because it has long ago been dissolved and carried away by streams to the ocean. In arid regions salt is abundant, and some basins of interior drainage contain salt lakes or salt crusts. Some of these are utilized in the western states, and California ranks fifth among the states in salt production. Probably the deeply buried salt beds of the East are the result of the evaporation of sea water in arid-land basins of long ago when the climates of the world were not arranged as they are now. The oceans contain now nearly 3 pounds of salt per hundred pounds of water. In some regions it is evaporated to get the salt but not much in the United States where purer salt is so abundant.

MINERAL FERTILIZERS. Among the elements that enter into the composition of common soils several are essential to plant growth. Of these the most important are nitrogen, phosphorus, potassium, calcium, sulphur, silicon, carbon, hydrogen, and oxygen. Most of these are found abundantly in the soil or in the water and air contained in the soil. Only the first three may be called "critical elements," because phosphorus is frequently deficient in soils, and potash and nitrogen, although they may be present, are often in chemical forms in which plants are unable to utilize them. Fertilizers are supplied to make up for these deficiencies and to replace the quantities of these critical elements removed from the land in the form of crops. In some parts of North America animal manures and straw or other plant refuse replace a large part of the fertility extracted by crop production. In regions where these are not available the deficiency is made up by commercial fertilizers, which, though they may contain slaughterhouse refuse and other organic material, are primarily mineral in composition.

NITROGEN is vital to the rapid vegetative growth of plants. Prairie soils have it in abundance, but old and much cropped forest soils commonly are deficient. Nitrogen is the chief component of air, but it is not available to plants until it is combined in the soluble form of a nitrate. This process is accomplished in nature through the agency of certain bacteria that live mainly upon the roots of leguminous plants, such as beans, clover, and alfalfa. It is also accomplished chemically, to an increasing extent but at considerable cost, by combining atmospheric nitrogen with a base through electric heat. The industry tends, therefore, to seek localities where cheap hydroelectric power may be obtained within reasonable distance of the fertilizer markets. Such localities in the United States are Niagara Falls and the Tennessee River power developments. In Europe, Norway is an important producer. Another growing source of nitrates is the sulphate of ammonia recovered in coal distillation (see page 206). This source is of growing importance in the United States, but Germany is the largest producer. Mineral nitrates are obtained almost exclusively from the desert of northern Chile (see Chap. XIX). Formerly they were the chief source of supply, but now they are less used.

MINERAL PHOSPHATES. Phosphorus is vital to the seed-producing function of plants and is therefore of great importance in the soil of grain-producing regions. It is likely to be depleted when grain is continuously sold from the farm. Mineral phosphates enter into the composition of many commercial fertilizers.

North America is fortunate in having a vast reserve of phosphate rock from which is produced about one-third of the world's commercial supply. The United States is the world's largest producer, but large quantities are mined also in northern Africa, Russia, and some of the islands of the Pacific. The rock now utilized in the United States is obtained mainly from deposits in Florida and Tennessee, three-fourths of it from Florida. Some of the material is obtained in pebble form from river gravels. A larger amount is soft rock mined in open pits in west central Florida by steam shovels. Much of the best has already been exploited by very crude and inefficient methods.

There have been discovered in Idaho, Montana, Utah, and Wyoming underground beds of hard-rock phosphate which constitute the greatest known reserve of this material in the world. At present only a small quantity of it is mined because of its great distance from the fertilizer markets. It will be very important in the future, when the Middle West demands more commercial fertilizers. The metal smelters of these same states now waste large quantities of sulphuric acid which might be employed in the treatment of the rock phosphate for the manufacture of the acid phosphate, the chemical form in which it is required for agricultural use.

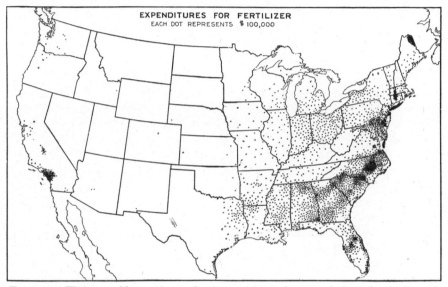

EXPENDITURES FOR FERTILIZER
EACH DOT REPRESENTS $100,000

FIG. 145.—The vegetable-growing and cotton-raising industries of the Atlantic Coastal Plain and the Appalachian Piedmont are the principal consumers of commercial fertilizers.

POTASH in one of its several chemical combinations is a common ingredient of mineral fertilizers. More than 90 per cent of the potash used in the United States goes into fertilizer manufacture, and the remainder into the chemical industries. Large but deeply buried reserves of potash are known to exist in the southern part of the high plains, but they are as yet mined in quantity only near Carlsbad, N. M. Some is produced also from the crust of mixed salts covering the dry bed of Searles "Lake" in the Mojave Desert of California. The total United States production is a little more than half that consumed. The balance is obtained by importation, mainly from Germany, whose great underground reserves are more actively mined than those of any other region in the world.

THE FERTILIZER INDUSTRY. One of the important chemical industries of the United States is the manufacture of commercial fertilizers.

The raw materials used in this industry include the mineral fertilizers already described; and organic materials, such as bones, slaughterhouse refuse, and fish waste, together with substances used as fillers or diluting agents. These materials are obtained from both domestic and foreign sources and are most economically assembled relatively near to the place of consumption. Figure 145 shows the expenditures for commercial fertilizers in 1935. It indicates the location of the great fertilizer market on the Atlantic Coastal Plain and the Appalachian Piedmont. Because of this market, and because of accessibility to the imported nitrates, potash, bones, the menhaden fisheries, and fish waste, as well as close proximity to the Florida phosphates, the manufacture of commercial fertilizers is established in nearly every Atlantic port. The Atlantic and Gulf Coast states south of New York produce nearly three-fourths of the total for the country; the section from Maryland to Georgia, half of it.

SELECTED REFERENCES

BAYLEY, W. S. "Non-Metallic Mineral Products," New York, 1930.
BOWLES, O. "The Stone Industries," New York, 1939.
FOX, C. S. "Bauxite and Aluminous Laterite," London, 1932.
LOUIS, H. "Mineral Deposits," London, 1934.
PARKINS, A. E., and J. R. WHITAKER. "Our Natural Resources and Their Conservation," pp. 395–422, New York, 1939.
RIES, H. "Economic Geology," New York, 1930.
ROUSH, G. A. "Strategic Mineral Supplies," New York, 1939.
TARR, W. A. "Introductory Economic Geology," New York, 1930.
VOSKUIL, W. H. "Minerals in Modern Industry," New York, 1930.
"World Atlas of Commercial Geology," Part I, U.S. Geological Survey, 1921.
ZIMMERMANN, ERICH W. "World Resources and Industries," pp. 666–741, New York, 1933.

# Chapter XV. American Transportation and Trade

THE FUNCTIONS OF TRANSPORTATION. It has been pointed out previously in many connections that we live in an era of regional specialization. Some regions are dominantly pastoral; others are agricultural or manufactural. Some of the agricultural regions specialize in one limited group of crops, and some manufactural regions in a limited range of manufactured wares. Only a few in America even approach the complete self-sufficiency that characterized most of the world only a few generations in the past. It is clear that regional specialization would be impossible without means of transportation to give added utility to goods by enabling them to move from areas of surplus to areas of deficiency.

THE FORMS OF TRANSPORTATION. Modern commercial transport has developed many new forms, but it has not completely freed itself from the old. A motor truck may take goods from the factory door to a railway car; the train may transport them to a port; and a ship may move them to a foreign market. Yet in the transfer from factory to truck, truck to train, and at every other stage the goods may require movement by human hands, just as they would have done in the past. We have added greatly to the number of modes of transport by introducing trains and airplanes and pipe lines, and we have greatly increased the volume and variety of goods that can be moved and the speed with which they can be transferred. It is obvious that the functions of some transport facilities are general and others restricted. Railway cars can carry goods of many kinds, but pipe lines can transport only fluids. Ships can carry goods, persons, and ideas, but the telegraph line is restricted to ideas. Pipe lines and the telegraph, telephone, and radio are nevertheless an integral part of the system of transportation and exchange.

PATTERNS OF TRANSPORTATION ROUTES. It has been noted previously that communication in a large part of northern Canada is restricted principally to the streams and airplanes, supplemented, one may add, by the radio. In this region the network of routes of land and water transportation is a very coarse one. It has large areas that are so far off any main artery of traffic as to require days or weeks to get into touch

255

with the world outside. In contrast, there are sections of the United States where no farm is so isolated as to be more than 5 miles from a railway or more than ½ mile from a road so well surfaced as to be passable all the year. The patterns of spacing and arrangement made by the avenues of transportation in these and other situations are an important part of the geographical scene and a clue to the state of economic development of a region.

## Inland Transportation

EARLY TRANSPORTATION IN THE UNITED STATES. In the colonial days the people were too few to undertake extensive road building. Trails were opened, or previous Indian trails were adopted, and some of them grew into bridle paths or even into traces for wheeled vehicles. But these primitive roads often were impassable for wheels, and much of the goods moving over them went by pack horses. Gradually the roads were widened and bridges were built, but this was usually at private expense. The cost was paid by the users who passed frequent toll gates and toll bridges. Rates for cartage on these early roads were high, and the services were restricted. For example, it cost about $100 per ton to haul goods from Philadelphia to Pittsburgh, and the freight on iron from England to Philadelphia by ship was less than it was by wagon from the small iron furnaces of that time only 30 miles inland. A long step toward our present system of highways was taken in 1806 when the Congress authorized a road to be built from Cumberland, Md., westward into Illinois.

The difficulty of road transportation caused the waterways to be much used. Many rivers that now seem too small for navigation were used, and the larger, such as the Hudson, Delaware, and Susquehanna, had hundreds of rafts, flatboats, and other craft carrying freight. The Ohio, Mississippi, and Missouri rivers were invaluable aids in the rapid settlement of the interior beyond the Appalachians. The movement of goods in large quantity, however, had to wait for steam craft and the construction of canals to link together the various major waterway systems and bring them nearer to the goods requiring shipment.

THE ERA OF INLAND WATER TRANSPORT. During the period when inland waters were expected to remain the principal avenues of transportation, canals were built to connect or to supplement the natural waterways. Many were short canals, but the major undertakings were of three types: (1) efforts to connect the Great Lakes with the Atlantic, (2) efforts to connect the Ohio River with the Atlantic, and (3) efforts to connect the Great Lakes with the Ohio and Mississippi. Both (1) and (2) involved the discovery of feasible canal routes across the Appalachian highland. Of four attempted, the only one to succeed was the Erie Canal, which had the advantage of the low gap of the Mohawk River and the level expanses of the plain south of Lake Ontario. Coupled with the estuary of the Hudson River, this route permitted boats loaded with heavy goods to move from New York across the highlands to Buffalo where Great Lakes transportation carried on into the far interior. It was a most essential transportation link in the development of agriculture and industry in the Middle West. Other canals in Ohio, Indiana, and Illinois and a short one in Wisconsin succeeded in linking the Great

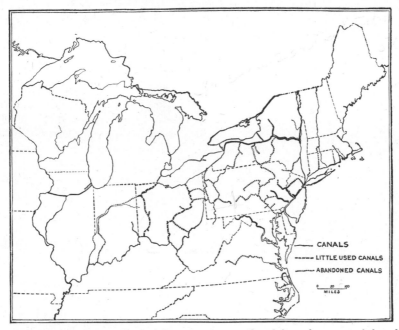

Fig. 146.—The canals served a useful purpose in prerailroad days, but most of them have now been abandoned or are little used. (*Courtesy of The Macmillan Company.*)

Lakes with the Ohio and Mississippi, but these canals never had as much use as the Erie Canal, and most of them have been abandoned (Fig. 146). The Erie Canal has been enlarged and still is in operation.

The period of steamboat transportation on the larger rivers began in 1811 and came to an end after the Civil War, through the competition of the railroads. During the time of their dominance the river boats greatly cheapened freight rates and moved great quantities of cargo. But for several reasons they were not able to compete with the railroads effectively. (1) Many of the rivers are closed by ice part of the year. (2) The depth of rivers fluctuates greatly between the flood and low waters of the changing seasons. (3) Rivers are crooked, increasing distances between points. (4) Rivers deposit sand bars and shift their courses, endangering boats. (5) The depths of water in the upper and lower parts of a river usually differ so much that a boat big enough to be profitable in the lower part is too big to be used on the upper part, thus preventing through shipment. (6) Relatively few places are directly on navigable streams, and much goods must be brought to the river by other forms of transportation and rehandled. (7) The shifting channels and varying depths of streams often make it difficult to build good terminal facilities for handling river freight (Fig. 147). Such freight as continues to be handled on United States rivers is principally imperishable bulk goods, such as coal, ores, stone, and sand. Some cotton and general cargo are transported on the Mississippi River.

Fig. 147.—River craft moored at the sloping bank of the Ohio River at Cairo, Ill. At high water the foreground is entirely submerged.

TRANSPORTATION ON THE GREAT LAKES.  The opening of the Erie Canal brought commercial activity to the Great Lakes; but unlike the traffic of the canals and rivers, that of the Lakes has continued to grow. Although they too are ice-fringed and useless several months each year, they do not share the other disadvantages of the streams. They are deep and of constant level and have required little expensive improvement except in the narrows, particularly the rapids of the St. Mary's River connecting Lakes Superior and Huron where a canal with locks is required. On the other hand, they have a most fortunate situation, since their general trend is east and west. They connect the iron- and grain-producing Northwest and Middle West with the populous, industrial, coal-producing regions farther east. The miscellaneous or package-freight traffic on the Great Lakes is not large, but the bulk-freight traffic is enormous. Special types of boats have been devised to carry ore, coal, and grain, and special wharf equipment has been made for loading and unloading them. This type of transportation is among the most efficient known, and the tonnage carried through the canal at Sault Ste. Marie is large even compared with that of the Suez and Panama Canals (Fig. 148).

RAILWAY TRANSPORTATION. The development of American railway transportation has paralleled the settlement and development of the land and its resources. It had a pioneer stage, a period of rapid growth, and it has now settled into a maturity that is accompanied by readjustments. The first railroads in the United States were short lines built to connect or to supplement the waterways (Fig. 149). They gave a type of service

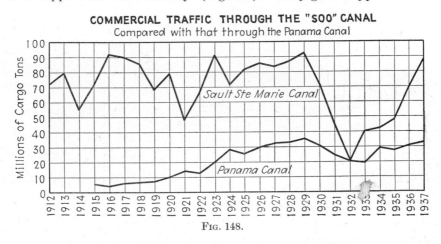

FIG. 148.

with which the waterways could not compete. Eventually they came to dominate the inland transportation facilities and extended into nearly all parts of the country. In the pioneer days of the Middle and Far West, railroads often were built in anticipation of the future settlement of what appeared to be good land. Most of these ventures were justified by experience. As the land was settled and new industries developed, more railroads were required. Sometimes they were built when they were not much needed, just for the sake of competition. The peak of railroad mileage was reached in 1917 when there were about 266,000 miles of roadway in operation, some of it with more than one track (Fig. 150). Since that time there has been some new road built and many hundred miles of double track laid, but other hundreds of miles of road have been abandoned. Thriving industry and productive farms have made a need for greater facilities in some areas. In other areas ravaged forests, exhausted mines, or ruined farm lands have failed to support existing railway services, and they have been withdrawn.

*The function of American railroads* is different in several respects from that of the waterways. The latter are most effective in the move-

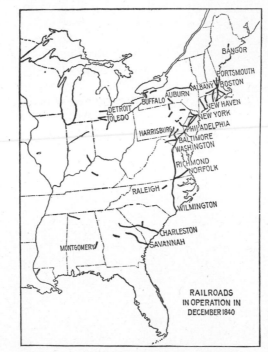

FIG. 149.—It is notable that in the early days of railroad building the southern states built several of the longest lines.

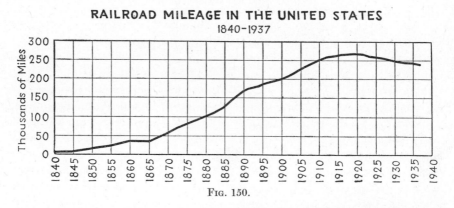

FIG. 150.

ment of heavy nonperishable goods in bulk, and the railroads and their equipment are designed for the rapid movement of passengers and perishable goods as well as miscellaneous freight and bulk commodities. They provide this service at all seasons. Collections and deliveries are not restricted to main lines, as is true of waterways. By means of secondary track and spur lines most American towns and even individual factories, warehouses, and some large farms have immediate connection with the markets of the country and the ports of overseas shipment. One of the fortunate aspects of American railroad development is that all the tracks are of the same standard gauge and that cars are permitted to move from one system to another freely. That is not true in all parts of the world, and in no other part is there so vast a mileage of railroads with complete interconnection as in the United States and Canada.

*The density of the railroad net* over the different sections of the United States and Canada is in large degree a reflection of the ability of each section to produce goods that require shipment by rail (Fig. 151). That there are great variations in the density of the railroads is indicated by the following facts. Each of the more than 250,000 miles of railway in the United States must, on the average, serve about 12 square miles of land area, but the figure varies from 4 to 50 square miles in different regions. In the manufacturing regions extending from southern New England to Illinois there is 1 mile of railroad for each 4.6 square miles of land; in both the Middle West and the "old" South the comparable figure is 10 square miles; in the livestock-grazing regions of the high plains and the intermontane plateaus it is about 45; and in California, 13. Although each mile of eastern road serves so many less miles of area, it carries much more freight than those of the South and West, in the ratio of about 2.5 to 1.8 to 1, respectively. This reflects again the greater goods-originating and goods-consuming capacity of the more densely peopled northeastern manufactural-commercial-agricultural regions as compared with the capacities of the other sections of the country.

*The patterns of railroad distribution* are much influenced by the location of certain focal points. Some of these are ports, such as Montreal, Boston, New York, Savannah, San Francisco, or Vancouver. Others are strategic physical gateways, such as the Mohawk Valley, upon which several rail lines converge to avoid highland barriers. Still others are the natural focuses between productive regions and the eastern markets, such as Minneapolis-St. Paul, Kansas City, and Fort Worth-Dallas. From the greatest of them, Chicago in the United States and Winnipeg in Canada, radiate nearly all the rail lines of their respective sections of the continent. In these cases the railroad centers do not merely lie between productive regions and their markets but are also affected by physical interruptions to rail traffic which prevent some of the roads from taking more direct routes. In the case of Chicago, it is the Great Lakes themselves and the less productive Upper Lakes region that lie across the shortest route between the spring-wheat region and the eastern ports. Winnipeg has a similar lake barrier and the unproductive northern forest region to the north of it to direct the traffic of the prairie provinces through this focal point, which is sometimes called the "Chicago of Canada" (Fig. 152).

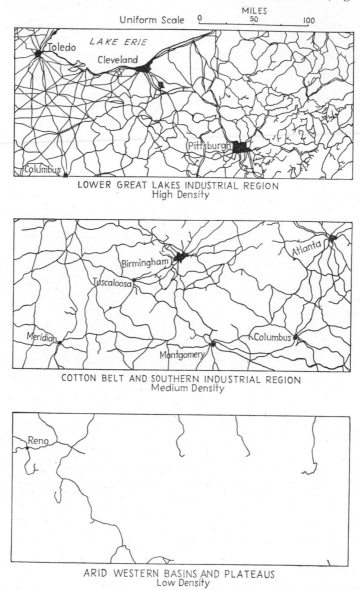

FIG. 151.—A comparison of railway-density patterns in parts of the United States.

American railway transportation has not been developed, and its conduct is not continued without meeting many difficulties. For some of these the railroad companies themselves are responsible; others have arisen from an unreasonable public hostility toward them; and still others arise from the competition of newer and more efficient means of transportation. The great development of pipe-line transportation for the movement of petroleum, gasoline, and natural gas has been noted previously (Figs. 123, 124). Although the airplane now competes principally for passenger traffic, the least profitable aspect of railway business, it carries the mails also and may ultimately be a larger factor in the

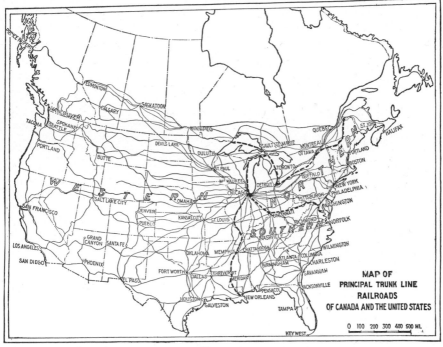

MAP OF
PRINCIPAL TRUNK LINE
RAILROADS
OF CANADA AND THE UNITED STATES

0  100  200  300  400  500 ML.

Fig. 152.

carriage of perishable freight. The most serious competitor at present is the motor vehicle on the public highways. Just as the water-transport industries complained, during the middle of the past century, that they were being strangled by the railroads, so the railroads now complain concerning competition by vehicles traveling on roads built from public funds.

HIGHWAY TRANSPORTATION.  The American system of public roads grew out of the need for local transportation. It was designed to give the farmer access to the market towns and to enable the towns to exchange goods and ideas with reasonable facility. But only to a limited extent were roads expected to permit the long-distance, interregional flow of traffic. This was because, when most of the roads were originally surveyed, it was not believed that means of highway transportation ever would permit of large-scale movement of commodities over long distances. There were some roads that had that objective. The eastern post roads, the Cumberland or National Road, and the Military Road of southern Wisconsin were such.

*The function of the public roads* remains dominantly local. This is indicated by the fact that, of the United States total of 3 million miles of roads, about 2¼ million are common earth roads. The total extent of modern roads with a high type of hard surface probably does not exceed 150,000 miles, and surfaced roads of all classes may reach a total of 750,000 miles. It appears from these estimates that the American road still is primarily the country byway, the link between the farmer and the market town or between neighboring towns. The development of motor traffic has greatly expanded the functions of highway transportation, however. The change has been wrought by the perfection of special types of motor carriers and by the investment each year of more than a billion dollars of special taxes and appropriations in the building and maintenance of roads. The modern reinforced concrete road is an artery of traffic fed from all the lesser roads, and it carries a large quantity of long-distance traffic as well as much that is local.

There are in the United States about 25 million passenger automobiles and nearly 5 million trucks, busses, and similar vehicles, about 70 per cent of the world's total. So effective are they as carriers that, in spite of a great increase in general travel, the number of passengers carried by the railroads is less than half that of two decades ago. The total quantity of freight to be moved in the country has obviously increased also in the same period, but the amount carried by the railroads has declined somewhat. The principal field in which motor vehicles compete with the railroads is that of short-distance transportation of both passengers and freight, and the competition for freight is mainly in miscellaneous goods that move in small lots. However, long-distance carriage of both passengers and freight is increasingly common.

*The density of the highway net* is not necessarily so closely related to the density of human population or the goods-producing capacity of the land as is the density of the railroad net. Roads enable people to reach their homes, and there must be roads whether homes are many or few, even if the road is only wheel ruts in the sand. Five miles of road in a city may serve several thousand homes or places of business but in the arid lands only one or two ranch houses. Data on the density of all country roads are incomplete, but the estimates available would indicate about 1 mile of road of some kind for every square mile of land in the United States. Of surfaced roads the mileage is only about one-fourth as great, or about 1 mile to each 4 square miles of land area. These are the

# SELECTED AMERICAN ROAD PATTERNS

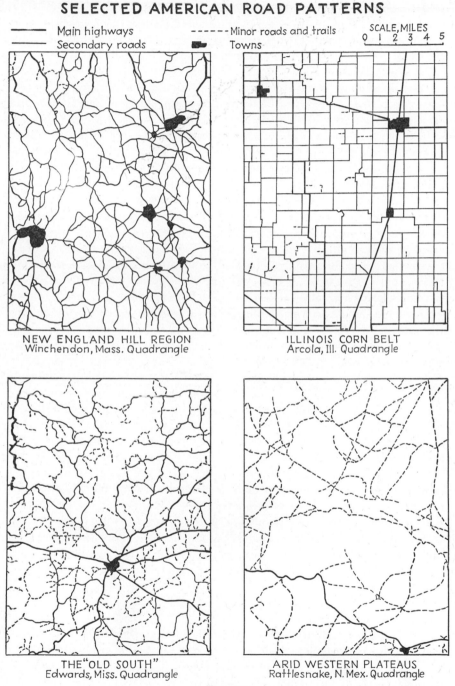

Main highways
Secondary roads
Minor roads and trails
Towns

SCALE, MILES
0  1  2  3  4  5

NEW ENGLAND HILL REGION
Winchendon, Mass. Quadrangle

ILLINOIS CORN BELT
Arcola, Ill. Quadrangle

THE "OLD SOUTH"
Edwards, Miss. Quadrangle

ARID WESTERN PLATEAUS
Rattlesnake, N. Mex. Quadrangle

Fig. 153.

rural roads which carry the major part of the motor traffic. Of roads having a high type of hard surfacing there is still less, the ratio being about 1 mile for each 25 square miles of land area. Differences in the densities of such roads in the several sections of the country are comparable with the similar figures given for railroad densities. The industrial regions, extending from southern New England to northern Illinois, have the highest density, and the arid western plateaus and basins the lowest.

*The patterns of road distribution* are related to both physical and historical conditions. In the East and the old South, where settlements were made early, the roads follow courses most of which are inherited from the trails of the pioneers or even the Indians. Many of them radiate from early settlements and proceed toward adjacent settlements by direct courses that are deflected in conformity with features of the surface of the land, drainage or cultural conditions. In flat lands they avoid areas of poor drainage. In rolling lands they frequently cling to ridge tops, descending into valleys only to climb to the next adjacent ridge. In very hilly land the roads generally follow the valley patterns and climb the ridges only to get into the nearest accessible valleys.

In the Middle West a distinctive road pattern was established through the system of rectangular land surveys. Some roads, even there, run directly from one village to another. They either are older than the land survey of the locality, inherited from Indian trails, guided by a physical feature; or are new, paved roads relocated without regard to compass direction to give the easiest construction and the shortest distances. The greater part are, however, rectangular in pattern. They bound the sections of land and divide it in checkerboard manner at 1-mile intervals. In some cases the intervals are more than a mile, and in others they have been divided and there are ½- or ¼-mile roads. Generally they trend north-south and east-west in conformity with the land surveys. The rectangularity of the pattern usually is most perfect in the areas of flattest land and of the most recent surveys. Examples of some of the patterns mentioned are shown in Fig. 153.

In the West and Southwest the road patterns show the affects of such conditions as mountainous relief, the old Spanish systems of land grants, ranch trails, and the more recent carrying over of the rectangular system used in the Middle West.

## Foreign Trade and Transportation

FOREIGN TRADE is like domestic trade in that it is a flow of goods from regions of surplus to regions of deficiency. Surplus and deficiency result from differences that are both physical and cultural in origin. Among the physical conditions related to the origin of trade those of greatest effect are climatic features, soil quality, and differences in natural resources. Among those of cultural nature are differences in racial backgrounds and aptitudes, differences in stage of economic advancement, political control, and religious adherence. Foreign trade is measured, of course, by the movement of goods across international boundaries, and the mere multiplication of states tends to increase the volume of the world's foreign trade. If Europe were a union of states without political barriers to trade, much of what now constitutes the foreign trade of the world would appear only as domestic trade and would perhaps not show in the records of trade at all. On the other hand, much of the present internal trade of the United States, such as that between the North and the South or the eastern manufacturing regions and the agricultural and pastoral West, would be recorded as foreign trade if these were separate countries instead of parts of one large and diverse political unit.

The great volume of the world's foreign trade may be grouped under the broad class headings of foods, the raw materials of manufacture, structural raw materials, fuels, and manufactured goods. The foods and raw materials tend to flow from the less densely peopled agricultural regions, the tropics, and the colonial dependencies toward the highly organized industrial regions, especially those having large resources in fuel and power. In return the industrial regions furnish manufactured wares and coal. However, the whole world moves steadily toward a higher plane of industrial organization, and the flow of goods established during the past century is breaking down as a result. This tendency is increased by the wave of sentiment for economic independence which is spreading toward the remote corners of the world, by the imposition of tariffs and other restrictions, and most of all by the demoralization wrought by war. Still, no modern nation is equipped by nature for complete economic independence, and trade must continue to be the basis upon which critical wants are satisfied and domestic surpluses are marketed. It will be better for all the world when a state of security is reached that will permit the removal of trade barriers and the resumption of a more natural flow of goods from those regions best able to produce them, but such a change cannot be brought about quickly.

Foreign trade involves, as does domestic trade, a consideration of the routes of transportation and the types of carriers employed. Some of the foreign trade of the United States is by rail with Canada and Mexico. A larger part is transoceanic. Some of the latter is carried in American ships, but a large part moves in foreign bottoms. It is not necessary that a country own enough ships to carry all its foreign commerce. Some great manufacturing companies own railways and locomotives, and several possess their own railway cars. None own all their own transportation equipment. In the same way, no country does all its own ocean carrying, although such countries as Britain and Norway own large fleets of ocean shipping which they hire in the service of others. The situation of the United States in this respect has varied through the years. So has the nature and volume of its foreign trade.

THE DEVELOPMENT OF AMERICAN SHIPPING. From the period of the earliest settlement the American colonists were dependent on overseas trade. The settlements on the Atlantic Coast were scattered; roads were lacking; and communication was almost altogether across the Atlantic with the "mother countries." The tobacco of Virginia, the pine trees of New England, and the furs of Canada were shipped to Europe in exchange for European wares. In New England particularly, the

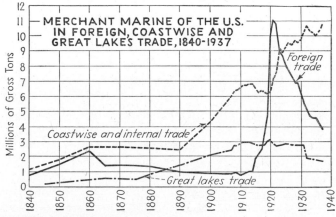

FIG. 154.—The gradual development of shipping in coastal and inland service is quite in contrast with the sudden increase in ocean shipping during the war boom of 1914–1921 and its great decrease since that time.

difficulties encountered in agriculture led many to seek a livelihood on the sea, where the close proximity of good fishing ground added inducements to a seafaring life. The abundance of oak and pine timber of the highest quality made shipbuilding an important industry, and ships themselves, made in New England and sold in Europe, became an important export commodity. In this period the same man often was shipbuilder, shipmaster, and merchant.

Following the American Revolution, numerous laws were passed for the protection of United States shipping, and the merchant marine kept pace with a growing foreign trade. In the period between 1800 and 1830 an average of between 80 and 90 per cent of the foreign trade of the United States was carried in American ships. For many years thereafter, until the period of the Civil War, shipping continued to increase in amount yet not so rapidly as the total value of foreign trade of the nation.

The years from 1861 to the close of the century marked a substantial, if somewhat irregular, growth in the total value of foreign trade of the United States but a progressive decline in the size of the American merchant marine (Fig. 154). About 1890 less than 10 per cent of the foreign trade of the country moved in its own ships. This decline may be attributed to a combination of political and economic causes, the latter fundamentally geographic, which discouraged the investment of American capital in shipping but afforded it new and vast opportunities elsewhere. (1) The period was one of rapid expansion westward into rich agricultural lands. Coal, oil, iron, other minerals, forests, and railroad building were attracting men, and interest waned in the modest returns of the shipping business. (2) The sailing ship was giving way to the larger and more dependable steamship, particularly to those constructed of iron and steel. In the building of steamships Great Britain, with her established iron and steel industries and her skilled and less expensive labor, had an advantage over the United States.

Of no less serious consequence were certain political and historical factors such as (1) the destruction of shipping during the Civil War and (2) the removal by Congress of protection to the shipping industry enacted at earlier dates.

It appears, therefore, that, at the opening of the present century, the United States had a large and growing foreign trade but a relatively small merchant marine.

THE DEVELOPMENT OF AMERICAN FOREIGN TRADE. Since the colonial period American foreign trade has been greatly increased in quantity and completely transformed as to character. In 1840 more than 85 per cent of the exports were (1) crude raw materials, such as timber and cotton; (2) crude foodstuffs, such as wheat; and (3) simply manufactured foodstuffs, such as flour and salt pork. Less than 15 per cent were finished and semifinished manufactures of more advanced types. At that date also, about 70 per cent of the imports were manufactured wares, including finished and semifinished wares and some foodstuffs of a more advanced type of manufacture. Only about 30 per cent were crude industrial materials and crude foodstuffs. The trade of the present is in striking contrast with that of a century ago. Now only about 30 per cent of the exports are crude raw materials and crude and manufactured foods; 20 per cent are semimanufactures; and 50 per cent are finished manufactures of great variety. In contrast, 40 per cent of the imports are manufactures, semifinished or finished; and 60 per cent are crude materials and foodstuffs, crude or manufactured. The general development of the American foreign trade will be seen in Fig. 155. It will be observed also that the great increase in the value of American trade that occurred during these years reached its climax during the war period

1914–1918 or shortly thereafter. It has since suffered from instability in the commercial world and the restrictions of nationalistic policies in this and other countries.

The recent development of the American merchant fleet is indicated in Fig. 154. The period of rapid shipbuilding induced by the War of 1914–

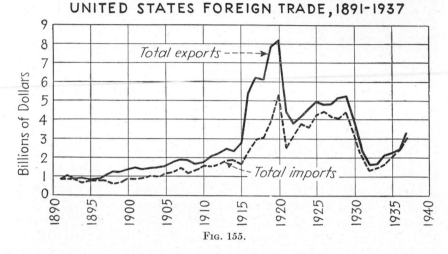

## UNITED STATES FOREIGN TRADE, 1891-1937

FIG. 155.

1918 is clearly seen, and the depression that has followed. Its nature is the more striking when compared with the development of inland and coastwise shipping.

## Gateways of American Trade

FACTORS IN THE DEVELOPMENT OF A PORT. The overseas commerce of any region flows in and out in response to fairly well-defined geographic and economic conditions, and the gateways through which it flows are the ports of the region. Ports do not thrive merely because they are located upon the seacoast of a country. Those which grow and prosper do so because of geographic and economic advantages that are lacking at other points. The following are among the more important of such advantages: (1) A *good harbor* with opportunity for the construction of terminal facilities. The ideal harbor is provided with (*a*) a safe entrance of ample depth, (*b*) abundant anchorage room with protection from storms, (*c*) freedom from ice, (*d*) an approachable and extensive waterfront capable of improvement at low cost (Fig. 156). (2) A *large and productive hinterland*. (3) *Easy access to the hinterland*. Where physiographic features are such as to concentrate many lines of traffic upon one coastal point, as at New York, the effectiveness of this last factor is greatly increased.

Fig. 156.—Locust Point Terminal, Baltimore. An excellent illustration of the land and water relationships of a port. (*Courtesy of Baltimore and Ohio Railway Co.*)

THE PORT OF NEW YORK.  New York is America's greatest commercial gateway (Fig. 157). Through it passes more than one-third of the total foreign trade of the United States. Its import and export trades are more nearly balanced than is true of most American ports, but the imports generally exceed the exports in value. As a port, it is not without defects, nor has it been without rivals for commercial supremacy; yet it has maintained its position for more than a hundred years. Several advantages lead to this condition: (1) New York has easy access to a large and rich hinterland. The easy grade provided by the Hudson and Mohawk valleys are not found on the routes reaching westward from

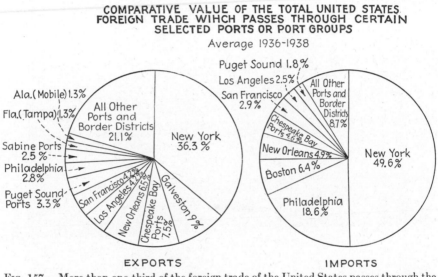

COMPARATIVE VALUE OF THE TOTAL UNITED STATES
FOREIGN TRADE WIHCH PASSES THROUGH CERTAIN
SELECTED PORTS OR PORT GROUPS
Average 1936-1938

EXPORTS

IMPORTS

FIG. 157.—More than one-third of the foreign trade of the United States passes through the port of New York.

Boston, Philadelphia, or other eastern ports. This easy route to the interior first suggested the Erie Canal, which did much to establish the preeminence of New York. Later the same route was followed by the New York Central railway lines which have served the same end. The dominant position attained by New York under these early advantages practically forced the railways that later connected Philadelphia and Baltimore with the West to extend to New York also, thus contributing to its further growth. (2) New York has an excellent harbor (Fig. 158). The entrances to it have required expensive improvement, but the expanse of protected water in its various bays and rivers is great. The water frontage of the entire port district, included within a radius of 20 miles, totals nearly 800 miles, an almost unbelievable figure. A total of about 350 miles of this frontage is now developed for the berthing of ships and for the loading and unloading of cargo. (3) The principal trade of North America has, up to the present, been transatlantic, and more

FIG. 158.—The harbor of New York has commodious bays and an extended water front, but the port is so divided that freight transfer is often difficult.

goods have been moved to eastern ports than to those of the South or the West.

Many economic factors have helped to maintain New York's supremacy in spite of the competition of other eastern ports and the inconvenience of handling goods through a harbor divided into more than 20 different bays, rivers, and terminal districts. Among these conditions the most important is the fact that, during the early period of commercial development, there became established in the city great financial and commercial interests, and many other types of service which facilitate the movement of foreign trade. Although the other eastern ports have long been made accessible by railways, and though rail rates have been equalized, yet the great volume of North American foreign trade continues to flow through the port of New York.

OTHER NORTH ATLANTIC PORTS.  A group of North Atlantic ports, of which the principal are Montreal, Boston, Philadelphia, and Baltimore, compete with New York for the trade of the northern interior.

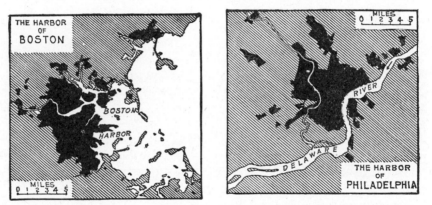

FIG. 159.—Boston harbor is a sheltered bay, while that of Philadelphia is a tidal river.

*Montreal* is the most important port of Canada. Its export trade is much greater than its import trade, since it is a port of shipment for wheat as well as for wood products, dairy products, minerals, and manufactures from Ontario and Quebec. It has an admirable location 1,000 miles in from the edge of the continent; and because of its position with respect to the "great circle route" of the North Atlantic, it is 300 miles nearer to Liverpool than is New York. Yet it has the great handicap of being closed to navigation by ice during 4 or 5 months of every year. During these months Canadian exports are shipped by rail to the ports of the Canadian maritime provinces or of the United States.

*Boston* is the commercial gateway of the great industrial district of New England. The value of its imports, including the vegetable fibers, wool, hides, and other raw materials of industry, is several times greater than that of its export trade. The harbor of Boston is commodious and convenient (Fig. 159); it is well situated with respect to Atlantic routes, is well equipped, and is served by railways that reach the whole of New England and even make a part of Canada tributary to it. Yet the total amount of trade handled through the port is hardly one-tenth the trade of New York. One explanation of this fact is to be found in the physical isolation of Boston from the trade that in former years flowed through the Erie Canal. Boston's isolation gave to New York a commercial advantage that even the efficient railway connections of a later day between Boston and the West could not overcome. Economic factors of a complicated character also enter into the question.

PHILADELPHIA AND THE CHESAPEAKE BAY PORTS. The trade of Philadelphia is, like that of Boston, characterized by much greater imports than exports, its ratio being nearly 2 to 1. Like Boston it serves a large industrial hinterland, and many of its imports, especially hides and wool, are of the same character. In Baltimore and Norfolk, on the other hand, the balance in favor of imports is much less, and in some years exports exceed imports. This is due largely to exports of coal from the Norfolk port district. Two decades ago the coal exports were so great as to far overbalance the import values, but the coal exports have declined and the general imports have increased until the latter usually exceed. The location of Philadelphia and Baltimore on long southward-facing bays is something of a handicap to them in north Atlantic trade. The distance from European ports to Baltimore is about 325 miles greater than to New York. In trade with South America, however, or in reaching the Panama Canal, this handicap does not exist.

THE COTTON PORTS. New Orleans, the Texas ports, and Savannah, Ga., are the principal gateways of the cotton belt. They also are primarily export points. New Orleans, although it is the gateway for the importation of much of the Caribbean produce—bananas, sugar, henequen, coffee, and petroleum—has a larger export trade. The exports of the Texas ports (Houston, Galveston, Corpus Christi, and several smaller ports) outvalue their imports many times. In addition to cotton, a large quantity of petroleum and grain and other agricultural produce from the northern interior is handled through these ports. In spite of the handicaps under which New Orleans competes with Atlantic ports (greater distance from Europe and more than 100 miles of river approach), it is one of the leading ports of the United States in foreign trade.

PACIFIC PORTS. Commercial gateways on the Pacific Coast of North America are few, and their total trade is considerably less than that of the combined Gulf ports. This is not for lack of harbors, although the coastline is generally much less approachable than that of the Atlantic side of the continent. Several Pacific ports have been provided with facilities where natural advantages were insufficient. San Francisco (Fig. 160), Los Angeles, Portland, Seattle, and Vancouver have large harbors with good shipping facilities. They are termini of the principal transcontinental railway lines, on the one hand; and of transpacific steamship lines, on the other. An explanation of the relatively small value of the trade flowing through these ports is to be found, rather, in other conditions, some of which are related to the geographic situation of the ports. (1) Their immediate hinterlands are small. The coastal slopes and valleys constitute the principal parts of the area directly tributary to the ports. The larger hinterland of the arid plateaus and intermontane basins is sparsely populated. (2) The ports are separated

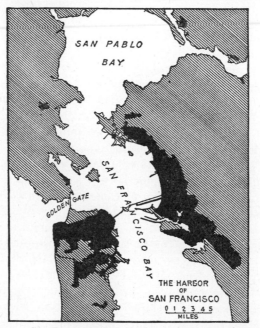

Fig. 160.—The ports on San Francisco Bay. Bridges span the bay between San Francisco and Oakland and at the Golden Gate. City areas are shown in black.

from the continental interior by long distances and difficult routes, and a large part of the intervening region is arid. (3) The coastal region has a limited industrial development. The principal export commodities are the products of natural resources—lumber, petroleum, and fish. Many of the most valuable agricultural staples, such as fruits and vegetables, are perishable and enter foreign commerce to a limited extent only. (4) The transpacific markets that are reached through these ports are small in size or have but a limited purchasing power. Both of the last-named factors are likely to be modified by the growth of manufacturing, both on the Pacific Coast and in the Orient, and the change will tend to increase the trade of the Pacific ports. Many valuable commodities from the Orient and the tropics are entered at these ports, and the values of the import and export business are more evenly balanced than in most of the Atlantic ports.

## Highways of American Foreign Trade

FACTORS IN THE LOCATION OF OCEAN TRADE ROUTES.  Connecting the ports of the world are ocean highways of fairly definite location and of widely differing importance. It may be considered somewhat strange that, when the broad oceans are free for all, ships should confine the direction of their movements to anything approaching definite routes. Yet there are several physical conditions that influence them to do so. (1) The spherical shape of the earth makes the shortest distance between any two ports lie along a "great circle" passing through these ports. Other conditions permitting, ships will go by the shortest route. (2) The shapes of the continents sometimes force ships out of a direct route and cause them to converge upon some point or along some line of travel as, for example, in narrow straits or around projecting capes. (3) The general circulation of the atmosphere, vastly important in the day of sail, has not yet lost its influence upon the routes of ships. When it is otherwise practicable, shipmasters lay their courses to take advantage of favorable, and to avoid unfavorable, winds. (4) In the same manner even the ocean currents are taken into account. It is indeed a small ship whose operating expenses do not run into scores of dollars per hour, and even so small a factor as a favorable or an unfavorable current is considered. At certain seasons some of the ocean currents bear arctic or antarctic ice which becomes a menace to navigation and influences the courses of ships, particularly in the North Atlantic. (5) The location of stations able to supply steamship fuel is a cause for the bending of lines of traffic into routes that touch at those stations. (6) The ability of certain districts to supply cargo is an attraction that operates in a similar manner.

THE FEATURES OF AN OCEAN TRADE ROUTE.  The oceans are indeed traversed by numberless ship tracks, but only when many of them, for some combination of the foregoing reasons, converge or coincide along a part of their way are the ships that traverse them said to follow a trade route. Such a route has two distinct features: (1) a central belt, or trunk, of varying length and width with (2) a set of branches, or feeders, at each end, reaching into the many ports tributary to this route. The principal ocean trade routes or highways of the world are shown in Fig. 161.

THE NORTH ATLANTIC ROUTE is the most traveled of any in the world. Its feeders reach more than 100 ports, spread from Panama to Labrador, and an even greater number in Europe extending from Norway to Spain.

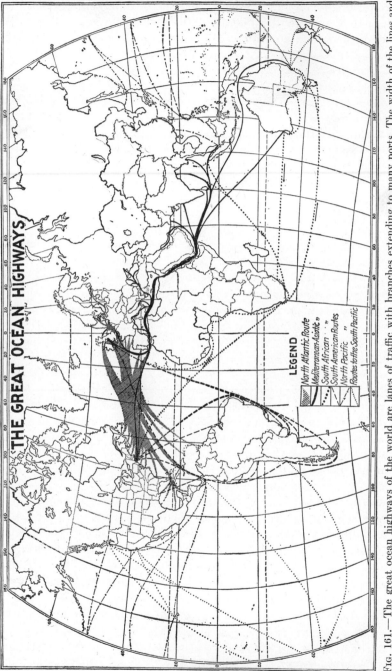

FIG. 161.—The great ocean highways of the world are lanes of traffic with branches extending to many ports. The width of the lines and bands on this map are not intended to do more than suggest location and approximate relative importance.

The trunk of the route, a broad, curved band of ship tracks, represents in its location a compromise between the great-circle route and various modifications due to the influences of the other factors mentioned. It might seem that ships from the Panama Canal bound for France would sail directly across from the West Indies, and some do so. Yet a course along the great-circle route brings them so far north that the advantage of cheap coal at Norfolk or of additional cargo at New York is sufficient to attract many and to cause them to complete their course along the North Atlantic route. The volume of traffic flowing over this great ocean highway is said to require one-fifth of all the shipping of the world. Both ends of the route are abundantly supplied with steamship fuel.

THE MEDITERRANEAN-ASIATIC ROUTE connects the whole North Atlantic region with the Indian Ocean by way of the Suez Canal. Although many American ships use this route in normal times, it is of much greater importance to the European nations, especially to Great Britain. It is the "life line" that connects Britain with her raw materials, food supplies, and markets in India, Malaya, Australia, and New Zealand. In 1940 its utility was jeopardized by the military and naval action of the Axis Powers, and Britain was forced first to divert much shipping to the South African route and then to make extreme military exertion to lessen the threat of danger against the Suez Canal. Much of the fuel required at intermediate stations on this route has to be carried from England or America.

THE SOUTH AFRICAN ROUTE connects the same regions as does the preceding. The trunk of the route lies between the Cape Verde Islands, where shipping from both sides of the North Atlantic converges, and Capetown, where it again diverges into the Indian Ocean. Although it is 2,500 miles farther from New York to Calcutta by this route and more than 4,000 miles farther from Liverpool than by the way of the Suez Canal, the presence of cheap coal in South Africa and the avoidance of the canal tolls attract many ships to the route.

THE SOUTH AMERICAN ROUTES. *East Coast.* Ships bound for the east coast of South America from both sides of the North Atlantic converge upon the eastward projection of Brazil. So far out into the Atlantic does this course take American ships that the distance from New York to Buenos Aires is only 400 miles less than the distance from Liverpool to that port. The southern feeders of this route extend from all the ports of eastern South America and from Cape Horn.

*West Coast.* The trade between North Atlantic ports and those of the west coast of South America has been provided with a new route by the construction of the Panama Canal. This effects a saving of nearly 1,600 miles between Liverpool and Valparaiso, Chile, and more than 3,700 miles between New York and the same port. Not even the delays and the tolls incident to passage through the canal are sufficient to offset this great saving.

On both of the South American routes, ship fuel is largely supplied by importation. Only on the west coast of South America are local supplies of coal and oil able to meet even a small part of the requirements.

PACIFIC OCEAN ROUTES. The size of the Pacific Ocean is so great, the ports upon its borders are so widely distributed, and the total volume of trade that moves across it is relatively so small that avenues of steamship traffic are not so well developed upon it as upon the Atlantic. Nevertheless, certain physical facts influence ships plying between the ports on the two sides of the North Pacific in the choice of their courses. They may take (1) the shorter great-circle route which swings far north toward the Aleutian Islands or (2) a longer and more southerly route touching at the Hawaiian Islands. The choice of the latter course adds 700 miles to the distance between San Francisco and Manila but has the advantage of additional revenues derived from passengers, mails, or cargo to be delivered or received at Honolulu or Guam. The most direct route even from the Panama Canal to Manila curves far to the north of the Hawaiian Islands and often makes calls at Los Angeles or San Francisco and some Japanese port advisable.

## The Foreign Trade of the United States

THE TRADE OF THE UNITED STATES WITH MEXICO AND THE CARIBBEAN LANDS (MIDDLE AMERICA). The United States is the principal buyer of the products of every important Middle American industry. On the average about half the total exports from Mexico and the Caribbean lands has been sold in the United States. Much more than half of certain commodities moves to the United States. This is notably true of sugar, bananas, tobacco, henequen, petroleum, and iron ore. Because of the geographical proximity of the United States and because the American people are the world's greatest consumers of some of these commodities, there is reason to believe that this region will retain at least its present importance as a source of imports into the United States.

As a buyer of United States exports the region has, in recent years, ranked third among the trade regions (Fig. 162). Its purchases amounted to 12 per cent of the value of all American exports, exceeding the purchases of all other trade regions except those of Canada and northwest Europe. They consist principally of grains, meats, and numerous manufactures of textiles, iron, and steel.

THE TRADE OF THE UNITED STATES WITH EASTERN AND WESTERN SOUTH AMERICA, both import and export, is less than that with the Middle American region. Exports to all parts of South America are similar and consist principally of manufactures of iron and steel, machinery, automobiles, and many other types of manufactured goods, together with petroleum and lumber. Imports from the several sections of the South American region differ widely. From the east coast the principal items are the products of farms and forests—coffee, grains, wool, hides, meats, forest products, and many other things. The leading imports from the west-coast countries are minerals—the ores of copper, iron, and tin, smelted metals, and nitrate of soda. These are the produce of the Andean mineral regions. There are some products of agriculture, but they occupy a relatively unimportant place in the list. In general the exports of the United States to South America, in spite of the fact that manufactures constitute a large part of the total, are slightly less valuable and very

## THE FOREIGN TRADE OF THE UNITED STATES, AVERAGE 1936-1938, BY REGIONS OF ORIGIN AND DESTINATION

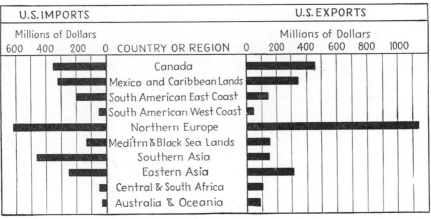

FIG. 162.

much heavier and more bulky than the imports. Especially is this true of the trade with the east-coast countries. As a consequence south-bound ships are usually well loaded, but many north-bound ships seek full cargoes in vain.

THE TRADE OF THE UNITED STATES WITH EUROPE. Europe, as a continent, is much the most important source of United States imports and the largest customer for her exports. In 1937 about two-fifths of the total United States exports went to the great industrial centers and consuming markets of Europe. These exports consist principally of fuels and raw materials of animal, vegetable, or mineral origin and even greater quantities of semimanufactures and highly manufactured goods. An increasing proportion of the total consists of the industrial wares that American manufacturers are able to produce in high quality and at low prices, such, for example, as automobiles and typewriters. United States imports from Europe are numerous and varied. In general, they are manufactures of high quality, although crude manufactures and even the unmanufactured products of European farms, forests, and mines are to be found among the exports of nearly all European countries to the United States.

TRADE OF THE UNITED STATES WITH EASTERN ASIA. Trade across the Pacific Ocean is small compared with transatlantic trade. The great population of the Orient has a relatively low per capita purchasing power. Moreover, in parts of the Orient, the penetration of Occidental ideas and appliances has been so slow that there is a limited knowledge of or use for American manufactures. The latter difficulty is gradually disappearing, and the large total population of the countries of eastern Asia indicates a market of great potential capacity. Its development will depend largely on the outcome of political changes now in progress there. The total value of American trade with the Orient in recent years has been similar to that with South America, and the values of imports and exports are fairly well balanced. The tonnage of the trade is, however, not at all well balanced. Among the more valuable American imports from the Orient are silk, vegetable oils, tea, and other commodities of small bulk and high value. Among the important American exports to the Orient are petroleum products, lumber, raw cotton, crude iron and steel, and machinery. There are also some exports of small bulk and high value, such as tobacco, but the total export tonnage is greater than that of the imports. Much shipping space must therefore return to America from the Orient in ballast or seek cargo in other regions.

TRADE OF THE UNITED STATES WITH SOUTHERN ASIA. With the exception of the Philippine Islands, the political divisions of the whole Indian Ocean trade region having the largest trade with the United States are the colonial possessions of European powers. Under this relationship the mother countries are the sources from which the colonies obtain a large part of their imports, mainly manufactured wares. Equal competition in this market by the United States is prevented by tariffs. There is nothing, however, to prevent the United States from making large purchases in this region; vegetable fibers, mineral ores, rubber, hides, tea, spices, oils, and gums are all important commodities obtained from that part of the world. The most important exports to the region are petroleum products and manufactures of iron and steel. From this region of the world, as well as from Middle America, the tonnage of American imports is normally greater than the tonnage of American exports to the region. Ships returning empty from other trade regions go to it in search of cargo for American ports. The value of American imports from southern and southeastern Asia, due to the restrictions on exports and the high value of some of the imported commodities, is three times as great as the value of the export trade to those areas.

THE TRADE OF THE UNITED STATES WITH AUSTRALIA AND WEST AND SOUTH AFRICA is relatively small, representing only 3 to 5 per cent of the total foreign trade of the United States. The European populations of both these regions are small, and the many political divisions included are under the commercial domination of European powers. Thus the foreign trade of Australia and New Zealand is predominantly with Britain and other British possessions. Nevertheless, the need of these regions for American timber, petroleum, ironware, and machinery enables American exports to these regions to outweigh the tonnage of imports from them several times and to have also a higher total value.

### SELECTED REFERENCES

*Ann. Repts.*, Mississippi River Commission.

BERGLUND, A. "Ocean Transportation," New York, 1931.

CRICHER, A. L. Ocean Routes in United States Foreign Trade, *U.S. Dept. Commerce, Trade Promotion Series* 96, 1930.

DAGGETT, S. "Principles of Inland Transportation," revised, New York, 1934.

HAWKS, ELLISON. "The Romance of Transport," New York, 1932.

JEFFERSON, M. The Civilizing Rails, *Econ. Geog.*, Vol. 4 (1928), pp. 217–231.

JOHNSON, E. R., G. G. HUEBNER, and A. K. HENRY. "Transportation by Water," New York, 1935.

LOCKLIN, D. P. "Economics of Transportation," Chicago, 1938.

LONG, W. R. Railway and Highway Transportation Abroad: A Study of Existing Relationships, Recent Competitive Measures and Coordination Policies, *U.S. Dept. Commerce, Trade Promotion Series* 155, 1935.

MEARS, ELIOT G. "Maritime Trade of Western United States," Stanford University Press, 1935.

MEYER, BALTHAZAR, *et al.* "History of Transportation in the United States before 1840," Carnegie Endowment, Washington, 1917.

MOULTON, H. G., *et al.* "The St. Lawrence Navigation and Power Project," Washington, 1929.

———. "Waterways versus Railways," Boston, 1927.

U.S. Army and U.S. Shipping Board. More than 20 monographs on various ports of the United States.

*U.S. Dept. Commerce Yearbook*, annual.

*U.S. War Dept., Ann. Repts.*, Chief of Engineers.

VAN CLEEF, EUGENE, "Trade Centers and Trade Routes," New York, 1937.

WYER, SAMUEL S. "Fundamentals of Transportation Problem," Ohio Chamber of Commerce, Columbus, 1928.

# Chapter XVI. The United States
# in the Pacific

THE UNITED STATES OVERSEAS.  Beyond the borders of continental United States are territories under the same flag which add 19 per cent to the area of the country and 11 per cent to its population. Of this total area 99 per cent lies in or faces upon the Pacific Ocean. It includes Alaska, Hawaii, the Philippine Islands, and some smaller island groups (Fig. 163). Alaska and Hawaii are United States territories, politically a part of the country, and large financial investments in the Philippines seem likely to

**A COMPARISON OF THE AREAS AND POPULATION
OF ALASKA PHILIPPINE ISLANDS AND HAWAII. 1938**

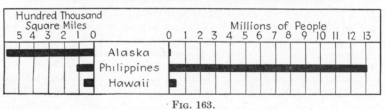

· FIG. 163.

continue American interest in those islands even after they have attained their political independence.

## Alaska

AN UNDEVELOPED TERRITORY.  The purchase of Alaska from Russia in 1867 increased the territory of the United States by nearly one-fifth. Although Alaska has made notable economic progress in certain particulars in the last two decades, it is still generally undeveloped. Its population (about 63,000, fully half Indians and Eskimos) is less than it was in 1910. Its mineral and forest resources are for the most part unexploited, and the total extent of its lands now under actual cultivation is less than that of an average township in Iowa. Various factors have contributed to this slow development, not the least of which are the geographical situation of Alaska, its climate, soils, and surface configuration.

REGIONAL CONTRASTS IN ALASKA (Fig. 67).  *The Pacific Coast section of Alaska* lies in the same latitude as Scotland and southern Norway, with

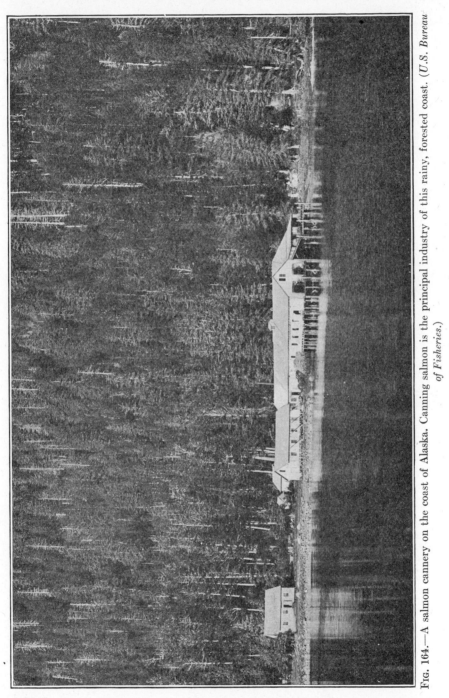

FIG. 164.—A salmon cannery on the coast of Alaska. Canning salmon is the principal industry of this rainy, forested coast. (*U.S. Bureau of Fisheries.*)

which it has much in common in its fiorded and mountainous coasts and its marine climate. The annual precipitation of the region decreases with distance northward (it is 165 inches at the southern boundary), but on the seaward slope it is everywhere ample for the maintenance of forests. The combination of steep slopes, rain, fog, cool summers, leached soils, forests, and long distance to profitable markets has not encouraged agricultural settlement (Fig. 164). The mountain-bordered Matanuska Valley in which settlers were located in 1935 has less than 200 farms and hardly more than 5,000 acres of cleared land. Short-season vegetable crops are raised and also hay and small grains that support dairy and poultry industries whose products can be got to a market. However, agriculture is not overly secure even there, because of the danger of unseasonable frosts. There is also some fur farming in the coastal district. Little has been done even in the exploitation of the forests, since the more readily accessible timber of British Columbia lies between the Alaskan forests and the markets that their products must reach. Two large government forest reserves, including most of the merchantable timber, have been created, and it is probable that in the future the forest resources will be in increasing demand (Fig. 73). However, much of the forest growth of western hemlock and spruce is likely to prove valuable as a source of pulpwood rather than as a source of saw timber. There are many excellent water-power sites on the glaciated mountain borders, but little present market for power. Most of the coastal settlements of Alaska are established in connection with the fishing industry or serve as gateways to the mineral regions of the interior.

*The Interior of Alaska.*    Between the Alaskan Mountains on the south and the Brooks Range on the north lies the great interior of Alaska. It consists principally of the basin of the Yukon and the lesser basin of the Kuskokwim River. Although the surface of interior Alaska is much more level than that of the coastal region, the rainfall and cloudiness are less, and the extremes of temperature are greater, bringing warmer summers and much colder winters. Here the forests are not extensive, and the timber is not generally suitable for lumber. The whole area may properly be considered a part of the great northern forest region or taiga (see Chap. II).

The long and relatively warm summer days of the Alaskan interior permit some agricultural crops to be grown, including potatoes, hay, and cereals, though the summer is short and there is danger of early frosts. Beef and dairy cattle, sheep, and swine also are successfully kept. Yet agriculture cannot be said to thrive, for the soils are generally cold and acid, and the region is isolated from all but the local market. The white population of the whole interior is not more than that of a good-sized village in the United States.

*Northern and western Alaska* are mainly tundra. The summers are not so warm, nor are the winters so cold, as in the interior, yet the ground is deeply frozen, and summer heat serves to thaw only the surface. In this region and in parts of the interior the vegetation of sedges, lichens, grass, and shrubs is range pasture suitable for reindeer, and the area has an estimated carrying capacity of 4 to 5 million head, though the number of reindeer is now only about 550,000. The industry is new, and most of the usable area is without people or convenient means of transportation; hence the existing reindeer industry is located near the west coast. At present the possibility of marketing reindeer meat in the United States is limited, but local use provides food and clothing for some 15,000 of the people who depend on them. In 1938 about 40,000 deer were slaughtered.

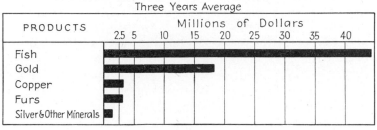

RELATIVE IMPORTANCE OF ALASKAN PRODUCTS
Three Years Average

Fig. 165.

THE MINERAL RESOURCES OF ALASKA. Alaska is rich in minerals. In the past the placer gold of the Yukon and of Nome attracted a large but temporary population. The most easily won placer gold is apparently about worked out; however, less accessible placers, dredging, and deep mining continue to furnish additional supplies. The placer mining and extensive dredging operations are conducted principally in the Yukon Basin; the deep mining is more productive in the coastal district, especially southeastern Alaska near Juneau. Large deposits of copper are known, and several properties are developed under the control of American copper companies, but the largest producing district has been about worked out and has discontinued operation. Up to 1937 the value of gold and copper taken from Alaska by American companies was more than one hundred times as much as the United States paid Russia for the entire territory. About 65 per cent of the total mineral values produced have been of gold, and 30 per cent of copper. Coal of various grades is found in the Alaska Range; it furnishes fuel for local and for railway use, yet the quantity produced is hardly sufficient for the limited local needs, and additional coal is imported from outside the territory, especially from the United States and British Columbia.

ALASKAN FISHERIES AND FURS. The sea yields to Alaska greater returns than all its land resources combined (Fig. 165). Of the sea resources the salmon fisheries are the most important, yielding about 90 per cent of the value of all fisheries. There are in addition minor catches of herring, halibut, shellfish, and the products of the whaling industry in Alaskan waters. Alaska is notable also for the catches of fur seals made on the Pribilof Islands. This industry, once so nearly ruined by ruthless slaughter of the animals, is reestablished under government protection. The total estimated number of seals is now about 2 million, and the annual catch is about 50 thousand.

THE PROBLEM OF TRANSPORTATION. Transportation difficulties arising from the location of Alaska, from its surface configuration, and from its long winters are not easily overcome. Communication with the rest of North America is mainly by water. Railways total less than 800 miles; three lines extend from the ports short distances inland to connect with the upper Yukon River or to tap mineral areas, but one that the United States government has built from the south coast across the mountains to connect with the river routes of the interior at Fairbanks is over 500 miles in length. It also serves the Matanuska Valley. The Yukon and Kuskokwim rivers offer many hundreds of miles of navigable waterways through which the interior is now reached, yet they are open to boats only 3½ months during the year. The frozen condition of the ground makes permanent road construction difficult, and dogs, used as work animals, are more numerous than horses, for dog and reindeer sledges must serve the needs of ordinary local transport in the sparsely settled interior during the winter.

## The Hawaiian Islands

THE LOCATION AND TOPOGRAPHY OF THE ISLANDS. The Hawaiian group consists of a number of volcanic islands situated in mid-Pacific just within the tropics. The situation is significant in connection with agricultural products and the commercial and political relations of the islands. (1) Mountainous surface gives rise to great local variations in temperature and rainfall. The lowlands have generally a marine tropical climate, but at moderate altitudes a more temperate climate prevails. (2) Situation in the northeast trade winds combines with mountainous surface to provide the northeastern slopes of the islands with abundant precipitation but leaves the southern and western slopes more dry and generally in need of irrigation. The development of extensive agriculture under these conditions requires large financial outlay. (3) The central situation of the islands in the North Pacific makes their principal port, Honolulu, a meeting point for Pacific interests and a crossroads of traffic. The situation is one of strategic importance for nations on both sides of the ocean. It also invites Asiatic immigration; the population of 411,000 is half of Japanese and Philippine origin. It is more than two-thirds of

Asiatic origin, little more than a quarter Caucasian, and only 5 per cent pure Hawaiian. However, 80 per cent of the total are American citizens.

The development of modern agriculture in Hawaii called for outside capital. Since both the necessary capital and the principal market for Hawaiian products were in the United States, the situation of Hawaii invited American control. The result was the annexation of the islands by the United States in 1898 at the request of the Hawaiian people.

THE HAWAIIAN SUGAR INDUSTRY. Only 11 per cent of the area of the Territory of Hawaii is improved farm land. Much of the total area is dry, mountainous, forest-covered, or composed of barren lava flows. A large part of the unimproved land is held in farms but serves only as pasture. Sugar cane is the most important cultivated crop in the islands; in 1937 the area of cane harvested was 35 per cent of all the improved

FIG. 166.—Sugar cane is grown on the windward (east) coasts without irrigation; on the leeward slopes irrigation is necessary. (*U.S. Department of Agriculture.*)

farm land. Sugar is grown on the rainy trade-wind coasts without irrigation, but much larger yields are obtained under irrigation on the leeward coasts (Fig. 166). In some instances the irrigation water is carried from the rainy eastern slopes through tunnels to the dry lands on the west. The soils of the lower levels used for sugar production are mixtures of weathered lavas with coral lime. To these favorable soil conditions provided by nature are added heavy applications of nitrate fertilizers, and large yields of sugar result. The large expenditures for irrigation and for fertilizer often involved in Hawaiian sugar culture do not favor small-scale cultivation. There are more small farms than large ones by number, but they are self-sufficing farms and gardens. More than 90 per cent of the farm land is in a few great plantations of more than 1,000 acres each. Most of these are sugar plantations, each with its own mill. The labor is provided mainly by people of Asiatic descent, but the ownership and management of the plantations are in American hands. Most of the raw sugar is shipped to refineries in the United States.

OTHER HAWAIIAN CROPS. The pineapple crop, grown without irrigation, mainly in Oahu, ranks next to sugar in value (Fig. 167). The perishable nature of pineapples does not permit of large exports over

Fig. 167.—A field of young pineapple plants in the Hawaiian Islands. (*Ewing Galloway*.)

the long distance to the United States in fresh form, though many are obtained from a nearer source in Cuba. The Hawaiian crop is canned (600 million pounds a year), making economical use of local sugar (Fig. 168). Other fruits are grown for local use, and there is some attempt to raise bananas for the Pacific Coast market. Rice and corn are the most important grain crops, but the quantities raised are not sufficient for the local needs, and food for the laborers is imported. Most of the minor crops, including rice, vegetables, coffee, and many others are produced by people of Asiatic origin on small privately owned farms.

THE LIVESTOCK INDUSTRY. Nearly one-half of the land of Hawaii is used only for pasture, being too dry, rough, or cold for crops. Most of the grazing lands are held in a few large cattle ranches, but the dairy industry is of growing importance. Although livestock raising is the third most

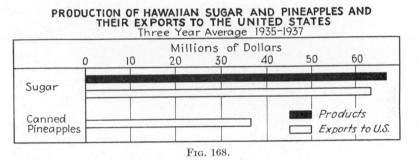

FIG. 168.

important agricultural industry of the islands, the beef produced is not sufficient to supply the local markets.

## The Philippine Islands

THE ISLANDS AND THEIR PEOPLE. The Philippine group consists of several thousand islands and islets, 11 of which are large enough to be of importance. The two main islands, Luzon and Mindanao, are each as large as the state of Indiana, and the entire archipelago has an area approximately equal to that of the British Isles or Japan and a population of about 13½ millions. The islands are mountainous and are characterized by the monsoonal phase of the tropical rainforest type of climate, except where that is modified by high altitude. The people of the islands are diverse, speaking eight basically different languages and more than 40 dialects. They adhere to different religions and differ widely in the stages of civilization that they have attained. The great majority, however, are of Malay stock. Spain was in control of the Philippines for 350 years, and Spanish continues to be the principal language of the educated class, although English is steadily gaining through the several thousand public schools that the American government in the Philippines has brought into existence. At present the islands are virtually independent. However, the fact that complete separation is likely to result in the erection of higher tariff barriers between the agricultural producers and their principal markets in the United States and disturbed political conditions in Eastern Asia may delay the conclusion of that act.

THE NATURAL RESOURCES. About half the islands are clad in forests owned by the government and comprise many species of tropical woods of commercial value. Another 10 per cent bears forest of no commercial value. Relatively little is definitely known of the possible mineral wealth of the archipelago, but there are reasons for believing that it may be considerable. Among the known minerals are coal, large reserves of low-grade iron ore, gold, and copper. The iron ore is little used now but may be important in the future, possibly in conjunction with the coal of China. Gold production has increased rapidly in recent years, and the

**PRODUCTION AND EXPORTATION OF PRINCIPAL PRODUCTS OF THE PHILIPPINE ISLANDS**
Average 1935–1936

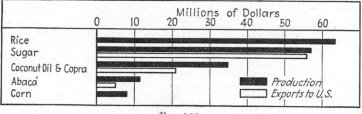

FIG. 169.

output now exceeds that of Alaska. The total mineral production is small, however, as compared with the value of agricultural products. The one outstanding resource of the islands is their agricultural land, from which most of the wealth is being derived.

AGRICULTURE IN THE PHILIPPINES. Nearly one-fourth the land of the islands is under cultivation; this is equal to the area of one of our smaller states, such as West Virginia, yet the annual value of the products is large. Much the greater part of the population is engaged in agriculture, and nearly 60 per cent of the national income is derived from it.

*Rice* is the main crop and chief food of the people. It occupies almost one-half of all the cropped land, or more than one-tenth the entire area of the islands. Yet not quite enough is produced to supply the domestic needs, and a small quantity is imported. Rice is raised on the diked and flooded alluvial plains of the coasts and valleys and on many terraced hill slopes. The copious rains and high temperatures, which the Philippine Islands share with monsoonal southeastern Asia, enable the rice lands to be irrigated even by primitive means and make rice the most productive and satisfactory food grain that can be grown (Fig. 169). In west central Luzon, where the dry season is long, only one crop per year can be grown. In most parts of the islands, however, two and even three crops per year are possible. Irrigation is used, not only to aid in rice production, but also in the districts having a long dry season to enable the cultivation of other food crops when rice is not on the land.

*Corn*, raised on unirrigated soils, ranks next to rice in acreage among the food crops and occupies about 16 per cent of the tilled-land area. Rice and corn are the principal food staples.

*Cane sugar* is by far the most important commercial crop. Promoted by American capital, it occupies only about 6 per cent of the land in crops but furnishes more than half the total value of all exports. The Philippine sugar industry is not conducted on a large plantation basis, as in Hawaii. Instead, most of the sugar is produced by small farmers who

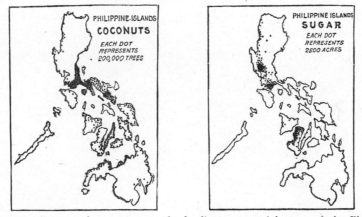

Fig. 170.—Sugar and coconuts are the leading commercial crops of the Philippine Islands. Southern Luzon is the most productive region since it is important in the production of rice and most of the commercial crops also.

contract with a sugar mill to raise a certain acreage of cane. The sugar lands lie mainly in the islands of Negros and Panay and in the coastal lowlands of Luzon, near Manila (Fig. 170). In recent years it has been found profitable to extend irrigation to some of the sugar-growing districts.

*Coconuts* and their products are important both for food and for export. They are produced abundantly on well-drained slopes and coastal margins where there is good circulation of soil water. The principal coconut-growing districts are the coastal plains of Luzon, near Manila, although some of the southern islands are important also. Large quantities of the coconuts are consumed fresh, and still larger amounts are converted into copra, coconut oil, and the dried and sweetened coconut used in confections. Copra is the coconut meat dried in crude form in a sort of kiln, or sometimes in the open. It is the material from which much coconut oil is obtained. It may be shipped in bags to distant oil mills and refining centers. Shipping space is saved, however, and superior grades of oil are produced if the oil is extracted from the fresh coconuts near the place of their origin. In this business the Philippines have become one of the most important countries of the world, producing about one-fourth of the world's supply. The area devoted to coconuts is almost as large as that devoted to corn and more than twice that given to sugar, but the value of the product is much less. A larger part of the coconut planting is done by small farmers, but to handle the large volumes of coconuts there are 10 local oil mills which produce oil for home use and 8 large ones engaged in crushing the coconut meats and pressing the oil

Fig. 171.—Abacá (Manila) fiber drying in a grove of coconut palms, two of the important agricultural crops of the Philippine Islands. (*U.S. Department of Agriculture.*)

for export markets. The volume of oil exported to the United States is so large that tank steamers are required to move it.

*Abacá*, or Manila hemp, is a product almost restricted to the Philippine Islands, although some is produced in Sumatra. It is a long, coarse fiber used in the manufacture of rope and is obtained from the leaf stems of a plant closely related to the banana. It occupies more land than sugar does, but its products are much less valuable exports. It is raised mainly by small farmers and must go through a process of crude manufacture to extract and dry the fiber before it is ready for market (Fig. 171). It is produced most extensively in southern Luzon and some of the more southern islands, and it occupies about 12 per cent of the total cultivated land of the islands.

*Tobacco* is grown, especially in the Cagyan Valley of northeastern Luzon, and is the basis of an important cigar and cigarette manufacture and export. It occupies less than 2 per cent of the cultivated area and is less important than formerly.

*Livestock* includes principally carabao (the water buffalo), cattle, and swine. Carabao are much more numerous than cattle and five times more numerous than horses. They are used in tilling the muddy or flooded rice fields and are thus vital to the food production of the country.

MANUFACTURING, TRANSPORTATION, AND COMMERCE IN THE PHILIP- PINES. Manufacturing is not highly developed in the Philippines and yields only about 15 per cent of the national income. It is essentially

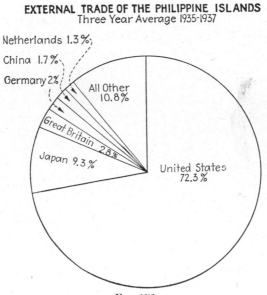

**EXTERNAL TRADE OF THE PHILIPPINE ISLANDS**
Three Year Average 1935-1937

FIG. 172.

an agricultural country. However, the cruder forms of manufacture were established long ago, and American occupation has promoted the improve- ment of some of these. Formerly small country sugar mills turned out crude sugar, and many of these remain, but the larger part of the crop is now manufactured in a few large sugar mills with modern equipment. Coconut-oil mills and cordage mills are representative of other mechanical processes that have developed. Besides them there are other industries that turn out wares of large value for use and for export almost entirely by hand methods. Most important among these are embroideries, cigars, and hats.

The islands are not well situated for heavy manufacture. There is abundant lignite coal, but even that is little mined, since better Australian and Japanese coal can be imported. There are earthy ores of iron, but hardly any of it is smelted. Such exploration for petroleum as has been done has not given encouragement to further search except by large companies with great capital. The principal minerals produced are gold, road materials, and cement, but the value of all these does not equal that of coconut oil alone. The estimated potential water powers are comparable to those of New England, but only about 1 per cent of them is developed. The people of the islands are not accustomed to deal with the problems of industrial organization and, without support of outside capital and organizing force, would not be likely to continue industrial development in the fields of resource exploitation and manufacture.

*Transportation* in the Philippines is confronted with peculiar difficulties because of the mountainous and insular nature of the country. Good roads and some 800 miles of railroad have been built, but all the external and much of the internal trade must be conducted by water.

*Commerce.* The present overseas commerce of the Philippines is large, averaging 250 million dollars. Over two-thirds of it is, however, with the United States, in spite of the great distance that separates them (Fig. 172). It is the possible restriction of that trade as well as the military and naval exposure of the Philippines that makes their future, after independence is granted, one of great uncertainty.

## Other United States Islands in the Pacific

For reasons of military and naval strategy and as refueling stations on the Pacific trade routes, the United States has acquired several islands. Guam is one of these. It lies 1,500 miles east of the Philippines and has an area of 206 square miles and a population of nearly 20,000. It is a naval base and a cable and radio station. Its principal exports are coconut products, and its other crops are much like those of the Philippines. Other important islands include the American Samoas, which lie on the ship route between Hawaii and Australia; Baker; Howland; the Midway Islands; and Wake. All have actual or potential strategic importance and are similar in their general tropical agriculture and products.

SELECTED REFERENCES

*Ann. Repts.*, Chief of the United States Bureau of Insular Affairs.
*Ann. Repts.*, the Governor of Alaska.
*Ann. Repts.*, the Governor of Hawaii.
*Ann. Repts.*, the Governor of the Philippines.
BUTLER, O. M. The Philippine Islands: A Commercial Survey, *U.S. Dept. Commerce, Trade Promotion Series 52*, 1927.
CHAPMAN, E. A. Hawaii, Its Resources and Trade, *U.S. Dept. Commerce, Trade Information Bull. 473*, 1927.
COULTER, J. W. Pineapple Industry in Hawaii, *Econ. Geog.*, Vol. 10 (1934), pp. 288–296.
CUTSHALL, ALDEN. Trends in Philippine Sugar Production, *Econ. Geog.*, Vol. 14 (1938), pp. 154–158.

FREEMAN, O. W. Economic Geography of the Hawaiian Islands, *Econ. Geog.*, Vol. 5 (1929), pp. 260–276.

HAAS, W. H. (*Ed.*). "The American Empire," University of Chicago Press, 1940.

McMILLION, O. M. Reindeer Trek, *Jour. Geog.*, Vol. 38 (1939), pp. 133–141.

SEEMAN, ALBERT L. Regions and Resources of Alaska, *Econ. Geog.*, Vol. 13 (1937), pp. 334–346.

VAN VALKENBURG, S. Agricultural Regions of Asia: Part X, The Philippine Islands, *Econ. Geog.*, Vol. 12 (1936), pp. 231–249.

WOLFANGER, L. A. Economic Regions of Alaska, *Econ. Geog.*, Vol. 2 (1926), pp. 508–536.

# Chapter XVII. Canada—*A Summary*

A SUMMARY FOR CANADA DESIRABLE. In the foregoing chapters Canada and Newfoundland have been treated as integral parts of North America, considered as one large economic region. Their physical and climatic features, their agriculture, and their other industries have been described in connection with the features of similar nature in the United States. However, the importance of Canada as a *political* unit recommends that the essential facts of its economic geography be brought together in a separate chapter.

A LARGE AREA WITH SMALL POPULATION. Canada and Newfoundland include a total area greater than that of the United States and Alaska, but they have a human population less than that of New York state alone. The principal reasons for this condition may not be attributed to youth or to lack of political organization, for Canada has a history as long and a political government as favorable to economic development as those of the United States. In fact even the peoples of the two countries are in most respects similar in abilities and outlook, since there has been for two centuries a continuous and free intermigration across the border. The great differences in the degrees of settlement and development of the two countries are to be attributed in large part to the restrictive influence of features of natural environment.

## Canadian Agriculture

CONSEQUENCES OF SURFACE RELIEF AND OF LATITUDE. Most of Canada lies north of the parallel of 49°N. This fact alone would not seriously retard the economic development of the country; all of the North Sea and Baltic countries of Europe are in a similar situation. Canada has, in addition, an unfortunate arrangement of its surface-relief features. The Cordilleran highland is an effective barrier against the moderating climatic influence of the Pacific Ocean; and in consequence the great interior of the country has the extremes of high-latitude continental climate. In most of Canada outside the maritime provinces, southern Ontario, the southern half of the central provinces, and the coast of

British Columbia the frostless season does not exceed 100 days. On the northern margin of the cereal zone of west central Canada the summer days are considerably longer than they are in the United States. In spite of this advantage, however, there is a large part of northern Canada in which the growing season is so short as to discourage any general dependence upon the cereal crops; and much of the extreme north is tundra, only the surface of which thaws out during the brief summer. As in the high plains of the United States, the crops of the western prairie provinces frequently suffer from lack of rainfall.

CONSEQUENCES OF THE CHARACTER AND DISTRIBUTION OF SOILS. The glacier-scoured crystalline rocks of the Laurentian upland (Fig. 3) have, in general, insufficient soil for agriculture. Over large areas the surface is covered with a scanty soil capable of supporting only forests, which are interspersed with lakes, bogs, and numberless patches of bare and polished rock (Fig. 173). Isolated areas of considerable extent, such as the "clay belt" of northern Ontario, are known to have soils deep enough for tillage, yet their very isolation, coupled with climatic handicaps and poor drainage, causes their economic development to be slow. The principal regions of agricultural land in Canada are therefore in (1) the maritime provinces, (2) the St. Lawrence lowland and southern Ontario, (3) the southern part of the prairie provinces, and (4) the valleys of the Cordilleran and Pacific Coast regions. The most extensive of these regions is that of the prairie provinces, in which, however, the northward expansion of agriculture is limited by the shortness of the growing season. There is now some permanent agriculture north of Peace River (56°15′N.) in the Fort Vermillion district and the upper Mackenzie Valley, but it develops under the handicap of a menace from summer frosts.

All the occupied farm lands of Canada comprise only a little more than 7 per cent of the area of the Dominion. The comparable figure for the United States is 55 per cent. Some of the occupied farm land is, however, actually forest land devoted to the raising of neither crops nor livestock. The land devoted to field crops is only about $2\frac{1}{2}$ per cent of the area of the Dominion. The comparable figure for the United States is about 19 per cent. Nothing else could show more strikingly the slow development of regions with pronounced physical handicaps for agriculture, so long as cheap land in better situations remains available elsewhere. It is estimated by the Canadian Department of the Interior that only about 16 per cent of the total land area of the Dominion is suited to any future agricultural settlement. That is a little more than twice the area now occupied, but it is, of course, the more desirable half that has been occupied first. We may watch with interest the attempts of settlers to establish new farms on the distant, cold, and forested frontier of agriculture in Canada. They must face hardship and losses there in their

FIG. 173.—The glaciated surface of the Laurentian upland yields little but timber and furs; the glacially disturbed drainage with its lakes and falls offers large resources in waterpower. (*Courtesy of Ontario Department of Mines.*)

endeavor to make a living in the face of competition from regions with less hazardous climates, better soils, and more advantageous relations to markets. This they must do, moreover, in a period of restricted international trade, agricultural overproduction, and low prices.

CANADA'S AGRICULTURAL REGIONS WIDELY SEPARATED.    The southward extension of the Laurentian upland to the Great Lakes and the western Cordilleran highland region divide Canada's best agricultural lands into widely separated parts (Fig. 1). Between the farm lands of southern Ontario and those of Manitoba lies an expanse of nearly 800 miles of land, sparsely settled and almost unproductive of agricultural crops. Between the grain fields of Alberta and the farms or ranches of the Pacific Coast valleys is a wide mountain barrier. It is clear that Canadian agriculture is faced with a peculiar problem in transportation.

AGRICULTURE IN EASTERN CANADA.    That part of Canada which lies east of the Great Lakes contains about 70 per cent of the entire population of the country and 6 of the 10 largest cities of the Dominion. The produce of this region has easy access to the greatest domestic markets and those of Europe. The humid, short-summer type of continental climate is favorable to pasture; hay crops; and, among the cereals, oats. This combination of climate, crops, and markets has led to the development of dairying, particularly for the manufacture of butter and cheese (Figs. 93, 95, 96), which are of high quality and compete for the English markets. Only in the southern tip of peninsular Ontario is corn an important crop, and here only do swine approach the numbers per square mile found in the American corn belt (Fig. 88). As an adjunct to the dairy industry they are, however, fairly numerous throughout the St. Lawrence Valley.

Many of the farms in the maritime provinces, in eastern Quebec, and along the northern border of agricultural Ontario lie on the forest fringe. Limited areas of tillable land are interspersed among areas of rocky forest land and glacial swamps. The farmers use cut-over lands and woodlands as supplementary pastures for dairy cows, and their fields and meadows provide hay, potatoes, root crops, and oats for winter feeding of cows and food for the families. This also is the principal region of fur farming, nearly 80 per cent of such farms being either in or east of Ontario. The province of Quebec has a third of the total for Canada. The meager income from these farms of the forest fringe is supplemented further by fishing and fur trapping, where situation permits, and by the cutting of pulpwood and timber from the farm lands or as the farmer hires his services to companies engaged in forest exploitation. A considerable income is also derived from the tourist trade, since the woods and lakes of these areas are a readily accessible part of the great playgrounds of Canada.

In a few places where the rigorous conditions of continental climate are moderated by marine or lake influence, fruits are grown in commercial quantities. The Annapolis-Cornwallis Valley of Nova Scotia, the Montreal district, and the northern shores of Lakes Ontario and Erie are noted apple regions (Fig. 40). The Niagara Peninsula successfully produces less hardy fruits, particularly grapes and peaches.

AGRICULTURE IN THE PRAIRIE PROVINCES. The great expanses of the central prairie provinces are given over almost entirely to the cereals and to a limited amount of grazing (Fig. 18). On these rich soils and under relatively low rainfall, wheat, barley, and flaxseed, mainly spring-sown, provide crops that can stand the cost of shipment to the distant markets of the United States or of Europe, and oats provide grain for local feeding. It is in wheat that the interest of the people centers. Grain elevators dot the level landscape, and many of the villages are little more than houses clustered about the elevator, the railway station, and the country store.

Prior to the coming of the grain farmer, cattle and sheep grazed the open ranges of the prairie provinces. The ranges are now mainly divided into farms, except in the sections of low rainfall. Yet grazing continues on the rougher and drier lands, and meat-packing plants operate in some of the larger towns.

The northern and western margins of the spring-wheat region encroach upon the great forest lands. There also are many areas of light soils and of stump and brush lands that are better suited to pasture and hay production than to grain. Mixed farming with dairying is more common along this fringe than in the heart of the region. Creameries are numerous, and butter provides an exportable product that can be profitably taken to distant markets. The southern margin of the wheat region, in Alberta and Saskatchewan, encroaches upon the dry lands of the northern high plains. There settlement is sparse, and livestock ranches occupy more area than grain farms.

Perhaps, in connection with the pastoral industries, attention should again be called to the livestock range of the far northern tundra and its possibilities for the future. This region still is the home of countless caribou, which are declining in number. Eventually domesticated reindeer will replace them. It is estimated that the ultimate capacity of that vast area may be several times as many deer as are now in Alaska. Whether there will be a surplus of meat for export or an expanding population of Eskimo herdsmen will require the entire production cannot be well foreseen.

AGRICULTURE IN BRITISH COLUMBIA is confined mainly to limited mountain valleys and to the environs of Vancouver and Victoria. It is more like that of eastern Canada than that of the neighboring province of Alberta. The abundant rainfall and mild temperatures of the Fraser

River Valley and of Vancouver Island encourage dairying and the production of small fruits. In the Okanagan and other of the dry mountain valleys apples are grown, as in Washington, with the aid of irrigation. The settled lands are confined mainly to the southern portion of the province. The rough, dissected "dry belt" of the intermontane plateau is a cattle-grazing region of some importance, with incidental agriculture. Although some good land is found farther north, it is forested, and settlement is proceeding slowly.

## Fuel and Power in Canada

COAL. Canada is unfortunate in the geographic relation of her most densely peopled industrial district to her own coal fields. In peninsular Ontario the sedimentary rocks that underlie the surface include the earlier Paleozoics up to, but not including, those of the coal age, which lie to the southeast in Pennsylvania and to the west in Michigan. The industrial region of Ontario is therefore dependent upon coal imported from the rich fields south of Lake Erie.

Canada has, however, a large reserve of coal, three-fourths of which is lignite. Great areas of low-grade coal are found in the prairie provinces (Fig. 109), and it is mined for local consumption. Some of it approaches bituminous coal in quality. Valuable deposits of high-grade coals are found in three widely separated regions: (1) Nova Scotia, especially the far northeastern section near Sydney, and New Brunswick; (2) the southern Rocky Mountain margin of Alberta and British Columbia; and (3) Vancouver Island, in which the most used deposits are located in the southeast, near Nanaimo, where they are readily available for ocean shipment. From each of these three regions coal is exported to the adjacent districts of the United States which are without coal, and some· is exported as steamship fuel. The total coal production of Canada averages about 15 million tons per year, a little more than one-half the amount consumed in the country. Its value is, however, about equal to that of the nickel output of Canada but only one-third that of gold. It constitutes about one-tenth the value of all mineral substances produced in the country.

The Canadian output of petroleum and natural gas is relatively less important than that of coal. The larger part of the country being underlain by the ancient crystalline rocks of the Laurentian upland, it is not reasonable to suppose that either petroleum or coal will be found there. Small amounts of petroleum and gas are found in the older sedimentary rocks of New Brunswick and peninsular Ontario, but the quantity is negligible, and it is likely that deeper drilling would do no more than penetrate the still older and less productive rocks. The petroleum output of the country increased rapidly from 1½ million to about 7 million barrels between 1936 and 1938. This was due almost entirely to new wells in the Turner Valley area of southern Alberta, a part of the Rocky Mountain field. Even that great increase does no more than raise the output of all Canada to about the level of that of Montana, one of the smaller producing states, and it reaches less than a half of 1 per cent that of the entire United States. Traces of oil and gas are found also in the Mackenzie Valley, but they have no present importance because of their great distance north.

WATER POWER. Canada has large water powers both developed and potential. The developed powers, nearly 11 million horsepower, are almost two-fifths that of the entire United States. The St. Lawrence Valley and southern Ontario are as fortunate in their possession of water power as they are unfortunate in their lack of coal (Fig. 126). The two provinces Ontario and Quebec have an installed capacity of more than 6½ million horsepower—about four-fifths of all the developed power in Canada. This large water power is due to (1) the geological structure of the region and the interruptions of drainage due to glaciation, resulting in Niagara Falls and the many falls and rapids that fringe the Laurentian upland; (2) the excellent conditions of water storage found in the Great Lakes and in the numberless glacial lakes and swamps and in the forest floor of the Laurentian upland; (3) the abundant and well-distributed annual precipitation of eastern Canada. It is believed that Canada has for the future about three times as much water power as is now developed. Nearly two-thirds of these undeveloped powers are in Quebec and Ontario, and Manitoba and British Columbia have most of the remainder.

## Raw Materials and Manufacturing

IRON AND STEEL. The amount and distribution of the iron ores of Canada are, as in the case of coal, unfortunate for the industrial development of the country. In spite of the fact that the most valuable deposits of iron ore in the United States lie on the margin of the Laurentian upland (Lake Superior region), the known and available resources in similar situations on the Canadian side of the international boundary are almost negligible in quantity. A comparatively small quantity of Newfoundland ore is shipped to the coal of Cape Breton Island, Nova Scotia, and is smelted mainly at Sydney. Some of this ore is exported also to the United States and to Europe.

In British Columbia some small bodies of ore are mined and smelted with the local coal. This iron is, however, too far distant from the Canadian industrial centers to be of much significance to the national manufactures, though a market for it may develop in Japan. Blast furnaces in Ontario, at Sault Ste. Marie, Port Colborne, Hamilton, and some other points, are so situated that Lake Superior ore is easily obtained from the United States by boat. In general the iron and steel industries of Ontario employ both imported raw materials and fuel.

OTHER MINERAL INDUSTRIES of importance, most of which have been previously mentioned, are located in various parts of Canada. In the hill region of southeastern Quebec is asbestos; and in the Laurentian upland of Ontario are the nickel and copper deposits of Sudbury, the silver of Cobalt, and the even more valuable gold resources of the Porcupine, Red Lake, and other newly discovered gold fields. In British Columbia lead and copper are the most valuable metals, yet the amount produced is not large. Gold alone accounts for one-fourth the value of all mineral products.

FORESTS AN IMPORTANT BASIS OF INDUSTRY. The forests of Canada rank second only to the soil in value as a natural resource. About one-third of all the land of the Dominion is classed as forest land, but of this at least one-third may be considered unproductive. The general character and distribution of these forests has been previously described (Chaps. II, VIII). The quantity of timber that they originally contained and, indeed, their present value are not accurately known. It is certain that, although vast areas of forested land remain, much of the best timber has fallen under the axe or has been destroyed by fire. The advent of the paper-pulp industry has created a market for a large part of the Canadian forests that were not valuable for lumber. On the southern margin of the great northern forests, from Manitoba to eastern Quebec and in the maritime provinces, pulpwood is being cut. Much of it is taken by private corporations from vast leaseholds on crown lands under conservative conditions that promise a permanent industry. Of the better timber, eastern Canada now has but little for export, and hardwoods for certain industries are even now imported. The forests of British Columbia, however, produce lumber for export to the Orient, Great Britain, and other markets.

MANUFACTURING INDUSTRIES. Canada has made great industrial progress in recent years. The nature and location of the industries reflect (1) an abundance of agricultural raw materials requiring manufacture, (2) great forest resources, (3) the water powers of Ontario and Quebec, and (4) a protective tariff on many classes of manufactured wares.

The principal centers of manufacturing industry are in the upper St. Lawrence Valley and peninsular Ontario. Ontario alone, especially the cities north of Lakes Erie and Ontario, turns out one-half of all the manufactured wares of Canada. Ontario and Quebec together are to be credited with four-fifths of the total.

Figure 174 indicates the relative importance of the leading classes of manufacturing industries of Canada, measured in terms of the number of wage earners employed and their value products. Although the woodworking and paper industries employ more workers and yield a greater net value of products than any one other class of industry, their national importance is not so great as that of the several food-preparing industries combined. In the latter group the most important items are contributed by flour and gristmill products, slaughtering and meat packing, and the manufacture of dairy products.

It is not likely that Canadian manufactures of iron and steel, with their geographical handicaps arising from lack of both coal and ore, could compete with wares of similar sort from the United States, were it not for a protective tariff. Many such industries now established in Canada are branches of concerns located in the United States. This is notably true of automobile manufacture.

RELATIVE IMPORTANCE OF CANADIAN MANUFACTURING INDUSTRIES

Three Year Average, 1935-1937

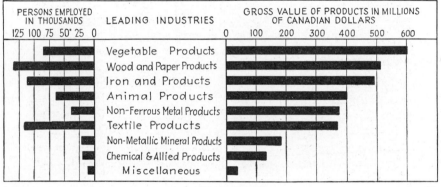

Fig. 174.

CANADIAN FISHERIES. About 8 out of every 1,000 persons in Canada are employed in some phase of the fishing or fish-preserving industry. The total products of the industry average nearly 40 millions of dollars per year, an amount considerably less than the value of the butter made in Canada. Nearly one-third of the total value of the Canadian fishery products is contributed by the salmon fisheries of the Pacific Coast. Including halibut and other fish caught on this coast, British Columbia is credited with nearly half the total value of the Dominion fisheries.

Next in importance are the lobster and cod fisheries of eastern Canada. Although cod are caught by Canadian fishermen on the Grand Banks, many are taken in the shore waters also, particularly in the Gulf of St. Lawrence. Lobsters and herring are the most valuable catch of the inshore fisheries, which employ many more men than do those of the offshore type. The value of the fish taken in the Great Lakes and in other inland waters of Canada is less than one-eighth that of the products of the salt-water fisheries.

Little more than one-third of the products of Canadian fisheries are required for domestic use. Efficient railway service permits fish to be sent fresh from both east and west into the interior, but the market is not large. The United States is the largest foreign market for fresh fish and takes about half the total Canadian exports. The United Kingdom, Europe, and Australia furnish the largest markets for canned salmon. Salt and dried cod and other varieties of cured and preserved fish are

Fig. 175.—Shipments of Canadian preserved fish awaiting transportation on the wharves at Halifax, Nova Scotia.

sent to many countries, particularly to the West Indies and South America (Fig. 175).

Furs and the Fur Trade. It has previously been noted that conditions of physical environment in the northern forests and tundra regions of Canada favor the growth and capture of fur-bearing animals. In more than half of Canada this is still the principal industry; the trading posts or "factories" of the Hudson's Bay Company are established at strategic points on the lakes and rivers as marketing points for the trappers, many of whom are Indians. Some of these posts have seen generations of service with but little change either in themselves or in the regions of which they are the centers. The total population of the trapping region is small, and its productiveness is slight in proportion to its great size. The sale value of the entire Canadian wild fur produced in 1936 (10½ million dollars) was, for example, hardly one-eighth the total value of the output of butter in the country. The value of the furs produced on farms is about two-thirds that of those taken from wild animals.

## Canada's Transportation Problem

CANADIAN WATERWAYS. The waterways of Canada have been of vital importance to the development of the country from its earliest history. The dense forests of the east were penetrable through the water route of the St. Lawrence. The Great Lakes led explorers to the far interior of the continent, and the streams of the Laurentian upland made the fur trade possible. So exclusively were the rivers the avenues of communication in the early settlements of eastern Canada that each inhabitant was granted land that had at least a narrow stream frontage. River transportation remains the sole means of communication in a large part of northern Canada. The canoe, the scow, the York boat, and the steamer are the carriers of people and goods on many hundreds of miles of waterways tributary to the Arctic Ocean and to Hudson Bay.

The most used waterways of Canada are, however, the St. Lawrence River and the Great Lakes. Owing to the estuarine character of the river it has, by some improvement, been made navigable for large ocean vessels as far as Montreal. Canals extend navigation for boats of 14-foot draught around the rapids and falls up to Lakes Ontario and Erie, beyond which Great Lakes transportation reaches to Port Arthur, 2,000 miles from the Atlantic. The usefulness of this and of the other waterways of Canada is greatly decreased by the long season during which they are closed by ice.

CANADIAN RAILWAYS. The problem involved in the connecting of the long, narrow, and interrupted strip of settled Canada from the Atlantic to the Pacific by means of railways has been previously mentioned. The construction of some of the Canadian railways has been so hazardous from the financial viewpoint that the Dominion government has felt called upon to do what private capital was afraid to risk. Railways constructed by the government, or taken over subsequently and united into the Canadian National Railways, now constitute more than half the entire mileage of the country. Most of the remaining mileage is comprised within the powerful Canadian Pacific system. The total length of railway line (about 43,000 miles) is only about one-sixth that of the United States. But it must be supported by a population that is only about one-twelfth that of the United States.

The difficulty of linking together the great expanses of Canada with their comparatively small populations is shown by the fact that whereas every 1,000 people in the United States must support about 2 miles of railway, the same number of Canadians must support about 3.8 miles. That is a large financial burden, and freight rates are high.

CANADIAN HIGHWAYS. The development of a system of highways in Canada is carried on in the face of difficulties much the same as those confronting the railway builders. There was in 1940, for example, no way to cross the country completely by automobile. The missing sections lay (1) in the region north of Lake Superior and (2) in the Rocky Mountains. It is likely that these gaps soon will be filled, but the cost of their construction through difficult and unsettled country is great. The total reported mileage of roads in Canada (exceeding 600,000 miles) is perhaps one-fourth, and the total extent of surfaced road (115,000 miles) about one-sixth, that of the United States. However, there are in the United States about 185 persons to support each mile of surfaced rural road, but in Canada less than 100 persons. These roads serve far more than the Canadian people, however, for they make the vacation lands of Canada accessible to the American visitor. In 1938 the tourist business of Canada was valued at nearly 270 million dollars, and two-thirds of that was derived from United States visitors who came by automobile.

## The Foreign Trade of Canada

THE DIRECTION OF CANADIAN TRADE. The geographic factors of greatest influence in Canadian trade are those creating dissimilarity between the provinces and giving rise to interprovincial trade. This, like the interstate trade in the United States, is much more important than the foreign trade. Second in importance is Canada's nearness to the United States. More than half Canada's imports come from the United States, and over a third of her exports come to this country (Fig. 176). Third in importance among the factors affecting the direction of Canadian trade are her political, economic, and geographic relationships with Great Britain. More than one-fourth the foreign trade is with the mother country, and nearly two-fifths of it within the British Empire.

THE CHARACTER OF CANADIAN FOREIGN TRADE. Until recent years Canada, although economically a young nation and a producer of raw materials and foods, had an unfavorable balance of trade. Expensive constructional materials and equipment required for the material development of the country caused the value of imports to exceed that of commodities exported. The extreme industrial effort of the war period of 1914–1918 and the great demand for Canadian foods changed this situation, and a favorable balance of trade is still maintained. The total value of foreign trade exceeds 2 billions of dollars.

The principal items imported into Canada are those required in industry: iron and steel, coal, raw cotton, wool, and silk. Sugar, fruits, and other foods that do not grow in Canadian climates are also important. Wheat is much the most valuable of Canadian exports. Next in importance are wood and wood products. Wheat and flour, wood, pulp, and paper combined comprise about one-half the total exports (Fig. 177).

CANADIAN PORTS. The importance of the port of Montreal in the commercial life of Canada has been noted. Through its harbor flows about one-fifth the total foreign trade of the Dominion. Doubtless the

### THE DIRECTION OF CANADA'S FOREIGN TRADE
Three Years Average 1936-1938

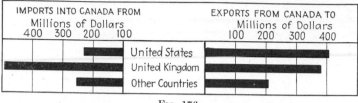

FIG. 176.

amount would be greater were it not for the handicap of winter ice. This difficulty is met by prolonged rail carriage into the ice-free ports of the east—Saint John, N. B., and Halifax, N. S. In part, also, the winter exports move in bond through the United States and out of ports as far south as Baltimore. In an effort to create a shorter rail route to get grain from the prairie provinces to a port for shipment to Europe, an

### PRINCIPAL ITEMS IN THE FOREIGN TRADE OF CANADA

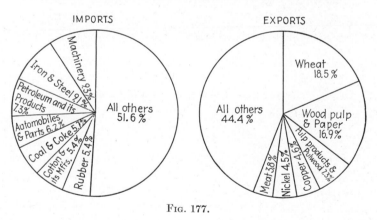

FIG. 177.

outlet was created at Fort Churchill on Hudson Bay. The government built an extension of the Canadian National Railway across 510 miles of Manitoba forests and swamps and constructed grain-storage and loading facilities at the port. However, the bay or its approaches are blocked by ice within a few weeks after the wheat harvest is over; and as yet only a small fraction of the grain exported is handled through it.

Vancouver is the principal Pacific port of Canada. It has a large
and well-protected harbor, is well provided with grain-handling facilities, and has a good position with respect to both transpacific and Panama
Canal traffic. It shares in the lumber business characteristic of the Puget
Sound ports of Washington. Prince Rupert, the northern Pacific terminus
of the Canadian National Railway, has but a very small trade. It is the
most northerly of all American ports served by transcontinental railway,
and it was expected to profit by this fact. However, the port is so far

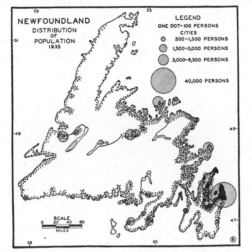

Fig. 178.—In Newfoundland most of the people live near the coast and fishing is their
principal occupation. (*Map by Earl B. Shaw, Econ. Geog., July,* 1938.)

from the interior and its immediate hinterland so poorly developed that
it is, in fact, much isolated. The foreign trade that passes through
Vancouver far exceeds that of Saint John but is hardly one-half that of
Montreal.

## Newfoundland

A LAND OF FISHERMEN.    Newfoundland was settled by fishermen,
and fishing still is the principal occupation of the people. It is a land of
deeply indented shores, with rocky inlets and peninsulas, a land of chill
and foggy coasts and an unsettled interior covered with taiga forest.
Most of the people are grouped in fishing hamlets on the bays of almost
the entire island margin (Fig. 178). Settlement is most dense in the
southeast near the city of St. John's and near the iron-mining district
of Bell Island. It is least dense in the far north. The fishermen are sometimes farmers also, but the extent of cleared land and tilled farm land
is but a small fraction of 1 per cent of the total area. Foodstuffs are the
largest imports.

As in eastern Canada, water powers make it possible to utilize the forests in the manufacture of pulp. Papermaking ranks next after fishing in the number of persons employed in it and first in the value of exports. The paper is sold principally in England. Minerals are found at several points on the island's margin, but the interior is only poorly explored. The most important mineral resource is the large deposit of hematite from which ore is supplied to Nova Scotia, to eastern United States, and some even to England.

The ice-scoured and mountainous coast of Labrador, which is politically a part of Newfoundland, is treeless except in the south and belongs to the realm of the tundra. Fishermen and Indians make up the sparse population of the south, and Eskimos the larger part of that of the more mountainous north.

SELECTED REFERENCES

BRUCE, E. L. "Mineral Deposits of the Canadian Shield," Toronto, 1933.
CRAIG, R. D. The Forest Resources of Canada, *Econ. Geog.*, Vol. 2 (1926), pp. 394–413.
HURD, W. B., and T. W. GRINDLEY. "Agriculture, Climate, and Population of the Prairie Provinces of Canada," Dominion Bureau of Statistics, Ottawa, 1931.
MACKINTOSH, W. A. The Laurentian Plateau in Canadian Economic Development, *Econ. Geog.*, Vol. 2 (1926), pp. 537–549.
MILLER, G. J., and A. E. PARKINS. "Geography of North America," Chaps. 22–27, New York, 1934.
PATTON, M. J. The Waterpower Resources of Canada, *Econ. Geog.*, Vol. 2 (1926), pp. 168–196.
RANDALL, J. R. Agriculture in the Great Clay Belt of Canada, *Scott. Geog. Mag.*, Vol. 56 (1940), pp. 12–28.
"The Canada Yearbook," The Dominion Bureau of Statistics, Ottawa, annual.

# PART II. THE WORLD OUTSIDE THE UNITED STATES AND CANADA

# Chapter XVIII. Middle America

REGIONAL ELEMENTS. The lands bordering on the Gulf of Mexico and the Caribbean Sea—which may be called Middle America—are of great importance to the United States, partly because of their situation with respect to the Panama Canal and vital American interests there and also because of our growing commerce with that part of the world. It is a region different in many ways from the United States and Canada and one having striking contrasts within itself.

The countries of Middle America include Mexico, the Central American republics, Colombia, Venezuela, and the West Indies. They have a total area nearly two-thirds that of the United States and combined populations of more than 50 millions. The average density of population is about 27 per square mile, a little more than half that of the United States. As in the United States, the population is very unevenly distributed. British Honduras, for example, has only about 7 persons per square mile; the island of Barbados (also British) has more than 1,100. The reasons for these great differences are many—landforms, climatic differences, poor drainage, soil contrasts, disease, economic isolation, political history, governmental instability, and many others. They are not, in the main, the same kinds of contrasts in density that are found in the United States, *viz.*, great centers of commerce and manufacture in contrast with the rural South or the arid livestock-ranching districts. With the exception of northern Mexico, no large part of Middle America is arid, but neither are there many large cities or great centers of manufacture. The population is principally rural and lives from the land.

PHYSICAL STRUCTURE. In its broader features Middle America is made up of mountainous lands. It is a part of the zone of instability in the earth's crust extending along the western sides of both the American continents and into the Caribbean Sea. It is a region of numerous earthquakes and several active volcanoes. The mountains of northern Mexico are, in a sense, southward continuations of the western highlands of the United States, and they trend southward to converge near Mexico City. Beyond that, the mountains have more nearly an east-west trend except

315

in southern Colombia. Some of them appear as the highlands of southern Mexico, Central America, and coastal Colombia and Venezuela. Others fringe the basin of the Caribbean Sea on the north and appear as the mountainous cores of Jamaica, Puerto Rico, and others of the Antilles.

Bordering the mountains, or included between them, are extensive plains, some at high elevations and others at low. Broadest are the interior plains of the Mexican highland, or plateau. Similar, but smaller and more dissected, are the highlands of Honduras and other sections of Central America. The lowland plains fronting the Pacific are mainly narrow, but those facing the Gulf of Mexico and the Caribbean Sea are broader. These include the coastal lowlands of eastern Mexico and Nicaragua, the northern valleys of Colombia, and the Maracaibo Basin of Venezuela. The most extensive lowlands are of two different types. One is a portion of the sea floor, broadly arched and slightly uplifted but not contorted into mountains. It includes the peninsula of Yucatan and the rolling surface of all Cuba except the mountains of the southeast. The other is the broad depression now occupied by the alluvial plains of the Orinoco River in Venezuela. Elevations and relief features in Middle America range from low delta plains, barely above sea level, to plateaus above 5,000 feet and to high peaks reaching three times that figure or more.

CLIMATIC CONTRASTS. In a region so extended and of such great contrast in physical features, climatic contrasts are inevitable. In general, the area lies in those latitudes where the tropical savanna climates prevail, with their hot and rainy summers and their warm but relatively dry winters. Uniformity in this respect is prevented by the relation between the persistent northeast trade winds and the relief features of the land surface. The broader lowlands do, in general, have savanna climate, but east-facing lowlands that are closely flanked by mountains have rainfall nearly all months of the year, owing to the forced ascent of the winter trade winds. These lowlands have rain in all seasons and partake of the characteristics of the tropical rainforest type of climate. On west-facing coasts, on the contrary, the descending air of the winter trade winds brings little rain, and their dryness is interrupted only by summer thundershowers. This is true of both Central America and the more mountainous islands. East coasts, therefore, tend to be rainy, and west coasts much drier. Only northwestern Mexico, however, is truly arid. This is because it lies on the west of a broad land area and under the . influence of the persistent high atmospheric pressures that are responsible for the deserts of southern Arizona and California, of which the Mexican desert is really a part.

A further modification results from the affect of altitude alone. The plateau climates generally are not only more dry, because they lie behind sheltering eastern mountain rims, but cooler. It is on account of this advantage that several of the political capitals and other important cities in the Middle American countries are located in the mountains or plateau uplands. The change in temperature is at the rate of about 3°F. per 1,000 feet of altitude, and on this basis it is common in tropical America to recognize three principal zones of altitudinal climate—the hot lands, which extend from sea level up to about a half mile of elevation; the temperate lands, from there up to 6,000 or 6,500 feet; and the cold lands, which lie at still higher elevations and, on some of the higher mountains, continue up into the zone of perpetual snow.

EARTH RESOURCES. Middle America offered to its settlers a great variety of natural resources in plants, soils, and minerals, and these have contributed to present differences in types and densities of settlement. The natural vegetation ranges from rainforest on the eastern lowlands through open savanna forest and grasslands on the west slopes and plateaus to shrub vegetation in the driest sections.

The soils vary also in accordance with the climates and vegetation types under which they have evolved and the nature of the materials from which they are derived. Some areas on the rainy coasts are characterized by poor and badly leached tropical red soils, but others are fresh alluvial soils of considerable fertility. On the savanna lowlands are some fertile grassland soils. Others derive their fertility from the decomposition of limestones. In the mountains some extensive areas of slope land have thin and rocky soils and are quite untillable, while near by are fertile basins filled with alluvium or deep accumulations of volcanic ash. These differences help to explain some of the sudden and pronounced changes in land use encountered.

Middle America furnishes also a striking variety of mineral products— iron and manganese ores in Cuba; petroleum in northern Venezuela, Colombia, and eastern Mexico; silver and other metals in the highlands. Some of these have been exploited for centuries and bear a relation to the oldest of settlements; others have been developed only recently and have clustered about them only the newest and most impermanent of population groups.

CULTURAL ELEMENTS. Among the most striking contrasts between parts of Middle America are those based upon population type and stage of cultural development. These, in turn, depend much upon differences in extent of European occupation and cultural history. The island portions, being more easily penetrated, were almost completely taken over by Europeans, especially the Spanish, English, and French, and their languages and customs were implanted there. Also, they largely exterminated the Indian populations and replaced them with African slaves as laborers. The continental highlands, on the other hand, were penetrated only by the Spanish, who imposed their language and some of their culture upon the Indians but never displaced them from their mountain strongholds. A majority of the island peoples of today are, therefore, of negro or mixed negro and white racial stocks, except in Cuba and Puerto Rico, where the white element is dominant. In the mainland countries, however, from Mexico to Venezuela, the people are mainly Indian with many white or mixed Indian and white elements. The white population generally is in political dominance, but in some of the more isolated sections there are many primitive Indians who speak little or no Spanish.

It has been noted that the population of Middle America is dominantly agricultural. The agricultural produce is extremely varied, ranging from tropical rainforest crops, such as bananas and cacao, to middle-latitude products like corn and livestock. Much attention is focused on a few of these, especially sugar, bananas, and coffee, because of their commercial importance. But these are not everywhere the staple crops. These latter are more often corn and beans, vegetables and root crops—the food supplies of the people—and most of them enter commerce little if at all. The settlements of the people are scattered over the lands that can produce food. The nature of their settlements and the emphasis upon one or another agricultural system depends much on the physical characteristics of the locality and the cultural tradition that the people have inherited.

The many basic differences between parts of Middle America make it desirable to subdivide it for fuller consideration. This might be done on the basis of various of the physical or cultural elements. However, it may serve as well as any if division here be made, in terms merely of location and political units, into Mexico, the West Indies, Central America, and northern South America.

## Mexico

CULTURAL FEATURES. Mexico is more than three times as large as France, but it has hardly half as many people and not a quarter as much tilled land. It has large mineral resources and a position fronting on both the great commercial oceans. Yet its agriculture does not supply sufficient food for its own people; its mines yield far below their possibilities; its foreign trade is small; and all its manufacturing establishments do not employ more people than those of Boston and the eastern Massachusetts industrial region alone. Some, but not all of these facts may be explained by reference to the primitive stage of economic development of a large part of its Indian population and by noting the unfortunate trend and turbulence of much of its political and economic history. Quite as significant are certain physical handicaps to its development.

THE MEXICAN PEOPLE AND GOVERNMENT.   Only 10 or 15 per cent of the people are white; 30 to 40 per cent are Indians of many different tribes and languages; and 40 to 50 per cent are of mixed blood. Few of the Indians are educated, and the larger part are a docile, unambitious people who live in agricultural villages of primitive construction and till the land. Many of the middle class—artisans, tradespeople, and minor officials—are recruited from the population of mixed blood. The descendants of old Spanish families are the educated higher classes. Formerly they held much of the land in great estates and controlled the govern-

FIG. 179.

ment. Under the modern political system most of these estates are being broken up, and new holdings are being created which are allotted to the villages for communal tillage or to small farmers.

In fact the recent political changes in Mexico are responsible for radical alteration of the whole system of ownership of the land, minerals, and other resources. What may be the effects of these changes is hard to foretell. Doubtless they will have far-reaching influence, for they have already brought about changes in the appearance of the rural scene. Certain things, however, they can change but little. These are the features of climate and surface configuration and the forms of agriculture and resource exploitation that are distributed directly in response to them.

THE PHYSICAL REGIONS OF MEXICO.   Mexico may be divided into many sections that differ in features of climate, landforms, and modes of settlement and use. For the sake of brevity, these may be grouped into six of great contrast, as shown in Fig. 179.

*The Sonoran desert* includes the peninsula of Lower California and the arid lowlands bordering the Gulf of California. Settlement in this region is sparse, and most of it is restricted to livestock ranching. In a few localities, especially toward the south, short streams from the western Sierra Madre provide irrigation water, and crops are grown, including corn, cotton, and others for domestic use. Many tons of winter vegetables,

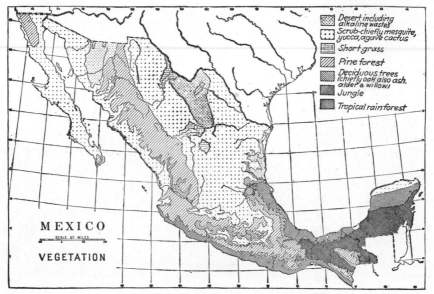

FIG. 180.—The cross-lined areas (forests) show where the rain chiefly falls. (*From the Geographical Review, published by the American Geographical Society of New York, Vol.* 11, *p.* 218.)

especially tomatoes, green peppers, and peas, are also raised in this district for sale on the United States market. The largest area of tilled land is in the extreme north, the most arid section. This is where the great delta of the Colorado River provides rich alluvial soil, irrigated from the river itself. It is continuous with the Imperial Valley of California and produces some of the same crops, especially cotton and alfalfa.

*The dry northern plateau-basins* region is the largest in Mexico. It opens northward into western Texas and New Mexico, which it resembles in some respects. East and west it is fringed by highlands. Internally it is a broad plateau, broken by escarpments, short blocklike mountain ranges, and volcanic ridges into many broad valleys and shallow basins. Its climate is generally dry, and some of the basins are deserts (Fig. 180). In the extreme north along the Rio Grande and in certain of the central basins, irrigation water is available. Important towns are located there and also agricultural villages, which produce food-supply crops of corn, beans, vegetables, and nearly two-thirds of Mexico's commercial cotton crop. Other important towns are related to the mineral resources, especially silver, for some of the basin ranges are highly mineralized, and in one of the basins is the best coal resource of the country. However, the general population is sparse, and cattle ranching is the most widespread use of the land.

*The Sierra Madre.* The eastern and western margins of the Mexican plateau are elevated and dissected by streams into belts of mountains. The western, especially, is high, rough, and of complicated geological structure. They are known as the "western" and "eastern Sierra Madre," respectively, and both get higher toward the south. The slopes of both ranges are partly forested, but their valleys are narrow and have little agricultural land. The rainy slope of the eastern range furnishes some water power, and both yield mineral ores.

*The Central Plateau.* Not only do the mountain rims of the northern plateau increase in height toward the south, but they also converge and meet. Between the southern mountains lies a narrower and higher plateau broken by volcanic peaks and ranges into basins that are smaller and more pocketlike than those of the north. These generally are floored with deposits of volcanic ash and alluvium, and they include the beds of former lakes. Because of its great elevation (5,000 to 9,000 feet above sea level) the plateau has a much cooler climate than the adjacent coastal lowlands, winter frosts being common, and occasional snows occurring in the higher basins. Because of its lower latitude it has a longer rainy season in summer and more rain than the northern plateau. The bordering mountains are well watered; their higher portions are forested; and they yield water supplies for irrigation and for power generation.

This region is the most densely peopled of any in Mexico. Agricultural villages are distributed thickly over the basins, and it includes most of the industrial towns and also the metropolis and capital of the country (Fig. 181). Mexico City, with more than a million population, lies near the southern and highest point of the triangular plateau, hemmed in by snow-capped ranges and volcanic peaks. In and about it are manufacturing centers for textiles, foodstuffs, and many other products. In the plateau ranges also are mineral ores, the occasion for the development of silver-mining centers, such as Pachuca. The greater part of the population, however, lives from the land. Corn and beans are the principal food-supply crops, but the urban markets give a commercial outlet for wheat, dairy products, and fresh fruits and vegetables. Although the plateau is not arid, supplementary irrigation is widely practiced, and some crops, such as wheat and alfalfa, grow throughout the winter. The drier lands are commonly used to grow maguey, the species of Agave used to produce pulque, the alcoholic drink in general use. Occasional dry years and a shortage of irrigation water bring great hardship to the rural population, many of whom have little beyond bare necessities.

Although the plateau has superior advantages in many respects, it is handicapped in its relation to the regions beyond it. Routes to the

Fig. 181.—A mountain basin, or "bolson," in the plateau of Mexico. The town, the intensively tilled floor and piedmont slopes of the basin, and the mountain rim are characteristic features. (*Photograph by H. S. Sterling.*)

north are open; but toward the south and the ports of the Atlantic and Pacific, transportation is difficult because of mountain barriers.

*The Southern Slopes and Highlands.* South and west of the plateau rim is an area of mountains and inaccessible valleys, ending in a narrow coastal lowland. It has a bold coastal outline with few good harbors and few connections with the plateau. Its climate is hot and humid in the summer, but the winters are dry. Agriculture is restricted to the narrow valleys, and the farmers have almost no market outlet. Agriculture is, therefore, mainly self-sufficing.

*The eastern coastal lowland* is wider and more accessible than that of the west. Its northern portion is similar to the adjacent coast of Texas and includes cotton and sugar fields and grazing lands. In it also are the famous petroleum fields of Tampico and Tuxpam, which were for a time the most productive outside the United States.

The southern part of the lowland extends from the principal port of Vera Cruz eastward, where it broadens into the undulating plains of Yucatan. It is prevailingly hot and humid, and its products are mainly those of tropical agriculture and the forests. In the drier sheltered valleys coffee is grown, and cattle are grazed in open forest lands and savannas. On the alluvial soils of the coastal districts bananas, cacao, and sugar are grown as commercial crops. The most important of the commercial staples, however, is *henequen*, the coarse, cheap fiber used in great

Fig. 182.—The broad fleshy leaves of henequen furnish the principal fiber used for binder twine. Henequen is grown in plantations in the scrub and jungle region of northern Yucatan. See Fig. 180. (*U.S. Department of Agriculture.*)

quantity as binder twine in the grain harvests of all the world. Henequen is produced from one of the species of Agave which finds particularly favorable environment in northwestern Yucatan (Fig. 182). Here the undulating plains are thin-soiled and underlain by a porous limestone. The summer rainfall is about 30 inches, but the underground drainage is so complete that the land has some of the aspects of aridity, to which this crop is well adapted. It is grown in extensive plantations; the fiber is extracted by machinery in small mills and exported through the ports of Campeche and Progreso, mainly to the United States.

## The West Indies

PRINCIPAL ISLANDS AND GROUPS OF ISLANDS. The West Indies include (1) the Greater Antilles: Cuba, Hispaniola, Puerto Rico, and

Jamaica; (2) the Bahamas; and (3) the Lesser Antilles, consisting of a number of groups of small islands. It has been noted previously that these islands have a common climatic situation but that they are different in other respects. Some are mountainous, and others low plains of coral or sea-bottom limestone. Some are dominantly negro, others white. Some are independent republics; others are dependencies of European countries or the United States. One other thing they have in common: On practically all of them sugar cane is either the dominant source of income

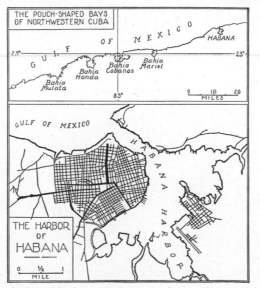

Fig. 183.—The pouch-shaped harbor of Habana is only one of many on the coast of Cuba.

or at least a very important crop. Only a few of the more important islands may be considered more fully.

## CUBA

THE ISLAND.    Cuba is as large as Ohio and in length nearly equals the distance from New York to Chicago. The greater part of it is an undulating plain with occasional hills, ridges, or groups of hills, the latter especially in the west. Only the southeast is mountainous. Its climate is of the savanna type, the long, hot, humid summers being relieved by cooler, but frostless, winters having light rain and a high proportion of clear, bright days. The original vegetation was mainly woodland, with some open spaces and grasslands on sandy, thin-soiled, or ill-drained lands. In large part the forests have been cleared to make way for agriculture. The soils are of several types, but the most valued are red, brown, or black clays derived mainly from the weathering of limestones. The best of them are well drained by seepage downward into the porous limestones and are easily tilled. The proportion of the island that is capable of tillage is high, and there is more potential farm land than there is in the island of Java in the East Indies, which supports a population ten times greater. The long coastline of Cuba is peculiar in having many deep, spacious, and pouch-shaped harbors (Fig. 183). Ports are numerous.

Of the total Cuban population of more than 4 millions, about two-thirds are classed as white. Most of the people are agricultural, but there

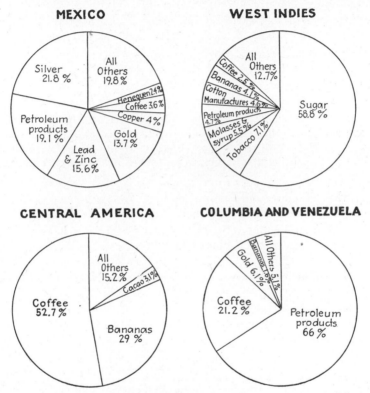

FIG. 184.—The principal exports from each of the four subdivisions of the middle American region are in striking contrast.

are several large towns; there are seven cities of more than 75,000 each, and more than one-eighth the total population lives in the capital city of Habana alone. Although the island is dominantly Spanish in language, customs, and architecture, it is greatly influenced by its close proximity to the United States. Financial investments and corporate management have come largely from that source. From it come two-thirds of Cuba's imports, and 80 per cent of the Cuban exports are sold there.

SUGAR-CANE PRODUCTION. The agricultural crops of Cuba are many. Food-supply crops include corn, vegetables, and fruits, and many cattle are raised also. But, unlike that of Mexico, the agriculture of Cuba is highly commercial, several important crops being raised for export (Fig. 184). Of these the sugar cane is dominant. Its products of sugar and molasses usually constitute about 80 per cent of all the exports of the island. This is, in part, a reflection of a very favorable physical environment. In part, also, it is the result of a large sugar market in the United States, the impetus given to sugar production by the introduction of United States capital and management and by a favored position under American import tariffs. Great agricultural specialization carries with it a great economic danger as well as benefits. Depression in the American market demand, shift to other sources of sugar supply, or increases in the tariff brings disaster to the Cuban sugar growers.

Most of the sugar cane is grown on great estates of hundreds or even several thousands of acres. Some is produced also on smaller independent farms and sold to the sugar mills. The great estates are distributed throughout the sugar-growing sections of the island, particularly the central portion, and are linked by roads and rail lines with the ports that are their several outlets. The typical estate is divided into blocks of a few tens of acres each, and these are farmed by tenants, called *colonos*, who live in simple palm-thatched houses placed singly or in groups near the fields for which their inhabitants are responsible. Each house has its garden plot, and the estate is likely to have other land devoted to minor crops, woodlands, and pasture for the grazing of oxen and other livestock. The cane fields are separated by wagon roads which lead to narrow-gauge railroads, and these in turn focus upon the great *central*, or sugar mill, which is the industrial heart of the estate (Fig. 185).

The ground is prepared for planting by plowing and harrowing. If new land is to be used, it must first be cleared of its timber and brush. Cane is planted by placing sections of cane stalks in furrows and covering them. The new crops spring up from buds at the joints of the stalk. Planting may be done in the autumn at the close of the rainy season or in the spring just before the next rainy season sets in. In Cuba a large part of the cane is not planted each year but springs up from buds on the stubble of the recently cut cane. This is called the "ratoon crop," and from three to six or more ratoon crops may be had from one planting, although the yields of the later crops usually are much decreased, and eventually the field is plowed and replanted. The young plants must be kept free of weeds and usually require a year or a little more to come to maturity.

The winter is the harvest season. From December to April inclusive the cooler and drier weather induces a higher sugar content in the cane, makes the heavy labor of cutting cane and stripping off its leaves more endurable, enables the heavy carts to traverse fields and dirt roads with less difficulty, and permits cutting operations with less damage to the stubble and hence to the succeeding ratoon crop. It also reduces the rate of fermentation in the exposed ends of the cut cane, which saves losses in the sugar mill. An acre of good cane yields 20 to 25 tons, from the juice of which 2 to 3 tons of sugar is extracted at the *central*. There it is reduced by evaporation and dried in centrifugal machines, into a soft sugar with a by-product of molasses. Most of the Cuban sugar

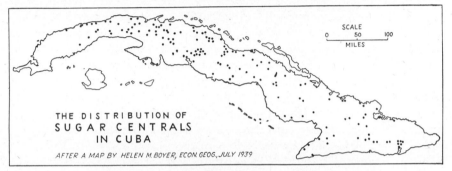

THE DISTRIBUTION OF
SUGAR CENTRALS
IN CUBA

*AFTER A MAP BY HELEN M. BOYER, ECON. GEOG., JULY 1939*

Fig. 185.

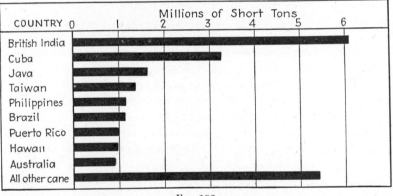

**WORLD'S IMPORTANT CANE SUGAR PRODUCERS**
Three Year Average 1936-1938

Fig. 186.

goes to the world's markets in this raw form, but about one-eighth of it is refined into granulated sugar before it leaves the island. There are about 160 sugar mills in Cuba, and their produce of nearly 3 million tons gives it first place among the commercial cane-sugar producers of the world (Fig. 186). Its output is far exceeded by that of India, but Indian sugar is almost entirely of low grade for home consumption.

OTHER CROPS. Just west of Habana is a small area about 90 miles long and 10 miles wide having localities with sandy soil underlain by red clays. These are famous for their production of aromatic tobaccos used in the manufacture of expensive cigars. This and other minor districts grow sufficient to make tobacco the second in value among all Cuba's exports. Some of it leaves the island in the manufactured form of cigars.

Other agricultural products of importance in the list of Cuban exports include tropical fruits and winter vegetables, especially bananas, pineapples, grapefruit, and others, sent fresh to the United States market. Their value is small compared to that of the sugar exports or even tobacco. The crops grown for home consumption are many, including corn, beans, and vegetables. Cuba has also a large livestock industry. Cattle raising, both for meat animals and for work cattle, is particularly important. There are more cattle than people in Cuba, whereas in the United States, by comparison, there are twice as many people as cattle.

MINERAL PRODUCTS. In the southeastern highland of Cuba are ancient rocks that include valuable mineral ores. Those most exported are copper, iron, and manganese. The importance of the latter with respect to steel manufacture in eastern United States has been noted. The iron ores are conveniently located near the sea, and the reserves are considerable. Exports of these ores vary greatly with market demand, and their average value is hardly 3 per cent that of sugar.

## HAITI AND THE DOMINICAN REPUBLIC

These two unfortunate republics constitute the island of Hispaniola, second largest of the West Indies. The people of Haiti are largely negro with an admixture of Indian and French blood, and the official language is French. The population of the Dominican Republic is largely mulatto, with Spanish blood and language.

The island is mountainous, but there are extensive cultivable lands. The Dominican, or northeastern, side is much more rainy. Its mountain slopes and exposed valleys are hot and humid, but the leeward slopes of mountains and sheltered valleys are less rainy. The drier climate is characteristic also of the whole western, or Haitian, side of the island. These differences are reflected in the order of relative importance of the principal exports of the two republics. In the Dominican list the order is sugar and molasses, cacao and coffee. In that of Haiti it is coffee, cotton, sugar, and sisal (a crop closely related to the Mexican henequen).

Agriculture occupies almost the entire populations, and practically all the exports are of agricultural origin. The islands are believed to have mineral resources of some variety, but lack of capital, lack of initiative, and the insecurities of unstable government have caused them to be almost entirely undeveloped.

## PUERTO RICO

This island, like Hawaii, is a territory of the United States. It is hardly three-fourths the size of Connecticut, but it has a rapidly increasing population of nearly 2 millions. Two-thirds of the people are classed as white, the remainder being negroes and mulattoes. The island is mountainous, less than half being under cultivation. Yet the population is dominantly agricultural, and the density of population is more than 525 per square mile of the entire area. This in itself constitutes the most serious problem of Puerto Rico.

The commercial agriculture of the island is concerned primarily with products of the same kind as those exported from Cuba, and most

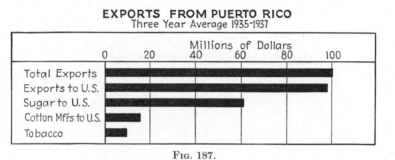

EXPORTS FROM PUERTO RICO
Three Year Average 1935-1937

FIG. 187.

of them are sent to the United States (Fig. 187). Pressure of population on the land requires the use of even the hill and mountain slopes for food-supply crops, and some high hills are cultivated almost to their summits. The value of the sugar, molasses, alcohol, and rum exported is more than two-thirds the total exports. Sugar fields occupy the coastal lowlands and broader valleys. On the north and east the crop is grown under ample rainfall, but on the south and west it requires supplementary irrigation. Other export crops are tobacco, some coffee, and fruits. Minerals are not abundant, although a little manganese is mined. Manufactures are principally hand products, such as wearing apparel and cigars.

The Virgin Islands, which lie immediately east of Puerto Rico, also are United States possessions, but they are of much greater value in naval defense than for their economic products.

## THE BRITISH WEST INDIES

These include Jamaica and Trinidad—large islands—the Bahamas, Barbados, several of the Leeward Islands and Windward Islands, and some others. Jamaica has more than a million people, most of whom are colored. Barbados is very densely populated. Their products are almost entirely agricultural and include mainly the crops of the rainy tropics—sugar cane, bananas, cacao, and coconuts. Bananas constitute more than half the exports of Jamaica, and that island usually is one of the largest producers, but its principal market is now in the United Kingdom. In some years the crop is severely damaged by hurricane winds; for example, high winds and heavy rains in November, 1939, are reported to have destroyed at least four-fifths of the crop for the year following. However, it was in Jamaica that large banana plantations were first successfully established, and the English-speaking Jamaica negroes perform much of the labor on banana plantations in the neighboring countries also. Barbados has been a sugar producer since its earliest settlement. Trinidad exports sugar, cacao, and coconuts, but it also yields petroleum and asphalt. The latter is a natural residue of ancient petroleum seepage. It occurs there in a "lake," or reservoir, which slowly fills from below as the hardened crust is removed from the top.

There are several good harbors among the British West Indies, the best of which is the important naval base at Kingston, Jamaica. The exports of these islands go more largely to the British Isles than elsewhere, but the imports come increasingly from the United States.

## Central America

Central America is made up of six small republics—Guatemala, Nicaragua, Salvador, Honduras, Costa Rica, Panama, and the little colony of British Honduras. Like Mexico the whole region includes hot and rainy eastern lowlands, widest in Nicaragua; a central highland or plateau, much narrower than in Mexico; and drier western slopes. Most of the people live either on the western slopes or on the plateau. The entire population of Central America is less than 8 million, and 3 million live in Guatemala alone. Of the several countries only Salvador lies wholly on the western slopes, and only British Honduras wholly on the eastern lowland. It is in some degree a reflection of the climatic conditions that Salvador has the greatest density of population per square mile (124) and British Honduras the lowest (7). The people of all the countries are predominantly Indian and of mixed blood. Railways in all the countries combined are little more than 3,000 miles. They are supplemented by some modern highways, but these have not yet penetrated the countries thoroughly, and many districts, both of the coastal lowlands and of the interior highlands, have but little contact with the outside. The eastern lowlands yield some mahogany and other timbers, and the highlands produce some minerals, especially gold. Yet these are relatively small items in the list of exports.

The people mainly are agricultural, but most of the crops produced are for their own subsistence—corn, beans, vegetables, and fruits. The open forests and grassy slopes of the highlands and west coast support many cattle, and other livestock are raised also. But a commercial cattle industry is hampered by political instability, lack of transportation, and the cattle pests and diseases prevalent in tropical America. The important export staples of agriculture are only two—bananas and coffee.

THE BANANA INDUSTRY IN THE CARIBBEAN REGION. The extension of banana plantations and the organization of the banana trade constitute one of the best examples of modern business methods applied on a large scale to tropical industry. The crop is widely grown in nearly all world regions of rainforest climate as a source of local food, but only in the Caribbean region is it grown commercially on a large scale. This results from the association of several factors both physical and economic.

The banana plant grows, somewhat like a tulip, from an offshoot produced at the bulbous base of a parent plant. It matures and produces its one stem of bananas in a year or a little more and then is cut down, a new plant taking its place from the buds at its base. It is grown most abundantly in regions having continuously high temperatures, an average annual rainfall of 60 to more than 100 inches, and only a short dry season, if any. Because the plant is top-heavy it is easily blown down, and a whole crop may be destroyed by hurricane winds. This tends to restrict its planting in the West Indies and has encouraged the migration of the industry to the west and south shores of the Caribbean, where these violent storms are seldom experienced. The rapid vegetative growth of the plant requires soils of natural fertility and good drainage. These are supplied by the alluvial lands at the bases of the Central American highlands.

The fruit is perishable and heavy and must be transported rapidly to as near a market as possible. The great market for bananas is in eastern United States and Canada. To develop the market and to supply it with fruit has been the objective of the several companies engaged in this business. This has required the organization of special car services and storage facilities in the United States; the provision of a unique form of ocean shipping; the purchase of large blocks of land, their clearing and planting; the building of wharves, plantation railways, roads, canals, villages, hospitals; and many other adjuncts to the business. Of all the possible banana lands in the world those of the Caribbean region are nearest, but these forested lowlands were sparsely peopled, mainly by Indians. Labor had to be brought in; problems of agriculture solved; and systems of planting, tilling, and cutting for shipment perfected. The larger share of this work has been done by one corporation, the United Fruit Company, and it does the larger part of the business that moves about 60 million bunches of bananas into the United States per year.

The producing region is not continuous along the Caribbean Coast but is found in localities where there are good soils that can be reached by short railroads from one of the many ports. The lowlands of southern Mexico and the narrow plain of northern Honduras are most productive. The broad coastal plain of Nicaragua might appear to have the largest potential banana area, but much of it is ill-drained, and the good lands are so far inland as to be inaccessible. The relative importance of the several producing countries, as measured by their exports, is shown by Fig. 188.

COFFEE IN THE CARIBBEAN REGION. The coffee of the Caribbean countries is grown mainly in sheltered valleys of the highlands and on the western slopes where cooler weather and dry seasons are more

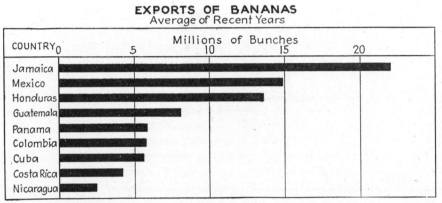

FIG. 188.

pronounced than on the eastern lowland. It is, for example, the only important export of Salvador. Other producing districts are the highlands of southwestern Guatemala, western Nicaragua, and the San José district of Costa Rica. These are also the areas of greatest population in those same countries. Some of the crop is grown on large plantations, but much of it is the produce of small farms. Hand labor, great care, and special varieties result in the production of high-grade coffees that are classed as mild in flavor. About half the Central American coffee exports normally come to the United States, but the mild coffees are much appreciated in Europe also, a market with which war greatly interferes.

THE PANAMA CANAL. Because of the distance that it saves, particularly in sea connections between eastern and western United States, the Panama Canal is of vital importance from both the commercial and the military viewpoints. It was feasible to construct it across central Panama because of the narrowness and low relief of the highland at that point (Fig. 189). It is about 50 miles long and has three pairs of locks

FIG. 189.—The steamship *Panama* passing through a portion of the Galliard cut in the Panama Canal. (*Panama Canal Official Photograph.*)

near each end. The degree to which the canal is used is indicated by Fig. 148. The tolls charged on traffic through it keep it in operation.

## The North Coast of South America

PHYSICAL FEATURES.  Colombia and Venezuela constitute a sizable part of the whole of South America. However, their most populous sections open upon the Caribbean Sea, and their commercial positions and relations are more like those of the Central American than of the other South American countries. Included within both of them are mountainous highlands that are the forked or frayed ends of the great cord of the Andes of Ecuador (Fig. 191). Venezuela shares also in the ancient Guiana highland which lies to the eastward across the broad alluvial plains of the Orinoco River. Southeastern Colombia extends into the basin of the upper Amazon River, a district with which it may be included for consideration later.

Between the mountainous highlands are north-trending valleys and broad lowlands, particularly those of northwestern Colombia and the basin of Lake Maracaibo in Venezuela. These are the most accessible parts of the region, but they are hot and in part ill-drained. Some sections are rainy and have dense forests, but those more sheltered by mountains from the rain-bearing winds have dry winters. In these are open forests and savanna grasslands.

LOWLAND AGRICULTURE.  Outside the port districts the lowland population is sparse. It consists largely of mulattoes and a few Indians. The lowland supply crops are similar to those of eastern Central America —corn, the usual food crops, some sugar cane, and cotton. On the narrow coastal plains of Venezuela cacao is the leading export crop. In Colombia great plantations of bananas have been established on accessible portions of the well-drained piedmont alluvial slopes. The producing districts are east of the mouth of the Magdalena River, near the port of Santa Marta. There the lower slopes of some coastal mountains provide suitable lands within a short distance of the harbor. These plantations are controlled by the corporations operating in Central America, and their produce is picked up by the same ships, as they make the rounds of the Caribbean ports.

Livestock are raised on the savanna lowlands. The greatest area of such land is in the llanos of the Orinoco Valley. This vast, flat plain is mainly grassland, but as a grazing region it has many handicaps. In the rainy season much of it is flooded. In the dry season the tall grass becomes coarse and unnutritious, and there are grass fires. There are also several insect pests and cattle diseases. Cattle raising is not in a prosperous condition, and the human population is sparse.

PETROLEUM.   The lowlands produce mahogany, tanning materials, and some other natural resources, but much the most important of them all is petroleum. The exploitation of this resource on a large scale did not begin until about 1927 in the Maracaibo Basin. So productive was the region that Venezuela soon displaced Mexico as the second most important country in petroleum yield. Although its output has been surpassed in recent years by that of Russia, the combined yields of Venezuelan fields and a Colombian field in the Magdalena Valley have maintained this north-coast region in second world place (Figs. 118, 190). New and

THE PRINCIPAL OIL FIELDS OF THE CARIBBEAN REGION.

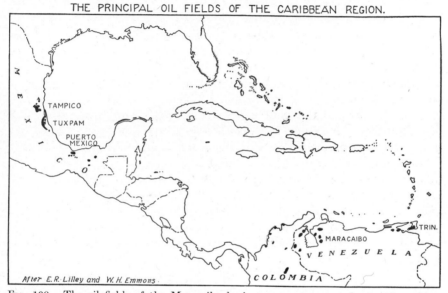

FIG. 190.—The oil fields of the Maracaibo basin are now more productive than those of Mexico.

large discoveries on the Colombian side of the boundary in the Maracaibo lowland seem likely to enable the region to increase its relative importance. A pipe line has been built westward from the new field in order to remain in Colombian territory. It crosses mile-high mountains and the Magdalena River swamps and ends at the port of Coveñas, 260 miles from the oil field. Petroleum is a most valuable resource for these countries. The income derived from taxes upon it have enabled the government of Venezuela to make many internal improvements. The new discoveries in Colombia should benefit that country likewise.

HIGHLAND SETTLEMENT.   Most of the white people and a large part of the Indians of northern South America live in the highlands. In Venezuela these are close to the coast and are reached by short but expensive railroads and a highway. In Colombia they are far in the interior, and the transportation problem is even more difficult to solve. The highlands are made up of several ranges and dissected plateau uplands, separated by basins and deep valleys. In this environment isolation is great. Some of the mountain areas are unsettled and almost unexplored. But they are so much more agreeable in climate that accessible highland districts contain the capital cities of both countries, most of the larger towns, and the areas of densest rural settlement.

HIGHLAND TRANSPORTATION. Venezuela has less than 1,000 miles of railroads, and Colombia less than 2,000 miles. They are mainly short lines of several different gauges, and most of them have been constructed at high cost. The longest railroad in Venezuela is only about 100 miles long, but it has 86 tunnels and 212 bridges. Imported goods going from the Caribbean coast to Bogotá, Colombia, 700 miles inland and at an elevation of over 8,000 feet, must change conveyance six times from river boats to railway links, requiring 2 to 5 weeks to make the journey, although passenger traffic may cover the same route in 1 to 2 weeks. Transportation and handling charges are high. Even in the settled highland areas transportation is difficult. There are some well-paved through highways extending from Venezuela into Colombia and from Colombia into Ecuador. These are valuable substitutes for railroads in difficult terrain. However, improved country roads are not abundant, and the movement of goods in rural districts still is largely by pack trains of mules or burros over narrow trails. It is not surprising that travel by air has quickly assumed an important place in this part of the world. The air trip from Barranquilla to Bogotá requires only 2½ hours.

HIGHLAND RESOURCES. The natural wealth of the highlands is considerable. Forests of great variety include tropical species in the lower valleys; oaks and other middle-latitude species at medium altitudes; and, still higher, bleak moors and pasture lands. There are great contrasts in vegetation resulting from differences in rainfall also, because some of the valleys and slopes are so exposed to the prevailing winds as to have abundant and well-distributed rains, whereas others have long dry seasons.

The complex geologic structures of the highlands yield several valuable minerals. They have been most actively mined in Colombia and include gold, platinum, and emeralds. Small quantities of coal and iron ore, for local use, are produced also.

As in most regions, the greatest resource is agricultural land.

HIGHLAND AGRICULTURE. Variety in temperature and rainfall conditions is productive of variety in agricultural crops. In a region so difficult of access, the subsistence crops are much more important than any produced for export. They include corn, beans, rice, and many other foodstuffs at the lower elevations and wheat, barley, and similar crops at the upper levels of dense settlement. Nonfood crops for domestic use include tobacco and cotton. Cattle and other livestock are raised on cleared mountain slopes and in the drier basins.

One commercial crop, coffee, dominates all others as an export staple and constitutes half to two-thirds of all the agricultural exports of the two countries. It is grown principally on the valley slopes at elevations from 2,500 to 6,500 feet and mainly on small farms. It is well adapted, as a cash crop, to these isolated districts, because it is valuable and little subject to damage. It can stand the expense and delays of the slow transportation to the outside markets.

MANUFACTURES AND COMMERCE. The manufactures of Colombia and Venezuela are varied but small. On the coast, petroleum refineries are outstanding. In the highlands, where imported goods are difficult to get and expensive, there are small industries. They include iron smelters, textile mills, sugar mills, and many others that supply local needs. These industries are better developed in Colombia than in Venezuela where imported manufactures are easier to transport.

The exports of these countries are mainly petroleum, coffee, bananas and other foods, and raw materials. The imports are extremely varied, but the largest items are machinery, vehicles, chemicals, textiles, and other highly manufactured wares, together with some middle-latitude foodstuffs such as wheat and flour. The United States is the source of more than half the imports and the largest single market for the exports.

SELECTED REFERENCES

LATIN AMERICA—GENERAL

BAIN, F. H., and T. T. READ. "Ores and Industry in South America," New York, 1934.
BRADLEY, J. R. Fuel and Power in Latin America, *U.S. Dept. Commerce, Trade Promotion Series* 126, 1931.
CARLSON, F. A. "Geography of Latin America," New York, 1936.
CUTTER, VICTOR M. "Trade Relations with Latin America," Boston, 1929.
FRANK, WALDO. "America Hispania," New York, 1931.
JONES, CLARENCE F. "South America," New York, 1930.
"The South American Yearbook," London (annual).
WHITBECK, R. H. and F. E. WILLIAMS. "Economic Geography of South America," New York, 1940.

MEXICO AND CARIBBEAN LANDS

BOYER, HELEN M. Distribution of Sugar Cane Production in Cuba, *Econ. Geog.*, Vol. 15 (1939), pp. 311–325.
BRATTON, SAM T. El Pacayal: A Coffee Finca in Guatemala, *Jour. Geog.*, Vol. 38 (1939), pp. 45–50.
CLARK, VICTOR S. and staff. "Porto Rico and Its Problems," Brookings Institution, Washington, 1930.
CUTTERIDGE, J. O. "Geography of the West Indies and Adjacent Lands," London, 1931.

DeGolia, Darwin. Porto Rico, What It Produces and What It Buys, *U.S. Dept. Commerce, Trade Information Bull.* 785, 1932.

Dicken, Samuel N. Corn and Wheat in Mexico's Changing Economy, *Jour. Geog.,* Vol. 38 (1939), pp. 99–109.

Jones, Clarence F. Agricultural Regions of South America: Part VI, *Econ. Geog.,* Vol. 5 (1929), pp. 400–421.

Jones, Chester Lloyd. "Caribbean Backgrounds and Prospects," New York, 1931.

———. "Costa Rica and Civilization in the Caribbean," Madison, Wis., 1935.

Hearst, L. Coffee Industry of Central America, *Econ. Geog.,* Vol. 8 (1932), pp. 53–66.

Mason, C. Y., and A. Rowlands. Panama Canal Traffic, *Econ. Geog.,* Vol. 14 (1938), pp. 325–337.

Miller, E. W. Petroleum in the Economy of Venezuela, *Econ. Geog.,* Vol. 16 (1940), pp. 204–210.

Pruitt, Fredonia M. The Coffee Industry of Colombia, *Jour. Geog.,* Vol. 35 (1936), pp. 68–72.

Simpson, E. N. "The Ejido, Mexico's Way Out," Chapel Hill, N. C., 1937.

The Coffee Industry in Colombia, U.S. Department of Commerce, 1931.

Venezuela, Commercial and Industrial Development, *U.S. Trade Information Bull.* 783, 1931.

*West Indian Sugar Comm. Rept.* (British), London, 1930.

# Chapter XIX. Western South America

The continent of South America is divided by its Andean highlands into two very unequal and unlike parts. On the east are broad plains, rolling uplands, and smaller ancient plateaus dissected by streams into low mountains. On the west the plains are narrow and merely fringe the rugged mountains which include high intermontane plateaus between their ranges (Fig. 191). Climatically the two parts are in strong contrast also. Much of the west is dry. It includes the most arid desert in the world. The east is prevailingly humid, and some of it has very heavy rainfall. Eastern South America fronts upon the greatest commercial ocean of the world. The west, until the completion of the Panama Canal, was a commercial backwater. From London or New York to Callao, Peru, by way of Cape Horn is 10,000 miles, requiring about 50 days for a freight steamer. The east is approachable, having broad river mouths and deep, commodious bays. The coastline of the west is straight and forbidding, being almost without a natural harbor from Ecuador to southern Chile, a distance of more than 2,500 miles. The few aborigines of the settled east were readily displaced, and the present inhabitants are almost entirely of European origin or the descendants of their negro slaves. The Indians of the mountainous west had a highly organized society and were never displaced. Although they are now dominated by people of European descent, they make up the larger part of the population of the inhabited highlands.

In view of these differences it is practicable to consider first the countries of western South America as a group set apart from those of the eastern side of the continent. However, there are strong contrasts also between north and south in that long and narrow western belt—contrasts in physical situation, climatic features, population elements, economic products, and political administration. For a discussion of these it will be convenient to group together the countries of the northern and central Andean region. Chile will be reserved for separate treatment. Colombia and Venezuela may be omitted, since they front northward upon the Caribbean Sea and have been discussed already.

FIG. 191.—Highlands and lowlands of South America. The unbroken chain of the Andes extending along the entire western coast is a formidable barrier. The moderate highlands of Brazil are a decided benefit to the east coast. (*Map from Miller and Singewald's "Mineral Deposits of South America."*)

FIG. 192.—Street scene in Quito, Ecuador. Though Quito is nearly on the equator, its high altitude makes the climate cool enough to cause the natives to wear heavy woolen blankets. (*Copyright Keystone View Co.*)

## Ecuador, Peru, and Bolivia

PHYSICAL SITUATION. These three countries occupy a long section of the western highland. They begin north of the equator and stretch southward more than 1,600 miles through the mountains and plateaus and along the coast. The physical site that they occupy may be thought of as belonging to three contrasting types. These are (1) a narrow belt of coastal slopes and valleys in Ecuador and Peru, (2) mountain-fringed plateaus which are narrow in Ecuador but expand through Peru into the broad highland basins of Bolivia, and (3) eastern lowlands which lie mainly along the headwaters of the Amazon River.

The climatic contrasts in the area are quite as distinctive as those of surface configuration. The eastern lowlands are a part of the Amazonian region of rainforest climate. Heavy precipitation and continuous high temperatures prevail except along the lower slopes of the Andean front, where moderate altitudes give some relief from the oppressive heat. The highlands are only moderately moist at best and are drier in the broad plateaus of Bolivia than in Ecuador. Temperatures vary with the altitudes of the several parts of the plateau. Generally they are cool; there is intense sunlight but much chill wind (Fig. 192). Frosts are not uncommon, for the plateau altitudes range from 10,000 to 15,000 feet above sea level. Perpetual snows lie in the fringing mountains. The western coastal lowlands are hot and humid in Ecuador, but the rainfall decreases rapidly to the southward. In Peru the coastal strip is arid. Its temperatures are somewhat moderated by a cool ocean current just offshore, and there are frequent fogs but little rain.

THE COASTAL LOWLAND OF ECUADOR. The coast of Ecuador is fortunate in that it has the only commodious bay and river harbor north of central Chile, the great Gulf of Guayaquil (Fig. 191). Elsewhere on this coast small streams terminate abruptly on a regular shoreline which affords little or no protection to ships. The Guayaquil lowland is in part ill drained, but there are some higher lands near the mountains that have been partly cleared of their dense forests. Here are located cacao plantations, which furnish the principal export of Ecuador. This was once the world's leading region in cacao production, but other countries now supply the larger part of a greatly enlarged world demand. Some coffee is grown also at higher elevations and in the drier district south of Guayaquil. To the northward the rainforest of Ecuador extends along the coast, little broken by settlement, and is continued in the forests of the Pacific lowland of Colombia. It yields little else than tropical woods and other forest products, such as tagua nuts, the "vegetable ivory" from which buttons are made.

The Coastal Lowland of Peru.   South of Cape Pariña, the western-most extension of the continent, the Peruvian coast becomes dry (Fig. 193), and its settlements are practically restricted to the many small irrigated valleys. These are narrow strips of fertile alluvium extending inland from the coast (Fig. 194). They are separated from one another

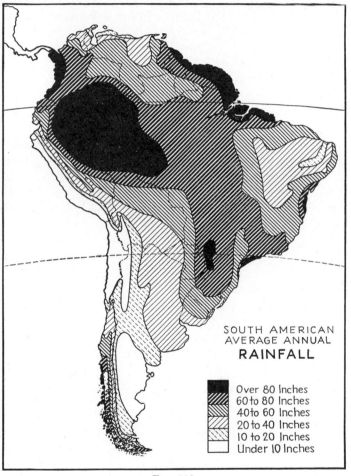

SOUTH AMERICAN
AVERAGE ANNUAL
**RAINFALL**

- Over 80 Inches
- 60 to 80 Inches
- 40 to 60 Inches
- 20 to 40 Inches
- 10 to 20 Inches
- Under 10 Inches

Fig. 193.

by treeless desert plains and hilly uplands which have little value except as poor grazing land. Irrigation water is derived from the headwaters of small streams back in the Andean slopes. In many of the valleys it is not abundant, and the irrigated strips are narrow. In a few places two or more streams join on the lowlands and furnish water enough to irrigate fairly broad expanses. Some of the irrigation works that control these streams are very old, dating far back of the period of European occupance. The present users have maintained and improved them.

Most of the irrigated land is held in large estates by old families of Spanish descent. The work on them is done principally by Indians who live on the estates as peons. Grains, beans, fruit, and vegetable crops of great variety are produced for home supply, and some livestock is raised also for meat and for work animals. However, there are only two important export crops in this arid coastal district. In the northern irrigated valleys of Peru, near Trujillo, sugar cane is dominant. It is grown on a large scale by the most modern methods, and there are large investments in the plantations and their equipment of field machinery and sugar mills. In the valleys of the central Peruvian coast, near Lima, cotton is the leading cash crop, but it is grown in most of the northern and southern valleys also. There are several varieties of Peruvian cotton that find special markets because they are fine and of long staple or because of their rough and crinkly fiber, which enables them to spin well with wool. Cotton is the most important export of Peru (Fig. 195). The valleys of southern coastal Peru have less irrigation water available than those of the northern and central districts. This is because of the growing aridity of the coast and the mountain slopes as the severe Chilean desert is approached.

FIG. 194.—Irrigated lands in river valleys along the coast of Peru. These are the chief agricultural areas of Peru. (*From the Geographical Review, published by the American Geographical Society of New York, Vol. 4, p. 219.*)

Settlement on the irrigated lands generally is dense, and near the lower end of nearly every valley there is a town or city that is its principal market and commercial outlet. The valleys are not completely connected by railroads along the coast, and most of the transport of goods is by coastwise shipping from the smaller ports to the larger ones, such as

Callao. Even the larger Peruvian ports have inadequate harbors, and the large ships that enter them must transfer cargo by lighters and move out to sea during storms for lack of protection near the shore. Callao and Lima are the largest cities in the country and, with other coast towns, do most of the manufacturing in textiles, leather goods, food products, and other supplies for the domestic market. Several short lines of railway extend inland from the ports along the valleys, but only two of them continue up the difficult grades into the highlands. These have their

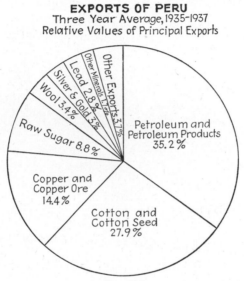

**EXPORTS OF PERU**
Three Year Average, 1935-1937
Relative Values of Principal Exports

Other Exports 3.1%
Other Minerals 1.1%
Lead 2.8%
Silver & Gold 3.3%
Wool 3.4%
Raw Sugar 8.8%
Copper and Copper Ore 14.4%
Cotton and Cotton Seed 27.9%
Petroleum and Petroleum Products 35.2%

Fig. 195.

coastal termini at the larger ports of Callao and Mollendo, with the development of which they have been closely concerned.

Peru has a large and varied mineral output, but most of it comes from the highlands. In the northern part of the Peruvian lowland, however, there are petroleum fields. Although the output of this district is small, compared even with that of the Caribbean region, it supplies Peruvian needs and leaves an exportable surplus of greater value than that of cotton.

THE ANDEAN HIGHLANDS. The difficulty of reaching the highland of Ecuador, Peru, and Bolivia is great. Only five railroads penetrate it—one in Ecuador, two in Peru, and two in Bolivia, the latter from ports in Chile. The Central Railroad of Peru, for example, climbs to 15,665 feet altitude in the first 106 miles from the coast; it has 16 switchbacks, 65 tunnels, and 61 bridges (Fig. 196). The cost of building it was so great that no profit is likely ever to be derived from its operation. La Paz, in Bolivia, is less than 500 miles inland, yet the freight charge on a ton of coal for this distance is several times as great as the normal ocean rate from England to the port terminal of the railroad, an ocean distance of some 10,000 miles. Railroads traverse the plateau uplands in several directions, and one from the Bolivian plateau extends southeastward to connect with lines in northwestern Argentina. It does not have a heavy traffic. There are improved highways on the plateaus also, some of them extending into the mountain fringes and toward the bordering lowlands. However, the great altitude of even the lowest passes, the steepness of the slopes, the depth of the canyons, the dangers from landslides, and other difficulties

Fig. 196.—A mountain town on the Oroya Railroad (Peru), which crosses one range of the Andes at an altitude of about 16,000 feet.

serve to create economic isolation in the highlands, even under modern conditions.

Isolated as it is, the highland is the principal region of population, agriculture, and mining. More than half the people are of pure Indian blood, the descendants of groups that were included in the empire of the ancient Incas. A large part of the remainder are mixtures of Indian and Spanish. There are perhaps few people in the world who would be less affected than these by a complete end to commerce with the world outside. The majority of the highland inhabitants are farmers and herdsmen, but a few are employed as laborers in mines.

*Agriculture* does not produce abundantly on the thin soils and steep slopes and under the cool highland climate. This is the region in which the potato originated, and it is cultivated still as a food staple. Barley and wheat have been introduced also, but the farming methods and implements are crude, and the crops yield less than enough to support the population. Foodstuffs are among the largest imports. The use of llamas as beasts of burden still persists, but many of the treeless pastures now carry flocks of sheep. Their flesh furnishes a domestic meat supply, and their wool supplements that of the llama and alpaca in the home spinning and weaving by which the blankets and warm clothing required in this highland environment are produced. The wool of both sheep and alpaca is exported also. The grazing ranges for these animals extend above the cultivated plateau basins to the bleak mountain slopes near the snow line.

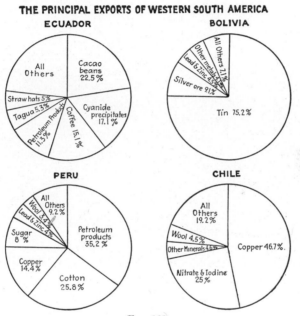

THE PRINCIPAL EXPORTS OF WESTERN SOUTH AMERICA

Fig. 197.

*Mining* in the Andes of Peru and Bolivia yields minerals, and especially metals, of great variety. During the colonial period the Spanish took large amounts of gold and silver from the Indians of the highland, and some still is produced there. The yield of both these metals is, however, much less valuable than that of either tin or copper. Copper is produced in many parts of the world, but tin is more rare, and the Bolivian highland ranks next after southeastern Asia in tin production (Fig. 197). The list of minor metals exported from this region includes lead, zinc, antimony, tungsten, and vanadium. The latter are not produced in large quantities but are important contributions to the world's supply of steel-alloy minerals. The metallic ores are obtained from mines far back in the mountains, hard to reach and expensive to operate; most of the copper from Peru is mined by an American company operating about

16,000 feet above sea level. Coal is found near one of the mines and is employed in developing power for mining operations and for the railroad. Unfortunately, however, most of the mining areas of Peru and Bolivia have no local source of fuel, and water powers are not yet developed.

*Cities and Manufactures.* There are several large towns in the highland region, but they are hardly to be considered industrial centers. There are mineral smelters and some woolen mills, but in general the situation is not favorable for manufacture even though imported wares are expensive. The lack of power resources is one reason for this, but more important is the nature of the local market. The Indians are poor, and more than half of them are illiterate. Their wants are few, and they are accustomed to make for themselves nearly all that they require. They do not make good factory workers. The towns are, therefore, market centers, mining districts, and political and administrative cities, some of them very ancient.

THE EASTERN SLOPES AND LOWLANDS.  It has been said that Peru is like a man who has a luxuriant garden from which, however, he is separated by a high wall, while his neighbor at the rear has free access to it. In this case Brazil is the neighbor, but it happens that she has a very large garden of her own and shows little disposition to make any use of that of Peru. This is essentially the situation of Ecuador and Bolivia also with regard to their eastern lowlands. In each case the Amazonian slopes make up more than half the area of the country but have only a small population. There are few exportable products, and most of these must find their exit down the Amazon through Brazil. Formerly it was a region of wild-rubber collecting, but that industry has been much depressed by the competition of cultivated rubber. Tribes of Indians live in the forests mainly by hunting.

The most habitable portion of this region is close to the base of the mountains and in their foothills. This is especially true in Bolivia, where the rise from the plains is less abrupt and there are deep valleys and sloping mountainsides at intermediate elevations. There the rainforest is replaced by more open vegetation, but the climate is not so dry and bleak as on the high plateaus. The lower valleys produce sugar cane, cacao, coffee, and other tropical food supplies. Little of them can get to any outside market, and they are merely subsistence crops. High up the slopes the crops are more like those of the plateau, and there are mountain grazing lands also. Corn is perhaps the most widespread of the crops, since it grows in the lower valleys and also well up into the zone of wheat, barley, and potatoes.

Commerce between the eastern lowlands and the plateaus is limited mainly to what can be carried on the backs of Indian porters or, at most, on the backs of pack animals. Representative items are a small quantity of boards and posts for the treeless plateau mining centers, the cinchona bark from which quinine is extracted, and the leaves of the coca shrub. Coca leaves are chewed as a narcotic by all the highland Indians, and an extract of them is exported for the manufacture of cocaine. This region is the native habitat of the cinchona tree, but it, like the rubber tree, has been so successfully planted in the East Indies that now only a small fraction of the world's supply of this important medicine is derived from its original source.

## Chile

THE COUNTRY AND THE PEOPLE.   Chile has the advantage of being mainly outside the tropics, a fact of much importance to its agriculture. The mountains near the coast are lower than those in Peru, and the country is readily entered from the sea. Chile is long and narrow but, unlike the countries to the north of it, is almost all on the Pacific side of the Andes. So long is the country—nearly 2,700 miles—that if it were placed in its proper latitudes in the northern hemisphere it would extend from southern Mexico almost to Sitka Alaska. The population—more than 4½ million—is largely white but includes also mixtures of Spanish with the energetic Araucanian Indians and a small proportion of pure-blood Indians. The government has been controlled by a small upper class who hold the land in large estates, although that control has been weakened in recent decades. About one-fourth of the people are illiterate, and the lower classes have little part in the government.

In its physical characteristics Chile has several points in common with the west coast region of North America. Its eastern border lies generally along the crest of the Andes, and the country is only 65 to 185 miles wide. This is comparable to the North American strip between the summits of the Cascade and Sierra Nevada Mountains and the coast. Chile has also some low coastal ranges, and between them and the Andes is a long but interrupted lowland somewhat like the great valleys of California, Oregon, and Washington. The climatic variations in this long strip also are similar to those in Pacific North America, with the compass directions reversed. Northern Chile is desert, like northwestern Mexico. Central Chile has a dry subtropical climate much like that of California. That of southern Chile is marine, characterized by cloud, fog, and rain, and is closely comparable with the climate of coastal Washington, British Columbia, and southern Alaska. The latter comparison is made more striking by the fact that in southern Chile the Andes descend to the coast. In the past they have been heavily glaciated, and the coastal area is a region of deep fiords with steep, forested or rocky slopes and fringing islands (Fig. 191).

Because of these striking physical contrasts the settlement and economic development of the several sections of Chile have proceeded in different ways in spite of the unifying influence of a central political administration. It is, therefore, convenient to attempt to understand the country in terms of its three principal regional subdivisions.

THE DESERT OF NORTHERN CHILE is continuous with that of southern Peru, and it extends southward to about the 27th parallel of south latitude. There the gradually increasing rainfall and a change in the surface configuration mark a zone of transition. The desert, in spite of its close proximity to the sea, is extremely arid, and in parts of it rain may come only as individual showers at intervals of several years. The land is practically devoid of any vegetation capable of use as forage, and there is no pastoral settlement. There also the plain is wider than in Peru, and the Andean slopes are even more arid. Small streams descending the mountains are swallowed up, evaporate in the desert basins, and fail to reach the ocean. The plain itself is partitioned by low mountains and ridges of hills into numerous small basins much like those of the Death Valley region of southeastern California. There is no available supply of irrigation water in them and no agricultural settlement. Yet the desert has population centers, railways, and several ports. They are supported almost entirely by mineral resources.

The mining industries are of two types—those concerned with the extraction of metallic minerals, especially copper, obtained from the hard rocks of the mountain ranges; and those which exploit the sedimentary accumulations of the basin floors. The latter are mainly the deposits of nitrate of soda, salt, iodine, and other products that have been left by evaporation in the arid basins of interior drainage.

Copper is found at several places in Chile, but operations on the largest scale are conducted at Chuquicamata on the Andean slopes of the desert region. There are large quantities of low-grade ores that can be mined cheaply. They are worked by a United States corporation which has spent large sums establishing a town, bringing a water supply from back in the mountains, and providing facilities for a mining population and the handling of the ores. The district is connected with the port of Antofagasta by a railroad which is one of the two that continues on up into the plateau of Bolivia. Copper is the most valuable export of Chile, but some export of gold, silver, and other metals is also derived from various sections of the country.

For many years the leading export of the country was nitrate of soda, and the income from its sale was the main source of support for the Chilean government. Although this region still is about the only natural source of this valuable mineral, which is used in industry and as a fertilizer, the growth of artificial nitrate production in North America and Europe has given serious competition to its production. It has declined to second place in the list of the country's exports. This easily soluble salt lies near the surface. It would have been dissolved long ago and carried away by streams had it not been for the extreme aridity of the region. It is mined in several basins of northern Chile (Fig. 198) and carried to local refining plants, where it is dissolved and separated from the earth, common salt, and other ingredients of the crude material. It is recrystallized by evaporation, sacked, and sent by rail to one of the several small ports that exist primarily for the handling of this commodity. A by-product of iodine is obtained from this mining process, and Chile is one of the important sources of that necessary substance also.

CENTRAL CHILE. Between latitudes 27 and 40°S. the rainfall of Chile increases from less than 10 to more than 60 inches per year, and the country is transformed from desert into a region of farms and pastures. It is the area of greatest population density. The principal cities are there, an improved highway system, and two-thirds of the railroad mileage, including the Chilean portion of the Trans-Andine Railroad, that little-used but only rail link with Argentina.

Agriculture in Chile produces for home consumption. The principal food crops are wheat and potatoes, but other grains, beans, and corn are much employed also. However, the dry subtropical climate of the great valley permits the cultivation of many horticultural crops of the type associated with Californian agriculture, and in part these are grown under irriga-

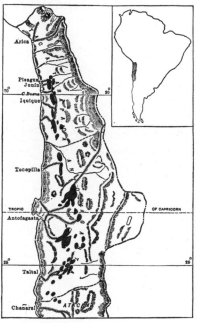

FIG. 198.—The northern end of Chile. Black areas represent principal nitrate-producing areas. (*After Tower, in Miller and Singewald's "Mineral Deposits of South America."*)

tion. Most important of them is the grape, for wine production. The basic element in the Chilean population being Spanish and wine-drinking by custom, the output of wine is more than 15 gallons per capita per year, and only a small quantity is exported. Some raisins are produced, also oranges and other subtropical fruits, but Chile lacks the large market for these products that California enjoys. In the cooler and more humid southern part of central Chile apples are grown under conditions comparable with those of the Puget Sound region, and dairying is well developed there also. Most of the agricultural land in this southern section of central Chile is in farms of moderate size, and many of the farmers are of

German or British origin. In the older settled northern part of the valley a much larger part is held in great estates by the descendants of Spanish colonists.

Central Chile has mineral resources also, some gold and copper being produced there, but more important are iron ore and coal. The iron ore is produced cheaply and so close to the coast that it may be loaded almost directly into ships. It is one of the sources of supply for the smelters in eastern United States. The total reserve is not great, however, compared with that of some in other parts of the world. The coal reserve is not great either, and most of it is coal of low grade. Yet it supplies the larger part of

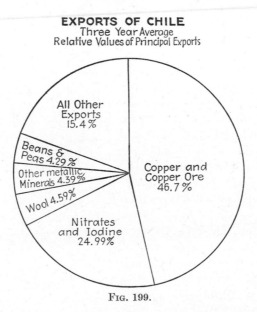

**EXPORTS OF CHILE**
Three Year Average
Relative Values of Principal Exports

All Other Exports 15.4%

Beans & Peas 4.29%

Other metallic Minerals 4.39%

Wool 4.59%

Copper and Copper Ore 46.7%

Nitrates and Iodine 24.99%

Fig. 199.

the national requirements, and some is exported, although a smaller quantity of better coal is imported from Australia and other sources. The iron is located near La Serena, and the coal farther south near Coronel. It is the largest coal reserve in South America.

SOUTHERN CHILE, as it has been previously noted, has many features in common with the coast of British Columbia. It is forested, but the timbers are not so valuable or so abundant as those of similar situation in North America. Some minerals are produced there also, but a large part of the fiorded mountainous coast is uninhabited. Much of the interior is but little explored, and some of the higher mountain basins are buried beneath permanent ice fields like those of the British Columbia coast ranges. This coast lacks the valuable fisheries of the North American coast. Far to the southward, especially on the island of Tierra del Fuego, the forests dwindlc, and open hillsides and bleak uplands afford grass- and shrub-land pastures. Here great sheep ranches have been established. The industry is principally controlled by Englishmen; British breeds of sheep have been introduced; and Scottish and English managers and shepherds make up an important part of the sparse population. Magellanes, the market center of this region of mountainous islands, rainy wind-swept fiords, and sheep ranches, is the most southerly city in the world.

MANUFACTURES AND COMMERCE. The manufactures of Chile are diversified but mainly small. That fact might readily be inferred from its geographical and economic situation. It is far removed from the great manufacturing centers of the world where surplus agricultural produce other than wool might be sold. Perishable products it cannot well market abroad. Of other products that it might exchange for manufactures there are left only the minerals (Fig. 199). These are important, but the value of the nitrates that formerly were the leading exports has declined. It has therefore been the policy of the Chilean government to promote domestic manufactures as a means of supplying the requirements of the country. These include textile manufactures, flour and lumber, leather, and other products. The low-grade coal does not favor the smelting of iron, but it furnishes some power. The rainy slopes of the central Andes make it possible also to provide hydroelectric power, of which large use is made. The centers of manufacture are mainly the cities of the great valley and particularly the region of Santiago and the port of Valparaiso.

Since the principal exports of Chile are copper and nitrates, their shipment is mainly through the northern ports of the desert region. These ports have little natural protection, and most of their cargo is transferred by lighter. Valparaiso, the principal port of import, is not much better situated; and although large ships can dock there, they are subject to great damage by storms and must sometimes interrupt cargo movement and put out to sea until storms are past. The numerous protected harbors of the fiorded south have few ports, because the population of that region is sparse and there is little to ship. Only the sheltered harbor of Puerto Montt is in a position to serve the southern end of the populous central region. The position of Valparaiso with respect to the valley may be compared with that of Los Angeles on the North American coast, and the location of Puerto Montt is somewhat like that of Seattle. But there is no central harbor comparable to San Francisco Bay. The principal imports of Chile are machines and various manufactures of iron and steel, petroleum and its products, textiles, and sugar. More than one-fourth of all the imports come from the United States, and nearly as large a part of the exports go to the United States. In the direction of this trade movement the shortening of the route due to the Panama Canal obviously plays an important part.

SELECTED REFERENCES

CARLSON, F. A. "Geography of Latin America," pp. 36–145, 332–348, New York, 1936.

CUNNINGHAM, C. H. Economic and Financial Conditions in Ecuador, *U.S. Dept. Commerce, Trade Information Bull.* 773, 1931.

DUGGAN, STEPHEN. "The Two Americas," New York, 1934.

JONES, C. F. Agricultural Regions of South America, *Econ. Geog.*, Vol. 5 (1929), pp. 277–307, 390–400.

———. "South America," New York, 1930.

WHITBECK, R. H., and F. E. WILLIAMS. "Economic Geography of South America," New York, 1940.

# Chapter XX. Argentina and Uruguay

The Rio de la Plata is a broad but comparatively shallow estuary into which the rivers Paraná and Uruguay discharge. Upon the shores of this embayment lie Argentina and Uruguay, and both are most easily and directly approached through it. They are sometimes called the River Plate Countries, a term derived from the English name for the estuary. They are very unequal in size, and Argentina, being sixteen times the larger, has greater variety in physical environment and resources. Culturally, however, they have much in common.

PHYSICAL CONTRASTS. That part of the eastern lowland of South America which includes Argentina and Uruguay is, in fact, not a simple unit. It includes areas having differences in surface configuration, climate, natural vegetation, and soils (Fig. 200). These several parts have offered contrasting advantages for human settlement and have developed unlike features of economy the meaning of which cannot be appreciated without an understanding of the physical differences.

*The Pampa* is the physical focus of the lowland. This is a gently

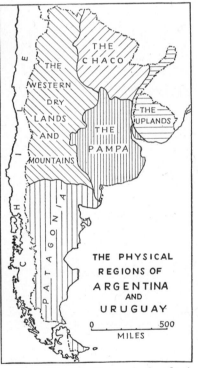

FIG. 200.—The Pampa is the physical and cultural heart of the River Plate countries.

undulating plain (very flat in places) which occupies about one-fifth of Argentina (Fig. 201). It lies adjacent to the Rio de la Plata and extends from the capital city of Buenos Aires southwest, west, and north in a great semicircle whose radius is about 300 to 350 miles. The plain is

355

FIG. 201.—The level grasslands of the Argentine pampa have produced horses, cattle, and sheep with comparatively little human labor for three centuries. (*Pan American Union.*)

underlain by deep accumulations of fine silt, in part washed down by streams from the dry lands bordering the Andes and in part wind-deposited from the same source. This section of the continent has a humid subtropical climate comparable with that of central Texas. Its average annual rainfall exceeds 20 inches, ample for the support of a close vegetative cover, and most of the plain was covered originally by a tall, coarse prairie grass. Age-long accumulations of these grass roots in the fine silty earth have resulted in the formation of soils of great depth and fertility. They are mainly dark loams of the prairie type, similar to those of the corn belt in Iowa or of the black prairies of Texas.

*The Uruguayan Uplands.*  Southern Uruguay, bordering the estuary and the lower Uruguay River, is an undulating plain similar to the Pampa. But the understructure of the country is essentially different. To the northward the surface elevations increase with approach to the highlands of southern Brazil. These are of old and complex rocks, and northern Uruguay is a land of ridges and valleys with some broad tablelands. Originally there were extensive grasslands in the south, but toward the north the prairies were interspersed with woodlands. Some of it is very tillable land; but in spite of the fact that all of Uruguay has abundant rainfall, not all of it has the natural utility for agriculture that characterizes the Pampa.

*The Chaco* is a broad lowland that occupies the northern one-fifth of Argentina. It includes tropical savanna forests and grasslands together with broad swamps. It averages 20 to 40 or more inches of rainfall, the larger amount on the eastern side. On that side are extensive forests; on the drier western margin, grasslands are predominant. Most of the land is flat, but some of it is so flat and so poorly drained, because of impervious clay soils, that it is somewhat like the swamp lands of Florida. The forest vegetation is tropical in nature, containing palms and various deciduous trees. In places the open forests and the shrub lands are replaced by tall tropical grasses.

*The Western Dry Lands and Mountains.*  From extreme northwestern Argentina southward to about the 38th parallel is a tropical and subtropical dry land, a belt about 200 miles wide and 1,300 miles long. The northern portion of it has both higher temperatures and lower rainfall, and in consequence it is more arid. It may be compared with northern Mexico or southern Arizona. The southern section is less hot but has not much more rain. The entire district is one of mountain and plains borderland. High mountains on the west break into foothills and detached ranges, and these enclose dry valleys and broad basins. The latter are deeply filled with alluvium, but the hill slopes and high plains are thin-soiled or are covered with desert gravel. They support a sparse dry-land vegetation of grasses and desert shrubs.

*Patagonia.* Nearly one-third of Argentina is south of the 38th parallel and the Rio Colorado. It lies in the rain shadow of the southern Andes in the westerly wind belt and is prevailingly dry, but its temperatures are those of the middle latitudes. They might be compared with the temperatures of the high plains of North America except that they are more uniform. The summers are more like those of Montana and Alberta, and the winters like those of western Texas. The surface is that of a sloping plain or low plateau deeply trenched by the valleys of semipermanent streams. The uplands are broad and contain expanses of thin soils interspersed with grassy depressions and alkaline areas. The high margin of the plateau merges with the glaciated slopes of the southern Andes and is characterized by morainic deposits and, in its southern portion, by long glacial lakes. These may be compared with the long lakes flanking the Rocky Mountains in Glacier National Park and the Canadian mountain parks.

LAND THE GREAT RESOURCE. The combined areas of Argentina and Uruguay are more than one-third that of the United States, but their combined populations are hardly one-ninth as great. The sparseness of the rural populations is the more striking when it is seen that about 60 per cent of the people in Argentina and 45 per cent of those in Uruguay live in cities. These include Buenos Aires, the largest city in the southern hemisphere. The occupations of the rural inhabitants are largely pastoral and agricultural. This may be attributed in part to a lack of other physical bases of support than the land. Neither country has large mineral or forest resources.

HISTORICAL ELEMENTS. It has been noted previously that the Indians were more easily displaced in the regions of eastern than in western South America. That displacement is practically complete in the River Plate lowlands, and the population is almost entirely white. The original settlements were made by the Spanish exclusively, whose language was established there. But the manner and purpose of these settlements were different from those which characterized the occupation of the mountain regions and certainly very different from those which governed the occupation of the interior farm lands of North America. These conditions have left their impress on the present-day use of the land and on the occupations and products of the people who use it.

The first settlers on the River Plate brought horses. The people were driven out by Indians, but the horses remained. Subsequently cattle and sheep came into the grassy plains by way of the settlements in Brazil, Bolivia, and Peru. These multiplied abundantly. Forage was plentiful, the climate mild, and predatory animals few. By the year 1600, when permanent settlement was well established on the estuary, the animals existed in great numbers. They were slaughtered for their hides, tallow, and wool alone, and dried flesh was even used as fuel in the absence of wood. So it was for nearly 200 years. Lack of improved transportation and the great distance to the European markets, small at that time, prevented any more economical use of this resource. A visitor to Buenos Aires in 1658 reports a fleet of ships that loaded 300,000 cattle hides in the port at one time. Their sale value is estimated to have been about $1 each, and the producers made a large profit even at that price.

Because livestock was cheap, the land was cheap also, and the few settlers were able to get it easily. Original grants of 5,000 to 100,000 acres were commonly made. These were sometimes added to by purchase, but some have since been subdivided. *Estancias*, or cattle ranches, of 50,000 acres were not unusual, and many large estates continue down to the present. In the United States we are accustomed to large livestock ranches in the semiarid parts of the country, but the eastern Argentine *estancias* constituted great wealth, because the land was potentially as productive as that of Kansas.

The market for beef was first enlarged in about 1800, when the salting of meat became an established industry. Salt beef remained the principal additional export for nearly another century, or until the era of refrigeration. That began, so far as the shipment of River Plate beef to Europe is concerned, in about 1880, but shipments did not reach large volume until 1900. This remarkable improvement in transportation immediately raised the value of Argentine beef, and that in turn increased the value of land and all the things that it could produce. As a result, a more intensive form of livestock raising was introduced, with better breeds of cattle and sheep and the introduction of better forage crops and grain farming. The agriculture of the region in the present is, therefore, centered mainly on livestock production. It is conducted on large estates. But it has taken on new features that are peculiar to more intensive farming, and this is mainly because improved transportation put the grazing lands within the economic reach of large and profitable markets.

## Modern Livestock Industries

BEEF PRODUCTION. Intensification in the cattle industry has resulted in the improvement of both the forage crops and the kinds of animals used. The old types of cattle have given way to early-maturing breeds of British origin, which are brought to maturity as quickly as possible on the best available forage. But the several regions differ greatly in their abilities to support cattle (Fig. 202). The pastures of Patagonia are poor, and the climate bleak and chill. That section has the smallest number of cattle. In the dry lands of the northwest a small number per square mile are pastured under range conditions much like those in western United States. Sparse grasses and shrubs serve as pasture and browse; irrigated districts furnish supplementary pasture and hay. In the Chaco and the northeast the tropical grasslands carry somewhat more cattle. They are more like the pastures of the Texas coast, warm and humid and subject to cattle diseases transmitted by insect pests. Much the greatest density of cattle distribution is found in the western part of the Pampas. Here are the rich pastures of alfalfa. It is the economic equivalent of the United States corn belt and of the livestock-farming industry as compared with cattle

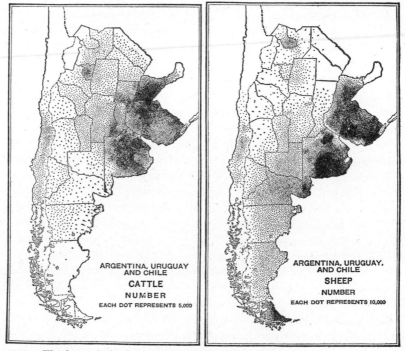

FIG. 202.—The best of the humid lands of the River Plate region is controlled by the stockmen. (*U.S. Department of Agriculture.*)

ranching. To it come many young cattle from the drier west or the more humid east to fatten on alfalfa. In some respects the cattle industry in the Pampa is different from that in the corn belt, particularly in its use of alfalfa rather than of corn for fattening cattle and in the fact that it is not a region of 160-acre farms but of great *estancias* of thousands of acres. Uruguay has also large numbers of cattle per square mile. It has generally more rainfall than even the Pampa, but its pastures have not been so well improved. Alfalfa is not widely used, and the cattle are not of such high quality.

The present number of cattle in Argentina is about 33 million, about 4 per capita of the population. In Uruguay it is 7 million, about 3½ per capita. In both countries cattle products make up about 15 per cent of the total exports. They include the principal items of frozen and chilled beef and also hides, canned meats, bones, and many incidental products. In one respect the character of the exports of the two countries differs. The fresh beef exported from Uruguay is about equally divided between the frozen and chilled forms. The latter is selected beef held at temperatures just above its freezing point until delivery in Europe. It gets a higher price than frozen beef, which transports more easily but tends to lose its flavor on cooking. From Argentina the exports of chilled beef are five to ten times greater than those in frozen form. This is a reflection of the more advanced development of the industry in Argentina and especially in the rich Pampa region, where choice young cattle are marketed especially for the chilled-beef trade.

THE DAIRY INDUSTRY. The Spanish tradition in River Plate agriculture was against the development of dairying, and until recent decades dairy products were imported in spite of the great numbers of cattle. However, Italian and north European farmers in Argentina were encouraged by the growing market in Buenos Aires to undertake dairy production. The industry still is most intensively developed on the south shore of the Rio de la Plata, but it has spread also over most of the Pampa and northward into the subtropical region. The average output is, however, small compared with that in the United States—about 4 per cent as much butter, 10 per cent as much cheese, and 60 per cent as much dried casein. People of Spanish tradition eat cheese but use oils rather than butter in cooking. Hence Argentina exports about one-fourth of its butter but must import cheese. It is also one of the great sources of export casein.

SHEEP AND WOOL. The sheep industry, like the cattle industry, in the River Plate region has undergone a transformation. It was established near Buenos Aires, and the range was first stocked with nondescript types of Spanish sheep. In the early days sheep were killed, and the wool was pulled from their half-decomposed bodies because it was cheaper than shearing. When the world's demand for fine wool was enlarged, following the industrial revolution, Merino sheep were introduced. When, still later, frozen mutton was added to the list of possible exports, English breeds of mutton sheep were introduced. As the value of land has increased and agriculture has become more intensive, the total number of sheep has decreased somewhat. But the decrease has been greatest in the grain-farming district of the central Pampa. The industry has, as in the United States, been pushed out into the less valuable lands of the arid and rough northwest, the dry lands of Patagonia and especially the bleak pastures of the far south, Tierra del Fuego and the distant Falkland Islands (Fig. 202). The industry has remained in the less cultivated regions south of Buenos Aires and in Uruguay. It has not advanced greatly into the warm, humid, and ill-drained lands of the Chaco, where sheep would be raised at a serious climatic disadvantage. From the entire region exports of wool and mutton nearly equal the exports of beef, but about four-fifths of the value is in wool and only one-fifth is in frozen and preserved mutton. Yet the River Plate is one of the leading world sources of mutton as well as of beef for the European trade and also of wool for both European and United States markets.

SWINE. As has been noted before, the swine industry usually is most developed in regions of settled agriculture and not in areas of livestock ranching. It is understandable, therefore, that, at the beginning of the era of refrigeration, there were 50 cows and 150 sheep for every hog in Argentina. The present ratio is 8 cows and 11 sheep for every hog; and in Uruguay, 24 cows and 60 sheep. Growth in the importance of the swine industry in Argentina is clear. It is a part of the general intensification of Argentine agriculture, dependent upon the raising of alfalfa and of corn. As a result of the mild Argentine winters swine can be kept the year around on alfalfa pasture and are less dependent on corn than is the case in the United States. Some corn is fed in finishing them for the market.

## Agriculture in the Pampa

FORAGE CROPS. In search of a better forage than the native grasses, the Argentine *estancieros* have found alfalfa a most satisfactory crop. On the western irrigated lands, as in those of the United States, it is almost the only hay crop. In the Pampa, however, it will grow without irrigation, because in dry seasons its roots go deep into the soil for water and enrich the land at the same time. Under the mild winter weather it grows the year around and furnishes pasture most of the time. It will provide feed for four to six times more livestock than the native grasses. Moreover, it is such good feed that it fattens cattle for market without the use of a grain ration, and it is used also in feeding lambs and swine. It is not surprising, therefore, that livestock raisers have turned readily to it and that it is now the most extensively cultivated crop in the country. The deep and porous soils of the central Pampa region seem particularly suited to alfalfa, but it is grown in nearly all parts of the region except the east, where the soils are heavier and the drainage less good.

Alfalfa is not the only forage crop, however, and it occupies only a part of the land. It dies out after a few years and must be replaced. This is done in a crop rotation. In times of drought and cold weather it must be supplemented by other forage, such as grasses, corn fodder, and young cereal grains.

CEREAL CROPS. The Pampa is well suited to grain crops, but the owners of great estates who had become wealthy by raising livestock had little interest in cereal culture save as a means to the end of getting land in alfalfa. This was often done by plowing the land and securing one or more grain crops that served as shelter crops to get alfalfa started. Once established, the alfalfa can be cut or pastured for several years before its yield declines. Then the land must be plowed again, and the crop sequence repeated.

Ranch managers and herdsmen had no facility for or inclination to do that type of farm work, and their numbers were few on the great estates.

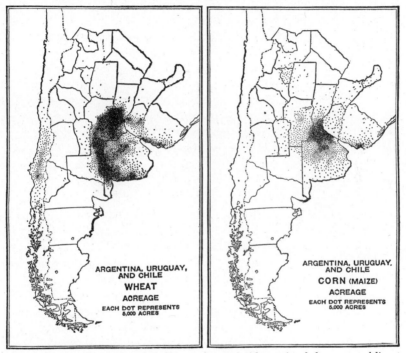

FIG. 203.—The Argentine wheat belt lies on the semiarid margin of the corn and livestock regions. (*U.S. Department of Agriculture.*)

It has been done almost entirely by immigrants, mainly Italian but some Spanish, French, and Swiss also. Few of them own land, but farm portions of the *estancias* under some kind of contract or lease. They live on the estate for a few years in temporary houses. Sometimes their tools and animals are supplied by the ranch owner. They farm extensively and produce little besides grains—so little that some of them do not even have gardens from which to supplement their restricted diets of cereals, eggs, and meat. Among the cereals grown, wheat leads in acreage, occupying nearly twice the area of any other. Corn is planted on about half as much land, but it usually yields a larger total return in bushels. Flax for seed often is the first crop raised on newly plowed prairie, and it occupies nearly as much land as corn. Some oats, rye, and barley are grown also, but their areas and yields are small compared with those of the three first mentioned.

*The Wheat Crescent.* The region of greatest wheat production lies in a crescent-shaped area, broader in the north and narrowing southward, on the western and drier side of the Pampa (Fig. 203). It is limited on the

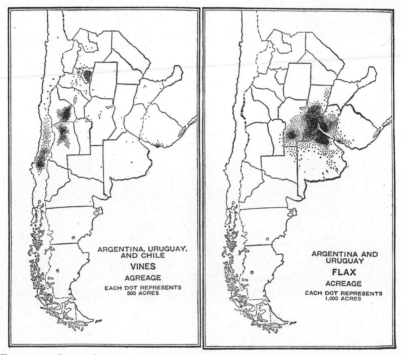

Fig. 204.—Grapes for wine, raisins, and table use are grown under irrigation in Chile and western Argentina. The ruled district in Tucumán, Argentina, marks the principal sugar-cane district. Flax for seed is an important crop in the cereal region. (*U.S. Department of Agriculture.*)

west where the rainfall decreases to less than about 20 inches per year. The eastern Pampa, south of Buenos Aires, is more humid, has less tillable soils, and is in parts poorly drained. It is better for grazing land than grain fields. The crescent extends from the southerly port of Bahía Blanca northward about 600 miles to the river ports of Rosario and Santa Fé, and it thus has outlets by water at either end and by rail to the port of Buenos Aires. The average crop of wheat is about one-fourth that of the United States, and a large part of it is exported.

*The corn region* lies in the central Pampa, west of Buenos Aires (Fig. 203). In part it is the same as the northern, and therefore warmer, end of the wheat crescent but is especially developed on its more humid eastern side. Most of the corn grown is of the "flint" type, with small, hard kernels which keep better in storage than North American corn does. Argentina is the second largest corn-producing country of the world, ranking next to the United States. However, its average crop is only about one-sixth as great, and only about one-fourth of that amount is fed on the Argentine *estancia*. About three-fourths of the crop is exported, mainly to Europe. For this reason the location of the producing district near to Buenos Aires and the river ports is an advantage.

*Flax* is grown for its seed in the same general region as corn (Fig. 204). It is one of the crops used in starting alfalfa, and it yields a cash return. Like corn, little of it is used in the country. It moves through

Fig. 205.—Ranch houses in Uruguay made of sods and thatch; a country with little timber. (*Copyright Keystone View Co.*)

Buenos Aires mainly to the United States, where it supplements the domestic crop in the manufacture of oil for the paint industry. Because of the rich prairie soils flax can be grown cheaply, and the normal Argentine crop is nearly half the world's supply of linseed.

THE GREAT ESTANCIA, which is the representative agricultural unit in the Pampa, is so different from the North American farm or ranch as to require brief comment. Owners of many of the large estates built palatial residences on them, but often they actually resided in Buenos Aires or even in Madrid or Paris. The land was supervised by a resident manager, sometimes Scottish or English. In the early period the pastures were unfenced, and even the boundaries sometimes were vague. When the value of livestock began to increase and the need for improved pasture was felt, the *estancias* were fenced and subdivided into great blocks, often several times the size of an average United States farm. Some of these are now occupied by tenant farmers and are again subdivided by wire fences into large fields of wheat and corn, other small grains, or alfalfa. Among them also are the homes of the tenants, often constructed of mud or sods and without barns or other buildings (Fig. 205). These bare and humble structures are in striking contrast to the owner's residence, set amid groves of planted trees on the otherwise treeless plain, surrounded by gardens and hedges, and flanked by granaries and workshops in architectural harmony.

## Other Agricultural Regions and Crops

OASIS FRUIT CULTURE.   Beyond the agricultural region of the *pampa* are others of different type. In part these are fruit-growing oases in the arid west. The more important of them include the pear and apple district of the Río Negro Valley and the grape- and wine-producing areas in the provinces of Mendoza and San Juan (Fig. 204). In these arid basins are fertile alluvial soils, unproductive save where irrigation water is available from the rains and snows of the high Andes to the west. Where the land is irrigated, alfalfa is grown as a general crop, but the tree fruits and the grapevine have also been established (Fig. 206). Under the care of Spanish and Italian growers the vine yields wines to supply the large requirements of a nation of nearly 13 million people, most of whom are of Mediterranean origin.

Table grapes and some raisins are produced also. Not only are grapes in demand in Buenos Aires and other Argentine cities, but they have an export market as well. The same is true of pears and apples from the Río Negro district. Brazil is the largest purchaser of Argentine fruits in general, but special markets have been developed for some of them.   Because of the difference in seasons between Northern and Southern hemispheres the Argentine harvest for pears, apples, and grapes comes in March and April, when such fruits are scarce in the northern countries. Pears have been sold especially in Great Britain, France, and Sweden; apples in Brazil, Germany, and Sweden; and grapes in the United States. The trade grew rapidly, and in 1938 the total fruit exports exceeded 70,000 tons, of which more than half were pears.

OASIS SUGAR CULTURE.   To the north of the vine regions is the great oasis of Tucumán, one of the earliest colonial settlements of Argentina and its colonial capital, located on the overland route by which the Pampa was first reached from Bolivia. The vine-growing oases are hemmed in on the east as well as the west by mountains, and their environs are barren. Tucumán, however, is open on the east, and the mountains to the west of it are luxuriantly forested at moderate elevations. The plain is dry and must be irrigated. The principal cash crop there is sugar cane. About Tucumán and other towns on the piedmont are fields of cane, whose total acreage is only a little less than that of all the vineyards to the southward.

Fig. 206.—An irrigated vineyard in Mendoza, Argentina. The development of fruit and wine production in this region is restricted by a limited market. (*Pan American Union.*)

The towns have sugar mills, which supply most of the Argentine requirement, and there is usually a small surplus of sugar for export.

COTTON CULTURE. The subtropical climate of the Chaco makes it a potential cotton-producing region, and the area planted in cotton is slowly increasing. There is much cheap land, but unfortunately the climate is not ideal. In the western part the rainfall is too light; in the east it is too heavy, especially in the picking season; and in all parts it is erratic. The frequency of droughts, locust pests, and the inadequacy of transportation have retarded the development of the industry. Its present output is about equal to that of Mexico or Peru but is less than 3 per cent that of the United States. However, one-third or more of the crop is usually exported (Fig. 213).

HORTICULTURAL CROPS. The growth of a large and rich urban market in Buenos Aires and some of the smaller cities of the Paraná Valley has encouraged specialization in vegetables and fruits, but the industry has much more limited possibilities than in the United States. It is best developed in a zone along the south side of the estuary and in the delta of the Paraná, all within a short distance of the capital city. It supplies a variety of vegetables and middle-latitude fruits, but grapes come from Mendoza, and citrus fruits from the subtropical Chaco and the northeastern province of Missiones.

## Extractive and Manufacturing Industries

QUEBRACHO. The forest industries are but poorly developed in Argentina. The only one of importance is located principally in the north, especially in the eastern Chaco near the great rivers. It is concerned with the cutting and preparation of quebracho trees, whose extremely hard wood is rich in tannin. Formerly the logs were exported, and some still are, but it is generally more economical to chip the wood in small mills and extract its tannin by hot water and steam. The condensed extract is conveniently shipped to the leather-tanning centers of North America and Europe. Large areas have already been cut over, but considerable supplies remain. The operations are conducted principally by corporations, both Argentine and foreign. They control large leaseholds of the thinly forested land, mainly in those areas easily accessible to river transportation.

LACK OF MINERALS. It has been noted previously that Argentina and Uruguay are peculiarly lacking in mineral resources. A small quantity of petroleum is produced in western Argentina, but it is barely half the national requirement. Neither country has any domestic coal supply. This is most unfortunate in relation to the development of manufactures and the transportation of goods. The arid western mountains have but little potential water power either, and the flat plains even less. The only important water-power resources are in the far northeastern corner of Argentina, where a tributary of the Paraná descends from the Brazilian highland over the great falls of Iguassú. These are so far removed from the centers of population that it has not yet been feasible to develop them. Most of the resources of industrial and motive power must, therefore, be imported.

Metallic minerals also are few. The mountainous west wall of Argentina shares in the mineralized rocks of Bolivia and Chile, but the actual discoveries and output of minerals remain small. Silver, lead, and tungsten ores are among the exports, but their combined values average only a small fraction of 1 per cent of the value of all exports, and they fluctuate greatly from year to year. So much of eastern Argentina is deeply silt-covered that there is hardly even a supply of rock and sand for building purposes in Buenos Aires and the other eastern cities. However, these can be supplied from Uruguay, and they enter the list of Uruguayan exports because it is cheaper for Buenos Aires to get them from that source than from the western highlands.

MANUFACTURING INDUSTRIES. The greater part of the manufactured goods used in Argentina and Uruguay come from the United States and Europe, but certain lines of manufacture are growing up in the region. The wine industry of Mendoza, the sugar industry of Tucumán, and the quebracho industry of the Chaco have already been mentioned. It would be expected that forms of manufacturing that can succeed would be (1) those using raw materials produced in the region, (2) those requiring a comparatively small amount of coal-driven machinery, (3) those demanding a relatively small force of technically skilled employees, and (4) those producing articles that require local manufacture in order to fill immediate local needs or to fit the exact nature of the local markets. It will be seen that most of the leading manufactures fulfill those requirements. They are meat and other animal products, flour and other food products, textile manufactures, manufactures of machinery and vehicles, and many other commodities of local importance. The number of persons employed in all manufacture in both Argentina and Uruguay is about the same as the number so employed in Canada and only about 7 per cent of the number in the United States. Of the total more than five-sixths are in Argentina. Protective tariffs have encouraged the development of certain classes of domestic manufacture and are partly responsible for the high prices of manufactured goods, especially in Argentina.

## Facilities for Transportation

RIVER TRANSPORTATION. The Paraná and its large tributaries, the Paraguay and the Uruguay, are navigated by river steamers for more than a thousand miles above Buenos Aires, and these waterways are the main outlets for parts of Uruguay, Paraguay, northern Argentina, and southern Brazil. Down these rivers come Brazilian lumber, some livestock, and other products. Ocean vessels drawing 26 feet ascend the Paraná to Rosario, and the Plata estuary is, of course, the great commercial gateway upon which are located Buenos Aires and Montevideo. The port of Bahia Blanca is the only important one not located on this estuary or its tributaries.

POOR ROADS. The most densely peopled portion of the River Plate countries, the Pampa, is so flat that there are few obstructions to road building. However, it is also the region of deep loessial and alluvial accumulations, where road materials are practically absent. Good roads must be built from imported materials and are expensive. Beyond some stretches of paved highway near Buenos Aires and along the lower Paraná good roads are almost lacking. The common roads of the Pampa are little more than broad traces, deeply trenched from rain erosion and the removal of dust by wind. Over them move ponderous high-wheeled carts heavily laden with wheat or wool and pulled by many horses. This style of two-wheeled conveyance, with wheels perhaps 10 feet in diameter, is a special adaptation to the soft, unimproved, but level roads. Fortunately, cattle and sheep can transport themselves to market, and this may be one reason for the continued dominance of the livestock industry.

A GOOD RAILROAD SYSTEM. The level Pampa has made railroad building easy, and Argentina has an excellent system totaling more than 25,000 miles. It is the best in South America. The greater part of it consists of a network radiating from Buenos Aires to the margin of the Pampa with some interconnecting cross lines (Fig. 207). Beyond the margin of the more densely settled areas long lines extend northeast, northwest, and west connecting with railroads into Brazil, Paraguay, Bolivia, and across the Andes to Chile. Much of the capital invested in Argentine railroads is British. Unfortunately, the roads have been built on several different gauges, thus preventing the free interchange of cars among the different lines. The rail lines of Uruguay radiate from Montevideo, but the country is less well served than the Pampa, having a total of less than 2,000 miles.

## Summary

The essential economic and geographic features of the River Plate countries may be summarized in few words. European settlement in this region is older than in eastern United States, but the regional economy remains simple in contrast with the industrial complexity of the United States. This may be attributed to a variety of causes—the origin and ideas of the dominant population element; the system of land holdings and the political dominance of the great landowners; the simple physical surface of the lowland; its lack of mineral resources, even including road materials, in the Pampa; its large area of humid, middle-latitude climate and prairie soils; its Atlantic frontage but great distance from its principal markets in the Northern Hemisphere. The striking dominance of agriculture and pastoralism in these countries is exhibited in the lists of exports and imports, because, since they are agricultural, these countries live in large degree by foreign trade. Among the exports corn takes first rank in value. It is sold mainly to the swine and poultry farmers of northwestern Europe. It is followed by wheat and linseed. The principal market for Argentine wheat and flour has been until recently in Great Britain, but currently the largest purchaser is Brazil. Next in the list of exports come the animal

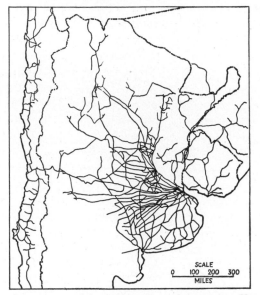

FIG. 207.—Railroad patterns and densities in Central Argentina, Uruguay, and Chile.

products—wool, beef, hides, mutton, and others. Formerly the animal products made up the larger part of the total exports, but now the exports of grains and other products of the soil far exceed in value all the many products of animal origin combined. In the list of imports the leading groups are crude-metal products and machinery of all types, textiles and clothing, petroleum and its products, coal, timber, and a great variety of minor items. The latter are in part manufactures but also foods of tropical and foreign origin such as cannot be raised in the River Plate climates or are not included in the prevailing type of agriculture.

In spite of the dominance of agricultural interests the size of the urban population is notable. Uruguay, which is least urban, is dominated by Montevideo (population nearly 700,000), but it has only one other city exceeding 50,000. Argentina, on the other hand, has nine cities of more than 100,000; and Buenos Aires, a city of great wealth and architectural display, reaches nearly 2½ million.

SELECTED REFERENCES

CARLSON, F. A. "Geography of Latin America," pp. 147–202, New York, 1936.

ELLIOT, L. E. "The Argentina of Today," New York, 1926.

ESTABROOK, L. M. Agricultural Survey of South America: Argentina and Paraguay, *U.S. Dept. Agr., Bull.* 1409, 1926.

JEFFERSON, MARK. "Peopling the Argentina Pampas," American Geographical Society of New York, 1926.

JONES, C. F. Agricultural Regions of South America, *Econ. Geog.*, Vol. 4 (1928), pp. 1–30, 159–186.

———. "South America," New York, 1930.

LEMERT, BEN F. Uruguay and the Uruguayans, *Jour. Geog*, Vol. 33 (1934), pp. 289–303.

WHITBECK, R. H., and F. E. WILLIAMS. "Economic Geography of South America," New York, 1940.

# Chapter XXI. Brazil and Paraguay

## Brazil

Brazil, the largest country of South America, is nearly a hundred times the size of Portugal, of which it was once a colony. It is larger than the United States without Alaska and three times the size of Argentina. Its 43 million people include (1) a small minority of descendants of old Portuguese families; (2) immigrants from southern Europe, Germany, and Poland; (3) a large number of negroes and persons of mixed negro and white ancestry; and (4) Indians and persons having an admixture of Indian blood. Popular education has been neglected, and two-thirds of the population is illiterate.

HIGHLAND SUBDIVISIONS
1-Rainy east coast
2-Dry northeast cotton and cattle region
3-Coffee region
4-Savanna forest and grazing region
5-General farming and livestock region

FIG. 208.—The principal regions of Brazil.

Brazil lies upon the equator, but it also extends beyond the southern tropic. It includes one of the greatest plains of the earth but also some extensive highlands. In so large a country it is not surprising to find great differences in the adaptability of the land to human use, especially by people of European origin. In order to appreciate these differences some of the physically contrasted regions should be noted.

### Physical and Cultural Elements

Physical Contrasts. With respect to its surface configuration Brazil may be divided into two large and unlike districts upon the margins of which are others of smaller size (Fig. 208). In the north is the broad, low, and generally level plain occupied by the drainage basin of the Amazon River. It is bordered on the north by the highlands of the Guianas and on the south by the second major subdivision of the country, the great

373

Brazilian highland. The plain lies mainly between latitudes 5°N. and 10°S. and is therefore almost entirely within the area of rainforest climate. The highland extends south to latitude 33°S. on the border of Uruguay. It is of so great diversity in elevation, exposure, and latitude that it has in consequence a diversity of climates.

*The northern lowland* occupies more than a third of the area of Brazil. The larger part of it is underlain by poorly consolidated sediments of relatively recent geological origin. It is traversed by the accessible thoroughfare of the Amazon, which has the largest volume of any river on earth. The river gradient is very slight—a fall of only 35 feet in the lower 2,000 miles of its course, throughout most of which the water is from 100 to 200 feet deep. This may be contrasted with the Mississippi, which with difficulty is kept 10 or 12 feet deep between New Orleans and St. Louis. Almost at the base of the Andes the Amazonian plain is only 500 feet above sea level, about the same elevation as southern Illinois. Heat and humidity prevail over the entire lowland, and dense rainforest occupies most of it. The forest is rich in species but is not itself a great resource, since most of the trees have little commercial importance. Neither have these vast plains any great agricultural value at present. The bottomlands are poorly drained or subject to flood; and the soils of the low interfluves, badly leached and infertile. The lowlands have as yet yielded little of value in mineral resources. In spite of its level surface, its great extent, and the deep river routes that penetrate its far interior, the great northern lowland of Brazil supports a sparse population and offers even less attraction to human occupancy now than it did a generation ago.

*The Brazilian highland* is a region of complicated geological structure and many rock types. Old sedimentary rocks, still more ancient crystalline masses, intrusions and extrusions of igneous origin all are encountered in parts of the region, and in some areas they are closely intermingled. The entire region is the eroded remnant of a once higher mountain and plateau upland. Its present surface is that of a great plateau which slopes gently upward from the back country in the basins of the Amazon and Paraná rivers. It reaches its greatest heights near the southeast coast and then falls abruptly toward the sea. The surface is by no means level. Rolling uplands in part, it is interrupted by numerous escarpments, ridges of hills, and low mountains. The highest summit exceeds 9,000 feet above sea level, but the plateau surface descends from a general altitude of about 3,000 feet in the southeast to 1,000 feet on its inland borders northwest and southwest.

The narrow seaward margin of the highland has a rainy, tropical climate. It differs little from that of the Amazon Basin. The west-sloping plateau surface, however, is sheltered from the moist sea winds, but it gets abundant thundershower rain during the summer. It has, therefore, the savanna type of climate and has both a lower average annual rainfall than the coastal slopes and a distinct winter drought. Only in the northeast is the rainfall so low as to produce an aridity even approaching that of the dry lands of Argentina. The southeastern sections of the plateau, although within the tropics, are high enough so that altitude reduces the temperatures appreciably. Winter frosts are not uncommon there, and chill winter mornings are associated with clear, dry days and strong sunlight.

The forests of the savanna uplands are much less dense than those of the rainy lowlands. They are more easily cleared to make room for agriculture and are at the same time more valuable as timber. In the southern part of the plateau are forests of Paraná pine, the only tree in South America that grows in pure stands at all like those which were characteristic of the pine forests of Florida, for example. Also, it is the best South American source of lumber for ordinary uses.

The soils of the uplands are generally less leached than those of the more humid regions, and some of them have good productive capacity. The complicated rock structures of the plateau have a variety of mineral resources also. There is neither coal nor petroleum, since most of these rocks, like those of Lauretian Canada, are very old. But they do contain ores of the metallic minerals, especially iron, manganese, and gold.

CULTURAL ELEMENTS. Brazil was easily approached only through the rainy lowlands of the Amazon or the southeast coast. It was not, therefore, so attractive to early settlement as the pampas or the mineral regions of the west coast. Forest products and sugar planting did enable a fringe of Portuguese settlement to maintain itself in the coastal region. Through these the Portuguese claim to the colonial region was established, the Portuguese language was rooted in the country, and negro slaves were introduced. As was true elsewhere, the native Indians were killed off in fighting or in slavery, and African slaves took their place on the sugar plantations.

However, it was not until the discovery of gold and diamonds on the plateau that there was a large movement of settlers from Portugal or from the coast to the interior. Gold was the attraction that led to the exploration of the far back slopes of the plateau, the penetration of the Amazon Basin, and the ultimate unification of so great an area under one language and one government. It also gave rise to the establishment of agriculture and the pastoral industries on the plateau, because these were necessary to supply the mining centers. The political and economic control of Portugal over Brazil was very strict, and for three centuries colonial Brazil could be little else than a supplier of foods and raw materials. The colonial status ended in 1808, and the country became the independent center of the Portuguese empire. In 1889 it became a republic. Since its independence the various regions of the country have undergone kinds of development that reflect their physical character and economic resources.

## REGIONS AND INDUSTRIES

SETTLEMENT AND INDUSTRY IN AMAZONIA. The great northern lowland of Brazil is much alike throughout in spite of its vast extent. It has a small population for so large an area, and that is located mainly along the streams and particularly along the lower course of the Amazon. The major concentrations are in the two cities of Belém (Pará) and Manaus. The former is situated near the mouth of the Amazon and is the principal port of the entire region. Manaus is an interior distributing and collecting point 1,000 miles upriver, near the stream junctions at the center of the lowland. The interstream and upstream districts along the tributaries are almost unbroken forests, inhabited by Indians, some of whom are still in their primitive state.

The industries of the lowland are confined almost entirely to the exploitation of the forest resources. The tillage of the soil is very limited, and that mainly near the river settlements. The principal forest resources collected for export are Brazil nuts, carnauba wax, and rubber. Formerly the rubber industry was the most important of these, but now it contributes least of the three to the value of exports.

*Rubber Production.* Among the many trees of the Amazon forest are several that produce resinous gums. The most important is *Hevea brasiliensis*, which secretes the latex from which the best grades of rubber are obtained. Individual trees are scattered through the mixed forests, and the collection of the latex requires the workman to travel from tree to tree on daily rounds scoring the trunk of the tree and collecting the milky exudations. About a century ago the first shipments of rubber began coming down the Amazon. Year by year the demand for rubber increased. By 1880 the Amazon forests were yielding 9,000 tons a year; and in 1910, 40,000 tons; but this did not supply the demand, and the price rose to $3 a pound. Seedling trees had already been transported to the East Indian region, where climatic and soil conditions are similar to those of the Amazon Valley but labor was cheaper and management better. Great plantations were developed there, and now they supply more than 98 per cent of the world's requirement, whereas Brazil contributes only a little more than 1 per cent. The actual shipments from Brazil have declined from a peak of nearly 47,000 tons in 1912 to recent annual exports of only a fourth that amount. Rubber planting has been undertaken in Brazil also, but it is hardly past the experimental stage. Low prices, sometimes less than 25 cents per pound, have made it unprofitable to collect wild rubber. The gatherers have disappeared from the less accessible forests;

many of their settlements have been abandoned; and much of the land has reverted to the Indians. The white population is less than it was thirty years ago. Even the cities, such as Manaus, have been faced with severe depression and have had to adjust their economic life to new conditions.

*Other Forest Products.* Brazil nuts are collected in the Amazon forests. They grow in coconutlike pods holding 20 to 30 nuts. Gathering them occupies some of the inhabitants, and the United States alone buys 2 or 3 million dollars worth per year. However, it is reported that even this industry is threatened by plantation products from the Far East. Carnauba wax is a hard wax obtained from the leaves of a palm. It is used in the manufacture of phonograph records, electric-insulation compounds, shoe polish, and other preparations. Many people are employed in the collection and preparation of this wax, the exports of which amount to 5 or 6 million dollars per year. There are also exports of cabinet woods, but the trees are widely scattered through the forest, and the expense of finding them, cutting them, and getting them to the rivers and to market is so great that there is little profit in the undertaking. Altogether, it

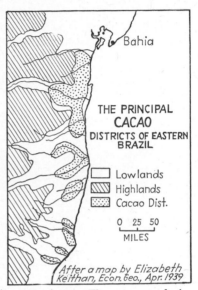

THE PRINCIPAL
**CACAO**
DISTRICTS OF EASTERN
BRAZIL

☐ Lowlands
▨ Highlands
▦ Cacao Dist.

0  25  50
MILES

*After a map by Elizabeth Keithan, Econ. Geo., Apr. 1939*

FIG. 209.—The cacao-producing districts of Brazil lie on the alluvial lands south of the port of Bahia.

appears that this vast forested plain is the least productive part of Brazil and that its development is now stagnant, if not in actual decline. It can hardly be doubted that the region could support a large population under conditions like those now existing in Java or Malaya. Yet it may be a long time before that will be realized with a Brazilian or European population.

SETTLEMENT AND INDUSTRY ON THE RAINY EAST COAST (Fig. 208). The east coast of Brazil is like Amazonia in its climate but is much more accessible. A series of ports from Recife to Rio de Janeiro are the outlets of narrow forested plains whose streams and alluvial soils are derived from the rainy slopes of the plateau. These are the sites of some of the colonial sugar plantations, and sugar still is grown in the north near Recife and also near Rio de Janeiro. However, the central and most rainy portion is noted particularly for its production of cacao, of which Brazil is the world's second largest producing region. Most of the crop is raised in the district south of São Salvador, a region of more than 80 inches of average annual rainfall. The plantings are made on the better drained slopes and alluvial lands. They are located near the coast or the rivers to secure transportation, because roads and railways are almost lacking (Fig. 209). The plantations are not large, and often they are merely collections of small patches purchased from the natives, many of whom are of mixed Indian and negro blood. The owners are mainly Europeans, but the natives are hired by them to produce the crop. Cacao exports, valued at about 15 million dollars, are worth three times more than Brazil's present rubber exports and rank third in the list of all exports from the country.

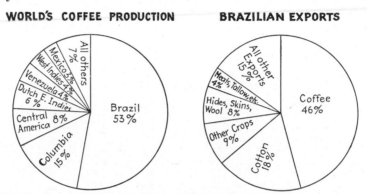

WORLD'S COFFEE PRODUCTION　　BRAZILIAN EXPORTS

Fig. 210.—Brazil supplies about half the world's coffee, and coffee comprises nearly half the exports of Brazil.

COFFEE PRODUCTION AND PLATEAU AGRICULTURE. In no other large country does a single product dominate the economic life of the nation as coffee dominates that of Brazil. The coffee planters constitute the aristocracy of the nation, whose prosperity rises and falls with the annual sale of 12 or 15 million bags of coffee (132 pounds per bag). When coffee prices are low, the whole nation is depressed; and when they are high, nearly every other business feels their influence. The value of the coffee exports is nearly equal to that of all other exports products combined (Fig. 210).

*The Coffee Region.* Practically all the coffee is grown in a district on the plateau in the state of São Paulo, west of Rio de Janeiro (Fig. 211). The region is only about 200 miles square, and a relatively small part of it is actually in coffee trees, yet Brazil produces about 65 per cent of the coffee of the world. Many features of the physical and economic environment of this region are involved in an explanation of this unusual crop concentration.

Coffee growing was first attempted 150 years ago on the rainy coastal lowland near Rio de Janeiro, but it did not prosper there. When the crop was moved to an enclosed and dryer valley on the seaward slope of the plateau, it did better; and when finally it was planted on the uplands and savanna margins, it found a most favorable environment. In its expansion into this region the crop was planted where routes of transportation, especially the railroads, penetrated, thus making the shipment of the crop possible. Expansion was limited, however, and still is, by conditions of climate and soil.

The districts most suited to coffee growing have the following climatic characteristics: (1) Temperatures that do not average more than 72°F. in the warmest month or less than 63°F. in the coldest month. (2) Absence of severe frosts or, at least, their infrequent occurrence. Light frosts may occur, and the quality of the coffee seems generally better near the cool margin of the producing area, though yields are likely to be low. (3) An

THE PRINCIPAL COFFEE-GROWING DISTRICTS OF BRAZIL

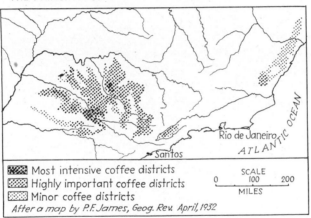

Fig. 211.—The principal coffee districts of Brazil are located on the uplands of the state of São Paulo, away from the coast.

average annual rainfall of between 40 and 60 inches. (4) Relatively dry and sunny winters, with rainfall averaging less than 8 inches for the three winter months. This promotes the uniform maturing of the coffee berries during that one season and facilitates the picking and open-air drying of the crop.

Coffee is grown in several types of soil, but that considered best is called *terra roxa*. It is an unusually porous red soil of high iron content which is derived from the weathering of dark-colored basic igneous rocks. It is generally low in both organic and mineral plant foods. Large areas of terra roxa soil are found in the southern Brazilian highland in districts not climatically suited to coffee, but within the climatic limits that soil type is utilized for this one crop to a high degree.

The surface configuration of the coffee region is that of a rolling upland. Many of the larger ridges stand in relief because of the resistance of the basic rocks to erosion. In general, the coffee districts are located on the ridges and avoid the lower lands, but they do not occupy the highest lands, above 3,000 feet elevation, because of the lower temperatures there. Locally, the uplands are cut into hills and valleys by stream erosion, and the great coffee estates occupy all kinds of land. However, the coffee trees are confined mainly to the hills and valley slopes; the valley bottoms are used for corn, rice, beans, and other food crops or as pasture for the animals, or they remain in woodlands. This has the advantage of leaving the terra roxa of the ridges and slopes for the coffee trees and, at the same time, providing them with better soil drainage and air drainage in times of light frost (Fig. 212). The plantation buildings, which include houses, stables, storage sheds, coffee-cleaning plants, and drying floors, also occupy the valleys, and it is through the valley that the road usually leads down to the nearest railway station, from which the coffee is sent to market.

*The Coffee Fazenda.* Brazilian coffee is produced mainly under a system of plantation culture. The great estates, called "fazendas," sometimes include several thousand acres. One of them may occupy the entire drainage basin of a small stream. It will include several hundred acres of coffee on the uplands and still larger areas in woodland, pasture, and supply crops. The coffee land is divided into blocks, each under the charge of a workman who may be an Italian immigrant. Workmen live in barracklike houses at the plantation center. The plantation, like the Argentine *estancia*, is run by a manager, and the owner commonly lives in a near-by city.

New land is cleared and coffee trees are planted as older plantings cease to be productive. New plantings require 6 to 8 years to come into production. Unlike the general practice in Middle America, the trees can be grown without shade in the Brazilian climate. This makes cultivation easier and promotes large-scale operation. The cool, dry winter (May to August) is the principal harvest season. The picking is done by hand but more rapidly and with less selection for maturity than in some other regions. This reduces labor costs but also, in general, the quality of the product. The picked berries are taken to the cleaning machines, where the exterior pulp and hulls are removed, and they are then spread to dry on paved floors. These are sometimes colored black so that they will absorb more solar heat and thus hasten the drying process. The dried beans are sacked for shipment. Most of the coffee goes for export to Santos or Rio de Janeiro—especially the former, the world's leading coffee port.

One difficulty encountered by the planters is that of securing enough laborers when they are needed, particularly at harvest time. In an effort to provide laborers the government has encouraged immigration from Italy, Spain, and Portugal, even paying the passage of immigrants.

FIG. 212.—A coffee plantation on the hilly upland of São Paulo, Brazil. Coffee trees clothe the upper slopes; the drying floors and buildings of the fazenda occupy the valley. (*Pan American Union.*)

Many Japanese have settled in this region also, but they prefer to own land and become small farmers rather than plantation laborers. Another serious difficulty is low prices. The crop being perennial, it cannot be expanded or contracted readily to fit changes in demand. Moreover, there are great variations in yield from year to year. A large yield coinciding with a restricted demand reduces prices to ruinous levels, and the state and national governments in Brazil have adopted various measures to

Each dot represents 5,000 bales

FIG. 213.—The cotton-growing regions of South America include four principal areas: (1) the Brazilian coffee region; (2) northeastern Brazil; (3) coastal Peru; and (4) the Chaco region in Argentina and Paraguay.

control them. Some of these have been temporarily beneficial, but Brazil is not the only coffee producer, and in some degree her competitors have profited as much as the Brazilian planter by these measures. Control now appears to be abandoned, and a free competition with other regions may be expected to reduce Brazil's advantages more largely to those that are inherent in her natural equipment for coffee production.

BRAZILIAN COTTON.   Cotton culture was introduced into Brazil very early, but it did not progress rapidly until the years of the American Civil War, when European spinners were deprived of their customary supply. After that time it declined to a relatively low level of output, and only recently has Brazil again taken an important place among the world's producers. Its 1937 crop of more than 2 million bales was six times greater than the average production of a quarter century earlier.

Cotton is grown in two distinct regions in Brazil: (1) the older region, in the northeastern states (Fig. 213), which produced about three-fourths of the supply prior to 1920; and (2) the southern states, where cotton growing has expanded so rapidly that in recent years this region has produced more than two-thirds of the total Brazilian crop. The two regions are very different in soil, climate, and growing conditions, and they produce different kinds of cotton. In southern Brazil, the state of São Paulo has the largest acreage. The cotton grown is of the American upland varieties, and it is grown both in the coastal districts and in the coffee region. Its rapid increase in importance there has resulted in part from the fact that planters, discouraged with the outlook for coffee, have turned to cotton as an alternative cash crop. Small farmers also, especially the Japanese, find cotton more suited to their requirements and abilities than is coffee. In northeastern Brazil the long-staple tree cotton, a perennial plant, still predominates, especially in the interior districts, which are subject to erratic rainfall and long periods of drought. There is a great abundance of cotton land in Brazil. The future of the crop there is restricted more by low prices, lack of labor, and poor transportation facilities than by lack of area having suitable soils and climate.

GENERAL FARMING AND LIVESTOCK PRODUCTION. Only a small part of the agricultural lands of Brazil are planted to coffee, cacao, cotton, and minor cash crops. Even in the regions of specialized agriculture, general-supply crops occupy much of the tilled land. That is particularly true in the southernmost states, which extend toward Uruguay (Fig. 208). There the population has a large north-European element, especially German, and general farming and livestock raising is more widely practiced than plantation culture. The region is intermediate in surface and climate between northern Uruguay and the coffee region, and most of it is a low rolling plateau with humid subtropical climate comparable with that of the state of Georgia. It was originally a forested region but now produces corn, wheat, beans, potatoes, and other supply crops, especially in the more densely settled section near Porto Alegre. The principal cash income, however, is from livestock. Cattle, sheep, and swine are raised, but in large part they are of poor quality and get comparatively little attention. Packing plants at Rio Grande do Sul and other centers provide an outlet for the commercial surplus.

The great forests of northern Brazil obviously cannot be utilized as grazing lands. If ever they are more densely settled, it will be by farmers who chop small farms out of the rank woodland growths. On their savanna margins, however, there are large areas that have some possibilities as grazing lands. These include the Mato Grosso and other parts of southwestern Brazil on the Paraguayan borders (Fig. 208). Some of these lands already are stocked with cattle of low grade, which are tended by indifferent half-cast herdsmen. The cattle are subject to disease and insect pests, and there is little incentive to improve them so long as better lands are available in the plateau region. Present transportation facilities are limited to one railway line extending west from the coffee region and the river traffic southward through Argentina. These are too restricted to permit the profitable movement of much other than hides, meat extracts, and preserved beef. The potential utility of a large part of these savanna lands is not known. Some are believed to be capable of future agricultural settlement, but large sections have poor soils or are otherwise unsuited for farming even if provided with adequate transportation and markets.

MINERAL RESOURCES AND INDUSTRIES. For a century and a half Brazil supplied the greater part of the world's diamonds; but when the remarkable mines of South Africa were discovered, the Brazilian output declined. Only recently, however, the second largest diamond ever found was taken from Brazil. In colonial days gold was an important product, but now it is less than a half of 1 per cent of the world's average annual output. Some silver is produced also, and manganese is exported. In the far south, on the Uruguayan border, a little low-grade coal is mined, but not nearly enough to supply the country's needs. All these minerals and some others are obtained from the complex rocks of the eastern highland, but the value of all the mineral products combined is not half so great as that of the sugar or one-sixth that of the coffee produced. However, a statement of the present value of the minerals produced is not a true reflection of the mineral resources of Brazil, for undoubtedly the plateau region has large potential resources, particularly of iron ores. In the state of Minas Geraes, about 200 miles north of Rio de Janeiro, there are several ore bodies, some hematite, some magnetite, of very high grade and at the surface of the ground. Unfortunately, Brazil has no coking coal, and the small quantities of ore now smelted are reduced with imported fuel. Moreover, the transportation difficulty of getting the ores to the coast over expensive railroads on steep grades has been restrictive. So have Brazilian export regulations, and little of the ore is mined. They are mainly controlled by American, English, and French capital; and when they are mined in quantity, they probably will be taken to Europe, and coal brought back in the same ships. For the future, these are probably among the most important iron-ore deposits in the world.

## MANUFACTURING AND COMMERCE

THE GROWTH OF MANUFACTURING. Nowhere in South America has manufacturing progressed far, but under a high protective tariff it has made more progress in Brazil than elsewhere. Factory production is restricted to a relatively small list of articles, foremost among which are textiles, metal products, clothing, chemical products, foods, and lumber.

The relative importance of these is indicated by the fact that the value of textile products, mainly cotton, is more than twice as great as that of all metal products. Yet in this greatest of all Brazilian industries the number of cotton spindles in operation is only one-tenth that in the United States, and the quantity of cotton spun is about equal to that spun in Alabama. In general, the Brazilian manufacturing establishments are small, and the value of products per worker indicates the lack of some of the elements of skill, management, power, transportation, and experience that enable large-scale manufactures to grow.

The principal centers of manufacture are in the south, especially the state of São Paulo. There are several reasons for this. The south is the principal center of population both urban and rural; two cities, Rio de Janeiro and São Paulo, together have more than 3 million of Brazil's 43 million people. The south has the larger part of the white people with a higher standard of living, the negroes, since the abolition of slavery in 1888, having migrated generally to the northeastern coastal region, where many of them already were employed in the sugar industry. The south has the best transportation, as the railroads have been built into the coffee and mining districts of the plateau more extensively than elsewhere (Fig. 214). The south has also the greatest actual and potential water powers. The heavy rainfall of the plateau region, especially its abrupt seaward face, and the steep stream gradients there provide large potential powers which are only slightly developed. These are particularly adaptable to the textile industries. The south, and especially the plateau upland, has the coolest and most generally healthful climate in which to establish manufacturing industries.

BRAZILIAN PORTS AND COMMERCE. Brazil has 12 cities of more than 100,000 population each, and with two exceptions (São Paulo and Bello Horizonte) they are all on the coast. Several of them have excellent harbors; this is particularly true of Rio de Janeiro, which has one of the best protected and largest natural harbors in the world (Fig. 215). Yet the foreign commerce of Brazil is little more than half that of Argentina, which has only one-third as great an area or population. Brazil is not a country of great per capita wealth, though it has greater natural (but undeveloped) wealth than Argentina. So varied are the products of Brazil that it is more nearly a self-sufficient country and does not need to buy so many things abroad.

The export trade of Brazil consists largely in the sale of the products of plantation, range, and forest; mineral exports are small. Coffee makes up more than 40 per cent of the total, and cotton nearly 20 per cent (Fig. 210). The United States is much the most important market for Brazilian exports, since it is the world's largest coffee market. Cotton is exported to Great Britain, Germany, and Japan. Brazilian imports come in about equal amounts from the United States and Germany. Large purchases are made from Great Britain and Argentina also and from many other countries in smaller quantities. The largest classes of imports are machinery and vehicles, foodstuffs (especially wheat and flour), miscellaneous manufactures of iron and steel, coal, and petroleum.

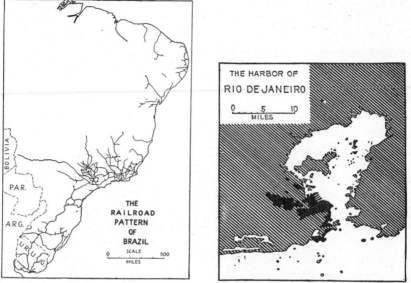

Fig. 214.

Fig. 215.—The large and protected harbor of Rio de Janeiro.

## Paraguay

Paraguay—three times the size of Pennsylvania—has a population of less than a million, the majority of whom have Indian blood. It is the least developed of the South American republics, owing in part to its inland situation and in part to long and bitter wars. Much of it is low, partly forest covered and partly open grassland and swamps. It shares in the characteristics of the Argentine Chaco and the Mato Grosso of Brazil, between which it lies. Its capital, Asunción, is an unpaved, unsewered town of 95,000 people, reached by one poorly built railroad from the south. Most of the small external trade of the country is carried by river boats on the Paraguay and Paraná rivers which connect with Buenos Aires.

Only a few lines of industry have developed an exportable surplus. They are (1) the raising of cotton, which has increased considerably in recent years; (2) cattle raising; (3) the preparation of quebracho extract; (4) the growing and collecting of yerba maté (often called "Paraguay tea"); and (5) tobacco raising. Many other products, such as sugar, mandioca, corn, beans, and oranges, are extensively grown but mainly for home consumption. The country is reputed to have reserves of iron ore, manganese, and copper, but they are even less developed than those of Brazil.

AGRICULTURAL EXPORTS. The development of the cotton industry in recent years has provided Paraguay with a valuable, relatively light, and imperishable product. It has taken rank as the leading export of the country, accounting for one-fourth to one-third of the total export values. The region of its production is on the border of the Argentine Chaco, where the same industry is making progress. The total Paraguayan crop of less than half a million bales is about equivalent to that of one of the less important cotton states, such as Missouri.

*Yerba maté* is a small tree growing wild in Paraguay and southern Brazil. Its leaves when dried and pulverized make a tea that is much in demand in parts of South America, especially Argentina. So great is the demand that foreign corporations have acquired large tracts of land and are developing plantations, both in Paraguay and Brazil, after the model of coffee estates.

*Meat Products.* It is estimated that there are four times as many cattle as people in Paraguay, but the cattle, like those of the Mato Grosso, are of poor quality. The meat-packing plants do not attempt to ship fresh beef. Canned and preserved meats, meat extracts and concentrates, and cattle hides are among the important products that can be got profitably to an outside market.

SELECTED REFERENCES

BYNUM, M. L. The World's Exports of Coffee, *U.S. Dept. Commerce, Trade Information Series* 110, 1930.

CARLSON, F. A. "Geography of Latin America," pp. 203–331, New York, 1936.

JAMES, P. E. The Coffee Lands of Southeastern Brazil, *Geog. Rev.*, Vol. 22 (1932), pp. 225–244.

———. The Expanding Settlements of Southern Brazil, *Geog. Rev.*, Vol. 30 (1940), pp. 601–626.

JONES, C. F. Agricultural Regions of South America, *Econ. Geog.*, Vol. 5 (1929), pp. 109–140.

KEITHAN, E. Cacao Industry of Brazil, *Econ. Geog.*, Vol. 15 (1939), pp. 195–204.

McCREERY, W. G., and M. L. BYNUM. The Coffee Industry in Brazil, *U.S. Dept. Commerce, Trade Promotion Series* 92, 1930.

NASH, ROY. "The Conquest of Brazil," New York, 1926.

NORMANO, J. F. "Brazil: A Study of Economic Types," Chapel Hill, N. C., 1935.

TEWKSBURY, H. H. Motor Roads in Brazil, *U.S. Dept. Commerce, Trade Promotion Series* 117, 1931.

WHITBECK, R. H., and F. E. WILLIAMS. "Economic Geography of South America," New York, 1940.

# Chapter XXII. The Continent of Europe

EUROPEAN DOMINANCE IN WORLD AFFAIRS. All Europe is only a little larger in area than Canada or than the United States and Alaska. In spite of its small size it has attained a dominant place among the continents. It includes one of the four great centers of world population (Fig. 5) and has accumulated the world's greatest concentration of tangible property in lands, buildings, consumable supplies, and transportation equipment. It conducts, in normal times, the greater part of the world's commerce. Moreover, it is a remarkable fact that the peoples of Europe have extended their languages, type of civilization, and political ideas throughout the world. Both Americas have been occupied by Europeans and their descendants. All Africa is under European rule or dominance, and so are Australia and most of the islands of the Pacific. Only Asia includes important non-European nations. So far as political and commercial control are concerned, the world is under the domination of Europeans. To what extent this position represents only a stage in the unfolding of human history, to what degree it was inevitable that Europe should be the dominant continent, these and other like questions are matters that it does not suit the present purpose to debate. They are, in any case, vastly complicated by the military operations and political changes of recent times. However, political governments may rise or fall and boundaries may change, as they have in the past, but the physical Europe remains essentially the same. It is desirable, therefore, that we give some thought to the physical characteristics and equipment of the seat of this unique development of strength and cultural potency, the continent of Europe as a whole. These include a combination of geographical elements used or neglected by men according to their knowledge or abilities.

EUROPE'S ADVANTAGES OF FORM AND OUTLINE. Of all the continents Europe is least massive and most articulated. It is, in fact, a great peninsula on the Eurasian landmass. But it is a peninsula fringed with lesser peninsulas and islands, and these in turn carry a greater number of still smaller peninsulas upon their margins. Finland, Scandinavia, Britain,

Iberia, Italy, and the Balkan area are the larger units. Denmark, Cornwall, Brittany, Calabria, and southern Greece are of the second order of size. These coastal projections are separated by more or less enclosed bodies of water. In the early stages of European history separation promoted a degree of isolation, permitting periods of development in relative seclusion. There were, to be sure, conquests and great migrations, but there was not quite the same exposure to seasonal raids and incursions, the tribal shifting and pushing, that characterized the relations of the

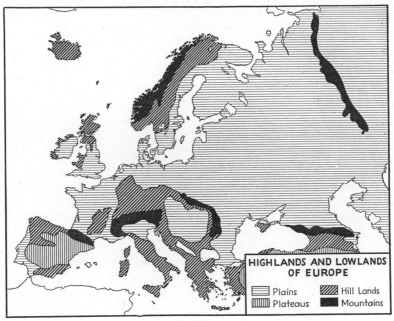

HIGHLANDS AND LOWLANDS
OF EUROPE

☐ Plains   ▨ Hill Lands
▦ Plateaus   ■ Mountains

FIG. 216.

Indians in the open spaces of the great interior plains of North America, for example. Later, after the conquest of the sea but before the improvement of land transportation, this same indented coastline made much of Europe accessible to the penetration of commerce and the interchange of ideas. It still does. No other continent has half as long a coastline in proportion to its area.

FEATURES OF SURFACE CONFIGURATION. The land surface of Europe is one of great diversity. Mountains, hill lands, nearly enclosed basins, and broad plains are interwoven in a manner that produces great diversity within relatively small areas. This is much more true of western Europe than of eastern, and it is one of the reasons why travel in western Europe has been so much enjoyed. Although the distribution of these features may seem the result of mere chance, a study of them shows that in geological age, type, and arrangement they have an order or system the major features of which are readily understood. Briefly these features include three systems of highlands: north, middle, and south (Fig. 216). Between them are two types of lowlands, very unequal in extent.

In the northwest are ancient rocks, comparable with those of Laurentian Canada. The western margins of these are broadly uplifted and carved by erosion into the highlands of Norway, Scotland, and northern Ireland. Eastward in Sweden and Finland the same kind of rocks are worn down to a low level. Both high and low, these hard rocks have been

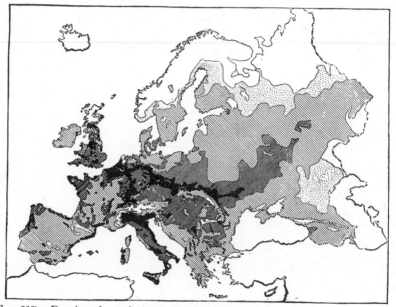

FIG. 217.—Density of population in Europe. Black, very dense, in places reaching 500 or more per square mile; dots, less than 10 per square mile; white, still less dense. (*After Weise in Petermann's "Mitteilungen."*)

heavily ice-scoured by continental glaciation, with results similar to those in Canada—disturbed drainage and innumerable lakes, thin soils, boulder-strewn surfaces, and areas of bare and polished rock.

Midway in Europe between north and south are isolated hill lands, also of ancient rocks but less extensive than those of the north. They, too, are a part of the foundation structure of the continent. These appear in southern Ireland, Wales and Cornwall, Brittany, central France, and the hill regions of central Germany, such as the Black Forest and the mountains of Bohemia. They were not overridden by the continental glaciers. A great block of land in western Spain and Portugal belongs in this same category. It is mainly a tableland, or plateau, traversed by mountain ridges.

Southern Europe is characterized by rugged mountains. These trend in a generally east-west direction and include the Pyrenees, Alps, Apennines, Carpathians, and Caucasus. They are so young in age that they appear to be still in a process of growth. Occasional displacements of the rocks by internal forces jar the region in the severe earthquakes that visit the Mediterranean border. Such have occurred in southern Italy many times, and the disastrous Turkish earthquakes of December, 1939, were of the same origin. The active volcanoes of Italy may be thought of as a related phenomenon.

Between the northern highland and the central hill region is the North European Plain. This begins in southern France and extends north and east, including eastern England, Belgium, the Netherlands, Denmark and the Baltic plain of Germany and Poland. At that point it expands greatly, both north and south, and includes most of Russia from the Black Sea and the Caucasus Mountains to the Arctic Ocean. It terminates in the east against the low ridges of the Ural Mountains. This plain is one of rolling surface and has underlying rocks much like those of the central plain of North America.

Fringing the Alpine mountain chains are the lesser plains of southern Europe. They include basin lands in southern France, the Po Valley of Italy, and the Danubian plains of Hungary, Yugoslavia, Rumania, and Bulgaria.

The significance of the plains of Europe will be seen from the maps showing density of population (Figs. 5, 217). The central plain in particular, from England to central Russia, is the focus of industrial and commercial activity. Tillable lands, sources of industrial power, and highly developed communications enable it to support the larger part of the total population of the continent.

THE RIVER SYSTEMS OF EUROPE. The rivers of Europe include several of sufficient size to serve as navigable waterways, and these have played a large part, and still do, in commerce. Those most used are the Thames, the Rhine, the Danube, and the Volga. But the Vistula, the Oder, the Elbe, the lower courses of the Seine and Scheldt, and many of the rivers of Russia besides the Volga also carry a large traffic.

In northwestern Europe the sinking of the land relative to sea level deepened the lower courses of several of the rivers and converted them into estuaries that admit ocean vessels for considerable distances. On these estuaries most of the great ports are located—London, Liverpool, Hull, Antwerp, Hamburg, Bremen, and many others.

THE CLIMATES OF EUROPE have played an important part in the development of its resources, civilization, and industries. The essential conditions that have shaped its climates are two: (1) position in the middle latitudes on the eastern side of one of the great oceans and (2) the nature and arrangement of the surface features. In Europe, in contrast with both North and South America, an open and deeply indented coast-line is presented to the westerly winds, and mainly it is the ends rather than the bold and continuous fronts of the mountains that face the sea. Under these conditions mild and moist winds penetrate far inland along the North Sea, the Baltic, and the Mediterranean. One of the results of this is that Europe is the only continent that has no arid desert, unless a

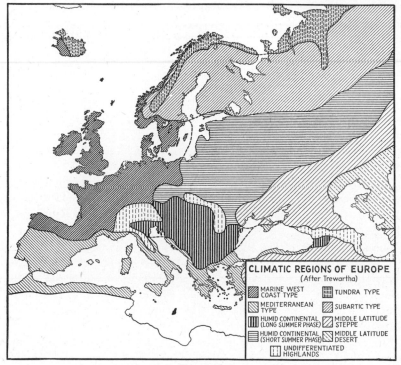

CLIMATIC REGIONS OF EUROPE
(After Trewartha)

MARINE WEST COAST TYPE   TUNDRA TYPE
MEDITERRANEAN TYPE   SUBARTIC TYPE
HUMID CONTINENTAL (LONG SUMMER PHASE)   MIDDLE LATITUDE STEPPE
HUMID CONTINENTAL (SHORT SUMMER PHASE)   MIDDLE LATITUDE DESERT
UNDIFFERENTIATED HIGHLANDS

FIG. 218.

small area in southeastern Russia bordering the Caspian Sea be rated as such.

Europe has, in fact, seven rather distinct types of climate, each of which is reasonably comparable with the climate of some part of North America (Fig. 218). (1) The far north includes a strip of tundra climate. (2) South of it is a subarctic zone much like the larger part of Canada. (3) Western European climate is marine, generally not so rainy as the climate of the Puget Sound region of North America but otherwise similar. This mild-winter, cool-summer type of climate penetrates inland to the Alps and central Germany. (4) Beyond that, in the eastern Baltic plain and central Russia, the climate is similar to that of the Great Lakes region of North America. (5) The climate of the Po and Danube Basins is much like that of the American corn belt. (6) That of the Black Sea borders and southern Russia is comparable with American high plains climate. (7) All the lands of the Mediterranean border from Portugal to Greece have dry, subtropical climates comparable with the conditions found in most of California.

FOREST RESOURCES.   Northwestern Europe has large forest resources. Sweden, Finland, and northern Russia in the zone of subarctic climate

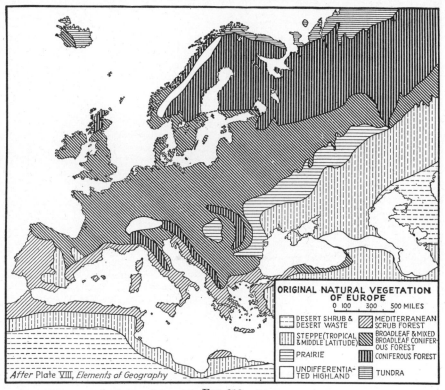

FIG. 219.

have coniferous forests that are comparable with the better forest districts of eastern Canada (Fig. 219). Eastward they grade off toward the taiga of the Ural district and Siberia. Southern Germany and the Carpathian and Balkans regions have mixed forests more like those of the Great Lakes region. England, Belgium, the Netherlands, and France had such forests originally, but they have been more largely cleared to make place for farm lands and pastures even on many of the hilly areas of types that in central Europe have been kept in forests. In the Mediterranean lands, with their scant summer rainfall, the original forests were thinner and consisted largely of oak. They have suffered much from grazing animals and lack of attention and are now generally sparse. In most of Europe the timber has been largely removed from lands capable of cultivation, but this is less true in central Russia than elsewhere. Southeastern Russia, on the other hand, was not originally forested but was prairie grassland or even short-grass steppe.

SOIL ZONES IN EUROPE. The soil zones of Europe have developed as a consequence of climatic conditions, the character of the natural vegeta-

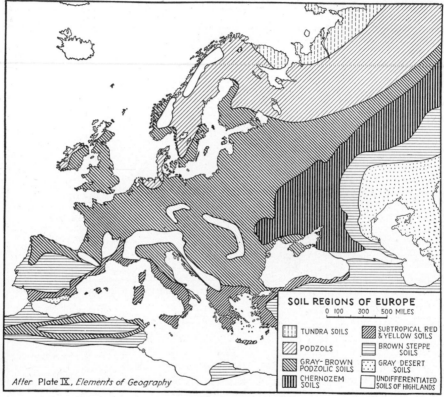

SOIL REGIONS OF EUROPE
0   100   300   500 MILES

TUNDRA SOILS
PODZOLS
GRAY-BROWN PODZOLIC SOILS
CHERNOZEM SOILS
SUBTROPICAL RED & YELLOW SOILS
BROWN STEPPE SOILS
GRAY DESERT SOILS
UNDIFFERENTIATED SOILS OF HIGHLANDS

*After Plate IX, Elements of Geography*

FIG. 220.

tion that occupied the land in prehistoric times, and the nature of the surface and its geologic history. There are several broad zones (Fig. 220) in which the soils are of contrasting types. Those of the north are of the light-colored, leached podsolic type, like those of the Canadian forest region. In most of the North European Plain the prevailing soils are of the brown, forest type like those of southern Michigan or Ohio, fertile if properly managed. In southern Europe types of subtropical red soils of only moderate fertility prevail. The old grasslands of southern Russia, however, yielded soils of dark color and high fertility. These are comparable with the soils of the Dakotas or Nebraska. Near the Caspian

Sea are alkaline desert soils. The fact that some of the soils of western Europe are actually more productive of crops than the naturally rich lands of southern Russia is more a tribute to the greater and more dependable rainfall of that region and to the skill of the farmers than an expression of the natural productiveness of the soils themselves.

MINERAL RESOURCES. Europe is rich in some of the vital industrial mineral resources but poor in others. Her production of gold, silver, copper, and tin are small, and only in southeastern Russia and in Rumania

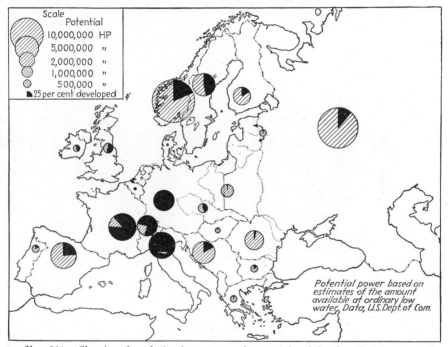

FIG. 221.—Showing the relative importance of potential and developed water powers in Europe. Norway has the largest potential power resource, but Italy and Germany have developed theirs most completely, having already exceeded their minimum potential.

are there considerable supplies of petroleum. Of coal, iron, manganese, bauxite, and potash, however, the resources are large, but these are very unequally distributed. The coal is confined almost entirely to the sedimentary rocks of the northern plain. Deposits are found in England, northern France and Belgium, Germany, and central and southern Russia. In contrast, the ancient rocks of Scandinavia and the complicated structures of the Mediterranean lands are almost without this essential fuel. Iron ore is found most abundantly in the older rocks of central Europe, as in northern Spain, northern England, northeastern France, the mountains of Bohemia, southern Russia, and the Ural region. Some is found also in North Africa, and ores of the highest grade are mined in the far north of Sweden. It appears therefore that the countries that occupy the North European lowland are best equipped with coal and are well supplied with iron, the prime mineral essentials of modern industrialism. This same region has also the principal deposits of zinc, lead, potash, and several other minor minerals.

The mineral resources of Europe as a whole are highly utilized. The continent has far less than half the known coal and iron ore of the world, yet normally it mines as much as all the rest of the world. Europe and Anglo-America together produce more than 95 per cent of the world's coal and iron both. This expression of the high industrial development of these regions, more than anything else, shows why the North Atlantic Ocean is the greatest highway of international trade.

WATER POWER. Since the potential water power of a continent depends upon the area of the continent, as well as upon the rainfall and runoff and the relief of the land, Europe could hardly rank high in total potential water power (Figs. 125, 221).

ESTIMATED POTENTIAL AND DEVELOPED WATER POWER IN 1936*

| Continent | Potential Horsepower | Developed Horsepower |
|---|---|---|
| Africa | 274,000,000 | 175,000 |
| Asia | 148,000,000 | 5,400,000 |
| North America | 77,000,000 | 26,000,000 |
| South America | 74,000,000 | 1,100,000 |
| Europe | 74,000,000 | 27,200,000 |
| Oceania | 24,000,000 | 600,000 |
| Approximate world total | 671,000,000 | 60,500,000 |

* Data from U.S. Department of Commerce.

From the preceding table it will be seen that Europe ranks highest among the continents in *developed* water power, exceeding North America. In both these continents about a third of the potential power has been brought into use. In Europe two regions yield a large part of the total. They are (1) the glaciated highland of Scandinavia and (2) the Alpine region of France, Italy, Germany, and Switzerland. It cannot be said that the use of water power has yet assumed large importance in the industries of Europe as compared with coal, although it is increasing rapidly.

## The Three Economic Regions of Europe

### THE NORTH SEA COUNTRIES

A MARINE CLIMATE. It already has been pointed out that the Atlantic Ocean exerts a profound influence upon the climate of western Europe. Note on a map of Europe that the British Isles, the Scandinavian countries, Belgium, Holland, most of Germany, and a part of France are north of the 49th parallel of north latitude, which is the northernmost latitude of any of the states of the United States. Even the northern boundary of Minnesota and North Dakota is several degrees farther south than London or Berlin. The North Sea countries lie between the parallels of 50 and 60°N. latitude, but they have winter temperatures resembling those of our eastern states that lie nearly 1,000 miles farther south, for example, Virginia and Maryland. These countries have ample rain for agriculture, little snow except on the mountains, mild winters, temperate summers, and ever changing weather.

A REGION OF DROWNED COASTS AND MANY HARBORS. The western edge of the real continental block of Europe is out in the Atlantic well to the west of Ireland. The British Isles are a part of the actual continent, and the North and Baltic seas are shallow parts of the ocean which now cover portions of the North European Plain. A moderate sinking of the land in the recent geologic past cut the British Isles off from the rest of the continent. Sinking coasts are usually irregular coasts, with offshore islands and broad river mouths which make good harbors. The North Sea countries have such a coast—an excellent coast for the purposes of ocean commerce. Of 12 leading ports of the world, 6 are on the borders of the North Sea—London, Antwerp, Rotterdam, Amsterdam, Hamburg, and Bremen. In normal times more overseas commerce is handled by the North Sea ports than by all the other ports of Europe.

IMPORTANCE OF THE FISHERIES OF WESTERN EUROPE. The shallow waters that border the coast of western Europe are ideal breeding grounds for fish, and one of the most productive sea-fishing regions of the world is there. Many people in all the West European coast regions are engaged in fisheries, especially in the North Sea and off the coast of Norway. Thousands of fishing boats go out from the ports of England, Scotland, France, Norway, and Holland. Cod, haddock, mackerel, herring, and many less familiar fish are caught in enormous numbers; the annual catch by British and Norwegian fishermen has exceeded a billion pounds for each of these countries. The ocean fisheries have been one of the most effective of all agencies in making the North Sea peoples seagoing and sea-loving. The ocean fisheries are a training school for seamen, an incentive to boat designing and boat building, and the invariable first steps in the making of maritime nations; and all the North Sea nations are maritime nations. Moreover, the 4 billion pounds of fish caught yearly in these waters constitutes a very substantial item in the food supply of Europe and a not inconsiderable item of commerce.

THE NORTH AND BALTIC SEAS BORDERED BY PLAINS. With the unimportant exceptions of a short strip of the Norwegian coast and the Scottish coast, the North Sea is bordered by plains. This, of course, is to be expected when it is recalled that the North and Baltic seas are merely drowned portions of the North European Plain. The absence of mountain barriers in this part of Europe, the ease with which the rivers can be used for navigation, and the general utility of the land for agriculture have been favorable to the economic development of the North Sea countries. This condition is quite in contrast with the mountainous lands around the Mediterranean Sea; and the relative decline in the commercial importance of the Mediterranean countries and the rise of the North Sea countries is, in no small part, due to the surface features of these two regions.

THE ABUNDANCE OF COAL AND IRON IN THE LANDS AROUND THE NORTH SEA. This region of Europe was highly important commercially even before the rise of steam-driven machinery, notably during the period of the Hanseatic League, a league of commercial cities that flourished between the fourteenth and seventeenth centuries in the region around the North and Baltic seas. The greatest expansion of the commerce of western Europe, however, has taken place in the last century—the century of coal and iron. Most of the great coal deposits and iron deposits of Europe are in the lands that surround the North Sea, and practically half the factory manufacturing of the world is done in these same lands—England, northern France, Belgium, and Germany, especially.

## THE MEDITERRANEAN REGION

PAST IMPORTANCE OF THE MEDITERRANEAN REGION. Early European civilization grew up on the shores of this sea, and during the long period when Rome was mistress of the world the Mediterranean bound together nearly all the known world. It was small enough and had islands and peninsulas at sufficiently frequent intervals to permit the small vessels of that period to navigate its waters. But with the discovery of the New World and of the routes around the southern end of Africa and of South America, a new era of navigation began. The Atlantic grew in importance, and the Mediterranean suffered a relative decline. After the opening of the Suez Canal (1869) the Mediterranean again increased in importance as a route of commerce and is now one of the chief ocean trade routes of the world (Fig. 161).

THE MOUNTAINOUS SHORES OF THE MEDITERRANEAN. Unlike the North Sea, the Mediterranean is almost everywhere bordered on the north by mountains and on the south by mountains or deserts. Here there are no broad, fertile plains traversed by navigable rivers. Entrance to the interior of the continent is somewhat difficult, the Rhône Valley in France being the principal open gateway to the north. The mountainous character of southern Europe, its less abundant mineral resources, and its dry summers are reasons for the lower industrial development of the Mediterranean lands and the general poverty of the people, the majority of whom seek to obtain a living from the scanty soil.

THE UNIFYING INFLUENCE OF CLIMATE.    The distinctive features of Mediterranean climate as well as frontage upon an almost enclosed sea tend to draw together the fortunes of all Mediterranean lands in both Europe and northern Africa (Fig. 218). In this region mild and moderately rainy winters alternate with hot and very dry summers. Under these conditions agriculture acquires a distinctive character. Its outstanding features include (1) cereal crops, especially wheat, which are able to grow during the cool, moist season and come to maturity before the summer

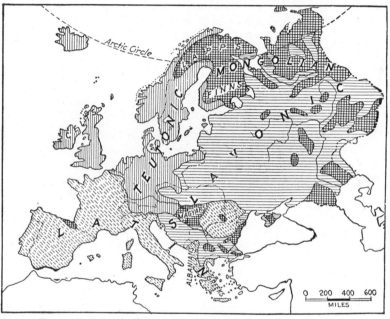

FIG. 222.—Distribution of the principal racial stocks of Europe.

drought is established; (2) perennial crops, such as the olive and the grape-vine, which are able to endure drought or send their roots deep for sub-terranean water supplies; (3) intensive horticultural crops, such as citrus fruits and vegetables, which depend upon irrigation; and (4) animal industries, especially sheep and goats (Fig. 223), which are able to make efficient use of the hilly, nonagricultural lands and the sparse, dry pastures of the summer season. So general are these types of agriculture that in one form or another they are to be found from Spain and Algeria on the west to Palestine and Turkey on the east, in spite of the differences in race and religion and the contrasts in cultural history among the peoples who inhabit the various portions of the Mediterranean borders.

## EASTERN EUROPE

The three outstanding characteristics of eastern Europe are as follows: (1) It is occupied almost wholly by Slavs (Fig. 222); (2) it is mainly (but not wholly) a region of plains; (3) it is dominantly agricultural, with manufacturing developed to any large extent only in restricted areas, especially those which touch the highly industrialized districts of western Europe.

The vast plains of eastern Europe extend through many degrees of latitude from the Black Sea borders northward to the shores of the Arctic Ocean. They include wide variations in climate, vegetation, and soils (Figs. 218, 219, 220) and corresponding differences in agriculture and land utilization. Their inhabitants are predominantly agricultural peasants who dwell in rural villages and live by the tillage of the soil or the exploitation of forests and other natural resources. However, recent decades have seen the rise of manufactures and manufacturing centers, a trend that is making rapid progress under the present Russian political regime.

SELECTED REFERENCES

BLANCHARD, W. O., and S. S. VISHER. "Economic Geography of Europe," New York, 1931.
BOGARDUS, J. F. "Europe, a Geographical Survey," New York, 1934.
CUNDALL, L. B. "Western Europe," London, 1932.
HUBBARD, G. D. "The Geography of Europe," New York, 1937.
LYDE, L. W. "Peninsular Europe," New York, 1931.
JONASSON, OLOF. Agricultural Regions of Europe, Econ. Geog., Vol. 1 (1925), pp. 277–294; Vol. 2 (1926), pp. 19–48.
NEWBIGIN, MARION I. "Southern Europe," New York, 1933.
SHACKLETON, M. R. "Europe: A Regional Geography," London, 1934.
SINGEWALD, Q. D. Europe's Fuel and Metal Deposits Evaluated, Econ. Geog., Vol. 15 (1939), pp. 384–394.
VAN VALKENBURG, S., and E. HUNTINGTON. "Europe," New York, 1935.
WOODS, G. G. "The Baltic Region," London, 1932.

# Chapter XXIII. Great Britain
## and Ireland (Eire)

THE POSITION OF BRITAIN.   Great Britain has long had the most valuable foreign trade of any country in the world and has been the commercial and political focus of the largest and most widespread empire ever to exist under one flag—nearly one-fourth of the land of the earth. This position is unique, and Britain has not maintained it without challenge. In the acquiring and holding of her position she has at various stages found herself in conflict with European competitors—Spain in the sixteenth century; the Netherlands in the seventeenth century; France in the eighteenth and nineteenth centuries; and Germany in the twentieth century. Because the empire is widespread, it has been held together mainly by sea power, and British supremacy has been challenged only by nations that had attained sea power also. Russia, too, has been in economic and political rivalry with Britain, but it has not been able to force the issue in open conflict because it never has had great power at sea. The reasons why Britain has been able to wield such great world power are many, and the question of how long she will be able to hold it depends upon many factors. Some of these are historical and have operated slowly and for centuries. Others are inherent in the resources of the country and have made their influence felt in any large degree only upon recent generations. Whether they are considered to be of historical nature or of economic origin, there can be little doubt that the conditions leading up to the position of Britain in the twentieth century have rested upon the solid foundation of her geographical situation, the nature of her land, and the natural resources with which human enterprise had to work in creating political as well as economic power.

THE LOCATION AND INSULARITY OF GREAT BRITAIN.   No other country except France has a situation so favorable for ocean commerce as that of the British Isles. They occupy the center of the land hemisphere; they lie at the front door of Europe; they border on the North Sea, the most used of all the commercial seas, and on the Atlantic, the most used of the oceans; and they are the nearest of the European countries to North America. In latitude, they are much further north than is commonly realized. But, as already indicated, the prevailing winds from the Atlantic give mild summers and mild winters to all parts except the Scottish Highlands. On an average, London has only 14 days of snow during the year, and no snow at all falls there during some years. There is much rain in Ireland and on the highlands of western Scotland, Wales, and England; but on the plain of eastern England the annual rainfall in one locality averages as low as 25 inches, yet this is sufficient for agriculture. The temperature is cool enough to invigorate but not cold enough at any season to retard the economic life of the country. The fact that the islands are close to the continent but severed from it has exerted a constant influence upon the country's development. An attack upon England could in the past be made only by sea, and great standing armies have never been necessary. The defense of the nation generally has rested with the navy, which withdraws relatively few men from productive occupations. From the days of William the Norman down to the present time no foreign foe has been able to invade England. Until today her lands have not been devastated by foreign armies, and her industries have not been crippled. For this her insularity has been in part responsible. To what extent aerial warfare may be able to overcome the protection afforded by a sea barrier the present struggle with Germany is likely to decide.

THE COUNTRIES FORMING THE BRITISH ISLES. The British Isles include England, Scotland, Wales, the north of Ireland, the Irish Free State (Eire), and many smaller islands. Their areas total about 121,000 square miles. That is less than the combined areas of Ohio, Indiana, and Illinois and is about the same as the area of the state of New Mexico alone. It seems remarkable that so small an area with a present population of about 50 millions can have exerted so great an influence on world affairs. A part of Britain's strength has lain in an internal diversity. The basis for this is the character of the land and its resources.

*Ireland.* For centuries Ireland was held in a more or less unwilling relation to the other three countries of the United Kingdom, and strong parties demanded first home rule and then complete independence. A compromise was finally effected under which all of Ireland except Ulster became a free state, self-governing yet continuing as a part of the British Commonwealth of Nations, with a status similar to that of Canada. Certain northern counties, forming Ulster, remain an integral part of the United Kingdom but not a part of the Irish Free State.

Ireland, the Emerald Isle, is characterized by abundant rainfall and mild temperatures. Low mountains or hills, not far from the sea, partly encircle the island, surrounding an interior plain and forming a shallow basin. The larger part of the land is low and level, and a considerable portion is covered with peat bogs. There is a little coal of low grade, but the quantity mined is unimportant. Some water power has been developed, but the total resources of industrial power are relatively small. Ireland is distinctively an agricultural and stock-raising country, and only in the north has manufacturing attained any considerable growth. The population declined almost one-half between 1840 and 1910, quite largely due to emigration to America. The present population of the island is about 4¼ million, but it is unequally divided. The Free State is five times larger in area and has more than two-thirds the total population; but since it is dominantly agricultural, the density of population is much less—about 110 per square mile as compared with 240 per square mile in Ulster, which is more highly industrial.

*Scotland* is the most mountainous part of the British Isles, and only 17 per cent of the land is suited to cultivation, as against 33 per cent in England. The rugged, lake-dotted northern Highlands are bleak in winter but delightful in summer; the Lowlands—which are of relatively small extent—are fertile, intensively cultivated, and densely populated in the neighborhood of the coal beds, where manufacturing centers have developed; 75 per cent of the people of Scotland live in these central lowlands. With a population of nearly 5 million, Scotland has a half million more people than Ireland, but neither has so many as the single city of London.

*Wales* is small and mountainous, and only 15 per cent of the land is adapted to crops. The population is more than 2½ million. In the south are coal beds of large extent and high quality—the best in Europe for the use of steamships. On or near these coal fields is one of the important manufacturing sections of Great Britain; it is especially devoted to the smelting and metallurgical industries, including iron, tin, lead, zinc, and copper.

*England* is the most favorably located and most richly endowed country of the British Isles and contains over 75 per cent of the people. It is one of the most densely populated of countries, averaging nearly 750 per square mile, due mainly to the high development of manufacturing. However, more than one-fifth the total is in the city of London and its suburbs. England alone has 47 cities of more than 100,000 population each; England, Wales, Scotland, and North Ireland combined have 55; and the Irish Free State has only one. The major part of England consists of rolling plains; the Pennine Range of low mountains in the north is the only highland of importance, but there are other hilly portions. A third of the land is suited to cultivation, but not all of this is cultivated. The resources that above all others have given England its place of industrial leadership are its wealth of coal and iron, upon which the great manufacturing industries are based. The iron ore is not sufficient for domestic needs, but coal has been one of the leading exports.

## Agriculture

BRITAIN A LAND OF MEADOWS AND PASTURES.   It is estimated that, on the average, Great Britain does not produce at home more than about 35 per cent of its total food requirements. From the accompanying table it will be seen that only in fresh milk, fish, potatoes, and certain vegetables does Britain approach self-sufficiency; in wheat flour only 12 per cent of the requirement is home-grown.

PROPORTION OF ESTIMATED BRITISH FOOD REQUIREMENTS THAT WERE PRODUCED AT HOME*

| Commodity | Percentage Produced at Home |
|---|---|
| Wheat flour | 12.1 |
| All meat | 49.5 |
| Beef and veal | 53.0 |
| Mutton and lamb | 43.0 |
| Fresh pork | 80.7 |
| Bacon and ham | 29.1 |
| Fish | 88.4 |
| Fresh milk | 100.0 |
| Butter | 10.0 |
| Cheese | 31.2 |
| Eggs | 65.0 |
| All fruits | 25.3 |
| Apples | 53.3 |
| Potatoes | 96.0 |
| Green beans and peas | 99.0 |
| Other green vegetables | 79.0 |
| Sugar | 26.1 |

* Foreign Crops and Markets, U.S. Department of Agriculture, Vol. 3 (1939), p. 564.

No other great nation is so dependent on imported food. Yet up to 1800 it was primarily an agricultural country and was an exporter of foodstuffs. Now, less than 7 per cent of the workers in all industries are engaged in agriculture. More than 75 per cent of the land is productive, yet only about one-fourth of it is cultivated, and part of that is hay land. This figure is lower than it was a half century ago. Much of the remaining productive area is in permanent pasture. Nearly one-third of the land in the United Kingdom, and nearly one-half in Eire, is used for pasture only. These proportions are higher than they were a half century ago, which implies an increase in the importance of the animal industries over cereal production. In a country so needful of imported food this seems an uneconomical use of the land, but it is a condition brought about by a combination of physical, historical, and economic factors.

The cool, moist weather of the British summer is highly favorable to hay and grass production, but it is often unfavorable to the ripening and harvesting of grains. In 1921, which was the driest summer Britain had seen in 100 years or more, crops generally were poor and the hay crop was the poorest on record. Yet, the wheat crop of England and Wales was very large, and the average yield of 35.3 bushels per acre was the highest ever recorded. Wheat and barley are raised most abundantly on the drier plain of eastern England. Oats are better able to withstand the prevailingly high humidity of Scotland, Ireland, and western England. All the grains are frequently discolored by excessive moisture and are, on the whole, of as great importance for animal feed as for human food. Corn (maize) does not mature in the cool summers of Britain, and its place in crop rotation is taken by potatoes and the root crops (beets and turnips). The latter are better feed for cattle and sheep than for swine and are widely used in animal feeding. British farms average nearly 100 acres in size, large for Europe, and this also reflects the great importance of the animal industries there as compared with the tillage of the soil.

THE ANIMAL INDUSTRIES.    In consideration of the general insufficiency of agriculture for the support of the population, Britain produces a surprising proportion of her required meat (around 50 per cent). This is in part due, however, to the importation of quantities of concentrated feed, grains, and oilseed cake with which to supplement the domestic rough feed of hay, straw, and root crops. Meat production is more economical of labor than is grain farming. As in America, the young men have left the farms for the factories. Moreover, British agricultural labor is unionized, and wages are high. As a result the tendency toward more intensive agriculture has been checked.

High-grade beef production for the home market is an important source of income on many British farms. Many beef cattle are raised on English farms, but others are raised in Ireland and shipped to English farmers for fattening, somewhat as western-range cattle in the United States move to the corn belt.

The importance of sheep in Great Britain is something of an anomaly, since sheep are, in general, the inhabitants of dry regions (Fig. 223). A partial explanation is to be found in the fact that some of the most famous of the sheep pastures are on the "Downs," or low ranges of chalk hills of southern and eastern England, where the soil is porous and well-drained. In general, it is in the hilly lands of Britain that sheep reach their greatest importance. The fleeces of British sheep are of coarse and of medium wool; the fine wools used by English spinners are imported. The home-grown wool averages considerably less than half that used in the great domestic woolen and worsted industries, and the proportion of the requirement for mutton and lamb that is produced at home is less than for beef.

Although Great Britain has never developed a swine industry comparable to that of cattle and sheep raising, Ireland and parts of England have been famed for the excellence of their pork products. The amount of fresh pork consumed in Britain is only a quarter that of beef, and most of it is home-grown, but bacon and ham imports are twice as great as the domestic output.

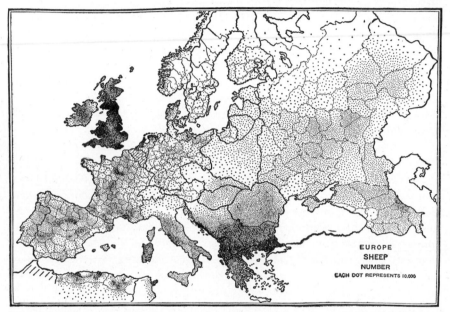

EUROPE
SHEEP
NUMBER
EACH DOT REPRESENTS 10,000

Fig. 223.—Sheep raising in Europe reaches its greatest importance in Great Britain and in the rough, dry lands of the Mediterranean regions. (*U.S. Department of Agriculture.*)

The animal industries of Britain yield a considerable revenue also through the exportation of breeding stock. Economic conditions have for two centuries encouraged careful selection and improvement of live-stock. Of the breeds of beef cattle that have found general favor in the New World, Britain has produced five or six, and the continent of Europe none; of dairy cattle, Britain five or six, and the continent two or three; of sheep, Britain 10 or more, and the continent only two; and of horses, Britain a number at least equal to that of the continent.

PERISHABLE FOODS PRODUCED AT HOME. Since food must be imported to supply the great industrial population, it is desirable to import from a distance those things which can best stand the delays and the costs of transportation. Thus wheat is much more largely imported than the bulky and perishable meat. Milk is, however, still more bulky and more perishable than meat, and all of it is produced at home. Formerly butter and cheese were important products of the British dairies; now nearly three-fourths of the milk is consumed fresh. It is carried to the great population centers by fast milk trains, though 90 per cent of the butter and 70 per cent of the cheese have customarily been imported from Ireland, the continent, and the colonies.

For this same reason the more perishable fruits and vegetables are raised at home. The mild, moist climate is also very favorable to vegetable production, including potatoes. Market gardening is common near the great cities, and in the milder climates of Cornwall and the south of Ireland early vegetable growing is of some importance. County Kent, in the extreme southeast, close to the London market, is the most important fruit-growing district of the country. About half the apples consumed are home-grown, but the large requirements of oranges, bananas, and other tropical fruits have had to be imported from the Mediterranean, the West Indies, and elsewhere. Many out-of-season vegetables have come from France or French North Africa.

## Mineral Resources

THE SIGNIFICANCE OF COAL. Great Britain, with a quarter of the estimated coal reserves of Europe, is one of the most richly endowed countries. This island produces more coal than any other country except the United States and Germany, and its reserves are estimated to be enough to last 700 or 800 years at the present rate of mining. No other element in the geography of the British Isles has affected the course of recent economic development so greatly as this factor of abundant coal (Fig. 224). Its energy drives the machines in the British mills and factories and the majority of British ships; moreover, British coal supplies return cargoes to many ships that bring foodstuffs and raw materials to maintain the life of the British nation. Great Britain is the most distinctive industrial and commercial country in the world. The whole vast empire was originally acquired and maintained primarily for the benefit of the industries and commerce of the home country. The British Isles have relatively limited resources of soil, timber, metals, and most other materials, and the population and industries would starve in a few months if supplies from the outside were cut off. But Britain is rich in labor, in industrial skill, and in coal. Her problem is to market this surplus of human ability and mechanical energy. The mechanical energy of her coal cannot be adequately marketed in that form, but it can be marketed in the form of manufactured cottons and woolens, machinery and ships, and hundreds of other articles. A fundamental principle of trade is that countries shall exchange what they have in surplus for what they lack. Since the only salable natural resource that Britain has in great abundance is coal, or its energy, this is and must be in some form the basis of its international exchange. When the Australian buys English cottons or machinery he is buying a compound made of foreign raw material, British coal, and British labor, capital, and skill; and the goods are brought to him in British ships, whose earnings flow back to British owners. There is a

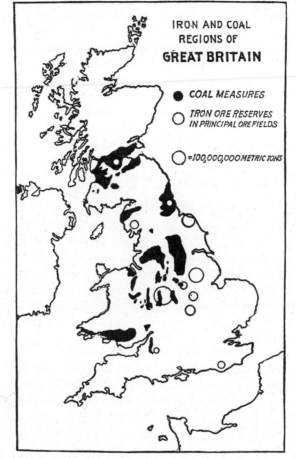

FIG. 224.—Great Britain produces much more coal than her own requirements, but imports about one-third of the iron that her industries use.

great weakness in Britain's position in this respect. Australia has coal, and so have New Zealand and Canada. To the extent that they establish industry the market for British textiles and machinery is reduced, and with it the consumption of British coal. The coal-mining and industrial districts such as South Wales and others have experienced severe depression in recent years, accompanied by bad social conditions among the laboring people. Rising tariff walls all over the world and the restriction of free trade have contributed to British industrial depression also, as they have in the United States.

In the British Isles there are upward of 20 different coal fields of varying degrees of importance; 5 of these produce the greater part of the coal (Fig. 225):

1. The Clyde field, surrounding Glasgow, in Scotland.
2. The Northumberland-Durham field, surrounding Newcastle.
3. The Yorkshire-Derbyshire field, surrounding Leeds and Sheffield.
4. The Lancashire field, near Liverpool and Manchester.
5. The South Wales field, with Cardiff as its sea outlet.

The coal varies in quality but includes some of the best in Europe, and it is important to note that no lignite is produced. None of it is equal

## EMPLOYMENT IN BRITISH FACTORY TRADES

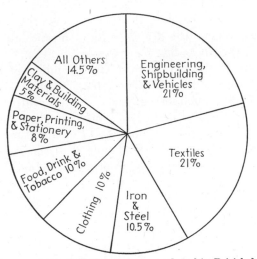

Fig. 225.—More than one-half of all the workers employed in British factories worked in engineering, iron and steel, and textile trades.

to Pennsylvania anthracite, though some is superior to any of the American bituminous coals. The best Welsh coals are nearly smokeless and are the favorite coals for steamship use. It will be seen from Fig. 224 that several of the coal fields are on the seacoast, and mines in these fields deliver coal cheaply into seagoing vessels, a condition that gives Great Britain an advantage over most other countries in the exportation of coal. Several of the iron-ore regions are in or near the coal fields, and this has made economies possible in the smelting of these ores.

IRON-ORE RESOURCES. For many centuries England has been a large producer of iron ore. Charcoal made from the wood of the forests was the first smelting fuel, and the early ironworks were placed near the ore and in the forests that supplied the charcoal. Iron ores of varying qualities are widely distributed in England and to a minor degree in Scotland, Wales, and Ireland. They are mainly of low grade, averaging only about 30 per cent iron, but most of them contain lime and are partially self-fluxing. Ore sufficient for about 65 per cent of the country's needs is obtained within the islands. It comes most largely from the Cleveland Hills in the northeast of England, which has very large reserves, and from the Furness area in the northwest. It is mined in small quantities in at least 50 different places in Great Britain. A further advantage is the presence of abundant limestone suitable for a flux in the smelting process. This nearness of iron to the coal, to limestone, and to the sea was an important advantage in the days of poor land transportation and aided materially in the upbuilding of the British iron and steel industries. The domestic ores have been supplemented by imports of higher quality, especially from North Africa, Sweden, and Spain, but in smaller quantities from France, Newfoundland, and other sources. Imports of scrap iron and steel further relieve the drain on the domestic ore supply, which is believed to be sufficient to last for 100 years.

TIN, COPPER, LEAD, AND ZINC. The tin mines of Cornwall in the extreme southwest of England have been worked since the twelfth century and possibly much longer. For five or six centuries they were the world's chief source of this metal, but the production is now small—less than 2 per cent of the world's output—and England is mainly an importer of tin. Copper, lead, and zinc are all mined in the British Isles but in quantities that have declined to small proportions, and they supply only a trifling fraction of the nation's needs. Of the various metals mined in the United Kingdom iron alone is of any present significance.

MINOR NONMETALLIC MINERALS. The most valuable of these minerals are (1) limestone, (2) building stones, (3) clay, (4) oil shale, and (5) salt, but none of these reaches any large annual value, and their total value ordinarily does not exceed 40 million dollars a year. The china clays are the basis of a large pottery industry, and some English clays are exported. There is a small production of petroleum by the distillation of oil shale in Scotland. The products obtained in this way are more expensive than similar products obtained in the usual way from oil wells and are wholly insufficient for British needs.

## The Development of Manufacturing

THE INFLUENCE OF EARLY INVENTIONS. In the growth of a nation's industries many other conditions interact with natural resources and other elements of earth environment. England's leadership in the textile industries is in no small measure due to four inventions that were made in that country in the latter part of the eighteenth century. These included the steam engine and power-driven machinery for spinning and weaving. Gradually these rapidly working machines replaced laborious hand methods, and England passed through the Industrial Revolution earlier than her rivals. This fact, coupled with her water power and her coal, her climate, her insular position, and the qualities of her people, gave England a leadership in manufacturing.

THE TEXTILE INDUSTRIES. The great development of British manufacturing and commerce gathers around the textile industries. The most characteristic product of the British soil for a thousand years has been wool, and wool and cotton both rank about on a par with wheat or butter among the leading present imports of the country. In no other country has economic life rested so largely upon textile manufacturing and exportation. This industry began with woolen and linen before the invention of the cotton gin made cotton cheaper than either of them.

FIG. 226.—Important towns in the Lancashire and Yorkshire industrial regions.

When cotton could be obtained cheaply from America, the trained spinners and weavers of wool readily changed to the working of cotton. Cotton must be spun and woven in a damp atmosphere to prevent the snapping or "fuzzing" of the fine threads, and before artificial humidifying was introduced this climatic requirement was better met on the west (rainy) side of England than on the east. Moreover, one-third of the cotton imports still come from America and are most conveniently landed at the west-coast ports. Water power and coal are available on the western side of the Pennine Chain, and the woolen industries had long been established there, providing a source of labor skilled in the textile trades. After cotton spinning and weaving grew to an important industry, the woolen mills gradually became concentrated on the east side of the Pennine Chain, leaving the cotton mills on the west side in Lancashire, with Manchester as the center and Liverpool as the chief receiving port. The Manchester ship canal permits ocean vessels to reach that city (Fig. 226). Nearly 25 per cent of the cotton spindles of the world are in this region, and many cities and towns are almost wholly devoted to cotton manufacturing. Oldham, Bolton, and others specialize in spinning; Blackburn, Preston, Burnley in weaving; some specialize in bleaching; and still others in dyeing and printing. Although most of the British cotton manufacture is concentrated in Lancashire, there are some mills in other districts. Since raw cotton must come by a long sea voyage, which adds to its cost, British mills find it to their advantage to make a large proportion of the finer and more expensive fabrics, leaving it to the countries with cheaper cotton but less experience, to manufacture the coarser goods. On the whole, the United States makes a higher proportion of the lower grades of cotton goods than does Great Britain. This tendency has been increased by the growth of cotton manufactures in many other countries since 1918, and especially in India and China, which were formerly the leading British markets. Much the same change has taken place in Lancashire as that observed in New England, and it has been accompanied by a similar depression of the cotton-textile industry. The quantity of cotton used in British mills in 1938 was only three-fifths that required in 1913, and British exports of cotton cloth in the same span of years declined to one-third its earlier volume. The outlook for British cotton manufacture is not good.

East of the Pennine hills, in western Yorkshire, the wool-using industries have become highly specialized also. Leeds is the center of woolen manufacture, and Bradford specializes in the high-quality worsteds for which England is famous. Wool is manufactured in some other parts of Britain also, especially the Scottish Lowlands. Linen has long been and still is the characteristic textile of the north of Ireland, with Belfast as its center of manufacture. Only a minor part of the flax for this linen is grown in Ireland or in the British Isles; it comes from Russia, Belgium, and elsewhere. Silk manufacturing has never held high rank among the textile industries of Britain. Rayon, however, has now become important, and exports of rayon nearly equal those of linen.

In the years just before the disturbances caused by the Second World War more than a million persons in the British Isles were employed in the textile industries, and a fifth of the value of British exports was made up of textiles and textile raw materials.

IRON AND STEEL PRODUCTS. In the great manufacturing countries generally iron- and steelwares and textiles head the lists of industrial products, because those classes of products include many different items, and some of them are in large demand both at home and abroad. Britain's iron and steel manufactures have been made possible by her large reserves of coking coal and coal for power. This resource not only has made the smelting industry and steel mills possible but has created a large home demand for steelworking machines, textile machines, and many other classes of machinery, equipment, and tools. There are important iron and steel industries on or near each of the great coal fields, but three or four of them are most important. (1) The oldest of them is the Midlands, in and near Birmingham and Sheffield, but its output is now exceeded by others. (2) The Middlesborough district lies on the northeast coast near the Northumberland-Durham coal field and the Clyde iron ores. The ports on the Tees estuary also have provided a convenient inlet for ores from Sweden and other foreign sources. (3) The Scottish Lowlands district, adjacent to Glasgow and the Clyde estuary, depends on Clyde and foreign ores. (4) The South Wales district has excellent coal but must import all its ore. The Middlesborough district has the largest production.

The British iron and steel industries, in general, are characterized by their output of heavy wares—steel plates and structural steel, tin plate and galvanized steel, heavy machinery such as locomotives and mining machinery, and electrical machinery. There are, however, large manufactures of smaller wares and more complex products such as textile machines, automobiles, and cutlery. The old Midlands district, especially near Sheffield, is noted for cutlery and small wares. Many factors have combined in recent years to hinder the growth of the British steel industry: (1) the high cost of coal mining due to a bad labor situation, (2) the increased cost of native and imported ores, (3) the increasingly severe competition of other countries where steel can be made at lower cost. In 1850 the United Kingdom produced four times as much pig iron as the United States; in 1937 the United States produced more than four times as much as the United Kingdom.

SHIPBUILDING. The insular character of Great Britain, her vast colonial empire, and her extensive ocean commerce combined to make a large demand for ships. There were (1) a demand for ships, (2) the materials for constructing them, and (3) a body of trained men competent to construct them; thus Great Britain became the greatest of shipbuilding nations—building for other countries as well as for herself. The Clyde River in Scotland stands first in shipbuilding. This is followed by the Tyne, the Wear, the Tees, the Thames, and by Belfast in the north of Ireland. On the banks of the first four of these rivers are built about 75 per cent of the total tonnage of the British shipyards. In normal times Great Britain builds about as many ships as all the rest of the world; and partly because of the great number constructed, British shipbuilders have been able to build them more cheaply than most other countries.

MISCELLANEOUS MANUFACTURES. Like other industrial countries Great Britain manufactures leather and rubber goods, chemicals, pottery, glass, food products, machinery, vehicles, clothing, and the whole long list of industrial products. Some of these, such as the leather, pottery, glass, and clothing industries, have long been established in the country, but others, such as the rubber and chemical industries, have undergone great expansion in recent decades. The chemical industries have become highly important, but they have not the world importance of those in the United States or Germany. The presence of salt deposits in Cheshire, together with limestone and the near-by markets in the Lancashire textile region and the industrial Midlands, has helped to locate an important part of the chemical industries in that section of western England. Miscellaneous manufactures are produced in nearly all the industrial districts of Britain, but one of the leading centers of such manufacture is London. Although that great city is primarily a commercial and administrative center, its great size makes it a large market in itself. Many establishments that manufacture mainly the lighter wares for local consumption have located there. As a rule British goods have a high reputation for dependability, and British manufacturers turn out mainly standard, staple goods, for which there is a fairly steady demand —differing in this respect from France, whose manufactures are more largely luxuries.

THE DEPENDENCE OF GREAT BRITAIN ON MANUFACTURING. For reasons already given, Great Britain has reached the point where her national life depends upon manufacturing and commerce. Her people must buy imported food and must pay for it with their coal and their labor, embodied in their manufactures. Heretofore, the advantages of various kinds possessed by Great Britain have enabled her to import raw materials and convert them into manufactured goods and sell them at a profit in competition with other nations. But this competition is growing ever more keen, and some of the advantages possessed by the British at an earlier date have one by one disappeared. Commerce is Britain's most vulnerable link with her empire and the world. It suffered heavy losses in the first twentieth-century war with Germany and is likely to suffer more heavily in the second.

TRANSPORTATION FACILITIES. Industry and commerce in Great Britain are greatly aided by highly developed transport facilities. There are, for example, about 2 miles of roads of all classes for every square mile of area—double the ratio of the United States—and a high proportion of British roads are improved. There is 1 mile of railroad line for each 4.6 square miles of area. The comparable figure for Ireland is 9.2. In Great Britain the density is about the same as that in the Great Lakes-New England industrial region and three times the average for the whole United States. Moreover, practically all the British lines have double tracks. The British merchant marine is the largest in the world. It included in 1938 more than 7,000 ships (of 100 gross tons or over), with a total gross tonnage of more than 20 million. That was nearly one-fourth of the entire merchant fleet of the world in number and more than one-fourth of the total world tonnage. But modern war is highly destructive of the shipping of belligerents, and the British merchant fleet has suffered heavy losses.

## The Foreign Commerce of the United Kingdom

Two Aspects of British Export Trade. The British recognize two aspects of their export trade: (1) the exportation of the products of British industries and (2) the reexportation of imported products in substantially unchanged form. The former group includes the products of British soil, mines, forests, fisheries, and factories; the latter includes such articles as rubber, tin, wool, hides, vegetable oils, and tea in the marketing of which the British act only as middlemen. Over five-sixths of the value of British exports belongs to the former group, and less than one-sixth to the latter.

The Principal Exports. Manufactured goods overshadow everything else in British exports, making up 85 per cent or more of the total (reexports not included). The only important export outside manufactures is coal. Among the exports cotton goods lead; yet if all forms of iron and steel, including machinery and vehicles, are grouped, they have a larger total value than cotton products. Woolen goods usually rank high. These three groups—goods made of iron and steel, of cotton, and of wool—make up about 70 per cent of the value of the exports of British manufactures. The remaining 30 per cent of exported manufactures consists of an endless variety of goods—leather and rubber goods, paper, glass, pottery, apparel, chemicals, oils, etc.

The principal imports have been, under normal trade conditions, largely included in the two groups: (1) foodstuffs and (2) raw materials for manufacturing. Meats and meat products, including bacon and lard; cereal grains and flour; and dairy products have made up the larger part of the food imports and one-fourth of all imports. Raw cotton, wool, wood, and woodpulp were the leading items in the long list of imported raw materials. Other imports usually having a high rank in value are petroleum and its products and tea (Fig. 227). Manufactured wares make up less than 20 per cent of the total imports.

The British Entrepôt Trade. The word "entrepôt" is applied to a commercial city that is extensively engaged in collecting products from various parts of the world and in reexporting them to other parts. During the past thousand years, six different cities have, in successive periods, held the place of the principal entrepôt of Europe—Venice, Lisbon, Bruges, Antwerp, Amsterdam, and London. The last-named city rose to its commanding position along with the rise of British commerce and the British command of the sea routes of the world. It is natural that a country with many productive colonies should collect the colonial products, bring them to a home port, and thence redistribute a portion of them to other parts of the world. The same merchants and ships that engage in this colonial trade may, with little additional effort, collect products from places near the colonies and redistribute these also. Thus, a world-wide entrepôt trade is built up by a favorably situated port in a commercial country. London is a great commercial port of the entrepôt type, although it has suffered from the competition of other European centers since the great war of 1914–1918. The reexport trade of Britain has had about one-eighth the value of the exports of British products. Its largest items are wool, hides, tea, and rubber. What affect the settlements terminating another war with Germany may have on this trade is hard to foresee. The trade probably will decrease and with it the outstanding importance of London as an enterpôt. However, even though the trade may be temporarily destroyed and the port itself ruined, war cannot change the advantageous geographical position of London. In time it

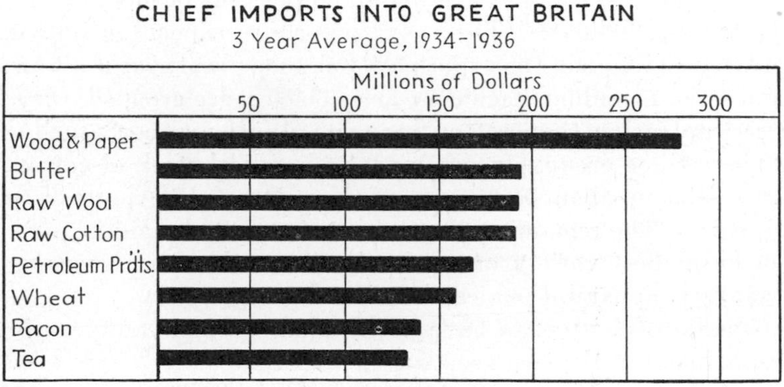

### CHIEF IMPORTS INTO GREAT BRITAIN
3 Year Average, 1934–1936

| | Millions of Dollars |
| --- | --- |
| | 50  100  150  200  250  300 |
| Wood & Paper | |
| Butter | |
| Raw Wool | |
| Raw Cotton | |
| Petroleum Prds. | |
| Wheat | |
| Bacon | |
| Tea | |

FIG. 227.

may rise again. The greater part of Britain's reexports are products from the Far East or from Africa. They include wool, mainly from Australia and South Africa; rubber and tin from the Malay region; skins from Asia and Africa; cotton from Egypt; tea from India and the Orient; and vegetable oils from Asia and Africa. A major part of these commodities comes from British colonies.

CORRECTING THE ADVERSE BALANCE OF TRADE. British imports normally exceed their exports by a large sum. In recent years the excess has averaged nearly 1½ billions of dollars annually. Since the British people annually pay out vastly more for goods purchased abroad than they receive for the goods that they sell abroad, a large yearly deficit results from these transactions; and if this deficit continues to pile up, the nation must become bankrupt. Yet, in spite of its continuous adverse balance of trade, Great Britain has accumulated great wealth and, next to the United States, has been the wealthiest of nations. This comes about as follows:

1. British ships have carried a great deal of the commerce of other countries and thus earned large sums annually.

2. A great many tourists have visited the British Isles and spent large sums of money.

3. British investors have been large owners of the securities (stocks and bonds) of foreign governments and foreign corporations, the dividends and interest from which have flowed back to the United Kingdom.

There are other sources of income, but these are the main ones, and in normal times these so-called "invisible exports" not only offset the adverse balance of trade but yield a surplus besides. Prior to the First World War Great Britain was the foremost of the creditor nations, but changes wrought by that war somewhat modified this situation. Another war, if it is long continued, may force British owners of foreign securities to sell them in order to raise money to buy food and military supplies.

THE PRINCIPAL BRITISH PORTS. The two outstanding British ports are (1) *London* and (2) *Liverpool* (Fig. 228). London is preeminently the port for trade with the continent of Europe, and Liverpool for the trade with America. Both share in the trade with Asia and Africa, but the entrepôt trade centers mainly in London. The London wharves extend for miles up and down the Thames, and those of

FIG. 228.—Showing some of the many docks by means of which Liverpool protects its shipping from tidal range.

Liverpool extend for an almost equal distance along the estuary of the Mersey. (3) *Hull* has about one-fifth of the commerce (in value) of London or Liverpool; it is situated on the estuary of the Humber and is the eastern sea gate for the great manufacturing district of north-central England. (4) *Manchester*, center of the cotton-manufacturing district of Lancashire, is connected with Liverpool by a ship canal 35 miles long. (5) *Glasgow* is in the coal fields and manufacturing district of southern Scotland and on the Clyde, the chief shipbuilding river of the world. (6) *Bristol*, on the Avon, a short distance up from Bristol Channel, is one of the ports engaged in trade with America. (7) *Newcastle* is the great coal-shipping port of northeast England. (8) *Cardiff*, in southern Wales, is the greatest of all coal-shipping ports. (9) *Southampton* is an important passenger and mail port in the south of England. (10) *Leith*, in the east of Scotland, or *Grimsby*, in the east of England, usually ranks tenth among the British ports.

COUNTRIES WITH WHICH BRITAIN MOST LARGELY TRADES.   The British have long been in the forefront of trading peoples. Their colonial empire, merchant fleet, and long experience enabled them to hold a share of the trade of nearly all countries. The trade with the colonies and political dependencies is larger in total than with any other group of countries, accounting (in 1937) for nearly 40 per cent of British imports and nearly 50 per cent of her exports. The United States, in the same year, was the source of more than 11 per cent of Britain's imports and the destination of more than 6 per cent of her exports. No other single coun-

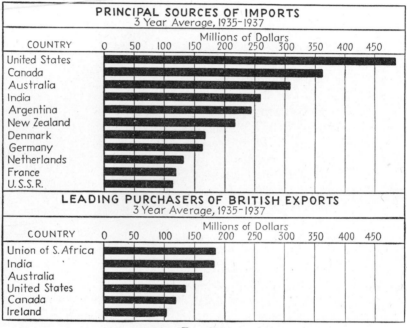

**BRITISH FOREIGN TRADE**

FIG. 229.

try had so large a share (Fig. 229). Other nonempire countries, in the order of their importance, were Argentina, Germany, Denmark, France, and the Netherlands. Nearly 40 per cent of all British imports came from five great producers of raw materials and foodstuffs—the United States, Argentina, Australia, Canada, and British India—three of which are British colonies. The large trade of Britain with the countries of western Europe is to be explained in terms of their nearness and the British entrepôt trade in colonial produce.

THE EXTENT OF THE BRITISH EMPIRE.   The widely extended British Empire grew by colonization and conquest. Australia, New Zealand, parts of Africa, and many islands were taken from the weak native peoples who possessed them. Canada was acquired from France as the result of the wars of the eighteenth century. India was gradually absorbed into the empire through commercial penetration and conquest. The Union of South Africa and the German colonies in Africa were acquired mainly through war. Besides these large territories, Great Britain gradually came into possession of many of the most strategic points on the trade routes of the world. Gibraltar, Malta, the Suez Canal, Aden, Ceylon, the Malay Peninsula, and Hongkong form an unbroken chain for 10,000 miles from England to the Far East by the Mediterranean-Suez route. British South Africa guards the Cape of Good Hope route. The Falkland Islands lie on the route around Cape Horn. Jamaica and other West India Islands guard the Panama route. Nova Scotia offers a naval base on the Atlantic side of North America and British Columbia on the Pacific side, and almost numberless islands under the British flag dot the Pacific and Indian oceans. On any of the great routes of trade, a British ship is seldom far from a British port. Of the 25 or 30 greatest ocean ports of the world about one-half are in those countries belonging to the British Commonwealth of Nations.

CONCLUSION. It has been noted to what a high degree the population of Great Britain is supported by the coal resource of the country and that this dependence carries with it a great danger. A great colonial empire is an asset in so far as it provides a protected market for British wares, but that market now has inside competitors. British foreign trade also must meet the competition of other industrial countries, such as Germany and the United States, which have coal, and Japan, which has very low labor costs. Wars cannot change the distribution of the natural resources that lie at the root of this conflict of interests. It can only be hoped that the minds that have been so inventive in the fields of industry and commerce can develop the political insight and make the adjustments and sacrifices necessary to solve the problem along other lines. Any permanent solution must, it would appear, involve not merely Britain but the cooperative effort of all the great industrial nations of the world.

SELECTED REFERENCES

ALLEN, G. C. "British Industries and Their Organization," London, 1933.

BRUINS, J. H. Present Status of the British Coal Industry, *Trade Information Bull.* 765, 1931.

BUTLER, H. D., *et al*. The Irish Free State: an Economic Survey, *U.S. Dept. Commerce, Trade Promotion Series* 62, 1928.

BUTLER, HUGH. The United Kingdom (Handbook), *U.S. Dept. Commerce, Trade Promotion Series* 94, 1930.

JONES, L. R. The British Fisheries, *Econ. Geog.*, Vol. 2 (1926), pp. 70–85.

OGILVIE, A. G. (ed.). "Great Britain: Essays in Regional Geography," 2d ed., Cambridge University Press, 1930.

STAMP, L. D., and S. H. BEAVER, "The British Isles: A Geographic and Economic Survey," 2d ed., London and New York, 1937.

"Statistical Abstract of the British Empire," government publication (annual).

ZIMMERMANN, ERICH W. "World Resources and Industries," pp. 643–647, New York, 1933.

# Chapter XXIV. France, Belgium, and the Netherlands

## France

ADVANTAGES OF GEOGRAPHICAL SITUATION. *Climatic.* Northern and western France are under the oceanic influences that prevail in the British Isles. Snow rarely falls in Paris; and Brest, on the northwestern coast, has the same marine type of climate as the coast of the state of Washington, which is in the same latitude. Over most of lowland France, except in the south, both summers and winters are mild, and rain falls frequently but not heavily. The conditions for agriculture and stock raising are excellent. The southeast has the Mediterranean type of climate, with hot, dry summers and warm, moist winters; this is the "sunny France" of tradition.

*Commercial.* All things considered, France has an unequaled location for world trade. Its northern ports are on the English Channel, one of the world's greatest commercial thoroughfares. Brest, Nantes, St. Nazaire, and Bordeaux, on the west coast, are nearer the Americas and Africa than are most British ports; and southern France is several days closer to the Near East and to the Far East by Suez than are the North Sea countries. France is the only European country (if Russia is excepted) that faces on both the northern and the southern ocean ways of the continent. Besides its advantages of location for ocean commerce, it has a good situation for overland trade.

### FRENCH AGRICULTURE

THE NATURE AND USE OF THE LAND. The area of France is about one and three-fourths times that of the British Isles, but its population is slightly less. Physiographic and climatic features divide the country into several contrasting regions. These may be arranged in groups which include: (1) The well-watered and generally fertile northern and western lowlands, containing the basins of the Garonne, Loire, Seine, and several smaller rivers. The northern part of this region is often called the "Paris Basin." (2) The hill lands of Brittany and of central France with their hard rocks and poor granitic soils. (3) The rugged lands of the Alps and the Pyrenees. (4) The Rhone Valley and the southern coastlands with the dry summers of the Mediterranean climate. Over one-half of France is lowland of more than average fertility; 50 per cent of the total area is under cultivation in field crops, vineyards, orchards, and gardens; and 20 per cent is devoted to pasturage (Fig. 230). France has more farm land of excellent quality than any other European country except Russia. Nearly 40 per cent of the population is engaged in farming, as against 7 per cent in the United Kingdom. Moreover, the greater part of the farms are tilled by their owners, a highly desirable condition but not one that

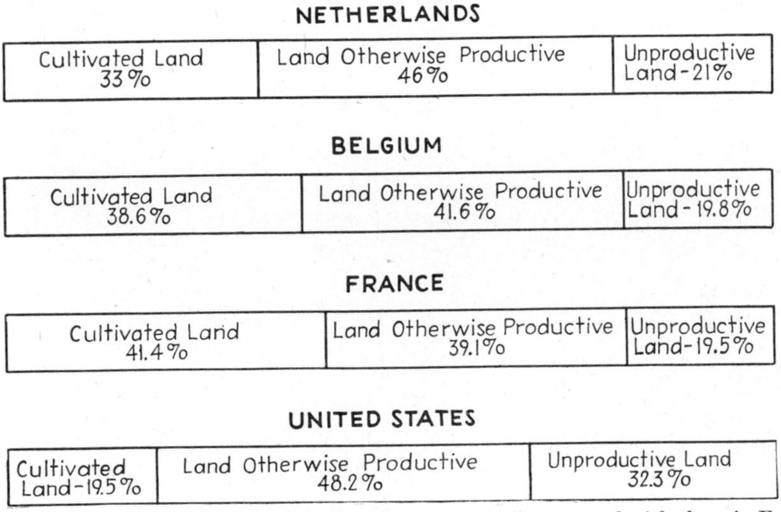

**NETHERLANDS**

| Cultivated Land 33% | Land Otherwise Productive 46% | Unproductive Land - 21% |
|---|---|---|

**BELGIUM**

| Cultivated Land 38.6% | Land Otherwise Productive 41.6% | Unproductive Land - 19.8% |
|---|---|---|

**FRANCE**

| Cultivated Land 41.4% | Land Otherwise Productive 39.1% | Unproductive Land-19.5% |
|---|---|---|

**UNITED STATES**

| Cultivated Land - 19.5% | Land Otherwise Productive 48.2% | Unproductive Land 32.3% |
|---|---|---|

Fig. 230.—The major uses of land in the "low countries" compared with those in France and the United States.

prevails generally throughout Europe. The farms, which average 20 to 40 acres in size, are industriously but not scientifically cultivated. As a rule the farmers live in villages and not upon their farms. Owing to an unfortunate system of inheritance a 30-acre farm may be made up of several small plats of ground almost entirely unfenced, marked only by cornerstones, and separated from one another by considerable distances. The land of France is naturally more productive than that of Germany, but the farming is so much less scientifically done that crop yields have generally been lower.

CEREALS.   Like the English and the Americans the French use white bread, and wheat is the most extensively cultivated crop in France. Wide stretches of level land and the mild West European climate, coupled with a high protective tariff, have brought France nearly to self-support in cereals and give the country a rank second only to Russia in wheat production in Europe (Fig. 231). About one-fourth of the cultivated land is devoted to wheat, and about half of the crop is raised in the Paris Basin. Oats, the other important cereal, are grown mainly in the cooler northern half of the country. Corn (maize) is grown only in the warm moist southwest; rye is found mainly in the bleaker climates and poorer soils of Brittany and the Auvergne hill lands of central France (Figs. 268, 274).

THE GRAPE AND WINE INDUSTRY.   France is the leading wine producer of the world. The modified Mediterranean character of the climate

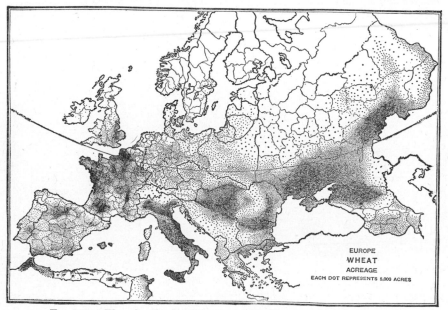

FIG. 231.—The wheatlands of Europe. (*U.S. Department of Agriculture.*)

of much of the country is ideally suited to the growing of wine grapes. Vine culture is commonly practiced on the well-drained river bluffs and hill slopes, where centuries of intensive tillage have greatly modified the soil. The total area devoted to vineyards is equal to that cultivated in potatoes and one-fourth that in wheat. More than 95 per cent of the vineyards are maintained for wine production. The principal vineyard districts are shown in Fig. 232. Each district produces its own brands of wine, some of which have become known throughout the world. The lighter wines are made in the west and south, and the stronger wines in the east. On the slopes of the chalk escarpments of the eastern Paris Basin, where vineyard lands command a high price, a limited amount of the famous and expensive champagne is produced. The total quantity of wine made in France is almost past belief, averaging in the past about 1 billion gallons a year; in some years it has reached 2 billion. Since more wine is imported than is exported by the French, it may be computed that, on an average, each person in France must consume a barrel of wine yearly. And it is mainly the cheap wines for common use that are imported. This is shown by the fact that the volume imported is sixteen times greater than the volume exported but the value of the imports is only three and one-half times greater.

In northern France, beyond the cool limit of vine culture, 400 million gallons of cider is made and used annually. It is at least an interesting speculation and by no means an impossibility that the abundant consumption of wines in the Mediterranean countries and of beer in northern

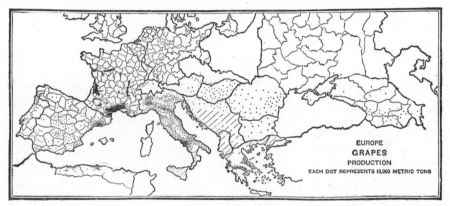

Fig. 232.—The Mediterranean countries are the leading wine producers of the world. (*U.S. Department of Agriculture.*)

Europe, like the use of tea in the Orient, may be in part in avoidance of bacterial infection in drinking water. The use of deep-drilled wells is comparatively recent. In many of these old lands the chief sources of water are shallow wells, springs, and streams, all of which draw upon surface waters that not uncommonly swarm with the bacteria of infectious diseases. The high quality of the best French wines is due not alone to climate and soil but equally to the care with which the wines are prepared. Generations of experience and a large amount of capital are invested in expensive appliances which are essential to the production of the uniformly superior article that commands a high price in foreign markets. However, much of the wine consumed by the common people of France is inferior.

Sugar Beets and the Sugar Industry.  During the Napoleonic Wars, France was at times cut off from her accustomed supplies of cane sugar from the tropics. The government thereupon offered a bounty for the production of sugar from the beet, which already was being used for this purpose in a small way in Germany. The industry thus obtained a start. The subsequent improvement of the beet as a source of sugar is due mainly to German scientists during the past century. By 1914, central Europe, from France to Russia, had become a producer of sugar to the extent of nearly half the world's supply (Fig. 233).

The principal sugar-beet lands of France are in the extreme north near the Belgian border, where labor from the industrial towns is available during parts of the year, for sugar beets require a great deal of hand labor. Before the First World War, France was about four-fifths self-sufficing in sugar. But the industry was nearly ruined by the German invasion and only slowly recovered after 1918. By 1930 it had regained

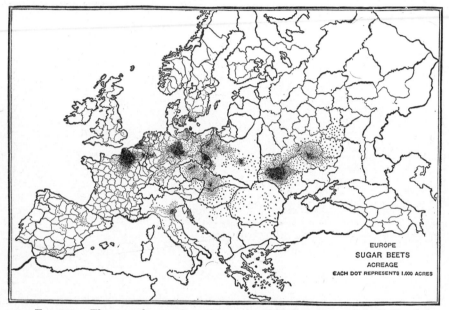

FIG. 233.—The sugar-beet regions of Europe. (*U.S. Department of Agriculture.*)

its previous importance, and in 1939 France was producing nearly her entire sugar requirement at home.

VEGETABLES AND TRUCK FARMING. Potatoes are less important in France than in Germany (Fig. 243), but the quantity produced is 50 per cent greater than that grown in the United States. The per capita production in France is about four times as great as that in the United States.

The vegetable crop of France furnishes an important part of the food supply of the people and also of their livestock. Potatoes, cabbages, and root crops, particularly in western France, are used in feeding cattle. In southern France and in the warmer parts of the western coast there are well-established horticultural industries. In the south, flowers are raised for the northern markets and for the manufacture of perfumes.

On the coast of Brittany several localities have developed extensive truck-farming industries because of early seasons and close proximity of the great industrial markets of England, France, and Germany. The earliest of all French vegetables are grown in the winter on the coast of Algeria and shipped to the Paris market.

THE ANIMAL INDUSTRY AND DAIRY PRODUCTS. Agriculturally, France is a well-balanced country; it raises cereals, vegetables, fruits, and livestock but specializes in none. With the exception of grapes, it does not rank first among European countries in any product of the land. The

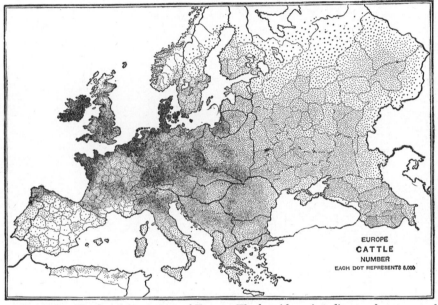

FIG. 234.—Cattle-raising regions of Europe. The humid marine climate of west central Europe is favorable to pastures. The uplands of central Europe also favor grazing. (*U.S. Department of Agriculture.*)

northwest of France is the most important horse-raising region of the country. This is the home of the Percheron draft horse. Near by, on this same well-watered lowland in Belgium and England, are the homes of similar breeds of nearly equal renown.

In most parts of France the cattle are not sharply distinguished as to purpose but are used for beasts of burden, for milk, and for meat. There are more breeds of cattle in France than in England, yet none of them has been developed to a point of superior excellence for either meat or milk production. Cattle are least abundant on the dry Mediterranean Coast. They are most abundant in the moist northwestern coastal region and in Brittany and the Auvergne, where humid climate or rough hill lands discourage tillage and encourage grazing (Fig. 234). Dairying is an important aspect of the industry in each of these regions and also in the French Alps. France is an exporter of both butter and cheese, especially the latter, and some of her cheeses have attained a wide reputation. These include the Camembert and Brie of the north and the Roquefort of southern France. Roquefort cheese is made from sheep's milk and is ripened in limestone caverns underground. Its manufacture furnishes a livelihood to upward of 50,000 people and yields 20 million pounds of cheese annually.

Sheep are most numerous in the drier and more mountainous southern half of France and upon the chalk hills of the Paris Basin, which are similar to the English "Downs." The high development of woolen manufacturing in France is closely connected with the domestic sheep industry, though the present number of sheep is much less than formerly and less than half the present number in the United Kingdom. Imports of wool are several times greater than the home production. Because of their ability to use waste products from house and garden, swine, poultry, and hares are particularly important in the domestic economy of the French, and they add much to the national meat supply.

## THE MINERAL RESOURCES AND INDUSTRIES

LARGEST IRON-ORE RESOURCES IN EUROPE. In one resource France has led all Europe—the iron-ore reserves of Lorraine, which nearly equal in quantity those of all the rest of Europe and have given to France a practically unlimited supply of that metal. The ore bodies are of sedimentary origin; they are partly on the French side and partly on the German side of the boundary as it existed from 1871 to 1919 (Fig. 235). One of the reasons for Germany's tremendous industrial growth was the possession of the iron-ore deposits taken from France in 1871 and developed by efficient German methods. These "minette" ores are not high in metallic iron (average, 30 to 40 per cent), and they contain so much phosphorous that some of them could not be economically used for making steel until the discovery of the Thomas process (about 1880). The quantity of ore, however, is enormous; and with the return of Alsace-Lorraine to France, Germany lost over two-thirds of her iron ore, and France came into possession of these reserves and of the furnaces and steel mills that the Germans had built. Control of this resource has again returned to German hands. Besides these major ore bodies in Lorraine, France has iron ores elsewhere, including those of Normandy and Brittany in the north, those of the eastern Pyrenees in the south, and those in her colonial possessions in northern Africa. However, upward of 90 per cent of the ore mined in France comes from the minette ores of Lorraine. Germany has also the necessary coal for smelting the iron ore, which

France does not have. With her coal and iron so largely in the northern and eastern part of the country the French steel industries naturally center in that part of the country.

THE COAL RESOURCES.    France is poor in coal. The chief coal field is in the extreme north, extending across the boundary into Belgium, and minor coal fields are located in various other parts of the country (Fig. 236). As a whole, the coal of France is of only moderate quality and is expensive to mine and hence is more costly to the users than is British, German, or American coal. After the First World War, France imported,

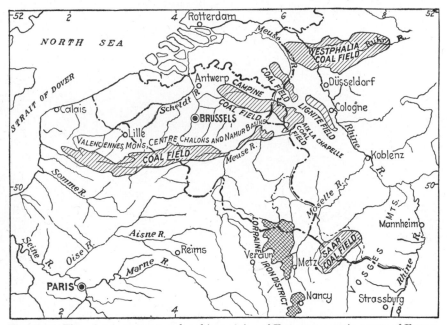

FIG. 235.—The most important coal and iron region of Europe, occupying parts of France, Belgium, and Germany. (*U.S. Geological Survey.*)

mainly from Britain, nearly half as much coal as her mines produced and also some of the coke with which to smelt her iron ores. Undoubtedly the different character of the manufacturing industries that have developed in France as compared with those in the United States, Great Britain, and Germany is partly due to her inadequate coal resources.

SHORTAGE OF OTHER MINERALS.    France is poor in nearly all metals excepting iron and aluminum. Copper, lead, zinc, gold, silver, tin, and nickel are either wholly lacking or very scarce. France has one of the two largest known reserves of bauxite, the principal ore of aluminum, in Europe or in the world, the other being in Hungary. Both of these are now readily accessible for use by Germany in her aircraft industries. France is also one of the two leading producers of antimony, used in various alloys, including type metal. China clays of the finest quality exist and are used in making the beautiful French pottery at Limoges and elsewhere.

THE DEVELOPMENT OF HYDROELECTRIC POWER. The enforced expansion of manufacturing into other parts of France during the four years of the First World War, when the Germans held the principal French coal field, led to a rapid development of hydroelectric power. France has great potential water power in the Pyrenees, the Alps, the Vosges, and the Auvergne regions. The amount of such power in use more than doubled between 1913 and 1921, and France now has more than a third as much water power in use as the United States has and more than any other European country except Italy. This is one method by which France can make up for her shortage of coal.

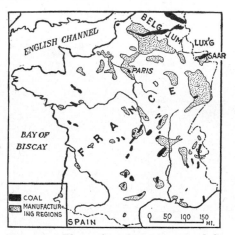

FIG. 236.—The coal-producing areas and the industrial regions of France.

FRENCH MANUFACTURES

TYPICAL FRENCH MANUFACTURES. With a shortage of coal and of many raw materials and with a people of high artistic ability, France has found it to her advantage to manufacture wares in which labor, skill, and artistic design contribute largely to the value of the articles. These manufactures are quite in contrast to the crude, heavy articles, such as lumber and timber and steel rails, bars, pipes, and plates, in which the material itself forms a considerable part of the value of the product. When one buys typical French manufactures, he pays mainly for the work and skill that the objects represent, not for the material in them. Such goods are the beautiful fabrics and laces, cut glass, porcelains, jewelry, millinery, gowns, toilet articles, tapestries, and hundreds of other things in the making of which the French have no superior. The variety of manufactures produced in France is great, and the total number of persons employed in factories is large—about the same as the number employed in Britain and two-thirds the number so engaged in the United States. However, 25 per cent of the French workers are employed in handwork factories which use little or no mechanical power, and the average French factory is a relatively small establishment. There are, in fact, about three times as many factories in France as in the United

States, but the average number of persons employed in each of them is less than 10, whereas in the United States it is more than 40.

THE TEXTILE INDUSTRIES. For generations France was the unchallenged leader in silk manufacturing, an industry that grew up in the region around Lyon, where in earlier days silkworms were raised and raw silk was produced. It is still an important European center of silk manufacturing. Silk, of all the textiles, is the one in which the fine French taste and workmanship find their best expression. Very little of the raw silk is now grown in France, but some is obtained from Italy, and the high value of the raw silk permits bringing it from Japan and China. The rayon industry has developed in France also, and it holds fifth place among the rayon-producing countries of the world.

The manufacture of fine woolens is an old industry in France. It was originally based upon home-grown wool, as it was in England and Belgium, but that is no longer true. The chief centers extend from the coal field of the north southeastward into Alsace, though other centers have grown up in the interior.

Again, in the manufacture of the finest and most beautiful cotton fabrics, France is unsurpassed. There are three cotton-making regions: (1) in Normandy, with Rouen as a chief center; (2) in the northern section near the coal fields, with Lille as a center; and (3) in Lorraine and Alsace, with Mulhouse as a center. The reasons for the emphasis on cotton manufacturing in these regions are (1) the convenience of receiving American raw cotton through Le Havre and Rouen in Normandy, (2) the advantage of local coal in the north, and (3) the advantage of water power in Lorraine and Alsace.

METAL PRODUCTS. Iron and steel manufactures have become increasingly prominent in France since the war of 1914–1918. The presence of large reserves of iron ore in France and the fact that modern military needs demand great quantities of iron and steel have promoted the growth of these industries even when fuel is scarce and much must be imported. Steel mills must exist in peacetime and produce goods of great variety in order that they may be ready for transformation to wartime needs. In recent years the iron and steel exports of France have reached nearly 200 million dollars, but that is only one-fourth the value of such exports from Britain. The principal steelmaking centers are in the north and northeast. The advantages there include nearness to the Lorraine ore deposits, the largest coal fields, and the best developed rail and canal systems of transportation. That region was, however, vulnerable from the military viewpoint, and the centers of arms manufacture were located farther south at Le Creusot and Saint-Etienne near small coal deposits in the eastern edge of the Auvergne highland. The classes of iron and steel goods normally exported from France include some pig iron and steel bars, pipes, and structural steel but also many highly manufactured products, such as machinery, automobiles, aircraft, and small wares.

FORESTS AND FOREST PRODUCTS.   The area of forest land in France is equal to more than half that used for tilled crops. However, the country is not self-sustaining in wood but must import both lumber and wood-pulp. Many of the forests in France are not densely wooded and yield some forage for sheep and cattle as well as acorns and chestnuts, which are feed for swine. The larger part of the forests occupy the rough lands of the eastern and southern parts of the country. The most densely forested region is the Landes district facing the Bay of Biscay (Fig. 237). This is a flat, sandy coastal plain, somewhat like the coastal plain of the United States. Formerly it was a waste land, furnishing scant sheep pasture at best. For several generations it has been reforested in pine trees, which yield turpentine and rosin as well as lumber.

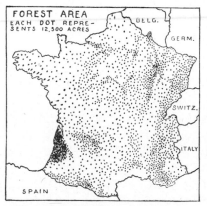

FIG. 237.—The forests of France are found mainly on the rough lands of the East and South but include the cultivated, turpentine forests of the "Landes," in the southwest.

FRENCH WATERWAYS.  Both France and Germany make more use of interior waterways than do Great Britain and the United States. France has about 7,000 miles of inland waters used for navigation; these include 17 canals, mostly shallow, and 17 improved rivers or parts of rivers (Fig. 238). Some of these are used very little; a few are used a great deal. At times in the past, waterways have carried nearly one-fifth of the traffic of the country. This was made up mainly of coal, ores, building materials, and farm products; yet even of these bulky commodities the railroads carry much more than the waterways. The Seine may be ascended as far as Rouen by fair-sized ocean vessels and as far as Paris by boats drawing 10 feet. The mountain-bordered Rhône is a swift, turbulent river, unsuited to navigation. The Saône, north of Lyon, is navigated for 170 miles, but its traffic is mainly downstream. The most important group of waterways is the one in the Paris Basin between Paris and the eastern boundary of France. In this region is a network of canals and improved rivers reaching to the coal fields, serving the many manufacturing centers and connecting French rivers with those of Belgium and Germany, and they carry a large quantity of heavy freight, especially such commodities as coal and building material.

FRENCH HIGHWAYS AND RAILWAYS.   France is a country of excellent roads. A large part of the country is fairly level; road-building material is abundant; and labor in the past has been inexpensive. There are some 50,000 miles of national roads of excellent quality and a total of nearly 400,000 miles of roads of all classes. This, as in Britain, is about 2 miles of road for every square mile of area.

The extent and distribution of French railways reflect the physical and economic conditions of the various parts of the country. There are six railway systems in France. Five of them radiate from Paris, which, because of its topographic situation, was the center of French inland transportation before the railway era. The regions best served by railways are the industrial north and northeast. Northwestern France has many railroads but is mainly an agricultural region and has not enough freight to make all these lines pay. Consequently, as in Canada, a large part of the railways in this district have been placed under government ownership. The rough and relatively poor central plateau has not so many railroads. One of the important lines of the south is that which connects Bordeaux with the Mediterranean Coast through the natural highway of the Garonne Valley. The most used of French railroads is the Paris-Lyon-Mediterranean, which connects Paris with the great port of Marseilles through Dijon and the Saône-Rhône depression. An important link in European transcontinental service is formed also by the French lines that connect England, via Southampton and Cherbourg or Dover and Calais, through Paris, Belfort, and the Swiss tunnels with the ports of Italy. The density of distribution of the French railways is somewhat less than that in Great Britain, there being about 1 mile of line for each 8 square miles of area.

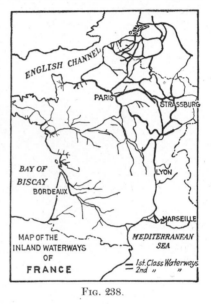

FIG. 238.

FOREIGN TRADE.   France, in normal times, is one of the important trading nations.   Like most European countries, it imports more than it exports, but the excess of imports over exports is not so large as it is in Great Britain. Owing to its high food-producing power, it pays out less for imported food than for imported fuels and raw materials.

The leading items of French import are, in the order of their importance, coal, wine, oilseeds and vegetable oils, petroleum and its products, wool, cotton, and machinery. The most important exports are metals and their manufactures, chemical products, cotton fabrics, wool, and wool fabrics.

France, of course, trades with all countries, but one-third of its foreign commerce in normal times is with four of them—Great Britain, Belgium, the United States, and Germany. Larger than its trade with any foreign country has been that with its colonial empire, of which Algeria is the leading member.

THE CHIEF PORTS OF FRANCE. France has upward of 40 ports capable of receiving ocean-going vessels; about 18 of these are of importance, but none of them is really excellent by nature. Through extensive improvements, many have been brought into highly serviceable condition. The leading ports on the English Channel are Le Havre, Rouen, and Dunkerque, with Cherbourg the chief port for the Atlantic passenger traffic. On the Mediterranean is Marseille (Fig. 239); on the west coast, Bordeaux, St. Nazaire, and Nantes. Le Havre is the chief port for the receiving of American cotton and Brazilian coffee. Marseille has a larger volume of trade than any other French port. It is the port of receipt and shipment from and to Algeria, the Mediterranean countries, and the Far East. It is one of the world's leading cities in receipt, preparation, and sale of vegetable oils and products made from them. These include olive oil, palm oil, soybean oil, peanut oil, cottonseed oil, and a number of others; numerous oilseed mills operate in the city, and there are many soapmaking establishments. Bordeaux is the principal wine-shipping port and is one of the leading ports for the receipt of South American products.

Fig. 239.

## COLONIAL POSSESSIONS

AFRICA. After France had lost or disposed of her extensive colonial possessions in America, including parts of the West Indies, eastern Canada, and the Louisiana Territory, the nation began a period of colonial expansion in Africa. Algeria on the Mediterranean Coast was acquired (1830); then from this coast as a base, French influence and control pushed into and across the Sahara and the Sudan and connected up with the colonies on the Gulf of Guinea. Tunisia, on the north coast, and the large island of Madagascar, off the east coast, were acquired; and, later, most of Morocco, in the extreme northwest of Africa, came under French domination. Finally, by the defeat of Germany in the First World War,

France became mandatory for the greater part of the German colony of Cameroon and about half of Togoland. The area of the French dependencies in Africa exceeds the area of the United States and also exceeds the area of British dependencies in Africa, but a large part of the area is included in the Sahara Desert and has a small population and low productivity (Fig. 240).

OTHER DEPENDENCIES OF FRANCE. French Indo-China in Asia is larger than France and is of considerable value. French Guiana on the north coast of South America is of small value. The French islands in the West Indies, the various groups in the Pacific and Indian oceans, the

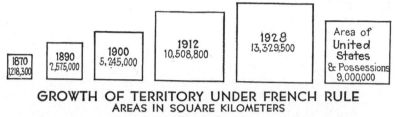

### GROWTH OF TERRITORY UNDER FRENCH RULE
#### AREAS IN SQUARE KILOMETERS
FIG. 240.

French mandate in Syria, certain small areas in India, and a few other minor possessions taken in connection with the colonies in Africa make up a colonial empire of wide extent. Most of the French dependencies are not in the attractive parts of the world; they are mostly tropical, arid, or semiarid and are peopled by economically backward races, although Algeria has been steadily developed and is a valuable region. The political and economic fate of these dependencies, like that of those in Africa and even of France itself, rests upon the outcome of the present conflicts in Europe and the Orient.

## Belgium

FAVORABLE COMMERCIAL SITUATION. Belgium is only about one-fourth the size of Pennsylvania but has a population of more than 8 million, making it the most densely populated country in Europe, with more than 700 persons per square mile, and one of the most densely populated regions in the world. Its greatest commercial asset and also its greatest political misfortune is its location. It lies near the focus of great ocean routes, touches three leading commercial nations—France, Germany, and the Netherlands—and is close to a fourth—England. It is also practically at the mouth of the Rhine, the chief commercial river of the continent. Belgium's strategic location insures that steamships from every part of the world will pass its doors in almost constant procession. It has long been, however, a buffer state between the great economic rivals of western Europe—and in time of war between them it is always in danger. Its location has made it one of the chief battlegrounds of Europe in war after war. The northern half of Belgium is occupied by Flemings, who resemble the Dutch and speak a language similar to Dutch; the occupants of the southern half are Walloons, who speak French.

REGIONAL CONTRAST. Although Belgium is small and climatically uniform, it is by no means alike throughout in other respects. Several physical subdivisions of the country are recognized, of which only three may be noted here.

1. *The northern lowland* extends from the coast eastward along the Netherlands border. Its seaward margin is fringed by sand dunes and is so low that it is diked and drained by pumps like the Dutch polder lands. Most of the remainder is a plain of marine sediments, largely sands. It is naturally infertile but has been much improved by the admixture of clays plowed up from underlying strata and by long-continued and heavy fertilization. This is a region of high agricultural development, especially in the lower western portion, but it has also several important industrial and commercial towns, including Ghent, Bruges, and the great port of Antwerp. Its industries mainly are of the lighter type, including textiles.

2. *The central upland and valley* stretches from the border of France eastward to Germany. Its surface is more rolling and its soils finer than those of the north. Its southern portion is traversed by the famous valley of the Sambre-Meuse rivers, which includes the coal-bearing strata that continue the principal coal field of northern France eastward (Fig. 235). More of the coal is in Belgium than in France. The region is densely populated, since it includes productive farm lands, a series of industrial towns, and Brussels, the national capital. This region, and particularly the valley, is the center of heavy industry.

3. *The southern highland* includes the hard rocks of the ancient plateau of the Ardennes, now carved by streams into a hill land having a local relief of 1,000 feet or more. The same hill region continues into adjacent France and Luxembourg. Where the hills descend northward toward the central upland, farm lands and dairying occupy much of the surface, but the rougher southern highlands are largely in forest with only interspersed pastures and farms. There are no important towns in this region.

THE HIGH DEVELOPMENT OF AGRICULTURE. More than 60 per cent of the entire area of Belgium is in crops and orchards, and 15 per cent more is in pasture. The agriculture is of a highly intensive kind. The population is dense; labor is relatively cheap; the people are industrious and fond of agriculture. The amount of food that the country yields is astonishing, yet it is insufficient for the large population. There are about 300,000 little farms averaging only 2 or 3 acres in size, and over one-fourth of them are cultivated by their owners, an excellent showing for a European country. Four cereals—wheat, oats, rye, and barley—and two vegetables—potatoes and sugar beets—occupy more than half the cultivated land, and the yield per acre is very high because of the intensive cultivation. The area about the city of Ghent is one of the greatest horticultural regions in Europe, growing market vegetables, plants, and bulbs for export. This district is noted also for its large area of gardens under glass, where flowers, vegetables, and even fruits are produced for the luxury markets of western Europe and Britain. Flax has long been one of the distinctive crops of Belgium, grown largely along the river Lys (in Flanders), whose waters are said to be peculiarly suited to retting the flax in preparation for the manufacture of linen. Strangely enough, Belgium has exported most of its fine home-grown flax to the mills of Great Britain and imported Russian flax for its own mills. The emphasis upon crops like sugar beets, potatoes, flax for linen, and plant bulbs, all of which are crops that demand a great amount of hand labor, is logical in a country like Belgium where land is scarce and labor is abundant. Although Belgium is one of the most highly developed countries in factory industries, it has nearly as many people employed in agriculture as in manufacturing. However, many factory workers live on small farms which they and their families cultivate.

THE FUNDAMENTAL IMPORTANCE OF THE COAL DEPOSITS.    One of the important coal fields of Europe is that of the Sambre-Meuse Valley (Fig. 235). Part of the coal is of coke-making quality and forms the basis of the great metallurgical industries of Belgium. Unfortunately, the coal beds have suffered folding and faulting, which make some of the coal difficult to mine, and a part of it extends to such depths in the earth that it can be recovered only at high cost. However, the abundant labor and moderate wages of Belgium have developed a great coal-mining industry which has won for the little country the name "The Workshop of Europe." The valley that contains the coal field is the great east-west highway between Germany and France. Along it extends one of the busiest industrial regions of Europe, with a variety of industries based upon coal. Most of these industries grew out of the earlier and simpler industries for which this region—especially Flanders—was famous in the Middle Ages.

THE METAL INDUSTRIES.    Formerly Belgium mined considerable iron within her own borders, but relatively little ore is now obtained from this source; however, the iron fields of Lorraine and Luxembourg are not far away, and from these sources the ore for Belgium's furnaces may be obtained cheaply. As a result, Belgium has become a leading manufacturer of machinery, arms, locomotives, rails, structural steel, and hardware. The city of Liége is one of the centers of heavy industry in this region.

Formerly Belgium mined important quantities of zinc and upon this source built up a zinc-smelting industry as a part of her metallurgical interests. These zinc ores are practically exhausted, but the smelters have continued and have grown, using imported ore, especially from Australia. The closely related lead-smelting industry is less prominent. In Belgium, as in all the leading industrial countries, the metalworking industries are among the first in importance.

TEXTILE MANUFACTURES. In the Middle Ages, Flanders was the center of textile manufacturing in Europe. A great many of the weavers and spinners whose skill built up British leadership in textiles were Flemings who came to England to work because the English industries were not disordered by the military operations that frequently interrupted or destroyed peaceful pursuits on the continent during the Hundred Years' War (1337-1453). Ghent, Bruges, Ypres, and a number of other cities were textile centers of great wealth and activity. During this period Ghent had five times the population of London, and Ypres four times.

### PRINCIPAL EXPORTS OF BELGIUM AND LUXEMBOURG
3 Year Average, 1935-1937

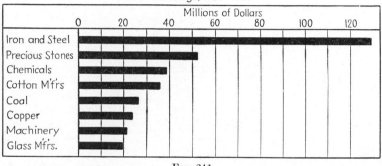

FIG. 241.

About 1040, Bruges was the chief wool market of the world, and in the sixteenth century Antwerp was the chief port. With the change from hand- to machine work, English leadership in textile making steadily increased. However, Belgium's skilled labor and her coal enabled her textile industries to continue and to grow. At one time the wool came mainly from near-by parts of western Europe, including England, but in recent times it has come mainly from overseas. Great quantities of unwashed wool are imported, washed, and reexported, causing wool to appear as both a leading import and leading export of Belgium.

The many linen mills owe their origin to the flax that is grown in Flanders and largely retted in the river Lys. The lace-making industry, which is said to have formed a household occupation for 150,000 persons at one time, has declined or given place to machine-made lace. The "persistence of a rooted industry" is excellently illustrated in the great textile interests of Flanders, which have been continuous for a thousand years.

OTHER MANUFACTURES. Belgium is one of the foremost countries in the manufacture of glass, including fine plate glass, some of which is exported to the United States. A large part of the so-called French plate glass is made in Belgium. Belgium is also a large manufacturer of carpets, of rayon, of aluminum goods, of chemicals, of paper, and of many other products. It is, indeed, one of the most highly developed manufacturing countries.

COMMERCE AND COLONIES.   Antwerp, the chief port of Belgium, is 50 miles up the Scheldt River, whose lower course is in the Netherlands, much to Belgium's dissatisfaction. The port of Antwerp not only serves Belgium but carries on a large transit trade for goods entering western Germany and even Switzerland. The foreign trade of Belgium is remarkably large, ranking about fifth in Europe, though it is one of the smallest countries. The exports are largely manufactured articles, notably metal products and textiles (Fig. 241). Belgium has one large colony, the Belgian Congo in central Africa, with eighty times the area of the home country.

## The Netherlands

SMALL SIZE, EXCELLENT COMMERCIAL LOCATION.   The Netherlands also is small; its area is only one-sixth larger than that of Belgium. The population is dense—over 600 to the square mile—yet less dense than it is in Belgium. The land is mainly built of the alluvium deposited by the Rhine and the Maas (or Meuse) to form a low, flat delta, over a part of which glacial drift has been laid down. Only about one-third of the land is highly productive, though three-fourths of it is utilized for crops or pasturage. The greatest geographical asset of this small country is its situation at the mouth of the Rhine, Europe's most used river, and on the shore of the North Sea. It touches Germany and Belgium and is near Great Britain and France, four of the leading commercial nations of Europe. The position of the Netherlands, even more than that of Belgium, gives the country excellent opportunities for transit trade with Germany. Like Belgium, from which it was separated in 1830, the Netherlands has constituted a buffer state, but its strategic location has enabled the Dutch to become one of the great commercial peoples of Europe. Whatever may be the fortunes of the Netherlands as a political unit, no change in government can alter the advantageous location of the region occupied by it.

THE FIGHT WITH THE SEA.   There are two physically unlike parts in the Netherlands: (1) An eastern upland, a low, sandy plain whose glacial ridges and more fertile alluvial valleys are dotted with forests, farms, and industrial villages. This region has much in common with that of western Germany, which it borders. (2) A western lowland: the polder land. This was once a region of peat bogs, marshes and shallow lakes fringed on its seaward side by a ridgelike belt of sand dunes thrown up by waves and wind. The region is so extensive that one-fourth of the area of the whole country is lower than the surface of the sea and another fourth is less than 3 feet above sea level (Fig. 242).

The upland was first utilized, but its sandy soils are relatively infertile; and not until modern methods of tillage and fertilization were employed could it be made very productive. It remains still the district of lowest population density and fewest large towns. The lowland peat bogs, silts, and clays are much more productive but require protection from flooding. This has been accomplished, a little district at a time over hun-

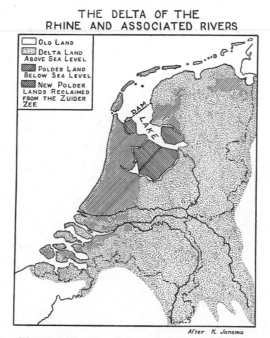

THE DELTA OF THE
RHINE AND ASSOCIATED RIVERS

☐ Old Land
▨ Delta Land Above Sea Level
▥ Polder Land Below Sea Level
▩ New Polder Lands Reclaimed from the Zuider Zee

After K. Jansma

Fig. 242.—The Netherlands and the reclaimed land of the Rhine delta.

dreds of years, by the construction of dikes. The seaward ridge of dunes made a principal bulwark, and gaps in it were repaired by artificial dikes. River banks had to be diked as well, and the whole lowland is traversed by dikes which partition the surface into innumerable little basins of a few acres to a few hundred acres each. These basins are the drainage units and are called "polders." Within the polder lands are thousands of miles of drainage ditches, large and small. Some of them can be drained directly into the sea or the rivers by opening gates in the dikes at low tide and closing them at high tide. Others are so low that they can be kept drained only by constantly pumping the water from lower ditches into higher ones and finally into the main rivers which carry the surplus water to the sea.

Formerly the picturesque Dutch windmills were employed for the pumping, and the countryside was thickly dotted with them, but more recently pumping engines have come into use. Many of the older polders are small and irregular in plan, but the newer ones have been planned on a larger scale and built by engineering science. The latest project for draining the half-million acres of the Zuider Zee has only recently been completed. The polder lands are more densely peopled than the uplands, and the five largest cities of the Netherlands are located there.

THE ABSENCE OF MINERALS.  Built of river deposits and sea muds, the land of the Netherlands is practically destitute of all minerals except clay. In the extreme southeast, behind the delta, are deposits of low-grade coal which were regarded as of little value until war economy forced the Dutch to use them. In this deficiency the Netherlands differs widely from its neighbors, all of which have coal, iron, and other minerals. Necessarily this lack, coupled with the absence of water power, has stood in the way of manufacturing. On both sides of the Rhine delta, in Germany and in Belgium, a great expansion of manufacturing has occurred, but the Netherlands has been unable to share in any large way in the heavy iron and steel industries.

THE INTENSIVE CHARACTER OF AGRICULTURE.  Only about 26 per cent of the land is suited to the cultivation of crops. In the past, farm labor has been cheap; the people are industrious; land is high-priced; and there are millions of people to be fed. Hence every acre must yield to its limit. On the sandy land potatoes, rye, and buckwheat are raised; in the clay loams wheat, oats, and sugar beets; and in particularly favored localities large quantities of flower bulbs, small fruits, and garden vegetables. The little country cannot feed its people, but it yields a surprising quantity of food.

A LAND FAMOUS FOR ITS DAIRY CATTLE.  The outstanding industry of the Netherlands is dairying and the manufacture of milk products (Fig. 234). Much of the richest land lies in the reclaimed areas, whose clay and peat soils are always moist, an ideal condition for the growth of the luxuriant grass upon which cattle feed and yield milk in abundance. The Dutch are excellent dairymen and have bred up a variety of cattle—the Holstein-Friesian—that leads all others in the quantity of milk produced. There are more than 2½ million cattle in this little country, most of them looked after with extreme care. In the Netherlands dairying is a science, and it is the countrypeople's greatest source of income. Famous brands of cheese are made, and butter of high reputation; also quantities of condensed and powered milk. More than 50 million dollars' worth of these products is annually sent abroad. They constitute the largest single group in the varied list of Dutch exports. Growing out of the dairy industry is a related one, namely, the manufacture of the butter substitute *margarine*, made from animal and vegetable oils and fats and widely used in place of the more expensive butter.

MANUFACTURING ONLY MODERATELY DEVELOPED. A country without good coal and without iron or any other metal is handicapped so far as manufacturing is concerned. Thus handicapped, the Dutch people have devoted a greater part of their energies to other economic activities for which their country is more favorably endowed, particularly to dairying and to commerce. Yet a large total amount of manufacture is carried on, some of it with imported coal. Some of the products also are of types that require relatively little power in their production. From the abundant clays, pottery, tile, brick, and other clay products are made. The distinctive blue pottery of Delft, for example, has been famous for centuries. Amsterdam has long been the greatest of all diamond-cutting cities, with many establishments and skilled workmen. The industry dates far back to the days when Amsterdam was one of the leading banking and jewelers' cities of Europe. The chief manufacturing industry is that of textile making—cotton, woolen, linen, and a small amount of silk. In some 600 mills—large and small—upward of 45,000 people are employed. Other important industries, measured in terms of the number of persons employed, are the machine industries, shipbuilding, and shoe manufacture. For these, as for the textile industries, a large part of the raw materials and even the coal must be imported in order to make employment for Dutch labor.

THE VALUABLE COLONIES. Two or three centuries ago the Netherlands was almost, if not quite, the leading commercial and maritime power of the world. Between the Netherlands and Great Britain a long and bitter fight for mastery of the sea was waged, and the British won. But the Netherlands held the Dutch East Indies—the richest of tropical colonies—and the area of the Dutch colonies of recent decades has been fifty-six times that of the home country, and the population eight times as great. The commerce between the East Indies and the home country has been large and profitable. The political fate of this island empire at the close of the world struggle now in progress cannot yet be predicted. It may remain in political dependence upon Europe, or it may quite as possibly become the ward of Japan. The only thing that seems reasonably certain is that its status will be changed. Dutch Guiana, on the northern coast of South America, and the near-by island of Curaçao are of relatively small importance as colonies, but their ownership is of great strategic importance, especially to the United States, because of their military value with respect to the defense of the Panama Canal.

FOREIGN COMMERCE. In spite of a regular coast and shallow river mouths the Dutch are a commercial and seafaring people. Their situation in Europe has had much to do with this development. Shipbuilding, the ocean fisheries, and the carrier trade are important phases of the economic life of the nation. In 1938 the Dutch merchant fleet ranked seventh in the world in total tonnage, and the per capita foreign commerce of the country was high. The total value of its imports and exports were more than twice that of Russia but less than that of Belgium and small when compared with the trade of Great Britain. Its trade was widespread, but the largest amounts were with Germany, Great Britain, Belgium, and its own colonial possessions in the East Indies. Normally about a fourth of the Dutch foreign trade has been carried on across the border with Germany. The country has many canals and canalized rivers which enable ocean-going ships to enter and discharge their cargoes into canal-boats which can be taken to German industrial centers. The rail service is excellent also. The trade with the manufacturing region of the Rhine Valley is particularly important. Dairy products, imported raw materials, and colonial products normally are exchanged for coal and heavy manu-factures. This trade is mutually beneficial in normal times, but during the period of German preparation for war it was subject to sudden restriction, and following complete German conquest it may develop new aspects. However, the basic differences between Netherlands and Germany remain unchanged, and eventually it is likely that similar products will flow in exchange much as they formerly did.

### SELECTED REFERENCES

BLANCHARD, RAOUL. Flanders, *Geog. Rev.*, Vol. 4 (1917), pp. 417–433.

—— and MILLICENT TODD. "Geography of France," Chicago, 1919.

BOGARDUS, J. F. The Population of the Netherlands, *Econ. Geog.*, Vol. 8 (1932), pp. 43–52.

CAMMEARTS, EMILE. "Belgium," London, 1921.

CHAMBERLAIN, E. T. French and German Waterways, *U.S. Dept. Commerce, Trade Information Bull.* 597, 1929.

JANSMA, K. The Drainage of the Zuider Zee, *Geog. Rev.*, Vol. 21 (1931), pp. 574–583.

OGBURN, W. F., and W. JAFFE. "The Economic Development of Post-war France," New York, 1929.

ORMSBY, H. "France: A Regional and Economic Geography," New York, 1931.

PIERARD, L. "Belgian Problems Since the War," New Haven, Conn., 1929.

SHAW, E. B. Land Use in the Upper Ardeche Valley of France, *Econ. Geog.*, Vol. 11 (1935), pp. 356–367.

# Chapter XXV. Germany and Central Europe

GERMANY'S ECONOMIC DEVELOPMENT BETWEEN 1871 AND 1914. The increase in manufacturing, commerce, and national prestige achieved by the German Empire in its 47 years of existence was phenomenal. The causes and conditions that promoted this achievement lay partly in the people and partly in the situation and resources of their country. It is probably true that they lay more in the German people than anywhere else. The vigor and forcefulness of their leadership; the centralized and aggressive government headed for many years by an ambitious emperor; the devotion of the nation to education, to scientific investigation, to efficient methods, and to industriousness and thrift; the exceptional degree to which science, education, government, capital, and industry joined hands in pushing forward everything that would advance the interests of Germany—all these and other similar conditions must be given full weight in considering Germany's progress between 1871 and 1914. However, a detailed consideration of the operation of these forces and their results may properly be left to studies other than economic geography.

On the other hand, there is another group of conditions that have played a large part in the economic upbuilding of modern Germany. These are elements inherent in the nature and resources of the land. Such are (1) the location of Germany in the heart of the leading industrial and commercial continent; (2) the resources of coal, iron, potash, and other minerals contained within her borders; (3) the extensive plains as related to the large food-producing power of her land under scientific agriculture; (4) great forest wealth under methods of strict conservation; (5) the waterways, both natural and improved; (6) the invigorating climate, including a moderate and well-distributed rainfall. These are some of the distinct physical advantages that were so energetically seized upon by the German people in building up a powerful nation.

All conditions in Germany since the beginning of the World War of 1914–1918 have been abnormal and may long remain so. Disturbed political conditions, attempts to recover from financial disaster, the setting up of a rigid nationalistic economy, and, finally, recourse to war again have so greatly distorted both the domestic industries and her foreign commerce that a true picture of Germany's economic geography is hardly possible.

THE GERMAN LANDS.   It is difficult to state even the extent of Germany. Its area was restricted by losses following the war of 1914–1918, but much of this territory was recovered and large additions were made in 1938 and 1939 by the annexation of Austria, most of Czechoslovakia, and part of Poland. How these and other lands, conquered but less formally incorporated in 1940, may be disposed of depends upon the outcome of the second great war of the present century and on the international settlements resulting from it. Even with the annexed territories included, the area of Germany is little more than that of the state of Texas, and its population, including the large non-German elements of Poland, Bohemia, and Moravia, is little more than 100 millions. Yet that total area is nearly as great as that of France and the United Kingdom combined, and its population is greater than that of those two western countries.

The German lands, *i.e.*, those in which people of German language predominate, include Germany as it was in 1937; Austria; the Sudeten fringe of Bohemia; and what was, in 1939, western Poland, where much of the Polish population was quickly dispossessed and Baltic Germans as quickly implanted. These lands are physically divisible into two strongly contrasting parts. These are (1) the North German Plain and (2) the southern highlands, basins, and valleys.

*The northern plain* of Germany is part of the great North European Plain. It is a region of low relief covered by glacial deposits and morainic ridges. In the west especially, near the Netherlands border, it includes sandy heath lands and coastal marshes and peat bogs. In the central and eastern parts, extending into East Prussia and Poland, are other morainic ridges also interspersed with numerous glacial lakes and swamps. It is a surface comparable with that of central Minnesota, parts of Wisconsin, or southern Michigan. The glacial deposits of this region are less sandy than those in the west, but associated with them are areas of gravelly and sandy materials deposited by streams that flowed from the margins of the ancient glaciers. Particularly along the southern margin of the plain, there is a nearly continuous east-west belt of fertile loess soils believed to result from the accumulation of fine dust carried by wind or water during the glacial period. In general, then, the North German Plain is one of undulating surface and soils of moderate to low fertility interspersed with areas of poor drainage. It is narrow in the west but broadens eastward toward Russia.

*The southern region of highlands, basins, and valleys* is one of extreme variety. It includes such ancient hills as those bordering the Rhine Gorge, the Black Forest, the Harz Mountains, and the mountainous rim of Bohemia. These are mainly dissected plateaus and short or broken ranges, some of them the eroded remnants of highlands once greater in both height and area. Included among them are basins and valleys. Some are of low elevation, such as the plains bordering the lower and upper Rhine. Others are higher and are traversed by bold ridges. Such are the basins of Thuringia, Bavaria and Bohemia, the uplands of Saxony, and the Alpine foreland. In general, the elevations increase southward in this region, ending in the high Alps of Austria. The basins include many districts of fertile soil and great agricultural productivity, but even the hill regions are cultivated on their gentler slopes, and the less tillable areas are devoted to forests. Within these highlands are most of the famous scenic places of Germany which, under normal conditions, are themselves a great resource, attracting thousands of foreign visitors and yielding a large revenue to the country.

*The climate* of western Germany has a strong marine influence; the winters are relatively mild; and the coast is free from ice. Eastward the average annual precipitation decreases from more than 30 to less than 25 inches, but it is everywhere sufficient for agriculture. The winters of eastern Germany are severe, and the use of the Baltic seaports is hampered by ice. The summer temperatures are warm but not warm enough to mature maize. Altogether it may be said that the climate of eastern Germany and Poland is somewhat like that of the northern Great Lakes district of the United States.

## Agriculture and Forestry

THE PLACE OF AGRICULTURE IN GERMAN ECONOMY. Until about 1890 Germany was more an agricultural than an industrial nation, but after that time industrialization progressed rapidly. At present less than a third of the population lives in rural districts and in villages of less than 2,000 inhabitants; more than two-thirds live in larger towns and cities. There are about 60 cities of more than 100,000 population each in Germany proper, and at least a dozen more in Austria, Bohemia, and the German section of Poland. In spite of a high degree of urbanization, Germany is more nearly self-sufficing in farm produce than Britain. This cannot be attributed to the natural fertility of the German soil and its climatic versatility but rather to the scientific methods of agriculture and the comparatively low standard of living that the German people as a whole have been willing to accept as a means of economic defense.

It has been stated already that much of the land is of poor agricultural quality. Some very sandy lands and marshes in the northern plain and some steep and thin-soiled slopes in the south are farmed with difficulty or are incapable of tillage. Yet a surprising proportion of the total area in Germany proper is productive. About 40 per cent is in tilled crops and orchards; 17 per cent is in meadows and pastures; and more than a quarter of the total area is in carefully tended forests. There is no uniformity in the system or size of land holdings, for there are many large landed estates, especially in the eastern districts, and also a large number of small and medium-sized holdings (under 25 acres). As a rule the smaller farms are owned by the farmers who work them, but only a part of them live on their land. As is true in France and many other sections of Europe,

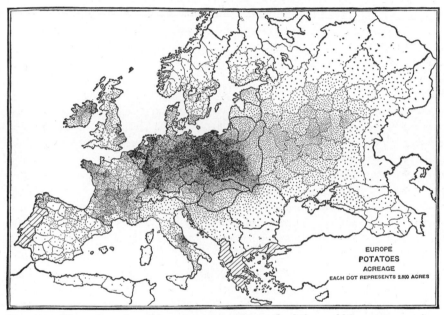

FIG. 243.—The cool, moist, plains of northern Europe lead the world in potato growing. (*U.S. Department of Agriculture.*)

it is common for the farmers to live in rural villages, from which they go out to till their near-by fields. The owners of the landed estates, especially in eastern Prussia, constitute a form of aristocracy who have long been a power in German political and military affairs, but their land also is worked by village peasants. The same is true in Poland.

Hay and root crops for the feeding of livestock occupy more land than any other single use, for Germany has a large and varied animal industry to be supported. Of the cereal crops, rye and oats are much more extensively grown than wheat and barley. Among other crops potatoes and sugar beets hold the leading places. However, there are regional contrasts in the relative importance of the several leading crops that require additional explanation.

POTATOES AND RYE. Sandy and ill-drained soils like those prevailing over much of North Germany are best suited to two food crops which thrive in light acid soils and cool summers—potatoes and rye. Enormous quantities of both are grown and used in Germany; 15 per cent of the cultivated land is devoted to potatoes, against 1.2 per cent in the United States, and the total potato crop is several times that of the United States. Not only are potatoes the commonest food of the German people, who consume about 30 per cent of the crop in that form, but great quantities (40 per cent) are fed to livestock and (nearly 10 per cent) are made into alcohol, starch, and flour. Nowhere else in the world are potatoes such an important crop (Fig. 243). Rye is the predominant cereal and occupies nearly four times as much land as either wheat or barley. It is more extensively grown on the North German Plain than in the southern uplands and, like potatoes, reaches its greatest importance in eastern Prussia and Poland (Fig. 274). Oats rank next to rye in acreage, and they are grown in nearly all parts of the country in about equal extent. Rye bread, potatoes, and cabbage are the staple foods of the peasant population throughout central and eastern Europe. Wheat and barley are widely grown, but they tend to occupy an important place only on the better soils, especially those of the loessial belt along the southern margin of the German Plain and in some of the southern upland basins. Barley is particularly important to Germany as a substitute for corn in the feeding of swine and in the brewing industry which provides the national beverage of the country.

SUGAR BEETS AND BEET SUGAR. To Germany is due a major part of the credit for the scientific studies by which the sugar-yielding qualities of the beet have been increased from 1 pound of sugar in 18 pounds of beets to 1 pound in about 6. The high development of the beet-sugar industry in Germany and in other parts of central Europe had a revolutionizing effect upon sugar production the world over (Fig. 233). For many years the industry was aided by substantial cash bounties on exported sugar paid by the governments of various countries on the continent; but this practice was discontinued. Before the war of 1914–1918 the sugar supply of the world came about equally from cane and from beets. Germany was the leading producer of the latter, for it is an industry to which the cool, moist summer climate; permeable, well-fertilized soils; cheap labor; and the German interest in chemical industries are especially suited. The sugar-beet crop occupies only about 2 per cent of the tilled land of Germany, less than half as much as that occupied by fodder beets for cattle, but it yields a highly valuable product, making imports of sugar unnecessary. It is grown on the more productive soils in both the northern and the southern regions and in Bohemia, but it is especially important in the loessial soils of central Germany near Magdeburg.

OTHER CROPS. In the more highly developed countries of Europe, population is much more dense than it is in the United States, and land is more expensive—often too expensive to justify its use for pasturage if it can possibly be used for crops. By planting turnips, beets, carrots, mangels, and other fleshy root crops a great amount of feed suitable for farm animals can be raised on a small area of land. Since corn cannot be grown successfully in the cool climate of northern Europe, root crops largely take its place in the agricultural rotation. Germany is a land of malt liquors, and hops are a characteristic crop in the south, especially

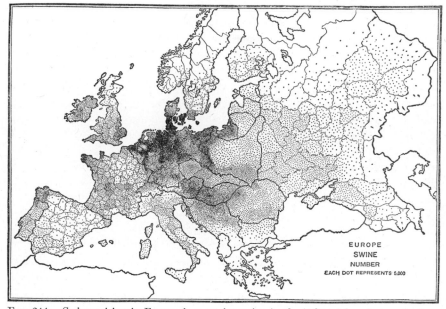

EUROPE
SWINE
NUMBER
EACH DOT REPRESENTS 5,000

FIG. 244.—Swine raising in Europe is most intensive in the industrial regions and where potatoes and dairy by-products are most abundant. (*U.S. Department of Agriculture.*)

in Bavaria. The grapevine is important in the west, notably so in the valley of the Rhine and its tributaries, the only part of the country warm enough for its successful cultivation. Tobacco also is locally a crop of considerable value.

THE RAISING OF LIVESTOCK. Because other activities stand out more prominently in Germany, the raising of livestock is seldom mentioned with any stress; yet only six countries report more cattle than Germany (India, United States, Russia, China, Brazil, Argentina), and each of them is much larger. Each square mile of Germany has an average of more than 100 cattle, as against 21 in the United States as a whole and 50 in the states that specialize in cattle raising (Fig. 234). Swine are as numerous as cattle, and Germany has more swine (Fig. 244) in proportion to area than any other country except Denmark—in fact about the same number per square mile as there are in Iowa. In meat, butter, and cheese Germany is much more nearly self-sufficient than Great Britain, her total imports of meat in particular being less than 10 per cent those of Britain and, of course, still less on a per capita basis. Sheep, however, are relatively few in Germany, and large imports of wool are necessary. Sheep do not fit well into the intensive use of land characteristic of the country, and there is only one sheep for every five hogs; in Britain both the actual numbers and the relative proportions of the two types of animals are almost exactly reversed, there being only one hog to five sheep.

All parts of Germany are well supplied with livestock, and regional specialization in one or another type of animal industry or animal product is not pronounced. Cattle are kept for work animals, for dairy production, and for beef, and in some cases the same animals ultimately serve all these purposes. In general the rough lands of the south and the ill-drained lands of the northwest coast do more commercial dairying than the central industrial regions and the large estates of the northeast. In swine production the western and northwestern sections of the country are particularly important. These districts are near the North Sea ports, into which are brought large importations of corn, barley, oilseeds, and other feedstuffs which supplement the potatoes and other domestic products used in swine feeding. As in Great Britain and in western Europe generally, it is only by imports of concentrated feedstuffs that the large domestic supplies of meats and dairy products are maintained.

SCIENTIFIC FORESTRY.   Germany reduced forestry to a science. More than one-fourth of the land in Germany proper and nearly half that of Austria is too hilly or mountainous or has soil too poor to be profitably used for agriculture. Such lands are set apart and studied to ascertain what use can best be made of them; if they can support forests of one kind or another, they are devoted to that use. Trained foresters manage these forests and determine what species of trees are best suited to the conditions, how thick the stand of timber should be, and what trees are ready for cutting. As fast as the mature trees are removed, young trees are allowed to grow up in their places, or others are set out from nurseries. So carefully are the forest resources husbanded that Germany is able to produce a large part, but not all, of her requirements of firewood, lumber, timber, paper pulp, and other wood products. Moreover, the forests protect the steeper slopes from soil wash and regulate the runoff. Largely under the influence of German methods, many other countries, including the United States, are introducing scientific forestry.

## Energy and Mineral Resources

LARGE AND WELL-DISTRIBUTED COAL DEPOSITS.   Germany has very large coal resources. Its most productive field and the one containing the best coking coal is in the Ruhr Valley of Westphalia in western Prussia, and 80 per cent of the good bituminous coal of the country is mined there and in the near-by Saar Basin (Fig. 235). Germany's greatest manufacturing region is situated on both sides of the Rhine in and adjacent to these coal fields. The next most important field is in Upper Silesia in the extreme southeast of Germany. Since 1918 and until recently the Silesian deposits have been so partitioned that part of them were in Germany, part in Czechoslovakia, and the larger part in Poland. They were the basis of the Polish industrial development near Kraców. Most of this coal is of lower grade than that of Westphalia. Other and smaller deposits of bituminous coal are located in the central provinces, especially in Saxony. Germany's total coal production of more than 300 million tons a year is somewhat larger than that of Great Britain and nearly equal to the bituminous coal output of the United States in recent years. However, more than half the tonnage of coal mined in Germany has been lignite, which has little more than two-thirds the heating value of good bituminous coal and is quite unsuited to some industrial uses. The principal lignite fields are in the central region. The possession of great coal deposits by Germany was one of the most fundamental factors in the expansion of its manufacturing and commerce, but coal probably did not play so large a part in German industrial and commercial development as in that of Great Britain.

ENERGY RESOURCES OTHER THAN COAL. Germany has only a small domestic *petroleum* supply. The reported output of 3 or 4 million barrels per year in recent years is much more than formerly, probably as a measure of preparation for war, yet it equals little more than 10 per cent of the recent imports of foreign petroleum into Germany. Even with the additional supply available through the occupation of Poland, domestic production can provide only a small part of the German petroleum requirement, especially in time of war.

The *water powers* available in Germany and its recent territorial additions are a valuable part of the total energy resources of the country. A moderate and well-distributed rainfall and numerous hill and mountain districts with glacial features and forested slopes give rise to extensive water powers and numerous power sites. These have been developed with characteristic German thoroughness, supported by the need to utilize all their natural resources. Moreover, most of the power sites are located within easy hydroelectric-transmission distance from urban and industrial markets for light and power. The quantity of power now developed in Germany, Austria, and Czechoslovakia is more than one-fourth that in use in the United States and about three-fourths that in France. In Germany proper the power possibilities are most highly developed, and the amount of power actually in use considerably exceeds the estimated potential of all the streams at ordinary minimum flow. This implies that a great deal of improvement has been made on some of the streams to regulate their flow and utilize their potential powers most efficiently (Fig. 221).

GERMAN RESOURCES OF IRON ORE. With the return of Alsace-Lorraine to France in 1918, Germany lost the minette iron deposits which had yielded 75 per cent of all the iron mined in the empire, reducing her reserves to about one-third their former quantity (Fig. 235). That was a serious loss. There were several other iron-ore deposits in Germany and Austria, but none of high grade or of large importance. One district, in the Sieg Valley, contains both iron and manganese and is near the Ruhr Valley coal, but it has never supplied more than a small part of the ore required there. Under the demands of a growing nationalism special efforts have been made in recent years to utilize more domestic ores. This has required the construction of several large and entirely new furnaces and steel mills using new processes of manufacture, but the products are considerably more expensive than those made with good foreign ores. In spite of great effort, about half the German iron output in 1938 still was made from imported ores; the other half from domestic ores and scrap iron reworked. Sweden was the chief source of the ore imports; France was second in importance but declining; and there were several sources of minor importance. Under the conditions imposed at the beginning of the Second World War the Swedish ore was about the only foreign supply available and hence was a vital necessity to Germany. With the military collapse of France in 1940 the minette ores again became freely available for German use, and Belgian and French coal and steelmaking facilities as well.

GERMANY'S POTASH. In 1843 there were discovered at Stassfurt in central Germany deeply buried beds of potash salt of fabulous extent— estimated at 20 billion tons—enough to supply the world's needs for 2,000 years at the present rate of consumption. The potash is mined by usual underground mining methods and can be produced rather cheaply. Less important beds of the same salt also exist in Alsace.

The principal use of potash is as an enricher of soils; it is one of three essential plant foods (potash, phosphorus, and nitrogen), and Germany had such a complete monopoly of the world's potash that she was able to use this monopoly to compel other countries to grant certain trade concessions to her. That monopoly was broken in 1918 by the loss of the Alsace deposits to France. Although Alsace is again under German control, it is doubtful if the German monopoly will be recovered. Other deposits have been developed in the meantime, especially in the United States. Although the United States output in 1938 was barely 10 per cent of the world's total, as against 75 per cent for mines now under German control, even that small amount was five times greater than that of 1932. The United States production appears capable of further increases if the competition of cheap German potash is reduced. Germany has used enormous quantities of potash (60 per cent of the total output) in building up her own agriculture, and, as already mentioned, the liberal use of this fertilizer is a large factor in the food-producing power of German soil. The presence of the potash and of large beds of common salt was also a factor in the upbuilding of the chemical industries in which Germany was so prominent.

OTHER MINERALS. Many of the mountains of southern Germany are ore-bearing. Upper Silesia is especially rich in coal, zinc, and lead. This region produced 57 per cent of the lead and 72 per cent of the zinc mined in Germany before 1914, but since then the industry has been largely in Polish hands. Only in 1939 was it returned to German control as a result of the conquest of Poland. Moderate quantities of graphite, pyrite, copper, and silver are mined—not enough, however, for the country's needs. As a by-product of iron-ore smelting by the Thomas process, large quantities of phosphate (for fertilizer) are produced.

## Manufacturing in Germany

RAPID GROWTH AND THE REASONS. The rise of manufacturing in Germany during the generation preceding the First World War was very rapid, and in 1914 that country ranked at least third and possibly second among the manufacturing nations of the world. For such an industrial expansion many conditions in Germany were highly favorable:

1. The geographical location of the empire gave it easy access to the markets of practically every European country.

2. It had ample supplies of coal, well distributed in various parts of the country.

3. It had iron, zinc, copper, lead, potash, salt, pottery clays, and a number of lesser minerals.

4. It produced a considerable variety of other raw materials including wood, sugar beets, hides, coal-tar products, and other chemical materials.

5. The government actively interested itself in everything that aided the upbuilding of industry—enacted a protective tariff, assisted the merchant marine, developed waterways, gave favorable rates on the state-owned railroads, actively promoted technical education, and encouraged scientific research.

IMPORTANCE OF THE CHEMICAL INDUSTRIES. Germany had for many years a place of world leadership in the varied field of chemical industries. This was based upon two main factors:

1. Its mineral wealth, especially coal, salt, and potash.

2. The scientific interests and training of its people, especially in the field of chemistry.

Just as the artistic leanings of the French are reflected in the artistic character of their manufactures, so the scientific leanings of the Germans were reflected in the remarkable development of their chemical industries. In the manufacture of aniline dyes, for example, Germany formerly had almost a monopoly—manufacturing about three times the quantity made by all the rest of the world. These dyes are made from coal tar obtained as a by-product of coke manufacture, and at the outbreak of the war of 1914–1918 Germany was in almost complete control of the secret formulas. But during the war other countries developed their dye industries. In scores of other phases of the chemical industries, including tanning, brewing, distilling, and the manufacture of drugs, medicines, explosives, glass, fertilizers, soaps, plastics, rayon, and other artificial fibers Germany was a leader. In these industries conditions have changed greatly in a quarter of a century. In recent years the German chemical industries have faced strong competition from Britain, Russia, France, and other European countries, also from Japan, and especially the United States which now has the largest and most varied chemical industries in the world.

THE METAL INDUSTRIES. With her basic resource of coal Germany produces more raw iron than any other country except the United States —more than Russia and, in recent years, as much as France and Britain together. This serves as raw material for a variety of metal industries. The industries include shipbuilding; arms manufacture; and the making of electrical and other machinery, vehicles, implements, and precision instruments for many uses. In part these manufactures require other metals, such as copper, zinc, and lead, of which the domestic supply has been insufficient. The recovery of the lead and zinc mines of Upper Silesia from Poland will increase the supply of those metals, but imports will still be necessary.

The industrial region of Westphalia includes the principal center for the manufacture of iron- and steelwares of all kinds, although many of the lighter wares are produced in other parts of the country also. The great arms and heavy steel industries of Essen have long been famous. In the same district are many other towns engaged in steel manufacture, such as Bochum and Gelsenkirchen, noted for heavy steel products; Solingen for cutlery; Remscheid for tools; and Duisburg-Ruhrort for shipbuilding. The port cities have developed shipbuilding also, especially Hamburg, which has access to the North Sea, and Stettin on the Baltic.

VARIED BUT NOT SPECIALIZED TEXTILE INDUSTRIES. It has already been pointed out that textiles and steel products are the leading articles of manufacture in practically all industrial nations. This is because they serve fundamental and widespread human wants. Germany, like the other manufacturing nations of Europe, produces only a minor part of the raw materials for its textile mills. Cotton is imported, about half of it from the United States, and enters through the port of Bremen. Silk comes from the Orient, wool from Argentina and Australia, flax from Russia, and coarse fibers from many lands. The importance of textile manufactures is seen in the fact that cotton, silk, rayon, and woolen fabrics and the manufacture of clothing from them normally employ more workers than any other German industry, even including the metalworking industries or the preparation of food products.

There are several districts in which the textile industries are well established, but those of western and southern Germany are most important. Alsace also is a textile-manufacturing area, and its control by Germany will increase the capacity of the western region. The industry has expanded in the Rhine industrial region, and several cities there are noted for their cotton and silk manufactures. Such are Gladbach-Rheydt, Wuppertal, leading cotton center, and Krefeld, which has large silk as well as cotton and woolen manufactures. The textile industries are important in Saxony and Silesia also, especially woolen manufacture.

OTHER MANUFACTURES. That Germany leads the world in the manufacture of beet sugar has already been indicated, and sugar refining is a leading industry in Magdeburg. The famous breweries of Bavaria (20 in Munich) use the hops and barley of that region. The chief source of toys is Bavaria and the Black Forest, where thousands of families spend their winter evenings making dolls and Christmas toys and clocks. In almost every one of the university cities are factories in which are made scientific and optical instruments, delicate apparatus, books, maps, and other articles in the making of which accuracy, scientific skill, and training are demanded. In such manufactures Germany leads the world.

## Communications in Germany

Germany has a highly developed and integrated system of communications. It includes nearly 34,000 miles of railway, largely owned and operated by the government, more than 200,000 miles of highways, some of which are paved through roads of the most modern type, and nearly 5,000 miles of inland waterways. The latter are comprised of about 1,000 miles of canals and nearly 4,000 miles of improved river routes. They are much more used than are the waterways in most other countries.

The average density of the railway pattern is high. Each mile of track must serve only 5.3 square miles of area. This is more than twice the average density in the whole United States and nearly as high as that in the Great Lakes-New England industrial regions. Much of the transport system has been designed with an eye to its military as well as its commercial utility. The rail network is well distributed over the country, but its focus is Berlin. From this center the lines of transportation radiate to all sections of the country, as do those of France from Paris.

Because the German waterways are so much more used than those of other countries, they may be described here in greater detail. First, it may be noted that the arrangement of the rivers is most fortunate. Flowing from the highlands of the south, the five great rivers trend not north but generally northwest, following the slope of the plain. Thus the Rhine, Weser, and Elbe all empty into the North Sea, and only the Oder and the Vistula flow into the ice-hampered Baltic. The ample precipitation of

PRESENT RIVERS AND ANCIENT GLACIAL SPILLWAYS IN N. EUROPE

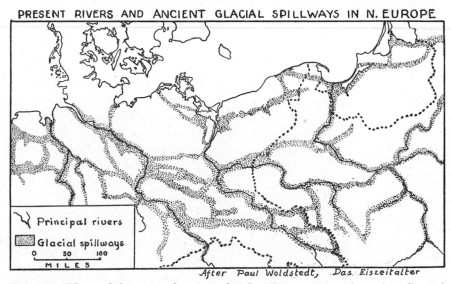

After Paul Woldstedt, Das Eiszeitalter

Fig. 245.—The graded courses of ancient glacial spillways connect the main valleys of Germany and have aided in the development of a unified system of inland waterways.

the whole of central Europe gives these major streams considerable volume, making them commercially usable. Cutting the central part of the German plain transversely to the trend of the major streams are several large stream channels now occupied only by small tributary streams. These are the graded courses, or spillways, of the large streams that carried the great volume of drainage from the continental glaciers westward along the ice fronts during the period of glaciation (Fig. 245). Being already graded, they are easily canalized and thus serve to link together the main rivers. By this means traffic originating far inland on the Vistula can be carried westward to the Elbe or the Weser and thus to the North Sea ports.

THE RHINE is the most important commercial river of Europe. It rises in Switzerland and enters the sea through the Netherlands and has been under the control of an international commission. The Rhine is not

FIG. 246.—Barge traffic on the Elbe River at Magdeburg. (U.S. Bureau Foreign and Domestic Commerce.)

quite so long (800 miles) as the Ohio River but carries vastly more commerce than the whole Mississippi system. It has been dredged and straightened and otherwise improved, and the many cities on its banks have built docks equipped with modern devices for loading and unloading cargoes. It is not a deep river, ranging between 6½ feet in the upper stretches to 10 feet in the lower. In the United States, the Ohio and the lower Mississippi are deeper and have had more money expended on them, but they are relatively little used. One important difference between the two countries in the development of water transportation arises from the density of population along the Rhine and along the Ohio and Mississippi. The Rhine has some 20 important cities on the river or directly tributary to it. Great coal and iron mines are near by, and a large tonnage of heavy, low-grade freight is available.

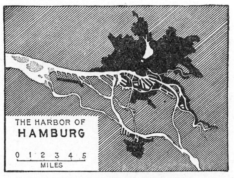

THE HARBOR OF
**HAMBURG**

0 1 2 3 4 5
MILES

Fig. 247.—The intricate harbor of Hamburg has been dredged out of the banks of the Elbe. City area in black.

OTHER GERMAN RIVERS AND CANALS. The Elbe (Fig. 246) and the Oder are the other German rivers of most usefulness. Near the mouth of the Elbe is the great port of Hamburg, whose peacetime river traffic, like that of Rotterdam at the mouth of the Rhine, was greater than its rail traffic (Fig. 247). The river rises in Bohemia and is navigable throughout its entire course across Germany; by means of this river Bohemia is made tributary to the North Sea rather than to the Mediterranean. The Oder is less used than the Elbe, and the Vistula, mainly in Poland, still less; yet all are used more than similar rivers in the United States.

Canals connect the German rivers not only with one another but with rivers in the Netherlands, Belgium, France, and other countries (Fig. 248). By means of canals now under construction the Rhine is to be connected with the Danube and the Vistula with the Dnieper in Russia. There will then be two water routes from western Germany to the Black Sea. Certain ones of these canals are used a great deal, especially for the shipping of coal, iron ore, and building materials. In Germany the government controls both waterways and railways, and they are forced to co-operate. Germany is sometimes pointed out as an example of what ought to be done with waterways in the United States, but evidence has been adduced that seems to show that if all actual costs are charged up to water transportation in Germany, they amount to more than rail transportation does in the United States.[1] If the waterways are provided and maintained from the public treasury and are made free to shippers, the water rates may well be lower than rail rates, but at the same time the actual cost of the service to the public may be as great as or greater than it is by rail. It has been said that Germany—all of whose policies have been shaped with reference to her possible military needs—was willing to

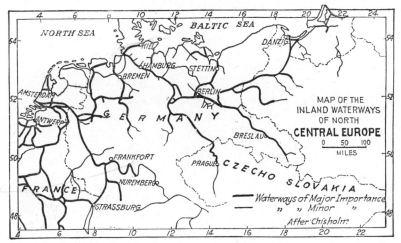

FIG. 248.—On the whole Germany has the most complete and most used system of waterways in Europe. (See Fig. 245.)

maintain her waterways at a loss because of their potential ability to relieve the railroads in time of war. This they ordinarily would do, but at a critical time in the war winter of 1940 unusually severe weather caused them to freeze for several weeks.

THE KIEL CANAL connects the North and Baltic seas across the narrow neck of land south of Denmark. The original canal, completed in 1895, had a depth of $29\frac{1}{2}$ feet and proved to be too shallow. Just before the First World War the depth was increased to 36 feet, and the canal was otherwise enlarged to accommodate the largest battleships and liners, though liners have used it but little.

## Colonies and Commerce

ACQUISITION AND LOSS OF COLONIES. Since modern Germany dates from 1871, it has had little opportunity to acquire colonies, because most

[1] Moulton, H. G., "Waterways versus Railways," Boston, 1927.

of the desirable regions had already passed into other hands. Africa, however, had not been entirely parceled out, and in 1884 and 1885 Germany took possession of parts of Southwest Africa, of East Africa, and of Togoland and the Cameroons on the Gulf of Guinea. These were colonies of small value at that time but of considerable potential value, for they are capable of yielding great quantities of tropical raw materials which the industrial nations need. Germany also acquired a number of insular possessions in the Pacific, all of which, together with her African possessions, were taken over by the Allies after the war of 1914–1918. The lack of such possessions to be used as secure markets and sources of raw materials has been a grievance to the nation in its program of national expansion, a condition leading up to the second great war for trade development and political control.

CHARACTER AND EXTENT OF FOREIGN COMMERCE.   German foreign trade has been influenced by abnormal conditions for many years: first by the period of financial instability following the First World War and later by the spirit of economic nationalism that dominated the political life of the country. This involved an attempt to restrict trade to such proportions as would bring to the country only essential imports and at the same time build up exports to provide a maximum of foreign credits to be used in emergencies. As a result, the trade of recent years shows a consistent surplus of exports over imports of about 4 per cent. The leading imports have been raw materials for German industries—vegetable oils and oilseeds, cotton, wool, petroleum and its products, iron ore, and other ores and metals. Smaller, but still considerable, have been the imports of foods, especially butter, eggs, meat, and fruits. The list of industrial raw materials is long and varied, but the value of the total import trade of all classes has been less than half that of the United Kingdom in the same years.

The exports are, of course, predominantly the products of German factories—steel products of all kinds standing first; cotton, woolen, and silk fabrics; beet sugar, paper, chemicals and dyes, leather goods, toys, furs, scientific apparatus, electrical goods, porcelain, and glass. Coal and coke are also sold abroad in large quantities.

PRINCIPAL REGIONS INVOLVED IN GERMAN COMMERCE.   Of all the influences that decide the countries with which other countries shall trade extensively, *nearness* seems to be the most important the world over. This would be expected, for neighboring countries can exchange products most promptly and most cheaply. It is easier for countries that are near together to understand each other's needs and wants and to supply them. This applies more fully to a country's exports than to its imports, for it can import products like cotton, raw silk, rubber, coffee, and tea only from a limited number of regions that produce them, but it may send its exports to practically all countries. Of the five countries that in recent years, have bought German exports most largely—the Netherlands, Great Britain, France, Italy, and Switzerland—four are near neighbors. Germany has also a large trade with the Scandinavian countries and with those of the Danube Basin. The United States ranks lower as a buyer of German goods than as a supplier of German imports. Argentina, China, and India are other distant countries whose total trade with Germany is large. It is an interesting fact that the three chief rivals for world trade have, in normal times, a large trade with one another—the United States, Germany, and Great Britain. Evidently the more our rivals' trade grows the more our trade with them grows; their prosperity becomes our prosperity, and their depression our loss. The whole commercial world is so closely knit together that in the long run all prosper and suffer together.

## The Annexed Territories

By political maneuvers and military force during the years 1938 and 1939 the German government brought under the control of Berlin all or part of three independent countries that lay upon its eastern borders— Austria, Czechoslovakia, and Poland; also the city and port of Danzig. The annexation of Austria and the Sudeten margin of Czechoslovakia brought dominantly German populations into the Reich, but in the Bohemian and Moravian districts of Czechoslovakia and in Poland the people were mainly Slavic. It remains to be seen what elements of economic and political strength or weakness the inclusion of these areas has brought to Germany, and there remains also the question of their final disposal after the conclusion of the present European struggle. Some of these matters have been touched upon previously, but they may be reviewed briefly here.

Germany's great need is not more coal and additional manufacturing facilities. Its need is good agricultural land, capable of producing wheat, corn, and livestock to supplement an inadequate food supply and to broaden the agricultural base of German economy. It also needs good iron ores and a variety of the metal ores. These the annexations have generally failed to provide.

AUSTRIA is largely a mountainous country; and although it is not so large as the state of Maine and less than one-fourth its land is arable, it has a population of nearly 7 millions and three cities of more than 100,000 each. Nearly 2 millions live in Vienna alone. The country has only a little coal, and that not of coking quality. Its other mineral resources include a small quantity of low-grade iron ore but little else of critical value. Its agricultural lands are not sufficient to support its own population adequately, and it has no seacoast or direct access to the sea. Two natural resources it has in relative abundance—forests and water power.

The population, like that of Germany, is largely employed in manufacture, trade, and the professions. Vienna has a strategic location at a crossing of two natural routes of traffic—one east-west, following the Danube Valley, and the other north-south, from the Adriatic Sea to Bohemia and Poland. It has long been a great industrial and commercial center. Prior to 1914 it was the rich and busy capital of the large and diversified Austro-Hungarian Monarchy. After 1918 it remained only the capital of a small and relatively poor country. A great depression overtook it, and a period of readjustment set in from which it has not recovered. Since the annexation of Austria to Germany Vienna has ceased to have much more governmental importance than attaches to a county seat, for most of the governing is done from Berlin. In general, therefore, Austria is a depressed industrial country which is much like southern Germany in agriculture and industry. Its textile manufactures and many of the others depend on imported raw materials, and it must import food. Its exports are diverse, but those of greatest value depend upon its iron ores and its forests resources. These industries are similar to those of Germany, compete for German markets, and in part depend on German coal.

BOHEMIA AND MORAVIA. These, the western parts of Czechoslovakia, are better endowed than Austria, but their possession involves the control of a large population, intelligent, industrially minded, almost fanatically patriotic, and traditionally anti-German. The annexed territory is mainly a mountain-bordered hilly upland. About a third of it is tillable, and it was nearly self-sufficient in food, but it produces the same kinds of crops as are found in southern Germany—potatoes, rye, wheat, and sugar beets. More than half the people are engaged in manufacture and trade, and less than a third in agriculture and forestry.

The great strength of the region is its industrial diversity. It shared with Poland the coal and iron deposits of Upper Silesia, most of which were taken from Germany in 1918, and it had some deposits of its own in Bohemia. Upon this foundation great industries had been built—iron and steel manufactures, including the production of armaments at the Skoda works; cotton and woolen textiles; leather and shoe manufacture; glassmaking, brewing, and many others. But most of these were dependent in large part on imported raw materials. Although their addition to the German economy increases the possible output of the national manufactures, it also increases the problem of marketing the surplus of goods. The industrial and commercial population that must be fed is also increased without a corresponding addition to the food-producing capacity of the country. The normal food imports of Czechoslovakia have been considerably greater than its exports.

WESTERN POLAND.    Poland, as it was in August, 1939, occupied a
part of the great European plain. Half of it was tillable land, and the
country was dominantly agricultural. Only a little more than a quarter of
the population lived in cities. However, there was a considerable difference between western and eastern Poland. Western Poland was in part
included in Germany prior to 1918. Its agriculture was better developed,
and its rural population more dense. Also it included part of the Upper
Silesian coal- and zinc-producing districts. It had developed considerable
manufacturing and included 10 out of the 14 Polish cities of more than
100,000 population.

The partition of Poland between Germany and Russia in 1939 added
the western portion to adjacent Germany, which, obviously, it is much
like in many respects. It shares the glacial moraines; the poor, sandy
outwash plains; and the lakes and marshes. It increases considerably the
industrial capacity of the country, adds coal resources and the critical
element of zinc to its mineral wealth. Its annexation increases Germany's
capacity to produce rye, potatoes, cabbage, and livestock, but it also
adds a large population. This problem is currently being met by the
summary ejection of peasantry of Polish blood and their removal eastward. They are being replaced by some 250,000 other Polish, Baltic, and
Russian people of German ancestry. Presumably they are better farmers.
Whether or not such measures can go far in making western Poland a
great asset to Germany is a question that only time can answer. Perhaps
an advantage to both Germany and Russia might have been created
if their respective spheres of control could have been reversed, for Russia
needs the industrial resources of western Poland, whereas in the more
sparsely settled and less intensively cultivated eastern portion Germany
could have found room for increased food production through scientific
agriculture.

## Switzerland

ECONOMIC CONDITIONS.    Switzerland has little agricultural land, does
not touch the sea, and has practically no coal or iron. It has mountain
pastures and is making the most of its opportunities for dairying. It has
much water power (Fig. 221) and a large population of industrious,
skillful workers. General agriculture and direct ocean trade are both out of
the question. With its necessity of importing coal and most raw materials,
Switzerland can scarcely compete in the ordinary lines of manufacturing
with more favored countries like Germany, England, or Belgium, but it
might succeed in highly specialized manufacturing that uses little raw
material and coal and a great deal of skilled labor; and this is precisely
the procedure that the Swiss have followed.

EFFECT OF LOCATION AND MOUNTAINOUS SURFACE.    The greater
part of Switzerland's 4 million people live in the northern two-fifths of

the country, which is a hilly plateau. Here agriculture and transportation are not particularly difficult, and here are located all the important Swiss cities (Fig. 249). The central location of the little country makes it the crossroads of several great routes of traffic and offers ready access to the markets of three of the important countries of Europe. Its glaciers, mountain lakes, Alpine peaks (Fig. 250), green valleys, superb roads, and 2,000 hotels have made it a summer playground. In normal times caring for tourists gives employment and income to a considerable part of the population. In point of money received this is one of the foremost indus-

Fig. 249.—The agricultural lands of Switzerland near Zurich, densely populated and highly cultivated. (*Photograph by Swiss Aviation Service.*)

tries of the country. Switzerland includes the very heart of the Alps, whose narrow valleys separated by high mountain walls have fostered in the people an intense spirit of independence and devotion to democracy. Its laws are the most liberal in the world, and it is the asylum of exiles from most of the countries of Europe. There is no national language; in 15 cantons, including 70 per cent of the population, German is spoken; in 5 cantons, including 22 per cent of the population, French is spoken; and in 2 cantons Italian or Romansh is used.

ALPINE PASSES, ROADS, AND RAILROADS. Many of the large rivers of Europe rise in the Alps; these include the Rhône, Rhine, Po, and Danube, flowing west, north, south, and east, respectively. The valleys of these rivers are the natural routes for the great railway lines of central Europe, and at the heads of these valleys and of other valleys of the Alps are the passes that have become famous in European history. Over the principal passes perfectly graded roads have been constructed, and under six of the passes (not all in Switzerland) railroad tunnels have been built. Three of the tunnels—the St. Gotthard (9¾ miles long) and the two Simplon tunnels (each 12¼ miles long)—are part of the chief north-south traffic routes of Europe. The presence of fairly easy passes in the Alps has made these mountains a much less serious barrier than some others, such as the Caucasus, which are conspicuously lacking in low passes. Furthermore, the situation of the Alps in the heart of Europe makes it far more essential that roads and railroads traverse them. Thus it is that the surface of Switzerland makes road and railway building difficult,

FIG. 250.—The high Alps of Switzerland, sparsely inhabited and little used. (*Photograph by Swiss Aviation Service.*)

but the location of the country makes such building necessary, and the result is favorable to the whole economic life of the republic.

THE IMPORTANCE OF DAIRYING. The heavy rainfall, cool climate, damp soil, and rugged surface of much of Switzerland make grazing (cattle and goats) the most practicable use for more than half the usable land. Sheep are raised but not in large numbers. Especially in the Alpine pastures with their rich growth of summer grass are the well-kept Swiss cattle herded. It is customary in summer for the cattle of a local community to be driven far up into the mountains, where their attendants live in temporary huts or cottages, care for the cattle, and make the cheese, while other members of the families care for the little farms in the valley. Swiss cheese, condensed milk, and milk chocolate are distinctive national products enjoying a world-wide reputation.

THE ABSENCE OF MINERALS AND THE SHORTAGE OF RAW MATERIALS. Trifling quantities of poor coal and iron are at times mined in Switzerland, but neither these nor any other minerals are of significance. Such a condition has necessarily militated against certain forms of general manufacturing, but it has by no means prevented a remarkable growth of *specialized* manufacturing. There is no other country destitute of coal and iron that has so highly developed its manufacturing industries as Switzerland has done.

THE DEVELOPMENT OF MANUFACTURING. Switzerland is one of the four or five countries of Europe in which manufacturing has grown to be a dominant industry, yet it is the most handicapped of them all in its lack of coal and raw materials and in the cost of securing them. All overseas raw materials must be landed in foreign ports and transported over foreign railways. Under such handicaps it is remarkable that the Swiss can succeed as a manufacturing nation. The reason lies in the characteristics of the people—in their mechanical ability, in their liberal government, in their six universities, their excellent technical and vocational schools, and in their ability and willingness to live on a small income. They probably could not compete with more favored nations if they did not follow the course of making goods in which water power can furnish much of the needed energy and in which the cost of power and raw materials is a minor matter and the cost of human labor a major one. These goods include textiles, watches, clocks, jewelry, musical instruments, optical goods, scientific apparatus, and light machinery. The industries are located principally in the western French-speaking cantons, especially the Jura Mountain valleys, and in the cities of Geneva, Neuchâtel, and Berne. For example, 20 to 30 million watches and clocks are exported in a year. In Basel and Zurich and other cities mainly along the St. Gotthard route, which brings in the raw silk from Italy and the port of Genoa, are some 200 silk mills, large and small, and silk and rayon goods are important items of Swiss manufacture. In the canton of St. Gallen are concentrated the cotton, lace, and embroidery interests. Milk-chocolate factories employ thousands of workers and send millions of pounds of chocolate yearly to other countries. These are examples of the highly specialized Swiss products which constitute about 80 per cent of the exports of the country.

THE LARGE FOREIGN TRADE. Switzerland ranks high in foreign trade. The bulk of the trade is, as may be expected, with the near-by countries of Germany, Britain, France, and Italy, but trade with the United States is almost equally large. The leading items in the normal import trade of Switzerland are, in terms of value, crude iron and steel, coal, wheat, chemicals, machinery, and raw cotton. With the exception of wheat these go to the maintenance of Swiss industries. The leading exports, also in value, are watches and clocks, machinery, coal-tar dyes, aluminum and its products, and cheese. Only one of these is agricultural, and the aluminum expresses the abundance of hydroelectric energy in Switzerland.

### Selected References

DICKINSON, R. E. The Economic Regions of Germany, *Geog. Rev.* Vol. 28 (1938), pp. 609–626.

JONES, CHESTER LLOYD. Switzerland: Resources, Industries, Trade, *U.S. Dept. Commerce, Trade Information Bull.* 421, 1926.

LAMING, R. V. Report on the Economic, Financial, and Industrial Conditions of Holland, Department of Overseas Trade, London (annual).

NIEHAUS, H. Agricultural Conditions and Regions in Germany, *Geog. Rev.*, Vol. 23 (1933), pp. 23–47.

SCHNEIDER, R. J. The Port of Hamburg, U.S. Department of Commerce, 1930.

ZIMMERMANN, ERICH W. "World Resources and Industries," pp. 636–642, New York, 1933.

# Chapter XXVI. Scandinavia and the Baltic States

The several countries of northern Europe, with the exception of Norway, share with Germany and Russia a frontage on the Baltic Sea. In spite of this unifying influence, differences in cultural history and political administration give rise to notable contrasts among them in degree of economic development. Yet they do share a relatively uniform climatic environment and some degree of similarity in economic resources. There are certain common elements in the type of economic development characteristic of the smaller Baltic States and Scandinavia, even though the degree of their development is different.

## The Scandinavian Countries

HISTORICAL INTERRELATIONS OF THE THREE COUNTRIES. Owing, no doubt, to geographical proximity, the three countries Denmark, Norway, and Sweden are peopled by the same racial stock—the Scandinavian—a branch of the Teutonic race that occupies northwestern Europe. During the past thousand years various of these countries have at times been united and again separated. They fall within the conflicting spheres of influence of Germany and Russia, and it remains to be seen if any of these countries can maintain independent political existence in the Europe that will emerge from a war in which small countries are but pawns in a gigantic struggle for world power.

THE PHYSIOGRAPHIC CHARACTER OF THE SCANDINAVIAN PENINSULA. The greater part of the Scandinavian Peninsula is an ancient landmass— among the oldest in Europe. The resistant rocks of this old plateau extend into Finland and give that country a similar geological character. Scandinavia was the principal center from which the great European ice sheet of the last glacial period moved outward, and, as a result of the scouring and transporting action of this ice sheet, the highlands of Scandinavia were robbed of most of their soil and are now a region of broadly rounded, nearly barren uplands and rough glaciated mountains. The southern end of Sweden belongs to the great European plain and is fair agricultural land.

## NORWAY

THE INFLUENCE OF THE NORWEGIAN COAST UPON THE ECONOMIC LIFE OF THE COUNTRY. The mountainous plateau that constitutes the greater part of Norway has heavy rainfall and snowfall, which gives the short, swift rivers great erosive power. Moreover, the many valleys leading down to the sea have been much overdeepened by glacial erosion, and their submerged lower portions now form the fiords that give to Norway its remarkable coast (Fig. 251). Besides these long, deep, narrow arms of the sea, some of which reach back into the plateau from 50 to 100 miles, there are almost countless rocky islands (said to be 150,-000) fringing the coast. These features in the physiography of Norway have been unfavorable to agriculture but have encouraged a seafaring life.

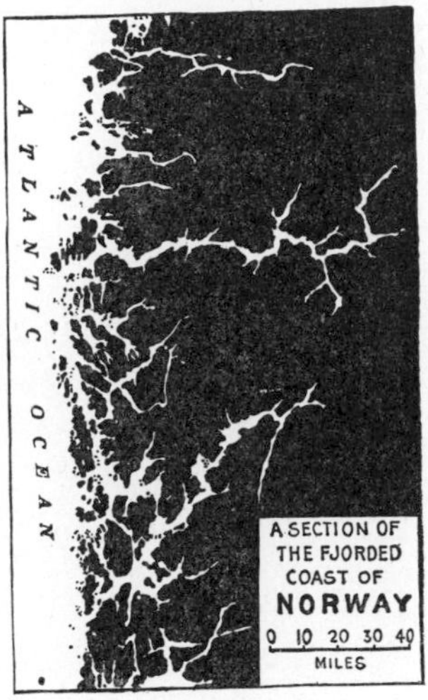

In the centuries when ocean navigation was in its infancy, when there were no charts of coasts, no lighthouses, no mariner's compass, and only small sailing vessels, an island-fringed coast like that of Norway or of Greece, where the mariner was almost never out of sight of land, was the most favorable place for encouraging seamanship and promoting a maritime life among the coast dwellers. If, in addition, the surrounding waters contained abundance of

FIG. 251A.

fish, then a motive for going upon the sea was added. Because of its unproductive land, its deeply indented and island-fringed coast, and the wealth of fish in the offshore waters, the people of Norway have turned toward the sea to a greater extent than any other European people, the British not excepted.

THE INFLUENCE OF THE OCEAN UPON THE CLIMATE OF THE NORWEGIAN COAST. Norway is in the same latitude as Greenland, in which all but the southern margin is a frozen waste covered by ice and snow and uninhabited. Yet Norway is one of the progressive nations, with modern cities, modern industries, and a population of nearly 3 million people. Throughout its great length of coast, extending far north of the Arctic Circle, the harbors of Norway are not closed by ice even in midwinter, and the January temperature along the coast is as high as it is in southern Russia, 1,500 miles farther south. Nowhere else, unless it be in Iceland, has the existence of a nation depended upon the moderating influence of the ocean as it has in the case of Norway and to a lesser degree in the case of Sweden and Finland.

FIG. 251B.—A Norwegian fiord. Four elements of Norwegian industry: a fishing boat and fish house in the foreground; a small farm on the alluvial terrace which also has summer pastures on the upland; forests on the lower slopes of the fiord walls; waterpower from the upland streams which fall precipitously as they enter the fiord.

IMPOSSIBILITY OF SUPPORTING THE NATION BY AGRICULTURE. So thin and scanty is the soil and so steep are the slopes in most of Norway that on an average only 2½ acres in 100 are under tillage, less than 1 per cent more is in meadows, and about 25 acres in 100 produce forests (of pine, spruce, and other evergreens), but in most places the stand of timber is not heavy (Fig. 252). Seventy per cent of the land is barren or, at most, is productive of a scant summer pasture. The growing season is necessarily very short, and only hardy grains and root crops can be raised. The larger part of the agricultural land is in the southeastern portion of the country, near Oslo. So rugged and barren is the surface of the rest of the country that only little strips of valley land here and there can be cultivated. The farms are small, two-thirds of them not exceeding 5 or 6 acres of tilled land; many of these are only little garden patches at the heads of fiords or in secluded valleys. Hay, oats, barley, and potatoes are

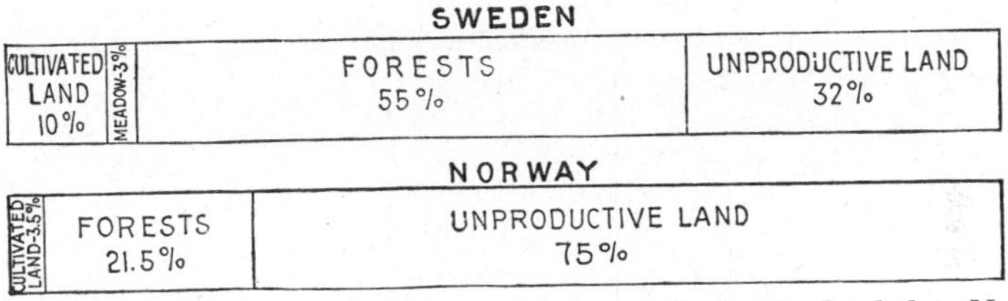

**SWEDEN**

| CULTIVATED LAND 10% | MEADOW-3% | FORESTS 55% | UNPRODUCTIVE LAND 32% |
| --- | --- | --- | --- |

**NORWAY**

| CULTIVATED LAND-3.5% | FORESTS 21.5% | UNPRODUCTIVE LAND 75% |
| --- | --- | --- |

FIG. 252.—Sweden has a much higher proportion of productive land than Norway.

leading crops, but the food production is much below the requirements of the population. In a land where most of the soils are thin and poor, farming is a discouraging enterprise, and this, in part, explains the heavy emigration of Norwegians to the United States and also the drift of the men toward the sea. Dairying has increased somewhat, and a surplus of dairy products permits some exportation of butter, cheese, and condensed milk. But as a whole the country must import a considerable part of its food.

NORWEGIAN FISHERIES. Important supplements to the Norwegian food supply and nearly one-fifth the value of the country's exports come from the sea (Figs. 97, 253). About 6 per cent of the people find full-time employment in the fisheries, but a still larger proportion includes small farmers and others who are part-time fishermen. Codfish make up more than one-fourth the total value of the catch, and large numbers of them are taken near the Lofoten Islands off the northern coast where they are salted and dried. Other fish, including small herring, are taken also, and the latter are packed as sardines in fish canneries, of which many are located along the southern fiords. Norway has a large whaling fleet also which carries on its works in all the whaling regions of the world.

FOREST RESOURCES AND HYDROELECTRIC POWER. Over half the limited forests of merchantable timber of Norway lies in the southeastern end of the country in the general region of the Swedish border and north of the capital, Oslo (Fig. 254). The manufacture of woodpulp and paper and of various forms of lumber are two of the leading mill industries of the country, but they are much less important than in Sweden, whose forest resources greatly exceed those of Norway.

Heavy precipitation and the features of mountain glaciation combine to give the country large potential water power (Figs. 125, 221); it is estimated that upward of 16 million horsepower is capable of commercial development, but less than 3 million is actually in use, and the greater part of this development has occurred since 1910. By way of comparison

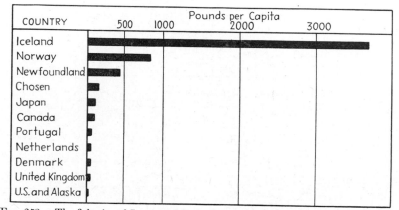

**THE PER CAPITA PRODUCTION OF FISHERIES IN SELECTED COUNTRIES**

Fig. 253.—The fisheries of Japan yield a larger quantity of fish than those of any other country (see Fig. 97), but not on a per capita basis. Relative to their populations the sparsely-settled fishing countries of the North Atlantic rank highest.

it may be pointed out that Italy has only one-third as much potential water power as Norway but twice as much already developed and in use. If placed on a per capita basis, however, Norway has more developed water power than any other country. So numerous and widely distributed are the water powers that small developments are available even in rural districts, and about two-thirds of the farm homes have electrical appliances. A large part of the power is transformed into electricity and is used in certain special industries that depend upon cheap electric current, including woodpulp manufacture, the electric smelting of ores, and the much more important manufacture of chemicals. Among the latter are compounds of nitrogen made by extracting the nitrogen from the air. This electrochemical industry of Norway is of special interest because it represents an effort to utilize the resource of water power in a country that has very small resources of raw materials. If, by the use of cheap electric power, free atmospheric nitrogen can be combined with other substances to make fertilizers or other valuable products, then Norway is making highly intelligent use of her limited resources. Other uses of water

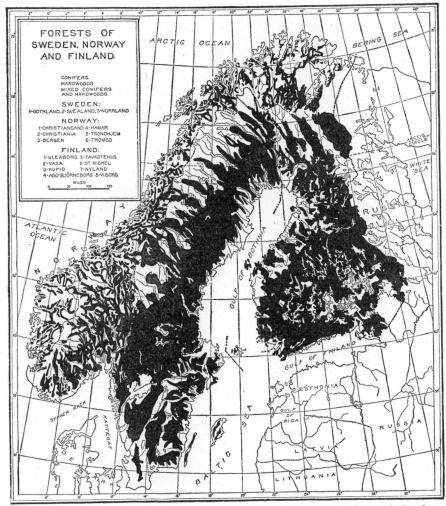

FIG. 254.—Areas in black are the lands that are wholly or partly forested. Southern Sweden, for example, has large areas that are partly agricultural land and partly timber land. (*After Zon and Sparhawk.*)

power are in aluminum smelting and paper manufacture. The industries of Norway use several times as much water power as steam power; those of the United States use more than four times as much steam power as water power.

VERY POOR IN MINERAL WEALTH. Norway is one of the poorest of European countries in mineral resources—no coal, almost no high-grade iron ore, very little copper and iron pyrite, and no other minerals worthy of mention.

HIGH RANK IN SHIPPING. In 1938 Norway ranked fourth among the countries of the world in the gross tonnage of her fleet of merchant ships, being exceeded only by Britain, the United States, and Japan. The Norwegians are among the best sailors of the world and are found as officers and seamen on the ships of many nations. Norwegian ships are primarily engaged in carrying the commerce of other countries, for Norway's commerce itself is not large. It is mainly by the earnings of these ships that Norway is able to offset her unfavorable trade balance, for her imports always exceed her exports in value. Because of its world-wide shipping services the Norwegian fleet, although neutral, suffered heavy losses in ships and men during the World War of 1914–1918, and the same fate has overtaken it in the second great struggle.

THREE CHARACTERISTIC EXPORTS. Norway's exports are small, but they reflect with clearness the three chief resources of the country. The three are (1) fish (dried, salted, canned, and pickled); (2) forest products (lumber, timber, woodpulp, and paper); (3) products of the electro-industries (metals, including aluminum, nitrates, and other chemicals). There is also a considerable export of ships, made in Norway with Norwegian labor and skill, largely out of imported raw materials.

SPITSBERGEN. Four hundred miles north of the northernmost part of Norway is a group of islands whose total area is twice that of Belgium or Denmark. Prior to 1919 these islands, in the far-off northern seas, definitely belonged to no one in particular, but that year they were placed under the Norwegian flag by the League of Nations. These islands contain mineral wealth, which includes coal of good quality, iron, copper, and lead.

## SWEDEN

NATURAL WEALTH GREATER THAN IN OTHER SCANDINAVIAN COUNTRIES. Norway and Denmark are poor in natural resources, and the same is true of Finland; Sweden has as much natural wealth as all these three combined. Fifty-five per cent of the land is forested, and a large part of this forest is of good quality (Fig. 254). About 10 per cent of the land is suited to agriculture (Fig. 252). There are rich deposits of iron ore (Fig. 255), equal in quality to the best in the world; and the water-power resources are among the largest possessed by any European country (Fig. 221). Thus, with an abundance of iron, timber, and water power and with fair agricultural land, Sweden is equipped to maintain a more varied industrial and commercial life than either of its sister Scandinavian nations.

UNFAVORABLE GEOGRAPHICAL CONDITIONS.  Sweden lies far to the north, on the leeward side of the Scandinavian mountains, but is much less rugged than Norway.  The northern half is comprised of ice-scoured uplands of crystalline rock, largely forested.  The southern portion also is ice eroded, but it includes extensive morainic deposits and many glacial lakes, several of large size.  Its physical features are much like those of

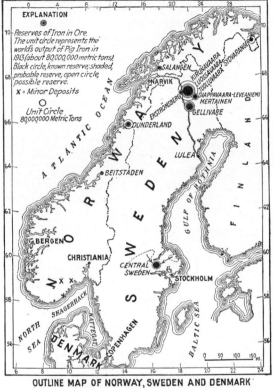

OUTLINE MAP OF NORWAY, SWEDEN AND DENMARK
SHOWING RESERVES OF IRON IN ORE

FIG. 255.—In the far north of Sweden is one of the most important high-grade iron-ore areas in Europe. (*Modified from U.S. Geological Survey.*)

central and northern Minnesota.  Most of the country is deeply covered with snow during the long winters; the growing season is short, and the summer precipitation is only moderate.  The lakes and rivers are frozen, and the water power is greatly reduced during the winter.  Only in the southern third of the country is agriculture profitable; yet this southern third could maintain extensive manufacturing industries based upon the raw materials of the country if cheap coal were available, but Sweden has very little native coal.  Eventually hydroelectric power may largely make up for this shortage of coal, but it has not yet done so.  However, when the natural advantages and disadvantages of Sweden are compared, they seem nearly to balance. Unlike Norway, whose economic life is so largely maritime, and unlike Denmark, which is mainly devoted to specialized animal husbandry, Sweden is not forced to specialize but is able to maintain a diversified, well-balanced economic life.

THE DIMINISHING RELATIVE IMPORTANCE OF AGRICULTURE.  Two generations ago the people of Sweden were preeminently agricultural, and more people were obtaining a living by cultivating the soil than by all other occupations combined. After the middle of the last century certain important changes came which greatly stimulated the forest industries and iron mining and a little later stimulated manufacturing. Today less than half the people of Sweden are farmers, against 85 per cent a century ago. The hardy cereals—oats, wheat, rye, and barley—and the hardy vegetables—potatoes, sugar beets, and the root crops for cattle feed— make up the larger part of the farm crops. The total population numbers only 6¼ millions (equal to Ohio), yet food has to be imported, although meats and dairy products are exported. The movement of population is toward the cities, as it is in all the industrial nations, and more than one-third of the total number live in cities, of which there are three that exceed 100,000 inhabitants.

THE RISE OF FOREST AND WOODWORKING INDUSTRIES.  A Swedish economist has declared that the future of Sweden lies in her forests. These forests of pine, fir, and spruce occupy the major part of the country and nearly all the northern half. The longer slope on the east side of the Scandinavian mountains gives rise to a great number of rivers that are excellently suited to the floating of logs. There are more than the natural facilities for the lumbering industry; Sweden has become one of the world's foremost wood- and wood-products-exporting countries; and Great Britain normally is the largest buyer of these products.

A great deal of the timber of Sweden, as of cold lands generally, is better suited to woodpulp than to lumber. Small, inferior trees that would not make lumber may be entirely suitable for pulpwood. Sweden is one of the foremost exporters of pulp and paper-mill products, even sending them to the United States. For this industry Sweden is especially well fitted, for it has raw material, water power, nearness to the sea, and nearness to the great consuming markets of Europe. Two other forest products are important: (1) tanbark for some 200 tanneries and (2) charcoal for fuel and for the smelting of iron ore. The match industry of Sweden is another that is based upon wood resources; Sweden has a factory that turns out 40,000 boxes of matches an hour, but much of the special wood employed in their manufacture is now imported from Russia. No other country except Finland depends for its prosperity so largely upon its forest products.

THE IRON ORES AND THE STEEL INDUSTRIES.  Sweden was once the leading iron-producing country of Europe. Iron ores of high quality have been mined in south-central Sweden and have been smelted with charcoal for centuries. The steel thus produced has no superior for certain purposes; for example, the cutlery industry of Sheffield, England, is based upon Swedish charcoal steel. In the far north of Sweden, beyond the Arctic Circle, are the largest high-grade magnetite and hematite ore bodies of Europe (Fig. 255). In fact, the largest known deposit of *high-grade* iron ore of that continent is located there, and the rest is in Russia. The ore is

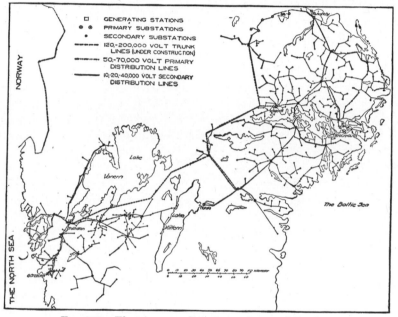

FIG. 256.—Electric power lines in south-central Sweden.

at the surface of the ground and is easily mined; in winter a railroad takes it to the ice-free port of Narvik on the Atlantic Coast of Norway, and in summer some of it is shipped from the port of Lulea on the Swedish coast on the Gulf of Bothnia, which is frozen over in winter. About these ores and the vital port of Narvik centered a part of the military struggle between Germany and Britain in the winter of 1940. Without coking coal with which to smelt the ore, Sweden is forced to export most of it, and Germany is the chief buyer in normal times, using the ore in her great metallurgical industries in the Rhine-Ruhr Basin. The Swedish government is opposed—and properly so—to the unlimited exportation of these raw ores, for the country derives but small return from the ore thus disposed of. It is, of course, desirable on the part of any country to work up its raw materials into manufactured goods as fully as possible, for only thus does the country employ its labor and itself derive a full return from its natural wealth. However, the Swedish steel industry is constantly struggling against the competition of German steel, which is partly made from Swedish ores. Yet the metal industries now far exceed the woodworking industries in value of product.

THE IMPORTANCE OF WATER POWER. The almost complete absence of coal in Sweden makes water power of unusual importance (Fig. 221). The amount theoretically available is very large, but the "amount worth exploiting" is placed at about 5 million horsepower, nearly half of which is already developed (Fig. 256). This is somewhat less than the amount developed in Norway, with its enormous electrochemical factories. Of all the mechanical energy used in Sweden, two-thirds is derived from water power. At present this is most largely developed in south and central Sweden and notably along two rivers—the Dal, with about 50 water-power plants; and the Göta, with about 25. The more rigorous climate of Sweden as compared with that of the coast of Norway places the water-power plants of the former at a certain disadvantage in competitive industries such as the electrochemical industries. But Sweden's vastly greater wealth of raw materials—especially iron and wood—are in that country's favor. A project has been completed providing for the transmission of hydroelectric power by marine cables from Sweden and from Norway to Denmark, which has neither coal nor water power. In looking ahead to the future development of Sweden, it is evident that its water power is destined to play a very large part.

NOTABLE INCREASE IN MANUFACTURING. The lumber, timber, pulp, paper, and metal industries have already been discussed. In the last quarter-century Sweden has had a rapid growth in general manufacturing —cotton, woolen, flour, tobacco, shoes, chemicals, beet sugar, butter, and many other products. In 1840 only 10 per cent of the people of Sweden depended for a livelihood upon manufacturing and commerce; today the figure is over 50 per cent, or as high as the percentage in France.

TRANSPORTATION AND COMMERCE. Sweden has a larger railway mileage in proportion to population than any other country in Europe. It also has a number of much used waterways in the southern quarter of the country, which has the major part of the population, agriculture, and manufacturing. A waterway with a minimum depth of 9 feet extends entirely across the southern end of the peninsula and connects the chief port Göteborg with the capital Stockholm. This waterway makes use of two large lakes (Vänern and Vättern), and along its course are many of the industrial plants of the country.

The foreign commerce of Sweden is fairly well balanced as to the value of imports and exports, although the imports generally exceed the exports by a small amount. Both are extremely varied in character, the imports including, as two large items, coal and manufactured articles, especially machinery. Woodpulp is the largest single export item, and manufactures of wood and steel and several million tons of iron ore make up 75 per cent of the exports.

## Denmark

DENMARK'S LIMITATIONS.    Denmark, like others of the small countries of western Europe, has worked out the main features of its economic life in a characteristic way. It finds itself compelled to take the fullest possible advantage of its geographical location and to make the most intelligent use of such resources as it possesses. The struggle for economic survival is severe in these countries because of their small size and consequent limited natural resources; they must import much of their food and raw material and must in some way earn the money with which to pay for them.

Denmark is a flat, sandy country with no coal, iron, or other minerals. Geologically and physically it is more closely akin to the plain of northern Germany than to the crystalline rocks of the Scandinavian highland. Nearly two-thirds of the land is tillable, and more than three-fourths is crop land or pasture. But it has small forest resources and produces very few natural raw materials that can be worked up into manufactured goods. Its location for conducting entrepôt, or transit, trade has not proved to be so favorable as that of the Netherlands or Belgium. With generous fertilization and intelligently directed labor the soil is made highly productive, but Denmark cannot successfully produce miscellaneous farm products for export in competition with Canada, the United States, or similar countries. If the country is to depend upon agricultural exports, they must be specialized products; and, furthermore, they must be such as are demanded by near-by markets. This is the course that the Danes have followed.

SPECIALIZATION IN DAIRYING.    One hundred years ago Denmark was trying to maintain its people mainly by general agriculture, including wheat raising; but the country was distressingly poor, and thousands sought relief by emigrating. The soil was run down, and the yields per acre were small. At that same time, the city population of England was rapidly increasing, and the demand for imported farm products was also growing. Among the products much in demand were butter, eggs, and bacon. Gradually the Danish farmers, under the influence of far-sighted leaders, began the study and practice of specialized dairying. By careful selection and breeding the dairy cows of the country were improved so that their average annual milk production was increased from 3,500 pounds in 1880 to 7,500 pounds in 1938. More and more of the land was devoted to clover, root crops, and succulent forage crops, and thereby larger quantities of milk-producing feeds were raised on a given area of land. Cooperative dairies and cooperative buying-and-selling organizations were formed all over Denmark. Experimental stations, special agricultural schools, and the distribution of printed matter among the farmers steadily raised the level of farm practice. Danish butter became famous in the London market for excellence and dependability and commanded from 2 to 5 cents a pound more than butter from other countries. So thorough was the inspection of this product by the cooperative marketing agencies that inferior butter under the Danish brands was almost unknown. Under this regime, fertility was steadily returned to the land; profits permitted the importation of oil cake, Argentine corn, and other feeds, which, in turn, increased the milk and meat production of the country. In recent years about four-fifths of the milk produced in Denmark has gone into the manufacture of butter, and the country has exported more than 300 million pounds of butter yearly. Most of it has gone to Great Britain, the world's largest importer of dairy products. It was a triumph of intelligence, integrity, and cooperation in making the most of the country's opportunities. Military invasion and naval blockade have cut off both the British markets and sources of imported grains and other feedstuffs. This is certain to destroy many of these advances. What may be the future markets for Danish butter in a war-impoverished Europe can only be conjectured.

OTHER ASPECTS OF DANISH AGRICULTURE.   Denmark is a country of small landholdings, and about 90 per cent of them are occupied and operated by their owners. About one-third of the entire population depends directly on the land for a living. Tenancy—which often leads to the depletion of the land—is rare. Education is widespread; in addition to rural elementary schools, there are over 100 rural high schools and over 20 agricultural colleges in a little country one-third the size of New York. Not only did Denmark develop her dairy herds and her soil; she went to the foundation of prosperity and developed her common people, more than half of whom live on the farms.

An outgrowth of dairying in Denmark is the raising of pigs, for skimmed milk has value as a feed, and this milk is made the basis of an industry of even greater importance than buttermaking, viz., the production of high-grade pork from which are made the famous Danish bacon and hams that bring top prices in the British market. To complete the breakfast menu, the Danes have also turned to poultry raising, and they send to the near-by industrial regions about 100 million dozens of eggs yearly (Fig. 257). However, the feedstuff- and forage-producing capacity of the Danish land is not sufficient to support such large numbers of livestock. The continuation of the industry depends upon the importation of supplementary feedstuffs from distant agricultural regions. By these intensive, intelligent methods, the land of Denmark annually exports from $20 to $25 worth of products for every acre—a figure attained by no other agricultural country. The value of *agricultural* exports per capita of the population in Denmark is much greater than the per capita value of *all* exports from the United States.

COMMERCE.   Copenhagen, the capital and chief city, is situated on the largest of the many islands that form a part of Denmark. It occupies a strategic commercial position between the North Sea and the Baltic. Most of the Baltic ports have rather shallow water, and Copenhagen, with its deep waters and "free port," has acted as a collecting and distributing center for this entire region. The hinterland of Denmark, unlike that of the Netherlands and Belgium, is only the small home coun-

## DANISH PRODUCE AND EXPORTS, 1939

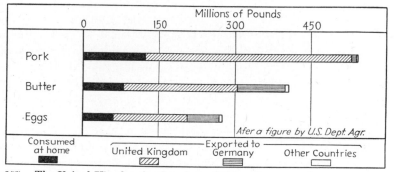

FIG. 257.—The United Kingdom has long been the most important buyer of Danish food exports.

try, and its exports have been therefore very largely the home products. Denmark is normally a large buyer of American cottonseed cake and meal and automobiles. It is also a large purchaser of Argentine corn and of other feedstuffs from various sources. But the agricultural countries buy only a trifling amount from Denmark, mainly because they produce a sufficiency or a surplus of animal products. About half the Danish exports normally go to the United Kingdom; about one-fifth, to Germany; and the other largest purchasers are Sweden and Norway. The import and export trades are very well balanced, and the principal sources of imports are the same as the export markets and also the United States.

ICELAND.   For centuries Iceland was treated as a colony or dependency of Denmark, as Greenland still is. This little-visited island on the border of the Arctic Sea is rendered habitable by the mild waters and winds of the North Atlantic. It contains about 115,000 people, mostly of Scandinavian ancestry. Since 1918 it has been an independent nation. The fisheries off the Iceland coast are frequented by the fleets of most of the north European countries. The largest industry of the island and one to which its climate is well suited is sheep raising. It has a highly educated people, a university, a national library, and newspapers and claims the oldest parliamentary assembly in the world. Its exports are mainly animal products and fish, and its trade is largely with the countries of north-western Europe. Its political fate, like that of other small countries, rests upon the outcome of the European war.

## Finland and the Baltic States

### FINLAND

THE COUNTRY AND THE PEOPLE.   Considerably larger than the United Kingdom, Finland has less than 4 million people. Except in the far north it is an undulating plain comprised almost entirely of old crystalline rocks, severely ice-scoured, much like Laurentian Canada. Lakes cover about 10 per cent of its area, and swamps another 30 per cent, and thousands of square miles are covered with infertile glacial deposits. Settlement is most dense in the coastal districts and more sparse in the interior region of lakes and forests. The northern portion lies beyond the Arctic Circle and averages only about one inhabitant to the square mile. Only about 7½ per cent of the land is cultivated; 2½ per cent more is pastured (Fig. 258); but even this is higher than the proportion in Norway. The agricultural land is mainly in the southern and southwestern coastal regions. The winters are, of course, long and cold; the growing season is short; forests and brush cover about three-fourths of the land, and there are about 15 acres of forest land for every inhabitant. In a country of so few natural advantages it is surprising to find a people of high culture, maintaining an excellent school system and supporting many newspapers and periodicals and numerous learned societies. The Finns themselves are descended from Mongolian ancestors who came into the country long ago. For 500 years they were under Swedish rule; large numbers of Swedes settled in the southwestern coastal belt of the country, and they have largely dominated the culture of the whole population. To them Finland owes much of the intellectual and economic advancement that it has achieved.

In 1809 Russia took the grand duchy of Finland away from Sweden and during the following century attempted its Russianization, but the

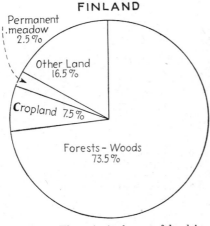

FIG. 258.—The principal uses of land in Finland.

FIG. 259.—A lumber port on the coast of Finland. The low, forested surface of the country yields a surplus of timber for export and large sawmills are found on the coast. (*U.S. Bureau Foreign and Domestic Commerce.*)

effort failed. The national spirit of the Finns is intense; they bitterly resented Russian control and, following the Russian Revolution of 1917, declared their independence and set up a republic which they were again called upon to defend against the Russians in the short but bitter war of the winter of 1939–1940. The terms of the treaty that brought nominal peace cost Finland some strategic territory and brought the country a little closer to Russian domination. Other and perhaps gradual steps in the process may be looked for in the future.

RESOURCES AND INDUSTRIES.    The ancient rocks of Finland contain no coal, little workable iron, and only a few other minerals of economic value. Among the latter are included the newly developed nickel deposits of the far north about which the Russian invasion of that region in 1939–1940 at first revolved. Only hardy grains, potatoes, root crops, and hay can be grown on a commercial scale, and not enough of these to supply home needs. The chief wealth of the country lies in its forests of pine and spruce, a continuation of the Swedish forests on the west and of the Russian on the east (Fig. 259). Lumber, timber, woodpulp, and paper are the most important exports, forming about 82 per cent of the value of all exports. Agricultural products, principally dairy products, make up about 8 per cent. The pulp and paper industry is second only to lumber and timber products among the few manufacturing industries of the country.

Agriculture and dairying employ the majority of the people. Dairying has become increasingly important, as the Finns have profited by the example and experience of Denmark. Hundreds of cooperative butter factories have been established, and butter is the largest agricultural export of the country, going mostly to Great Britain and Germany.

## THE THREE SMALL BALTIC STATES

During its centuries of expansion, the old Russian Empire absorbed many peoples that were not Russian. With the breakup of Russia in 1917, followed by the Allied victory in the World War, movements began among the submerged peoples of Russia that resulted in the establishment of three small republics—Estonia, Latvia, and Lithuania—on the eastern shore of the Baltic Sea. These former Baltic provinces of Russia were at one period under the rule of certain orders of Teutonic or German knights, and a large part of the land became the estates of the later German barons, who largely dominated these provinces down to the present. Although the German barons formed only 1.5 per cent of the population, they formerly controlled practically all commercial, political, and industrial activities because of their education, wealth, and aggressiveness. Over 80 per cent of the people are peasants living mainly by agriculture. After the establishment of the independent Baltic republics, many of the large landed estates were acquired by the governments and were divided into small holdings and sold to the peasants. All the Baltic States are distinctly agricultural. The land, a part of the low Baltic Plain, is partly forested, partly pastured, and partly cultivated in an indifferent way. Educational opportunities were much better in the Baltic provinces than in Russia proper, and four-fifths of the people are able to read and write. Roads are poor; railroads few; wages low; poverty is widespread; and life generally, an uphill struggle. Under such a regime the people produce relatively little beyond their own needs, and foreign trade remains small.

Under the political readjustments that took place in 1939–1940 these three small and weak states were again brought under the dominance of Russia. By apparent agreement between Russia and Germany several thousands of their German inhabitants, the so-called "Balts," who are the descendants of the former German landed aristocracy, were summarily uprooted after centuries of life in the Baltic States and returned to Germany. There they were largely resettled in the Polish territories taken by Germany in the very destructive war of September, 1939, and from which a large part of the Polish landowners were expelled.

Estonia, the northernmost of the three Baltic States, is one-third the size of Pennsylvania and has somewhat more than 1 million inhabitants, two-thirds of whom are rural. The Esths are close kin to the Finns and have been considerably influenced by Swedish culture. The boundaries of the country are so placed that 93 per cent of the inhabitants of the country are Esths, nearly all of whom have some education. The school system—including elementary and high schools, commercial and technical schools, normal schools, and a state university—is far ahead of the school system of Russia proper. Only a quarter of the total area is under cultivation, raising rye, barley, potatoes, hay, and flax. The forests, like those of Finland and north Russia, are mainly evergreen and supply some timber and pulpwood for export. Dairying is general, and butter is exported. The industrial development follows the pattern of that in Finland, the principal products being woodpulp and cellulose, paper, and cotton textiles. But, on the whole, Estonia is qualified to take a very small part in international trade or international affairs. Without mineral resources or any advantages for the development of manufacturing, with a severe climate and a small population, Estonia seems to have little out of which to build a modern nation. It seems probable that the military concessions made by its government to Russia in 1939–1940 have marked the end of its independent existence.

Latvia, like Estonia, came into existence as an independent nation in 1917. The Letts are not a Slavic people but together with the Lithuanians constitute a composite racial group whose origins are little known. They have been subjected to cultural influences from Russia, Germany, and

Sweden, but they have little in common with the Russians. Their country is half the size of New York state and has about 2 million people. The Letts are an able people and have maintained a state university that enrolls over 5,000 students. About one-third of the land is tilled; one-fourth is in pasture; and one-fourth is forested. Forest products constitute about 40 per cent of the exports, and they are in large part of the cruder types, only a small part being pulp, paper, and other highly manufactured wares. The Letts have, however, followed the Danish example, and much progress has been made in dairying. Butter is the largest agricultural export, but the leading crops for home use are potatoes, oats, barley, and rye. Latvia is included in that part of the European Plain which raises the largest part of the world's flax fiber, and the principal flax belt extends eastward into Russia. It is a crop requiring cool, moist summer weather and a large amount of hand labor. Only peasant labor can grow and prepare it cheaply enough; for, at best, it is a much more expensive fiber than cotton, and the world demand for it is limited. Agriculture and forestry occupy the greater part of the people, although Riga, the principal city, is a manufacturing center of some importance and one of the principal seaports of the eastern Baltic. It also was subjected to military control by Russia in 1939.

LITHUANIA. During a part of the fifteenth and sixteenth centuries, Lithuania was one of the large and powerful nations of Europe. Later, it fell under Russian and Prussian rule and was incorporated within those countries but mainly in Russia. The country is about half the size of Ohio and has a third as many people (2.5 millions). The greater part of the people are farmers of the peasant type, and about one-sixth of the population is illiterate. The uses of the land and the relative importance of the several crops are about the same as in Latvia. The country has no mineral wealth and but little manufacturing. The principal exports are forest products, butter, bacon, and flax fiber. Like its neighbors, after a short span of independence, it seems that Lithuania has reverted to practically the status of a Russian province, although it may not be called by that name.

SELECTED REFERENCES

NORWAY

KEMP, HAROLD S. Trondhjem: A Subarctic Phenomenon, *Jour Geog.*, Vol. 35 (1936), pp. 209–224.
THOMPSON, CLAUDIA. Norway's Agriculture, *Jour. Geog.*, Vol. 35 (1936), pp. 165–178.
———. Norway's Industrialization, *Econ. Geog.*, Vol. 14 (1938), pp. 372–380.

SWEDEN

JONASSON, O., *et al.* "Agricultural Atlas of Sweden," Stockholm, 1938.
KEKICH, EMIL. Forestry in Sweden, *U.S. Dept. Commerce, Trade Promotion Series* 56, 1927.

### DENMARK

BERGSMARK, D. R. Agricultural Land Utilization in Denmark, *Econ. Geog.*, Vol. 11 (1935), pp. 206–214.

JONES, H. "Modern Denmark," London, 1927.

SHAW, EARL B. Swine Industry of Denmark, *Econ. Geog.*, Vol. 14 (1938), pp. 23–37.

### FINLAND

EICHHOLZ, A. C., and RODECK. Finland, An Economic Review, *Trade Information Series* 681, Washington, 1930.

MEAD, WILLIAM R. Agriculture of Finland, *Econ. Geog.*, Vol. 15 (1939), pp. 125–134, 217–234.

ROTHERY, AGNES. "Finland, The New Nation," New York, 1936.

VAN CLEEF, EUGENE. "Finland—the Republic Farthest North," Columbus, 1929.

# Chapter XXVII. The Mediterranean Lands and Southeastern Europe

## Borderlands of the Mediterranean

GEOGRAPHIC UNITY OF THE MEDITERRANEAN LANDS. More than a dozen countries and political dependencies are situated about the borders of the Mediterranean Sea. Within these political divisions are included diverse conditions of local surface features and climate, many peoples, and many languages. Yet, from the standpoint of economic geography, they have a sufficient number of conditions in common to permit their being grouped together into one of the primary geographic regions of the world. The most fundamental of the unifying conditions is (1) similarity of climate. Others of consequence are (2) lack of extensive plains lands, (3) common frontage upon an inland sea, (4) a degree of similarity in location with respect to the principal landmasses of the world, and (5) a general meagerness of those natural resources which are fundamental to large industrial and commercial development.

CLIMATIC CONDITIONS AND ASSOCIATED FEATURES. A combination of climatic elements so distinctive as to have acquired the name "Mediterranean" characterizes all but the Libyan and Egyptian parts of the borderlands of the Mediterranean Sea. The outstanding features of this climate are (1) subtropical temperatures with smaller annual range than the average for the latitude; (2) low annual rainfall, with a winter maximum and dry summers; (3) a high percentage of sunshine. So characteristic is this type of climate that it is known by the name "Mediterranean" wherever it may be found, as in California, Chile, or Australia. The present region may, in fact, be further defined by it. On this basis the Mediterranean lands include southern Europe, Turkey, Syria, Palestine, and the coastal slopes of Tunisia, Algeria, and Morocco. Egypt and Libya are not included, since they get very little rainfall and may better be discussed later in connection with the deserts of northern Africa.

This type of climate, although it is favorable to certain crops and industries, imposes strict limits upon the development of others. The perennial crops must be those which are able to withstand summer heat and drought, such as the olive and the grapevine, or those which thrive under irrigation, such as citrus fruits. Fall-sown cereals which, in the mild winter temperatures, can make use of the winter rains furnish the staple foods. Because of the summer drought, good pastures are difficult to maintain, and their scantiness is evidenced by many sheep and goats but a relatively smaller number of cattle. The mild and sunny winters of the Mediterranean shores have made the region a winter resort for people of the more gloomy north European countries. Even northern Italy has 25 per cent of possible sunshine in its most rainy month.

SURFACE CONFIGURATION. The geologic history of the Mediterranean region has left its mark upon the coastal outline of the land and upon the configuration of its surface. A series of subsidences along the southern margin of the older landmasses of central Europe are responsible for the creation of the basin of the Mediterranean Sea. With these same processes were associated some of the mountain-building forces that have resulted in the hemming in of the region as a whole by mountains from whose northern axis project southward a series of peninsulas: Iberia, Italy, and the Balkan Peninsula. Fringing this irregular margin are the unsubmerged portions of other mountains which appear as islands, large and small.

Not only do mountains such as the Pyrenees, Alps, Balkans, and Atlas provide margins for the region, but other and lesser mountains characterize its surface. A degree of unity in the Mediterranean surface features may be indicated by calling attention to some of the repeating features. These include (1) limited coastal plains, as in southern Portugal, eastern Tunisia, and western Turkey; (2) alluvial basins and deltas, as in southern Spain and France and the Po Valley of Italy; (3) broad, dry plateaus broken by ranges of mountains, as in central Spain, the plateau of the Shotts in Algeria, and the Anatolian Plateau of Turkey; (4) the many included and rimming mountain ranges themselves.

The separation of the borderlands of the Mediterranean into many distinct physical units has had a profound influence upon the history of mankind. The total area of all the Mediterranean lands is not half so great as the area of the United States, yet they include, wholly or in part, eight independent states and several dependencies, at least eight distinct languages, and a large number of dialects. The latter, as in all old countries, are to be attributed in part to historic conquests and migrations and to the long separation of small groups of people by barriers that prevented easy intercommunication.

FRONTAGE UPON THE MEDITERRANEAN. There can be little doubt that, in the early stages of human development upon the shores of the Mediterranean, the sea was a barrier to human intercourse. Yet at a very early date the Phoenicians, who inhabited a part of the narrow plain at the eastern end of the Mediterranean, had pushed out from their shores to near-by islands and coasts. With this beginning they progressed from one island and peninsula to another until they penetrated to every corner of the sea and beyond its western portal. After them came the Greeks, the Romans, the Venetians, and the Genoese. The Mediterranean ceased to be a barrier and became a unifying influence, and powerful conquerors arose who welded these borderlands into great empires. Yet none has been powerful enough permanently to overcome the tendency to political disunion imposed by the expanses of sea and by the mountainous and disjointed surface features.

THE LOCATION OF THE MEDITERRANEAN AMONG THE LANDMASSES. European civilization owes much of its character to the peoples who inhabited the shores of the Mediterreanean, and modern commerce has sprung from beginnings in the same region. During the Middle Ages the Mediterranean was the great commercial thoroughfare of the world. The merchants of Venice and Genoa controlled a large part of the world's trade that flowed between northwestern Europe and the East. But historical events and important discoveries shifted the world's trade to the Atlantic Ocean, and the Mediterranean became for several centuries only a byway in the commerce of the world. Its importance was later increased by the reopening of connection with the East through the Suez Canal, yet its ancient position of predominance has not been regained. The closure of this route during the struggle to wrest its control from Great Britain is evidence of the fact that world trade may continue to flow without using the Mediterranean although not so abundantly or conveniently.

CHARACTER OF NATURAL RESOURCES. The early traders and merchants of the Mediterranean borders found in the natural resources of the region a wealth of materials for their purposes. For the craftsmen of the Middle Ages local raw materials were, in the main, sufficient. In this respect also the world has changed. Iron and steel have replaced wood and copper and bronze, and the energy of coal has replaced hand power. In the race for modern industrial and commercial supremacy the Mediterranean borderlands have been left behind, for nature did not abundantly endow them with the materials upon which modern commerce and industry depend.

## AGRICULTURE IN THE MEDITERRANEAN REGION

IMPORTANCE OF AGRICULTURE. Agriculture has developed in the Mediterranean lands under many discouragements. The hot, dry summers restrict the range of possible crops and of livestock industries. The rough surface and many steep slopes put large areas beyond the possibility of cultivation. In Italy less than one-half, in Spain only one-third, and in

Greece one-twelfth of the land is under tillage. These proportions average higher than the 20 per cent attained in the United States; and the percentage for Italy ranks among the highest in the world. That this is true attests dense and industrious populations dependent mainly upon the land for a living. About 45 per cent of the persons in all occupations in Italy and 50 per cent of those in Portugal are engaged in agriculture. In Greece 60 per cent and in Algeria 70 per cent are farmers. These figures may be contrasted with those of industrial countries—such as the United States, 22 per cent; Germany, 29 per cent; or the United Kingdom, 6 per cent—to get the full measure of the importance of agriculture to the people of the Mediterranean region.

WHEAT is the most important cereal crop of the Mediterranean countries, for it finds in the mild, moist winters the necessary conditions for its development (Fig. 231). It is harvested at the beginning of the summer drought, in May in northern Africa and in June in Spain, Italy, and Greece. Although wheat culture is widely distributed in the region, the most important districts are (1) northern Italy and (2) the plains of Old Castile in Spain, in which is situated the city of Valladolid, the chief milling center. The maximum importance of wheat is reached in Italy where it occupies above one-third of the cultivated land. In the Po Valley and about Naples it is cultivated very intensively; but in the drier portions of the country, including Sicily, less intensive methods prevail, and the yields are lower.

BARLEY as a winter crop is also well adapted to Mediterranean climatic conditions. It is, however, less desirable for food, and wheat tends to replace it where wheat can be grown. Because of the shorter growing season of barley, it is a more certain crop in the districts of scanty rainfall. It reaches its greatest importance in North Africa. On the desert margin in Libya the seed is plowed into the ground in November. If the rains are sufficient, a crop is harvested in April or May. In Algeria it occupies almost as much land as wheat (25 per cent of the cultivated area) and usually yields a larger return. The barley of North Africa and of Asia Minor, like that of California, is much in demand in northern Europe for malting because of its bright color and uniform quality, which are the results of dry weather during the ripening period of the grain.

Oats and rye, because of their larger water requirements and lower temperature requirements, are of very little importance in the Mediterranean countries (Fig. 274).

CORN (MAIZE). The Mediterranean lands do not have a good corn climate; the warm season is too dry. The principal corn regions are (1) northwestern Spain and Portugal, where the summer rainfall is considerable; and (2) the Po Valley of Italy, which has the most nearly continental type of rainfall of any part of that country (Fig. 268). Corn is an important food of the Italian peasantry, yet the acreage of corn in that country is barely one-third that of wheat.

VEGETABLE CROPS are cultivated in all parts of the Mediterranean region for local consumption and in some districts as market garden and truck crops. In Italy, particularly, they are grown by an intensive system of interculture in orchards and vineyards. Near the larger cities and along the principal railways they are grown for market.

Truck farmers on the warm, irrigated coastlands of Algeria and of the Mediterranean coasts of Spain and France have specialized in winter vegetables for the north European markets. In normal times special boats and rapid trains carried the produce across the Mediterranean and through France. This is, however, essentially a luxury trade, and it is likely to be restricted for many years to come by poverty in northern Europe.

VINEYARDS. The Mediterranean lands are believed to be the home of the viniferous types of grapes (Fig. 232). The vineyard is common to all the countries from Portugal to Persia. As in California, grapes are grown for wine, for raisins, and for table use. A number of famous wines take their names from Mediterranean places—sherry from Jerez in southern Spain, and port wine from Oporto in Portugal. Most of the wine of the Mediterranean countries is, however, for home consumption.

The production of table grapes on a commercial scale is best organized in southern Spain. In the Almería district numerous villages make this phase of vine culture their principal industry, and a large export trade is conducted with the cities of northern Europe. The grapes are packed in cork dust and shipped in wooden casks. The ability of California to supply the American market with this type of grape and the reduction both in production and in the European market resulting from wars has brought severe hardship to the Almería grape growers. Early table grapes are also exported from the coast of Algeria and from Greece.

Many parts of the Mediterranean coast have the requisite climate for the curing of raisins. A commercial industry has, however, developed principally in two regions—southern Spain and southern Greece. The Spanish city of Málaga has given its name to a type of raisin now produced in several other parts of the world. It is still the center of an important raisin district. On the shores of the gulfs of Corinth and Patras, on the islands of Cephalonia and Zante in southern Greece, are vineyards that specialize in a small, seedless grape. When these are cured into raisins, they are known as "currants" (a corruption of "Corinth"). As there is little domestic market for this product, nearly the entire supply (sometimes 150,000 tons) is exported. Currants rank second only to tobacco among the exports of Greece.

The drying of fruits other than raisins is favored by Mediterranean climatic conditions. Prunes are abundant in Jugoslavia, Italy, and southern France. The Smyrna district in Asia Minor is the center of the world's principal dried-fig-producing region. The same fruit is exported from Greece, Italy, Spain, and Portugal.

THE OLIVE.    Of all crops, the olive is perhaps most peculiar to the Mediterranean type of climate (Fig. 260). The tree is native to the Mediterranean lands and has been cultivated there throughout human history. It has been successfully introduced into all other regions having this type of climate, but it is still much more important in the borderlands of the Mediterranean Sea than in all other parts of the world combined.

The ability of the olive tree to thrive in the heat and drought of the Mediterranean summer is due to the plant's characteristics: (1) A finely

FIG. 260.—The olive is one of the distinctive crops of the borderlands of the Mediterranean.
(*U.S. Department of Agriculture.*)

divided and extensive surface-root system is able to make efficient use of very small amounts of rain; (2) the narrow, thick, leathery leaves are covered with densely matted hairs and, together with the stems, are equipped for economy in the utilization of the water collected by the roots (Fig. 261).

Figure 262 shows the relative importance of the leading olive-oil producing and exporting countries of the Mediterranean region. In Spain some olives are used for the preparation of pickled and preserved fruit, but most of the crop is raised for the manufacture of oil, a product that has long occupied the important place in the Mediterranean diet that butter and other animal fats occupy in that of the countries of northern Europe. Spain not only is the largest producer of olive oil but also leads in exports. Tunisia produces much less than Italy but has more to export because its domestic comsumption is proportionately far less.

CITRUS FRUITS are grown for home use in nearly all parts of the Mediterranean Coast. The principal commercial districts are (1) the irrigated valleys and coastal margin of the province of Valencia in eastern Spain (Fig. 263); (2) southern Italy and Sicily; (3) the coast of Palestine, especially near Jaffa; (4) Morocco and Algeria. The principal citrus fruit is the orange, except in Sicily, where most of the European lemons are

Fig. 261.—Olive trees about 200 years old. Their bulbous base, gnarled trunks, and narrow, leathery leaves indicate a high degree of resistance to drought. (*U.S. Bureau of Foreign and Domestic Commerce.*)

grown, and in Palestine where some grapefruit are produced also. England has furnished the chief market for the Mediterranean citrus fruits. Exports from Palestine and northern Africa increased greatly during the recent years when the Spanish industry was handicapped and in part destroyed bv civil war in that country.

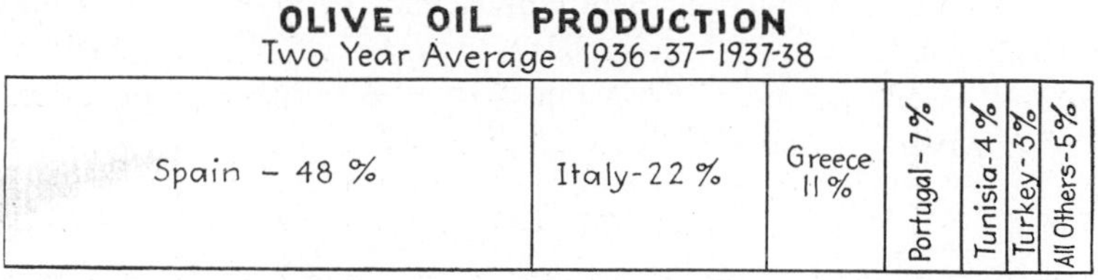
OLIVE OIL PRODUCTION
Two Year Average 1936-37–1937-38
Spain - 48 %
Italy-22 %
Greece 11%
Portugal - 7%
Tunisia-4 %
Turkey - 3%
All Others-5%

FIG. 262.—Per cent of the world's olive oil produced in leading countries.

TOBACCO is an important export crop in Greece and Turkey, and these two countries rank among the first ten tobacco producers of the world. The Greek crop is largely grown on the more fertile soils of the plains of Macedonia, and the Turkish crop is grown on the Black Sea borders and the lowlands of western Turkey. The export tobaccos are mainly of the highly aromatic types used in cigarette manufacture, and

PORTUGAL
SPAIN
IBERIAN PENINSULA
IRRIGATED LAND
BOUNDARY BETWEEN ARID AND HUMID SECTIONS OF THE PENINSULA

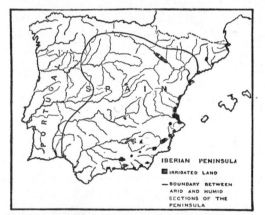

FIG. 263.—The irrigated lands of Spain. (*U.S. Department of Agriculture.*)

the markets for them are mainly in western Europe and the United States, the latter country normally taking nearly one-fourth the exports of both Greece and Turkey. In 1940 England abandoned her customary purchases of American tobacco and bought almost the entire Turkish crop. This shift was for the purpose of giving Turkey some financial support in exchange for political support against Germany's ambitions in the Near East, but it resulted also in a depression of the American tobacco market.

THE MULBERRY AND SILK RAISING. The mulberry tree is found in most of the more humid parts of the Mediterranean region, and silk raising is an industry of some importance in Spain and southern France but more particularly so in Italy. In the Po Valley the winter temperatures are too low for the olive and the citrus fruits. The mulberry is hardy and, with irrigation, produces an abundant crop of leaves during the warm season. The dense population of this valley and the many small farms furnish the necessary conditions for a supply of cheap but skillful labor and the close supervision required in silk production. Italy ranks next after Japan and China in this industry, but it produces only about 5 per cent of the world's raw-silk supply.

## PASTORAL INDUSTRIES

CATTLE AND DAIRYING. The statement previously made in regard to the unimportance of the cattle and dairy industries in the Mediterranean lands must be taken in a comparative way only. In Italy, which has twice as many cattle as any other Mediterranean country, the number per square mile is far less than it is in the north European countries (Fig. 234), yet it is more than twice the average in the United States, more, in fact, than in any state in the United States except those in the heart of the corn belt. In the Po Valley there are more cattle per square mile than in Iowa, and in no part even of southern Italy is the number so low as in Nevada. Relative to the human population, however, the number of cattle in Italy is less than one-half as great as in the United States.

Many of the cattle in the Mediterranean countries are draught animals. Some are raised for beef, and doubtless most of them are eventually utilized for food. Yet, in proportion to the population, the quantity of beef produced is small. Consequently the per capita consumption of beef is small, for the generally low purchasing power of the people does not permit of a large importation of foreign beef.

In most parts of the Mediterranean region dairy cows are extremely few. In the drier portions of southern Spain, Italy, and Greece they are found scarcely at all except a few near the larger cities. An organized dairy industry of the north European type exists in but few places, and only in northern Italy are dairy cattle numerous. On the irrigated lands of the Po Valley and the pastures of the Italian Alps cheese production is an important industry, and there is normally a surplus of cheese for exportation.

SHEEP AND GOATS. The ability of sheep and goats to subsist on rough mountain pastures and scanty summer forage has given them great importance in the Mediterranean lands (Fig. 223). Spain is the home of the fine-wooled Merino sheep, and for several centuries sheep raising was the most important industry of that country (Fig. 264). An organization of rich and influential sheep owners long had practical control of the civil affairs of the nation, much to the discouragement of settled agriculture. Large bands of sheep, under the charge of shepherds, moved about from lowland winter pastures to the mountain pastures of the summer, just as they now do in Arizona and Nevada. Throughout the Mediterranean borders, sheep and goats far outnumber cattle. This is particularly true in Greece and the Balkan Mountain area, where they outnumber cattle in a ratio of about 15 to 1. They furnish wool, hair, and skins for local manufactures and for export, meat for domestic consumption, and milk for direct use and for cheese. The number of sheep and goats employed in milk production is greater than that of cows in all Mediterranean countries but particularly so in the East. Much of the sheep's milk is used for cheese, more of the goats' milk being consumed fresh. The importance of the sheep in the dry lands of the East is seen also in

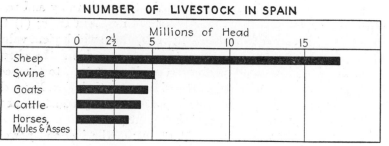

FIG. 264.

the wool used in the rug manufactures of Turkey. Asia Minor is the original home of the Angora goat, now raised also in other parts of the world for its fine hair, which is known commercially as "mohair."

OTHER DOMESTIC ANIMALS.  Swine are not numerous in the Mediterranean region (Fig. 244), in part because of the fact that most of the grain is required for human food. Yet in Spain and Italy they are raised in small numbers by the peasants on waste food products and in larger numbers upon the limited supplies of acorns and other forest feeds. In the Asiatic and African portions of the Mediterranean border, the prevalent Mohammedan religion encourages a prejudice against the use of pork products, and few, if any, swine are raised.

Just as the rough land surface, dry climate, and sparse forage of the Mediterranean region increase the relative importance of sheep and goats over that of cattle, so it increases the relative importance of the ass and the mule over that of the horse. Northern Africa and western Asia are believed to be the original habitat of wild asses, from which the domesticated breeds have descended. The largest and most valuable are now raised in Spain and southern France.

## NATURAL RESOURCES

FOREST RESOURCES.   In ancient times the more rainy parts of the Mediterranean border, such as the eastern shores of the Adriatic Sea, appear to have had considerable forest wealth of oak, chestnut, beech. pine, and other valuable timber trees, mainly hardwood. The drier portions probably never had more than the present shrub forests, or *maqui*, the European equivalent of the *chaparral* of California. Fire, destructive lumbering for more than 2,000 years, indiscriminate wood cutting, and the unrestricted browsing of sheep and goats have left for present generations but a small part of the forest resource. In most of the countries the supply of timber barely serves to meet the local needs, limited as the requirements are through poverty and lack of commercial and industrial development; in some, importation of timber is necessary. The principal forests remaining are (1) those which clothe the more rainy and remote mountain slopes, such as the Alpine forests of northern Italy; (2) those which are under government protection; or (3) those which yield valuable products other than timber. Among the last named are the chestnut forests of Italy, which supply an important item of food to the people, and the cork-oak groves of Spain, Portugal, and North Africa. In southern Portugal the cork oak is of particular importance. Its products rank with wines and fish as a leading export of the country.

SOURCES OF FUEL AND POWER.   A survey of the fuel and power resources of the Mediterranean countries provides at once an explanation of the predominance of agricultural pursuits and a basis for estimating some aspects of future developments in these lands. Of coal there is, in the entire Mediterranean region, extremely little. Of all the countries, Spain is best provided; yet its maximum output of coal and lignite is barely enough for a limited domestic requirement, and some is imported. Small amounts are mined in Italy, northern Africa, and other parts of the region, but they generally are not sufficient for local needs. Turkey produces less than Spain; but its requirements are less, and a small surplus has been available for export. Growing industries probably will require the total output shortly and perhaps need imported coal in addition. Italy, the most industrialized of the Mediterranean countries, has produced as much as 1 million tons of lignite in a year from its own mines, but generally its output is much less. Of good coal it has almost none. Imports of coal, principally from Germany and Britain, average about 12 million tons per year. Thus Italian industry is placed in a vulnerable position, and Italian politics are tied to the facts of resource distribution. In time of war between Britain and Germany the only route open for the export of German coal to Italy, so long as Britain commands the sea, is the expensive rail route across the mountains. The Mediterranean countries share with those of northern Europe a lack of domestic petroleum. In fact their situation is worse, because there is a small amount of oil in the former Polish territory, but none at present known on the Mediterranean borders.

The water-power resources of the Mediterranean region are considerable, much greater than the coal resources (Fig. 221). The low average rainfall and its great variability is not well suited to power production, yet the high altitudes and the many steep slopes and mountain valleys provide the necessary fall and also provide favorable conditions for storage reservoirs. In general, the shorter streams and the lower and more erratic rainfall of North Africa and of the eastern end of the Mediterranean region are not favorable for power development. Spain and Italy have the most water power in use and the greatest prospects for the future. The principal water powers of Spain, both developed and prospective, lie in the more rainy northern part of the country, especially on the southern slopes of the Pyrenees Mountains. However, the estimated resources, although greater than those of Sweden, for example, are much less than those of Norway, and only one-fourth the available resource is actually developed. For similar cause the principal water powers of Italy are in the north. The provinces at the foot of the Alps are particularly favored in this respect because of (1) the high altitudes and steep slopes of the mountains and their valleys, (2) the heavy rainfall fairly well distributed throughout the year, (3) natural regulation of stream flow due to (a) the summer melting of Alpine glaciers and (b) the presence of the large glacial lakes, such as Como and Garda, in the Alpine valleys. Italy's great need for power has led to the rapid development of her water-power resource in recent years. Storage reservoirs have been provided, and the 6 million horsepower now developed actually exceeds the total potential horsepower of the country as estimated on the basis of ordinary minimum stream flow. Italy has therefore more water power in use than any other country in the world except the United States and Canada, and its power resources are more completely utilized than those of any other country except France and Germany.

SOURCES OF MINERAL WEALTH.  Metals and minerals of moderate value and variety are found in the Mediterranean region, and a few of the deposits have had an important place in the history of the world's industrial development. The Rio Tinto copper mines in southwestern Spain, for example, have been worked since the days of the Phoenicians and still are among the larger producers in Europe, although they yield a comparatively small part of the world's output. The quarries of Carrara, Italy, and the Parian quarries of Greece yielded marbles for ancient works of art and are still producing for domestic use and for export. The mineral products of the Mediterranean region have, in general, been far excelled in value by the products of other regions of greater extent or of richer ores. In the supply of only a few of these substances do the Mediterranean countries rank high in world output. Examples are pyrite, of which Spain, Italy, Portugal, and the island of Cyprus mine one-third of the world supply; and sulphur, of which Italy and Spain are the only important producers outside the United States and Japan. They are minerals that are abundant and cheap elsewhere but that are produced in the Mediterranean countries also because of cheap labor. Large resources of phosphate rock are located in Tunisia and Morocco, and the produce of these

OUTLINE MAP OF SPAIN AND PORTUGAL SHOWING RESERVES OF IRON IN ORE

Fig. 265.—Regions of the Iberian Peninsula where iron ore is found. (*Bull.* 706, *U.S. Geological Survey.*)

mines is second only to that of the United States; they constitute more than one-fourth of the world's present supply.

Iron ores are found at several places in the Mediterranean countries; but since there is little coal with which to smelt them locally, large quantities are exported. The largest supplies are found in Spain, particularly the Viscaya district of the north. Nearly two-thirds of the quantity mined are sent in normal times to England, Germany, and the Netherlands, mainly through the northern ports of Bilboa and Santander (Fig. 265). These ores are almost as conveniently located with respect to the northern European smelting centers as are the Lake Superior ores with respect to the Lake Erie smelters and Pittsburgh. Other important iron-ore reserves are located in Algeria, Morocco, and Tunisia. The combined output of these African sources totals only about 5 million tons per year, equal to only a small part of the average annual production of the United States but very important to Europe. Italy, unfortunately for that country, has no adequate domestic supply of ore. There are several small reserves of low-grade ores, but only by the greatest of national efforts, projected but not yet realized, can she produce as much as half her requirements at home.

## INDUSTRIAL AND COMMERCIAL DEVELOPMENT

SPAIN AND PORTUGAL. The Iberian Peninsula has not kept pace with the countries of northwestern Europe in industrial and commercial development, but this fact cannot be attributed to its geographic location. Situated near the center of the world's commercial activity, streams of trade flow about it on all sides. Moreover, it is favored with extensive frontage on both the Atlantic Ocean and the Mediterranean Sea. Both Spain and Portugal were formerly possessed of vast colonial empires which have fallen away part by part until only small and relatively unimportant remnants are left. Many factors have combined to arrest the development of these two countries, among which those of a historical and geographic nature are clearly of great importance. The handicaps imposed by surface features, climate, and limited resources upon the Mediterranean region as a whole have been noted; certain others apply to the Iberian Peninsula in particular.

*Agricultural Contrasts.* Nearly half of Spain is used only as pasture and forest land, and only one-third is crop land, but the distribution of these land uses is significant. The bleak winters and snows of the central plateau restrict the agriculture of that part of the country to the grains and other hardy crops. The lower valleys and coastal margins on the other hand have a much more diversified agriculture. This fact, and the greater humidity of the western coast, explains why it is that in Portugal nearly two-thirds of the total area is in cultivated crops. It is then in the lowlands of Portugal, Andalusia, and the southeast of Spain that most of the commercial vegetable crops, grapes, citrus fruits, and other horticultural crops are grown. This is notably true in the southeast, which is the driest and most subtropical portion of Iberia, requiring irrigation for intensive agriculture (Fig. 263). Conversely, it is in the interior plateau and mountain uplands that sheep and cattle are most numerous and the larger part of the wheat and the other extensive crops are grown.

*Transportation.* The semiarid plateau-and-mountain character and the relatively sparse population of much of Iberia have made an extensive railway system financially impossible. Even before the destruction wrought by the recent war, there was in Spain only 1 mile of railway for each 19 square miles of area as compared with a ratio of 1 to 8 in France and 1 to 4.6 in Great Britain. The comparable figure for Portugal is 1 to

16. Many towns in Spain are without railway service and even without wagon roads. Owing to the plateau character of the peninsula and to the extreme seasonal fluctuations in stream volume, the use of the rivers for navigation is negligible. Although the coastline is long, its regularity is interrupted by very few natural harbors of a sort to invite modern shipping.

*Historical influences* of great significance also have retarded the industrial and commercial development of Spain and Portugal. Without adding detail in this connection, it may be said that, among other things, events in the history of Spain particularly have had much to do with the aversion of the Spanish people, especially the Castillians, toward industrial and commercial occupations.

FIG. 266.—The regular coast and artificial harbor at Barcelona.

*Barcelona the Industrial Center.* The province of Catalonia, and in particular the city of Barcelona, is the only important industrial center in the Iberian Peninsula. The Catalans are an energetic people with a different racial and historical inheritance from the Castillians. The region has considerable water power which renders it less dependent on foreign coal. The principal industries are textile manufacturing and papermaking. The raw materials, particularly cotton, are largely imported. Barcelona is the principal seaport of Spain (Fig. 266); it has an excellent harbor which is, however, almost entirely artificial.

ITALY. The natural advantages of Italy (coal, iron ore, and other mineral resources for industrial and commercial development) are somewhat less than those of Spain. Yet the industrial wares produced are more abundant and varied, and the value of foreign trade is notably greater. This difference may be attributed to a combination of historical and economic factors such as (1) the different attitude toward industrial pursuits from that held by many Spanish people, (2) closer political and economic association with the industrial nations of Europe and the desire to compete with them in material progress. The limited natural advantages for industrial development, have, however, notably influenced the character of Italian industrial wares and the places of their manufacture.

*Agriculture* in the Po Valley is very intensive. Rich, flat land and supplementary irrigation make it a highly productive region, but cold winters prevent the growth of olives, citrus fruits, and other subtropical products that are found in peninsular Italy and especially in Sicily. Much of the rest of the country is hill or mountain land, and the south is very dry in summer; yet a large population and small industrial opportunities cause nearly half the people to depend upon farming for their livelihood. More than 40 per cent of the total land area is sown to crops, and nearly 10 per cent more carries orchards and vineyards. Added to these are large areas productive of hay, pasture, and forests. It is surprising that less than 10 per cent of a country so hilly, so dry, and so continuously used for centuries is unproductive land.

*Transportation.* There is no important system of waterways in Italy. Only the Po River has a low gradient and large volume, but it is too shallow for any but small boats. On the other hand, its narrow peninsular form puts a large part of the country within easy reach of the sea, and much internal traffic is carried by coastwise shipping. Italy has also well-developed systems of roads and railways. Of the latter there is 1 mile for each 11 square miles of land, a network only a little less dense than that of France.

*Industrial Development.* Italy has 23 cities exceeding 100,000 population each, and 9 of them, including Milano, the second in size, are situated in the Po Valley. The large cities include also Rome, the administrative and cultural center, Naples, Genoa, Trieste, and others that are great ports; but the Po Valley cities are the leading centers of manufacture. In that valley are not only the most dense rural population in the country and the nine large cities but smaller industrial cities also. Several of these are arranged in a zone along the base of the Alps. The obvious advantage of this is the nearness of these towns to the only great Italian source of industrial power, the Alpine hydroelectric developments.

The industries of Italy, for lack of good and cheap coal, are largely of the lighter type. Of these the textile industries are most varied and important and occupy the largest number of workers. They include cotton and woolen manufacture, the making of silk goods from domestic raw silk, and a large rayon industry for which woodpulp must be imported. Because the textile industries use electric power most advantageously, they are strongly concentrated in the north, although cotton mills are found in the south also, especially at Naples. The machine, automobile, shipbuilding, and other iron and steel industries are more scattered. Only a small amount of special steel is made in the north with electric furnaces. To an even larger degree the ordinary grades of steel are made from imported ores or from scrap iron with imported coal. It is therefore quite as advantageous if the steel-using industries are located in any of the large cities or the port cities, such as Genoa. Most widely scattered of all the industrial groups is that concerned with the preparation of foodstuffs. It includes flour mills, macaroni factories, olive-oil and wine processing plants, and meat-packing establishments. A large part of them are of small size.

*Foreign Trade.* Italy has a large and varied foreign commerce more than half of which is carried in her own ships. In the export list, textile manufactures are most important. They are followed by automobiles and machinery, and these, in turn, by manufactured food products such as wines, fruits, canned goods, and cheese. The import list is headed by coal, and this is followed by wheat, raw cotton, heavy iron- and steel-wares and scrap iron, oilseeds, and a long list of other substances among which raw materials and crude foodstuffs predominate.

The direction of Italian foreign trade has in recent years reflected her political and colonial aspirations. Her African colonies have not proved great sources of raw materials, since less than 3 per cent of her imports comes from the colonies. Her hopes for trade with her newly conquered colony of Ethiopia are as yet largely unrealized. The largest part, nearly 20 per cent, has come in recent years from her political partner Germany, and the next most important source has been the United States. Italy can, however, see to it that a good share of her exports are bought in her African possessions, and 25 to 35 per cent of her export trade has gone in that direction since the conquest of Ethiopia. Germany is the second most important customer for Italian goods, taking 15 to 20 per cent; and the United States is next in rank.

GREECE AND THE LEVANT.  The countries that border the eastern end of the Mediterranean—Greece, Turkey, and the French and British mandate territories in Syria and Palestine—were once the seats of the world's greatest industries and the home of the originators of ocean trade. Today they are, by comparison with west European lands, almost wholly agricultural and have neither manufactures nor commerce of great world significance. In Turkey about 80 per cent of the population lives by agricultural and pastoral pursuits, and in the other countries the proportion is nearly as high. Turkey has a small amount of coal, sufficient for present domestic requirements, and both Turkey and Greece have some other mineral resources, such as chrome ores. Rapid economic progress has been made in recent years, in Turkey particularly, but there was little knowledge of modern industry to build upon, and few rich resources to be turned to industrial account. Communications also are poor; few improved roads exist. In Greece there is but 1 mile of railroad to each 28 square miles of area; in Turkey the ratio is 1 to 68. The settlement of Jewish Zionists in the coastal districts of Palestine in recent decades has done much to change the status of that region also. However, the occupation of these colonists is largely agricultural, and their principal exports are citrus fruits. They are in conflict with the pastoral Arabic natives, and the future of the region is uncertain.

The items that constitute the staple exports of Greece and the Levant are mainly those of agricultural and pastoral origin. These are shipped raw or after having passed through processes of manufacture that require much hand labor and but little power or mechanical equipment. Leaf tobacco is much the most important export from both Greece and Turkey in terms of value. Others are fresh and dried fruits, hides, skins, and wool, both raw and in the form of hand-made rugs and carpets.

MEDITERRANEAN LANDS OF AFRICA. Algeria, Morocco, and Tunisia have a large commerce which has been developed in recent decades largely under French protection and stimulation. The political divisions include the Mediterranean slopes and also the dry plateau uplands and, beyond them, large parts of the Sahara Desert. From the latter are derived only pastoral products and dates from the Saharan oases (Fig.

FIG. 267.—Date palms in the oasis of Biskra, Algeria. (*U.S. Department of Agriculture.*)

267). These come by caravan, motor transport, and short rail lines to the Mediterranean ports. Most of the population is concentrated on the more humid coastal slopes, and this region is most productive. Its exports are principally agricultural, pastoral, and mineral. The largest values are in wines, olive oil, cereals, vegetables, and wool. There are also the local productions of iron ore, phosphate rock, and other minerals to which previous reference has been made. Imports into the North African region include cotton cloth, prepared foods, metal products, fuels, and other wares in great variety. In general the trade reflects in that region a low state of development in manufactures and a more highly developed agriculture. It is a typically colonial type of trade, and the volume of the trade with France is greater than with any other country.

## Southeastern Europe

A COMPLEX REGION. Southeastern Europe is a region of great diversity, but in certain respects it is also a geographical unit. It is made up of small states in one of the most distinctive parts of Europe. On the whole, it is a region of mountains with two broad and well-marked plains. To a degree it is bound together by one of Europe's great rivers, the Danube, which touches all four of the countries Hungary, Yugoslavia, Rumania, and Bulgaria and plays a considerable part in their commercial life. This river is of sufficient unifying influence to have suggested a union of the small states in its basin into a Danubian confederation. There are, however, wide differences among the various parts of southeastern Europe, and the mountainous character of the region, with its many barriers to human intercourse, has kept alive racial antagonisms and has prevented the blending of the peoples. Hungary and Rumania are agricultural but are in a higher state of development than Yugoslavia or Bulgaria. Southeastern Europe, then, has two quite distinct economic regions: (1) the agricultural plains of Hungary and Rumania, which countries have reached a relatively high degree of advancement; and (2) mountainous states south of the Danube, still in a relatively backward condition and politically turbulent. The Balkans have been called the "cockpit of Europe," and they still harbor various causes of trouble. Although any military expression of their racial animosities is now held in check by the power of Germany, whose interests are not served by trouble in the Danube Basin, the causes of grievance still remain. Moreover, this important area has become a center of impending conflict.

CONSEQUENCES OF THE GEOGRAPHICAL LOCATION OF THE REGION. At various times in the past, Asiatic peoples have invaded Europe, and the paths of these invasions were determined by the major physical features of the region. The Caspian and Black seas forced the invaders to pass either north or south of these bodies of water, and the heavy forests of middle and northern Russia directed the invaders well to the south, where the open steppe lands made their movements relatively easy so far as natural obstacles were concerned. If the invasion was attempted by a route lying south of the Black Sea, the only convenient entrance to Europe was at the Bosporus and Dardanelles. The earlier invasions from Asia, including the coming of the Huns, Serbs, and Bulgars, followed the steppes of southern Russia and were stopped when they reached the mountainous lands of southeastern Europe. The last of these Asiatic invaders, the Turks, over four centuries ago came in by way of the Bosporus and pushed northward almost to Vienna, where they were stopped and were slowly forced backward for 300 years until they have been driven almost out of Europe. But the region that received both lines of invasion was this Danubian-Balkan region, and a part of it has been freed from Turkish rule less than a century. It may be said, then, that southeastern Europe is the least Europeanized part of the continent. Moreover, the extremely mountainous character of the Balkan Peninsula hinders that free intercourse of peoples by which civilization spreads. Such an environment breeds a spirit of personal independence, even lawlessness, which makes wars easy to start, and the Balkans have had rather more than their share of wars.

THE PRESENT COMMERCIAL OUTLOOK. The commercial connections of southeastern Europe extend mainly inland. Hungary has no sea outlet. Yugoslavia borders upon the Adriatic Sea; but its most productive lands are on its inner margin in the Danubian plain, cut off from the seacoast by a mountain barrier. Rumania and Bulgaria share an outlet through the Black Sea, but that outlet points in the wrong direction, considering that the produce of these countries is mainly agricultural and that the markets for it are mainly in central and western Europe. A commercially unifying influence is found, however, in the use of the Danube River and in the important line of railroad connecting the capital cities Budapest, Belgrade, and Sofia with Vienna on the one hand and Istanbul on the other—the route of the Oriental Express. This excellent rail connection and the large use of the Danube and its connecting canals tend to overcome the advantage of sea frontage in the southeastern countries and to link them commercially with the interior, especially with Germany. There these agricultural and pastoral lands find their natural market, and in recent years each of these four countries has got about half its imports from and has sent from 35 to 45 per cent of its exports to Germany, Austria, and Bohemia, all of which are now under German rule. In fact these lands serve Germany in somewhat the same capacity that the corn belt of the United States serves the Great Lakes industrial region, although the relationship in America is unimpeded by artificial trade barriers.

## HUNGARY

Hungary was united with Austria in the Dual Monarchy of Austria-Hungary until its dismemberment following the great war of 1914–1918. The Hungary that emerged from that war had only a third of its former area and population, having lost territory and people to Rumania, Czechoslovakia, and Yugoslavia. The boundaries imposed upon this defeated country were arbitrarily drawn and left it a total area equal to that of Indiana. About 60 per cent of that is arable, and much is distinctly fertile, though a part is subject to overflow by rivers. It is a country of corn, wheat (Fig. 231), hay, sheep, cattle, and horses—one of the distinctively agricultural plains of Europe (sometimes called the "Iowa of Europe"). Three-fourths of the inhabitants are farmers, and a surplus of farm products is available for export. The Hungarian Plain has long been one of the sources from which its neighbors have drawn part of their food. In the days of the Austro-Hungarian Monarchy, Hungary was the agricultural member of the union. In the Europe of 1914 only Russia grew more tobacco; only Russia and France produced more wheat; and no European country equaled Hungary in the production of corn (Fig. 268).

Within its present boundaries it has relatively little timber, water power, or minerals. However, it has small deposits of coal, some of which is of good quality, and one of the two largest sources of bauxite in the world. This was of great importance to German airplane manufacture when war and blockade closed French and other supplies of aluminum ore. The capital Budapest is a manufacturing city of importance. It formerly was the outstanding center of flour milling for all Europe. The other leading manufactures of the country are of the miscellaneous types

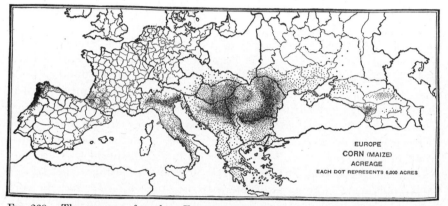

EUROPE
CORN (MAIZE)
ACREAGE
EACH DOT REPRESENTS 5,000 ACRES

FIG. 268.—The summers of northern Europe are too cool for corn; those of much of southern Europe are too dry. (*U.S. Department of Agriculture.*)

found in most countries where industry is protected by tariff—food products, textiles, leather, chemicals, and metalwares. The country is well equipped with railroads, having 1 mile for each 6 square miles of area, or more, relatively, than France. It has also about one-sixth as many miles of inland water routes as it has of railroads. These include the Danube River, its principal tributaries, and a canal system.

Although the capital city has a population of more than 1 million, there are only two other Hungarian cities exceeding 100,000 inhabitants. This fact alone testifies to the strong agricultural interests of the country. The Hungarian people are of a racial and linguistic group (Magyar) more closely akin to the Finns and Esths than any others in Europe. This makes it difficult for them to maintain common interests with their Slavic, Germanic, and other neighbors by whom they are isolated. By trade relations, however, Hungary is closely linked with Germany, since that country takes normally more than 40 per cent of its exports and supplies an equal proportion of its imports.

## RUMANIA

TERRITORIAL GROWTH.  The Rumanians speak a Latin dialect and claim descent from Roman colonists, but they include Slavic, Turkish, and other elements as well as Hungarian, Bulgarian, and Russian groups on the borders of the country. The modern Rumania began its successful

(a) - 1910    (b) - 1923

BOUNDARY CHANGES IN CENTRAL EUROPE

FIG. 269.—Political boundaries which are established by war are subject to change by war. Only the settlements resulting from the second great war of the century can determine their location in 1950.

struggle for independence from Turkish rule in 1829 but did not gain full independence until 1878. In 1914 it was about the size of England. It joined the Allies in the war of 1914–1918 and emerged with a territory about the size of the state of Arizona and its population doubled. The largest addition of land came from Hungary, but provinces of considerable size were also obtained from Austria and Russia (Fig. 269). These minority groups have clamored for reunion with their nationals, and Rumania doubtless will suffer partition as soon as it suits the convenience of

Fig. 270.—A scene in Transylvania. This was a part of Hungary in 1914, was added to Rumania after the First World War, and, under pressure, was ceded again to Hungary in 1940. Only a small part of this hilly land can be cultivated, and the principal towns and the few railroads are in the valleys. (*Copyright Underwood and Underwood.*)

Germany to see that it is done without jeopardy to her own interests. The territory of Bessarabia, taken from Russia, has already been reclaimed and occupied by that country without opposition.

An Agricultural Country. Rumania includes within its borders an important section of the Carpathian Mountains and other mountainous land (Fig. 270), but it also includes a large extent of the plains of the Danube Valley—good agricultural land. It is far enough south to fall within the corn belt of Europe and is at present the largest producer of corn (maize) outside of the Americas, yet its total average crop is only one-half to two-thirds that of Illinois. Wheat ranks next to corn in Rumanian agriculture, and western Europe depends considerably upon wheat from the Danubian countries. In addition to these crops, the country raises most of the products characteristic of the corn-belt type of climate, and cattle and sheep are numerous in the foothills and mountain pastures.

About 80 per cent of the people are engaged in agriculture, in part on large estates and in part on small holdings. Here, as in many other parts of Europe, an effort is being made to divide the large estates held by the gentry and nobility and to distribute the land in small holdings among the peasantry. Rumania has forest resources and mineral resources of value, but her national wealth and national strength lie primarily in her agricultural population. Not only are Rumanian imports of foodstuffs very small, but there is a large exportable surplus of wheat, corn, barley, and animal products, and from the income from these certain necessary imports can be paid for.

Mineral Wealth. On the lower slopes of the Carpathian Mountains the geological structure that is necessary to the preservation of petroleum deposits is found, and in various places oil fields of importance have been developed. Rumania supplies only 2 or 3 per cent of the world's petroleum, yet even this amount is significant in Europe, which requires so much oil and produces so little. This resource is of vital importance to Germany in her war effort. Its existence and the food resource available in Rumania are among the reasons why Germany has used all diplomatic pressure to prevent the outbreak of a war in Rumania which would certainly impede, if not stop, the westward flow of these commodities. The oil fields of Galicia—recently a part of Poland but now in Russian control —are on the northern side of the same mountains.

Rumania has large deposits of salt and small deposits of coal, mostly lignite, and of iron—enough to serve moderate local needs but not enough to form the basis of any large manufacturing industry. Other minerals occur but up to date have not been found in large quantity. Petroleum, however, is the principal export of the country, furnishing about half the total value of exports.

OTHER ECONOMIC INTERESTS. Rumania has about 16 million acres of forests; it has upward of 3 million horsepower of potential water power, very little of which is used. It has a waterway of some real value and still larger potential value in the Danube and 1 mile of railroad for each 16 square miles of its area. Manufacturing is moderately developed, and like the manufactures of Hungary it is of two main types: (1) those which process domestic products, such as foodstuffs and petroleum for home use and for export; and (2) those which manufacture textiles and other wares for home consumption under tariff protection.

## YUGOSLAVIA

This country, about the size of the United Kingdom or the state of Oregon, is made up of quite distinct parts; its official name is the Kingdom of the Serbs, Croats, and Slovenes. The former kingdoms of Serbia and

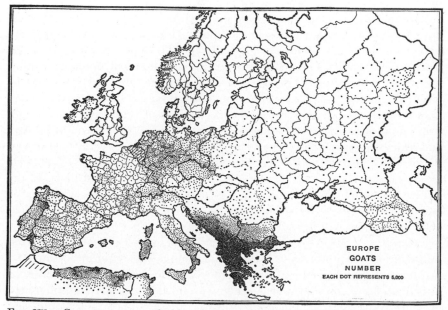

FIG. 271.—Goats are most profitable and numerous in the rough lands of Europe and are particularly so in the rough, dry lands of southern Europe. (*U.S. Department of Agriculture.*)

Montenegro and a number of provinces that were included in Austria-Hungary now make up the country which has a population of some 15 millions. It is by no means unified politically or otherwise. At best, not over one-third of the land can be cultivated, and most of that is in the northern part of the country, Yugoslavia's share of the Danube Basin. The south is almost entirely hilly or mountainous, and the land there must be farmed in small tracts. Another third of the country is covered with forest growth, a part of which contains merchantable timber and most of which supplies wood, the principal fuel of the people. The country is about as well served by railroads as is Rumania—1 mile of line to 16 square miles of area—but improved highways are few, and there are large numbers of secluded valleys hemmed in by mountain walls, into which people from the outside world almost never penetrate. The inhabitants are mainly peasants who occupy small farm tracts on which they raise enough for their own needs and a little more. Farming methods are crude; little machinery is used; the yield per acre is small; and the great majority of the people are poor. Corn, which can be grown more readily than the small grains on hilly, stumpy, or poorly prepared land, is the principal crop, but wheat is of nearly equal acreage (Figs. 231, 268). These two crops occupy nearly three-fourths of the cultivated area. Such a region as the Balkan Peninsula is rather better suited to grazing than to the cultivation of crops; cattle, sheep, and goats (Fig. 271) can find a living among the mountains, and pigs can feed on the acorns of the oak forests. The raising of animals and the exportation of various animal products is one of the country's chief sources of income.

A few million tons of coal—mostly of low grade—are mined annually, and some quantities of bauxite and iron ore. Manufacturing has made only a beginning, and foreign trade is necessarily small. It is carried on mainly with the near neighbor Italy and with Germany. The United States has relatively little trade with this part of the world. Belgrade, the capital, has over 240,000 people, and two other cities have in excess of 100,000. It is interesting to note, also, that although the country has three universities, one of which is reported to have over 7,000 students, and there are many lower schools, 2 persons out of 5 in the entire population are illiterate.

## BULGARIA

Bulgaria, the size of Kentucky, is rimmed on the west by the southward extension of the Carpathian Mountains, and the eastward projecting tongue of the Balkan Mountains cuts it almost in two. A high, stream-trenched plain on the north slopes toward the Danube. It is cold and dry in winter, a land of wheat- and cornfields and of sheep and cattle pastures. South of the mountains the land, although the winters still are cold, has some of the characteristics of near-by "Mediterranean" Greece. It is a region of wheat fields, tobacco raising, vineyards, gardens, and sheep grazing. In the mountains are mainly sparse forests and grazing lands.

Bulgaria's population of 6¼ millions is about 80 per cent rural; there are only two cities having more than 100,000 inhabitants. The dominant Bulgarian population is a mixed race of Slavic culture. The mountain valleys harbor several racial and religious groups that are turbulent elements. The country produces a small quantity of coal, but factory industry is but little developed; home industries still employ four times more workers than do factories. Roads are only moderately developed, and of railroad there is only 1 mile for each 19 square miles of area. In its general characteristics and economic conditions Bulgaria does not differ greatly from other parts of the Balkan Peninsula. Bulgaria also has territorial claims upon Rumania. The Dobruja, that southeastern corner of Rumania bordering the Black Sea, is inhabited by many Bulgarians, and Bulgaria has been pressing a claim for it. This also awaits a convenient time for settlement.

### SELECTED REFERENCES

#### THE MEDITERRANEAN REGION

AKERMAN, E. A. An Algerian Oasis Community, *Econ. Geog.*, Vol. 12 (1936), pp. 250–258.

BLANCHARD, W. O. The Plains of the Po, *Jour. Geog.*, Vol. 36 (1937), pp. 81–92.

————, and ELIZABETH R. BLANCHARD. The Grape Industry of Spain and Portugal, *Econ. Geog.*, Vol. 5 (1929), pp. 183–193.

BULL, W. E. The Olive Industry of Spain, *Econ. Geog.*, Vol. 12 (1936), pp. 136–154.

CUNNINGHAM, C. H. Portugal: Resources, Economic Conditions, etc., *U.S. Dept. Commerce, Trade Information Bull.* 455, 1927.

JONES, C. L., and E. A. Dow. Algeria, A Commercial Handbook, *U.S. Dept. Commerce, Trade Promotion Series* 8, 1925.

————. Power-using Industries of Italy, *U.S. Dept. Commerce, Trade Information Bull.* 772, 1931.

KNIGHT, M. M. "Morocco as a French Economic Venture," New York, 1937.

LONGOBARDI, C. "Land Reclamation in Italy," London, 1936.

ROBERTSON, C. J. The Italian Beet-sugar Industry, *Econ. Geog.*, Vol. 14 (1938), pp. 1–15.

ROUCEK, JOSEPH S. Economic Geography of Greece, *Econ. Geog.*, Vol. 11 (1935), pp. 91–104.

SEMPLE, E. C. "Geography of the Mediterranean Region," New York, 1931.

Spain, Resources, Industries and Trade, *U.S. Dept. Commerce, Trade Information Bull.* 739, 1931.

#### SOUTHEASTERN EUROPE

PASVOLSKY, LEO. "Economic Nationalism of the Danubian States," New York, 1928.

PATTON, KENNETH. Kingdom of Serbs, Croats, and Slovenes (Yugoslavia): A Commercial and Industrial Handbook, *U.S. Dept. Commerce, Trade Promotion Series* 61, 1928.

RANKIN, K. L. The Czechoslovak Iron and Steel Industry, *U.S. Dept. Commerce, Trade Information Bull.* 713, 1930.

ROBERTS, CATHERINE. Rumania Today, *Econ. Geog.*, Vol. 9 (1933), pp. 230–255.

ROCKWELL, A. F. Czechoslovakia: Its Industries, Resources, etc., *U.S. Dept. Commerce, Trade Information Bull.* 461, 1927.

ROUCEK, JOSEPH S. Economic Geography of Bulgaria, *Econ. Geog.*, Vol. 11 (1935), pp. 307–323.

# Chapter XXVIII. The Union of Soviet Socialist Republics

THE EXTENT OF THE SOVIET UNION. Soviet Russia is the largest contiguous political unit in the world. The British Empire has a greater total area, but it includes many separate dominions located in every continent. The area of the Soviet Union is approximately the same as that of all North America, including Central America and the West Indies, and it contains about one-sixth of the land area of the earth. The European portion of the Union comprises less than one-third of its total area but contains more than two-thirds of the total population of 170 millions. The inhabitants are mainly Slavic (true Russians, Ukrainians, and White Russians); but on the western and northern borders of the country and in Asiatic Russia are other races, some of them small in numbers. Altogether there are more than 150 ethnic groups in the Soviet Union, and they speak almost as many different languages or dialects. A large part of the population is directly dependent on the land for its living. Less than 25 per cent is urban, yet the city population has grown rapidly in recent years, and about 50 cities are reported as having more than 100,000 inhabitants each.

SURFACE CONFIGURATION. European Russia and more than half of Asiatic Russia consist of a great plain, the most extensive in the world. It is, of course, continuous with the North European Plain mentioned earlier. About 70 per cent of this great Eurasian lowland is under Russian control, and it can hardly be doubted that the plainsland character of that part of the continent has had much to do with the growth of the Russian dominion. Its great expanses are interrupted only by the low ranges of the Ural Mountains, which are no more effective as a barrier than are the Appalachian Mountains of the United States. The absence of natural barriers made it relatively easy to push the Russian conquests on until a large part of the weaker peoples of Eurasia had been incorporated in the heterogeneous Russian nation. This process was still going on when the revolution of 1917 checked it; and now it appears to have begun again in the reabsorption of Bessarabia, part of Poland, the control of the Baltic States, and the attempted reconquest of Finland. But, for a nation, such

great areal extent has its disadvantages; it means that a large part of
the country must be far from the sea and far from the markets of the
world. This, in turn, means long and expensive rail hauls to get the products of the interior to markets.

In the southern part of European Russia are the high, rugged, and
snow-capped Caucasus Mountains; and the trans-Caspian and Siberian
sections of the plain also are rimmed on the south by the high ranges of
central Asia. The surface of the eastern half of Siberia consists mainly
of highlands. In that region are elevated plains and ranges of hills which

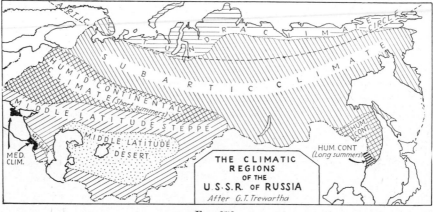

Fig. 272.

include broad valleys and basins. It is the great western plain, however,
that dominates the physical character of the Russian land surface. In
that part of the Soviet lands are the homes of most of the people and all
but a few of the larger towns and cities.

## Climatic, Vegetational, and Soil Regions of Russia

The vast area of the Soviet Union is impressive beyond that of any
other country in the world, but its ability to support population is not in
proportion to its area. It is sometimes said that the resources of Russia are
"unlimited." There is no doubt that they are large and that the great
size of the country increases both the probable variety of its resources
and the possibility of finding new ones. However, the principal resource
is the land itself, and Russia, like Canada, has large areas whose capacity
to support population is very low. About 25 per cent of the total area lies
north of the Arctic Circle, and another large section is arid. These facts
will be better understood from a consideration of the size and location
of the large regions into which the land may be divided on the basis of its
differences in climate, natural vegetation, and soils. In the formation of
these regions climate plays the leading role because, in large measure,

both natural vegetation and soils are directly or indirectly conditioned by it.

The general character of Russian climate is much influenced by the fact that the country has an interior, or continental, situation in the middle and higher latitudes (Fig. 272). The modifying influence of the Atlantic Ocean hardly penetrates even so far as Leningrad, whose Baltic approach is frozen most of the winter. The long seacoast of the arctic feels no moderating influence, either, because of the cold waters offshore. In eastern Siberia the winds are prevailingly from the land to the sea and so bring little Pacific Ocean influence to the land. In fact the upland of central eastern Siberia includes the area of greatest temperature extremes

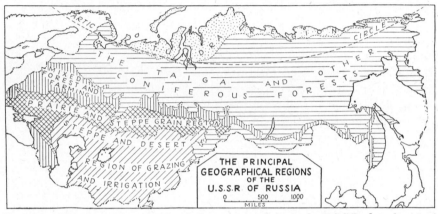

Fig. 273.—The taiga region occupies the largest area of any in the U.S.S.R., but the mixed forest and farming and prairie-grain regions are most densely peopled.

in the world, a district where the average temperature for January is more than 50°F. below zero. The extreme south of Russia, in Turkestan, lies in about the same latitude as Tulsa, Okla., but much the larger part of the country, in both Europe and Asia, is farther poleward than either Minneapolis or Montreal.

Nowhere in Russia is the precipitation very abundant. The climate is most humid in western European Russia and most arid in Turkestan. It is, however, the contrasts in temperature that have the greatest influence on the character of the climate and on the types of natural vegetation and soils. Since the temperatures are largely a function of latitude, it is not surprising that the principal natural regions of the country are arranged in the form of irregular belts trending roughly east and west. The nature and general utility of these regions is indicated below.

THE TUNDRA REGION.   The arctic coast region of Russia, like that of North America, has an average July temperature of less than about 50°F. This is too low to permit the growth of forests. Along this whole coast, from the Finnish border to East Cape and over a belt of varying width inland, the prevailing vegetation is the mosses, grasses, and low shrubs of the tundra (Fig. 273). Here the soil is permanently frozen, and no agriculture is possible. Reindeer graze in the summer, tended by semi-nomadic herdsmen who, unlike the American Eskimo, are accustomed to retreat southward to the forest fringe in winter. There are some inhabitants who live by mining, hunting, and fishing, but permanent settlements are few and small.

THE TAIGA REGION.    South of the tundra lies a region of subarctic climate in which long and severely cold winters alternate with short but warm summers. Within this region lies the "cold spot" of Siberia. It extends eastward from Finland; it crosses northern European Russia as a broad belt; and in central Siberia it widens to include all the rough uplands between the tundra margin and the mountainous borders of Mongolia (Fig. 273). This great region, which is 500 to 1,400 miles wide in its different parts and upward of 4,500 miles long, covers almost half the entire area of the Soviet Union. It is much like the taiga of Canada, except that only its western end was formerly covered by the continental glacier, and most of it does not have the numberless lakes characteristic of Finland and Laurentian Canada. Its sparse forests of spruce, larch, birch, and poplar constitute a great potential resource; but because of its extreme length, only the forests of its western and eastern ends are readily accessible. The former can send forest products to the European markets, and the latter to those of the Pacific, especially Japan. The region as a whole is poorly supplied with transportation facilities. Only in the Baltic and White Sea districts of the west do railroads penetrate deeply into the forests. To reach these the timber is floated down streams or is moved in winter on long sled trains pulled by tractors. Elsewhere, as in central Siberia, for example, transportation is served by the north-flowing rivers, and these are closed by ice for several months each year. Moreover, they open into the Arctic Ocean, upon which there is little commerce, although some timber is reported to reach European Russia by that route. During the open season the most feasible outlet is upstream on the rivers to points where connection is made with the Trans-Siberian Railroad or its branches, which skirt the taiga forest on the south. Such transportation is too expensive, however, to permit the exportation of bulky produce such as timber in large quantity.

Settlement in the taiga region is sparse, probably averaging less than two persons per square mile. Throughout the vast forests trappers take furs which can readily be got to outside markets. In this respect, as in many others, the great Russian taiga is like that of Canada. There are also some scattered agricultural settlements along the rivers, and tilled fields are located on south-facing slopes, where the more intense sunlight and better drainage enable hardy crops to mature in the short, frostless season, but the soils (mainly *podsols*) are unproductive. Some cereals, vegetables, and hay are raised for local consumption. There is some dairy production, and butter is shipped out, together with hides and skins from cattle, sheep, and reindeer. A few other products also, such as valuable minerals, can be got out profitably. However, the great interior forest remains as a resource for the future when the need for its wood shall make it profitable to provide transportation sufficient to enable its exploitation.

THE REGIONS OF MIXED FOREST AND FARMING. South of the taiga is a zone in which the original vegetation was forest of mixed hardwoods and conifers, much like that of Germany. It extends from the borders of Rumania, Poland, and the Baltic States to the Ural Mountains and beyond into western Siberia, becoming narrower eastward (Fig. 273). The climate of this region differs from that of the taiga in that its summers are longer and its winters, although cold, are less severe. It has a climate much like that of Minnesota or Wisconsin. The western portion of this region is covered in large part by glacial moraines and the deposits of glacial streams. It includes some lakes and extensive glacial marshes. Its soils are largely of the gray-brown forest type, similar also to those of the American Great Lakes region. Agricultural settlement in this part of Russia is much more dense than that of the northern forest. On the southwest the region of mixed forest and farming extends into that political division of Russia called "the Ukraine." In northern Ukraine the rural population is the most dense in Russia (Figs. 5, 217). The city of Kiev is its commercial center. Farther north is the great city and industrial center of Moscow which will be mentioned later.

Although farms are numerous in this region, much woodland remains. This is less true in the west and southwest where centuries of land clearing have reduced the original forests to groves. It is more true in the east, and especially in Siberia, where this region of forest margin still is in the pioneer stage, and land clearing and the making of new farms are still in progress. The prevailing farm crops of the region are rye, oats, potatoes, sugar beets, vegetables, flax, and hay, the typical crops of the plain of northern Europe (Figs. 233, 243, 274). The livestock and dairy industries are fairly well developed also in both the European and the Siberian portions, for in this region rail transportation is as well developed as in any part of the Soviet Union.

In the far east of Siberia, south of the taiga, there is another region of general farming somewhat like the one under discussion. It includes the Amur River Valley and the district immediately adjacent to the only good Pacific port, Vladivostok. In this area is settled most of the permanent farming population of the Far East, and along its border occurs much of the friction with Japanese interests in Manchuria.

THE PRAIRIE AND STEPPE GRAIN-FARMING REGION. (Fig. 273.)
South of the region of mixed forest and farming, and in part overlapping
with it, is a region of forest margins, open prairies, and steppes in which
a large part of the land is devoted to the raising of wheat and barley
(Fig. 231). The transition southward from the forest zone is similar to
that encountered in going westward from Wisconsin and Minnesota into
the old prairie and steppe lands, now the grain fields, of North Dakota.
These ancient grasslands of Russia have an undulating surface and rich,

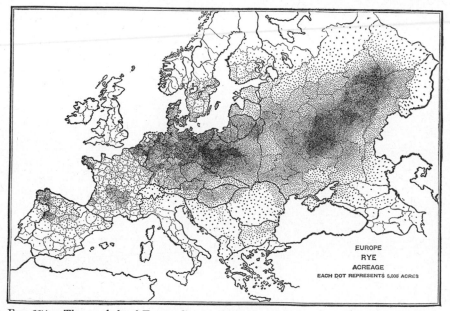

FIG. 274.—The rye belt of Europe lies on the cooler and more humid side of the wheat
belt and also in regions of poorer soil. (*U.S. Department of Agriculture.*)

dark soils (chernozem) underlain in part by accumulations of loess. The
southwestern portion of the region, near the Black Sea, lies within the
Ukraine. Its climate is more humid and less severe than that of the eastern
or Siberian part of the region, and the land is noted for its fertility. The
Ukraine as a whole not only produces wheat and barley but is the principal Russian center of the sugar-beet industry. Some tobacco and maize
are grown also. The Crimean Peninsula, which projects into the Black
Sea, has the mildest winters and most nearly Mediterranean climate of
any part of European Russia. It is a center of winter resorts, and its
agriculture even includes the growing of grapes, other fruits, and a little
cotton.

From the Ukraine, the black soils and wheatlands extend northeastward toward the southern end of the Ural Mountains. There they turn

eastward along the southern margin of the taiga and come to an end against the highland of Central Asia near Novosibirsk. In this long eastern belt the winters are extremely cold, and spring wheat is the principal crop. The relation between this wheat belt and the bordering taiga is almost exactly like that previously noted in Saskatchewan, Canada.

THE STEPPE AND DESERT REGION OF GRAZING AND IRRIGATION FARMING.   Last of the Russian regions to be noted is that of the south, a region of aridity surrounding the northern end of the Caspian Sea and broadening eastward to include the great lowland of Russian Turkestan (Fig. 273). The northern margin of this plain is grass steppe, the home of the Kirghiz, tribes of herdsmen whose livelihood depends mainly upon cattle and sheep. Although they are chilled to a bitter cold in winter by the dry winds that blow out of Siberia, the steppes are warm in summer. In some respects they are like the high plains of Wyoming and Colorado except in their elevations which, near the Caspian Sea, are several feet lower than sea level. South of Lake Aral the aridity is still more complete, and the temperatures are higher. There the steppes give way to desert vegetation and areas of drifting sands. These have low value even for grazing, except by sheep and goats and by the camels which are the burden bearers of the dry lands of central Asia.

In this southern region, however, are some of the most prized lands of Russia. They are irrigated valleys whose streams are fed by the snows of the mountains of Afghanistan and the high Pamirs. In that latitude cotton can be grown, and in some of the protected valleys of the foothills peaches and other tender fruits. The only other parts of Russia capable of supplying much cotton and other subtropical crops are the Crimea and the valleys on the south side of the Caucasus Mountains between the Caspian and Black seas. Hence these irrigated valleys are of great value in the Russian national economy. The limited areas of productive land are densely settled and are provided with railway transportation.

## Agriculture

PREDOMINANCE OF AGRICULTURE IN THE NATIONAL LIFE.   Russia is predominantly agricultural in its interests, the most completely so of any of the major European powers. Even after two decades of Soviet rule, with feverish attempts to industrialize the nation, less than one-fourth of the people live in cities. More than three-fourths are peasant farmers and farm laborers. The vast majority are more interested in the land and problems growing out of the land, its utilization and ownership, than in any other problems. The revolution of 1917, which greatly changed all economic conditions, was partly due to the poverty and discontent of the peasants. However, as has been noted above, a large part of the country is unsuited in climate and soil to agricultural use. In European Russia less than one-fourth the total area is under cultivation, and of the entire country less than 7 per cent produces farm crops. Yet the extent of the Soviet Union is so vast that even this small proportion has a greater area than the total areas of Germany, France, and England combined. A large amount of potential agricultural land still is forested, and some areas both in Europe and in Siberia, now unused, will eventually be brought under cultivation. Under the present system of government a large part of the farm land is held in some 250,000 collective farms and a few state farms. The collective farms range in size from 250 to 2,500 acres, and, on the average, each is worked by about 75 peasant families who live in farm villages on or near the land that they till. These are the true rural villages, for the majority of them have little, if any, commercial function. Each consists of a cluster or an irregular street of simple cottages built of logs, boards, stone, or clay, according to which type of material is most abundant in the region. The state is the owner of the land, and state officials make all the plans as to the crops that shall be produced and the methods to be employed. The work is supervised by local officials. The purpose of this enforced collectivization is to bring about a rapid improvement in the methods of Russian agriculture and an increase in crop production. The ignorance and poverty of the peasants prior to 1917 had resulted in very backward methods and low yields. However, plans imposed by governmental authority and enforced changes in practice do not always bring the expected results. There are also the difficulties of periodic droughts and other natural handicaps to be overcome. Whether or not the actual increases and improvements are as great as was anticipated is not certain.

CEREAL CROPS DOMINANT.   It has been noted already that the hardy crops and those which mature quickly dominate Russian agriculture. Of these the cereal crops are most important. Wheat, rye, oats, and barley together occupy about two-thirds of all the cultivated land, and wheat alone occupies nearly one-third of the total (Figs. 17, 231). Corn is raised only in the extreme southwest, near the Rumanian border, where the summers are longest and most humid. Until recently the area devoted to it has been less than 10 per cent of that devoted to wheat, but it is now reported to be increasing rapidly under governmental promotion. Another important group of crops on the Russian dry lands is the grain sorghums and millets, because of their drought resistance. The sunflower is also a seed-producing crop of importance. It is valuable for its yield of oil and as feed for animals. Potatoes, too, are widely grown and occupy about 5 per cent of the crop land.

Regional specialization among the several crops has been mentioned in connection with the regions of Russia and is shown by the several maps referred to. It may be noted again that food and feed crops such as rye, oats, and potatoes are raised in largest quantity in the cooler central regions, which have the poorer soils, and that they enter very little into commerce. Wheat and barley, on the other hand, are raised in the black soil belt of the south, and some part of the crop of each finds a commercial exit to foreign markets through such Black Sea ports as Odessa and Rostov-on-Don. Other crops have a high degree of regional restriction— flax fiber in the Baltic Plain, sugar beets in the southwest, and cotton in the irrigated southeast.

Other crops, notably the vegetables, have wide distribution. Cabbage is one of the most important of these. Bread, especially the black rye bread, cabbage, and potatoes are the staple foods of a large part of the agricultural peasants.

THE ANIMAL INDUSTRIES.    Livestock industries, such as exist in the United States, are not well developed in Russia. This is not for lack of animals. There are in the Soviet Union more horses than in the United States, although, owing to the increasing use of tractors and other causes, the present number is barely half what it was in 1914. The supply of sheep and goats is larger than that in the United States; the number of cattle is somewhat less; and of swine the United States has about 50 per cent more (Figs. 80, 81, 82). The great difference is in the manner of their production and management. There has been, for example, until recently little that was comparable to the American livestock ranch in the dry lands. Instead there was the nomadic herding of the Kirghiz steppes and the sparse but almost equally nomadic herding of reindeer in the far north. However, under Soviet rule, the Kirghiz are being required to abandon their nomadic customs and settle upon tracts of land where they conduct their livestock industries upon a ranching basis. In the central region of European Russia there is little of the commercial-livestock type of farming seen in the American corn belt and western Europe. Instead there is a self-sufficing type of general farming in which a peasant owns a horse or two, a cow, and a pig. On some of the collective farms the number of animals is greater, but still the larger part of the stock is kept for working the farms or for local food supply. Some are fed for the city markets but usually in small lots, one here and a few there, on surplus grains, hay, and pasture. The raising of crops to be devoted almost exclusively to animal production, as in the American corn belt, is little developed.

With the dairy industry the situation is a little different. In two regions previously mentioned, the Baltic area and western Siberia, modern dairying has made some progress. In the latter region particularly it has resulted from the need of a valuable product of small bulk suitable for shipment to distant markets. Butter is such a product, and progressive pioneer farmers had for many years, even before the revolution, hired Danish and German instructors to help them. Creameries have been built, and Russian exports of butter run into the millions of pounds. In fact the exports of Russian butter are greater than those of meat. However, the Siberian dairy farm is not much like that of Wisconsin. Barns and other equipment are primitive; there is not much winter feed provided; and dairying is mainly a summer industry. In its character and surroundings it resembles somewhat the dairy industry found on the northern, prairie-forest margin of the spring-wheat region of Canada.

## Industrial Resources and Development

THE POSITION OF MANUFACTURES IN RUSSIA. Prior to the revolution of 1917, the development of manufacturing in Russia was small. This was not for lack of industrial resources but is to be attributed to social and economic conditions that did not favor the growth of modern manufacture. These have been changed, so far as governmental desire and planning can change them, and manufacturing industries of many kinds have been started under the new system. Some of them have grown to large proportions in their endeavor to supply the domestic markets. However, they still are faced with serious handicaps, particularly the inexperience of Russian management and the inadaptability of the native labor for employment in the skilled trades and factory work. These handicaps are being overcome, and already the home market is being supplied with a large part of its essentials, if not with its full needs. The future expansion of manufacture in Russia appears likely to depend in part upon the nature and quantity of the basic industrial resources of the country.

ENERGY RESOURCES. The Soviet Union is well supplied with coal, petroleum, and water power, at least for its immediate requirements.

*Coal.* The total coal reserves of Russia are not well known, but they are of considerable size and are found in several parts of the vast area (Fig. 275). Recent estimates seem to indicate that the country may have as much as 1¼ billion tons of coal of all grades, an amount equal to nearly half the estimated reserves of the United States. The present average annual production is reported as about 130 million tons. That is about 10 per cent of the world's output, or about one-fourth that of the United States. The best coal in European Russia is found in the Donets Basin of southeastern Ukraine, not far from the Sea of Azov. Donets coal is of good quality and includes coking coal. A field of larger area, but one containing much less coal and of poorer quality, is located south of Moscow. Because of its central location the Moscow coal is much used, but it is mainly lignite, and as a source of fuel and power it has to be supplemented by coal shipped in from the Donets Basin and by peat dug from the local marshes. Other coal fields are known to exist in Siberia. The one being most rapidly developed is the Kuznetsk Basin, southeast of Novosibirsk.

It is estimated to be the richest and largest coal reserve in Russia; and since it is reached by railroads, it is the center of a newly promoted industrial region. Another but smaller field, also reached by the railway, lies to the west of Lake Baikal. In the isolated forest areas of the northern Urals and Siberia are several other coal deposits. Some are of low grade, but one of them, the Tunguska Basin, located near the place where the Yenisei River crosses the Arctic Circle, is estimated to rival the Kuznetsk in value. Even the far eastern provinces have coal, since reserves have been located in the Lena Valley and also within the angle of the

### THE COAL AND PETROLEUM FIELDS OF EUROPEAN RUSSIA AND CENTRAL SIBERIA

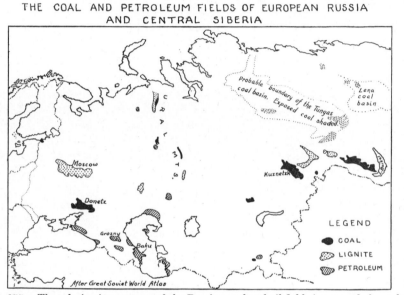

FIG. 275.—The relative importance of the Russian coal and oil fields is as much dependent upon their location as upon their size.

great southward bend of the Amur River. The latter is not far from rail transportation, via the line to Vladivostok. It is reported to have a much smaller reserve than the Kuznetsk region but to be nearly the equal of the Donets Basin.

*Petroleum.*    European Russia has one of the oldest and most productive petroleum fields in the world. It is located near Baku at the eastern end of the Caucasus Mountains. Other old fields lie along both the northern and southern flanks of the Caucasus, especially at Grozny. Newer discoveries include a large petroleum structure beneath the low plain at the north end of the Caspian Sea and several smaller ones in a chain along the western flanks of the Urals. The larger part of Siberia seems to lack indications of petroleum, but in the far eastern region some is obtained from the island of Sakhalin. The total Russian petroleum production of something over 200 million barrels per year is about 10 per cent of the world's output, sufficient to give the country third rank, following the United States and the Caribbean region.

*Water Powers.* The extensive plains and low rainfall that characterize so much of the Soviet lands would not seem to provide the conditions necessary for the development of large water powers. Yet the Caucasus Mountains, the Urals, and the extensive highlands of the far eastern region do furnish considerable power possibilities. The total is estimated to be nearly as great as that of Norway, but doubtless it would be more

IMPORTANT DEPOSITS OF MINERAL ORES IN EUROPEAN
RUSSIA, WEST AND CENTRAL SIBERIA

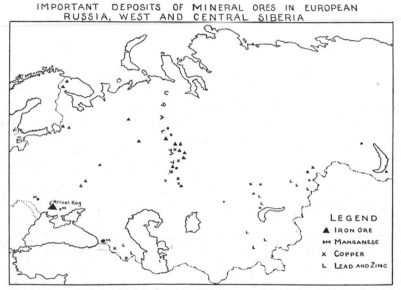

FIG. 276.—The principal mineral ores of the U.S.S.R. are distributed over a very large area.

expensive to develop, and much of it is in distant localities where it would find no local markets. Only about 10 per cent of the estimated resource is now in use, less than half the quantity used in Norway, and on a per capita basis the figure for Russia is very low.

IRON ORES AND IRON PRODUCTION. Iron ores appear to be relatively abundant in Russia. The output has increased rapidly in recent years but still is less than that of France and less than half that of the United States. Ore deposits are said to be located in several parts of Russia (Fig. 276). It is planned that some ores in the far eastern provinces are to be smelted with Amur River coal to supply needs in the Pacific Coast settlements, and ore from the Kola Peninsula near Murmansk is to supply Leningrad and the Moscow region. The utilization of some of the known deposits has, however, progressed but little beyond the stage of plans. About four-fifths of the ore actually smelted comes from two deposits.

Most productive are the mines of Krivoi Rog in the Ukraine, about 300 miles west of the Donets coal fields. Iron smelters have been built both in the coal fields and near the ore mines. Trains carry ore to the coal in one direction and coal to the ore on the return trip. These are hematite ores of high grade. The second region is Magnitogorsk at the southern end of the Ural Mountains where a good grade of magnetite ore is located. Furnaces are located there also, coke being supplied from the Kuznetsk coal field 1,200 miles eastward, and ore is sent in return to supply blast furnaces in the Kuznetsk region. Some iron is smelted also in the Moscow and Leningrad industrial centers, to which both coal and ore are brought from the outside.

Reports on the output of iron in recent years indicate that Russia has exceeded any other European country except Germany, and it has averaged nearly as much as United States during the period of American industrial depression. The iron industry has been particularly fostered by the Soviet government because of its basic relation to the industrialization and militarization of the country, including the manufacture of railway equipment, farm machinery, and armaments.

OTHER MINERAL RESOURCES. Russia has large known reserves of several important minerals but is only a relatively small producer of some, such as lead and zinc. Among those which are produced in large quantity are manganese, salt, and phosphates. Manganese, particularly, has long been an important export commodity. It is found in a convenient location on the south slopes of the Caucasus Mountains close to the eastern end of the Black Sea. Russian manganese has until recently constituted about half the world's supply, and it has been exported to most of the steelmaking centers of the world, but now about two-thirds of the ore mined is used at home. The great salt beds of Russia lie beneath the surface of the southern Ukraine, and the phosphates are hard rock deposits in the Kola Peninsula of the far north.

Russia holds about fifth rank among the copper-producing countries of the world. Its yield has increased nearly fivefold in a decade, but its output still is only about 5 per cent of the world's annual supply, an amount not sufficient for growing domestic needs. The Ural region is the principal area of copper mining, but new discoveries in the desert of Turkestan have been reported which may increase the output. The Ural Mountains formerly yielded about 95 per cent of the world's supply of platinum, the Republic of Colombia being the only other important source. In recent years, however, the Russian output has been equaled if not exceeded by that of Canada. The complicated geological features of eastern Asiatic Russia yield various metals, including copper, gold, and silver. It is known that new discoveries of the precious and semiprecious metals have been made in that large region, but the value of their output is a matter on which the Russian government chooses not to give full information

THE STATUS OF MANUFACTURING IN RUSSIA. A high development of manufacturing has evolved in most of the European countries only after centuries of economic evolution. Some other countries, particularly the United States and Japan, have gone through a more rapid industrial growth. In the Soviet Union a nation of agricultural peasants, with primitive industrial development, has been lifted into an industrial stage within two decades. This has been done by the application of a plan evolved by a highly centralized government and enforced with severe political pressure. In an attempt to secure economic independence it was not enough to encourage the textile and other simple factory industries such as have appeared first in many backward countries—India, and China, for example. The whole range of modern industry, heavy and light—steel, machinery, forest products, textiles, and the chemical industries—had to be got under way at once. The immediate result in Russia was industrial chaos and much waste of effort. That stage seems largely to have passed, however, and several well-marked industrial regions have evolved, some of which are associated with the principal coal deposits.

THE PRINCIPAL REGIONS OF MANUFACTURE. It is not to be understood that Russia was without factories before the revolution of 1917. There were many, but in large part they were not of the most modern type, and they were concentrated principally in the Moscow industrial region. The Donets Basin smelted iron, and the Ural region furnished metals, but these largely went to the Moscow and Leningrad centers for further manufacture. This tendency promoted the growth of those two cities which are still the largest in Russia. The changes that have taken place since 1920 have had the affect of modernizing the industries of the Moscow region and of expanding manufacture into new regions that formerly had little or produced only the industrial raw materials. As a result, manufacture is now widely distributed, even into Siberia. However, there are several outstanding centers in which a large part of the products are made, and they differ somewhat in their emphasis on one or another of the classes of industrial goods.

*The central industrial region*, with Moscow as its focus, had formerly the principal textile industries, and it retains its lead in that group of manufactures. Some of the mills of this region are of the older type, but newer ones have been built elsewhere, as for example south of the Caucasus, where there is local cotton, hydroelectric power, and labor needing employment. Moscow and adjacent towns also produce chemicals, metalwares, machinery, trucks, electrical equipment, and instruments for a great variety of uses. Gorki, 250 miles east of Moscow and the easternmost city of the central region, is the site of Russia's largest automobile factory. The power resources of the central region are not abundant, and the existing industries draw upon many sources. Much is furnished by steam electric plants that burn coal, the local lignite, oil, peat, and even firewood. Good coal comes by rail from the south, and petroleum comes from the Caucasus by rail and by barge up the Volga. In spite of the power handicap and the efforts of the Soviet planners to decentralize industry, Moscow with a population reported to be 3,600,000 has nearly doubled in size in two decades. This is perhaps in part the consequence of its central location, the focus of river routes and railways, just as are Paris and Berlin.

*Leningrad*, also with a power handicap in that it has no local coal supply, has become an industrial center and ranks second in population, largely because it is the only Russian port opening upon the Baltic and the North Sea trade. It manufactures engines and electrical machinery and has large shipyards.

*In the Ukraine*, with its good fuel, industry has been greatly expanded and diversified in recent years. Some of the industries are old, notably the blast furnaces and the beet-sugar mills. Others have been added, particularly those which use iron and cater to farm needs by the manufacture of such things as tractors, harvesters, and other agricultural machinery. But heavy industrial machines are made there also. The salt mined in the Ukraine furnishes, together with coal, the basis of important chemical industries.

*The Ural industrial region* makes use of the small coal fields near Perm and Sverdlovsk and also of the iron and other mineral ores of that region. It ranks second only to the Ukraine in raw-iron production, and it makes heavy machinery, chemical products, and many other things. New towns have been established, and several old ones have grown rapidly.

*In the distant Kuznetsk Basin* of Siberia is the newest and least developed of the larger Russian industrial regions. Coal is the obvious reason for its location, but it is designed also to supply the interior and far eastern regions with manufactures and to provide industrial employment for groups of people who had previously little opportunity. Metallurgical, machine, woodworking, paper, chemical, and general supply industries have been established.

Two classes of manufactures in Russia are not highly localized. One, the food-products industries, is distributed somewhat according to the density of population, the larger part of it being in the southwestern quarter of European Russia and along the western part of the Siberian railways. The other, the forest-products industries, such as sawmills and pulp and paper mills, is located in and along the southern margins of the northern forests. Such mills are most numerous in the northwestern and central sections of European Russia, in the Ural region, along the Siberian railroads from Tomsk to Lake Baikal, and again in the Amur Valley of the far eastern region.

## Transportation and Commerce

ROADS AND RAILWAYS. Russia has a problem in transportation somewhat like that of Canada—vast areas of land in forest and tundra, sparsely peopled and almost unreached by modern transportation except through air routes. Even in European Russia the country roads are little improved except on principal thoroughfares between larger towns. The

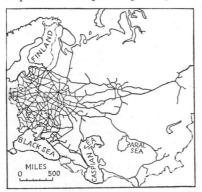

FIG. 277.—The railroads of Russia and western Siberia.

rail system also is in need of development. Although considerable additions have been made to it since 1917, railway progress appears not to have kept pace with expansion in manufacture (Fig. 277). In all the vast expanse of the Soviet Union there are only a few more miles of railroad than there are in Germany, less than one-fourth as many as in the United States, and each mile of it must serve about 150 square miles of area. However, this last figure has little meaning, since such large areas have no railways at all. Even in the most occupied portions of European Russia the spacing of the lines is much less dense than in most parts of western Europe. In Siberia the long line of the Trans-Siberian Railway serves to link together the distant portions of the country, but it has only recently been equipped with double track. The irrigated districts of southern Turkestan are linked with the west by one line that crosses the desert and by another that includes boat connections across the Caspian Sea.

WATER TRANSPORTATION. Inadequate road and rail transportation in Russia has given the water routes high importance, although most of them are closed during the long winter. The Caspian Sea and the Volga River have been much used for centuries, and great quantities of goods still move over them. The Don and the Dnieper also are employed, and in Siberia upriver traffic serves to feed the railway system which has only local branches. The flatness of European Russia causes most of the streams to have low gradients and makes them more usable. It also makes canal construction more feasible, and several hundred miles of canals serve to link together the waters of various navigable streams.

RUSSIAN FOREIGN TRADE. For so large and populous a country, Russia has a small foreign trade. This is in part due to the great size and diversity of the country, which enables it to produce most of its own requirements, and to the low standard of living, which creates a relatively low requirement for other than staple goods produced at home. It may be attributed also in part to the intense nationalism of the present governmental policy, which discourages or forbids imports in order to stimulate home production. This is evidenced by the fact that present exports and imports have less than one-fourth the value of those of 1913. The most important items in the Russian import list reflect certain facts: (1) that industrial maturity has not yet been reached; (2) that, great as the country is, it lacks a sufficient supply of several vital industrial resources of mineral or agricultural origin; and (3) that the animal industries are not adequate. These most important items of import are machinery, crude copper and tin, raw wool, and crude rubber. The exports of Russia generally exceed the imports in value by a small margin. The leading items in the export list are wood and its manufactures. These usually make up about one-fourth the total value. Other important items are petroleum and furs. In years of good crops wheat has ranked next to forest products in the list, but in other years little if any is exported. The produce of forests, farms, and mines comprises the larger part of the less important commodities shipped out of the country.

A LONG COAST WITH FEW PORTS. One of the most significant facts in the geography of Russia is its lack of ports on the open sea. With all its great length of seacoast, Russia has not been able to acquire a first-class harbor. Navigation in the eastern arctic region is endangered by ice, even in the summer, and is closed most of the year. Archangel and the White Sea outlet are closed for 3 or 4 months in the winter. The only northern port that is usable through the year is Murmansk, near the Finnish border, but that is a long way from the industrial regions. The port of Leningrad opens upon the Baltic Sea, but it occupies a shallow delta site, has a dredged approach, and also is closed by ice in winter. The recent war with Finland and the political control extended over the Baltic States involves an attempt to get more open harbors. The terms of the peace treaty of March, 1940, between Finland and Russia give Russia a naval base on the Finnish Peninsula of Hangö, which is less troubled with ice than is the approach to Leningrad. It provides also for Russian control of a railway across northern Finland to the head of the Gulf of Bothnia. This route will connect through Sweden, by way of the Kiruna iron-mining region, with the ice-free port of Narvik in Norway. Further political maneuvers to make these outlets more secure from outside control may be anticipated. On the south the Black Sea ports of Odessa and Rostov-on-Don are greatly reduced in value by the fact that

Russia has not political control over the Bosporus, which is the outlet to the Mediterranean. In time of war this outlet can be closed by Turkey or whatever maritime powers can gain the favor of the Turkish government. Recent Russian negotiations with Turkey appear to be directed toward an arrangement that will give the Soviet authorities control of this exit before Germany can secure it. The far eastern port of Vladivostok is kept open in winter by icebreakers, but it is too far away from the heart of Russia to have large commercial value except to eastern Siberia. Unless the freedom of commerce is ensured by some other means, it is almost certain that Russia will continue its efforts to gain better outlets by continuing its struggle in the Baltic; by attempting to wrest the control of the Bosporus from Turkey; by attempting to retake the ice-free Asiatic port of Dairen (Port Arthur), which it once owned but lost to Japan; or by gaining control of Persia and the Persian Gulf in conflict with the Indian interests of Great Britain.

SELECTED REFERENCES

Forest Resources of Russia, *U.S. Dept. Commerce, Trade Promotion Bull.* 378 and 798, 1925 and 1932.

GUBKIN, I. M. "The Natural Wealth of the Soviet Union," Moscow, 1932.

MIKHAYLOV, N. "Soviet Geography," London, 1935.

SINGEWALD, Q. D. Europe's Fuel and Metal Deposits Evaluated, *Econ. Geog.*, Vol. 15 (1939), pp. 384–394.

SVEC, M. MELVINA. Voyaging Down the Volga, *Jour. Geog.*, Vol. 38 (1939), pp. 297–304.

TVERSKOI, K. N. "The United Transport System of the U.S.S.R.," London, 1935.

ZIMMERMANN, ERICH W. "World Resources and Industries," New York, 1933, pp. 648–657.

# Chapter XXIX. China

THE LAND OF CHINA. China is an ancient land, a land of large area, large population (Fig. 5), and large agricultural production. Its most populous eastern provinces have been tilled for more than 40 centuries;

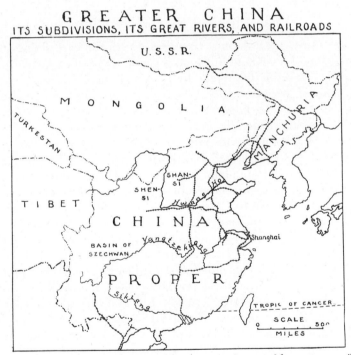

GREATER CHINA
ITS SUBDIVISIONS, ITS GREAT RIVERS, AND RAILROADS

FIG. 278.—The one great river highway of China is supplemented by a sparse railway net. Much of the country is reached only by roads and footpaths.

but far from being exhausted, some of them continue to support populations in excess of 600 per square mile, largely by agriculture. China is also a land of contrasts. Within its 28 provinces are flat alluvial plains, great areas of rough and hilly lands, plateaus, and mountains. Beyond these the influence of the Chinese extends westward and northward over

531

the high plateaus of Tibet and the deserts of central Asia, a total area much greater than that of the United States (Fig. 278). Although it was for centuries a realm of isolation, China has been within a few decades brought into violent contact with forces and ideas from the world outside, and it is now undergoing a period of turbulence with rapid social, political, and economic readjustments. Like most of Europe, it is engaged in military conflict the consequences of which can hardly be foretold. It may indeed result in the merging of China with Japan and other lands of Asia in a gigantic combination which will end, at least for a time, its separate political existence and alter its economic life in many ways. Yet the land of China will remain; and the people, although they may have undergone extensive migrations, still will occupy the land and till it much as they have done in the past, having the same advantages and subject to the same restrictions of surface, soil, and climate as before.

## The Physical Regions of China

SURFACE CONFIGURATION.    In contrast with the vast plains of Russia the proportion of level land in China is small, and some of even that part is rendered unsuitable for tillage by reason of unfavorable climate. The surface is one of great diversity. The high mountains and plateaus of the west project their long fingers eastward toward the Pacific Ocean in irregular pattern and generally with decreasing elevation. One of them, the Tsing Ling Mountains, is an effective partition between two strongly contrasted parts of the country, North China and South China. The north includes the broad deltaic plain of the Hwang Ho and the plains of Manchuria. These are fringed or interrupted by broken and isolated ranges of mountains and hills. South China includes the delta and floodplain of the lower Yangtze River and an extensive region of hills which rise westward into the tablelands of the extreme southwestern part of the country. Included in the south is only one extensive lowland district. It is the plain of the Yangtze which is continued westward by the rough but productive "Red Basin" of Szechwan in the far upper reaches of the Yangtze River, above the gorges of Ichang (Fig. 278). Elsewhere the land is largely in slopes, with only limited areas of alluvial plains. These latter are mainly near the coast and include especially the floodplain and delta of the Si Kiang, the only large river of the far southern part of China. The extensive plains of the country are therefore in the northern and middle regions; the southern portion is nearly lacking in them.

THE GREAT RIVERS OF CHINA.    Two of the great rivers of the world are in China (Fig. 278). The Hwang Ho or Yellow River, because of its shallowness and sand bars, is little used for navigation. It flows from that part of northwestern China which is covered with *loess*, a fine, yellow, wind-blown earth of desert origin. The water of the river carries a great burden of this material which gives the name (Yellow) to the river and to the sea into which it empties. Deposits of the loessial silt have created the larger part of the plain of North China, which is essentially the delta of the Hwang Ho. Across this plain the river flows between levees which it sometimes abandons to take a new course. Then disastrous floods occur, and large numbers of people are drowned—over a million in 1878, for example. The alluvium deposited by the stream has built the great delta plain outward until, through the centuries, it has reached and half sur-

rounded what once was the mountainous island of Shantung, converting it into a peninsula. The lower part of the river has changed its course—first north then south of that peninsula—thirteen times in the last 25 centuries (Fig. 279).

Much more important to China is the Yangtze, the most used waterway of the country. It, too, has an extensive floodplain and delta, which, on the north, joins that of the Hwang Ho but is less subject to disastrous floods. The Yangtze is the main highway of China, and it carries a large amount of traffic. Ocean-going vessels ascend 630 miles to Hankow, and river steamers can go 1,000 miles farther. They pass through the narrow gorges of

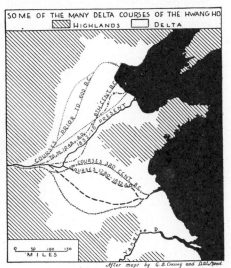

FIG. 279.—The great delta of north China, its relation to the Shantung Peninsula, and some of the many channels the river has occupied within historic times.

Ichang, where the river cuts across a mountain barrier, and beyond into the Red Basin of Szechwan. It is only by the river that heavy goods in large quantity can reach that densely peopled inland region.

CLIMATIC REGIONS. The situation of China in the continent of Asia gives considerable variety to its climates. On the eastern side of the landmass, it extends through a greater range of latitude than eastern North America from Cuba and the Gulf Coast to New England and southern Canada, and it has somewhat comparable climatic contrasts. Moreover, being a part of Asia, it shares in the monsoon influence common to the southern and eastern portions of that continent, a seasonal reversal of winds and weather much more pronounced than that brought about by the weaker monsoon of North America. Although the local variations of climate in China are numerous, they may be grouped for brevity into four major types. (1) The hill lands of the south and the valley of the

Yangtze River have climates that may be called "humid subtropical," a type somewhat like that of the American cotton region. The summers are hot and humid; the winters, mild and considerably more dry. The average annual rainfall varies from 40 to 60 inches. The rain is reasonably dependable and is distributed far inland. (2) North China also has warm summers, but the rainfall for the year is less, 20 to 40 inches, and it is less dependable. The winters are dry and cold. This climatic region includes the great northern plains—the best agricultural lands and the largest areas of dense population. It may be compared in climate with the United States corn belt, especially the drier portion of that belt in Nebraska and Iowa. (3) Only in the extreme north of Manchuria are there the short summers such as are characteristic of the American Great Lakes region. There the cold, dry winters and lower rainfall produce an environment somewhat like that of Minnesota or North Dakota. (4) In the far west and northwest of China, steppe and desert and highland climates prevail.

SOIL CONTRASTS. There are many types of soil in China, and most of them have been cultivated for so long a time that their present character is not necessarily like what it may originally have been. Generally the alluvial soils are most productive. The upland soils of the south appear to be mainly of the leached subtropical redsoil type found also in the American South. In the north lower rainfall has left a higher lime content in the soils, both in the alluvial plains and in the loess-covered uplands of the northwest. These are inherently more productive than the red soils, but they are associated with the lower and less dependable rainfall and are therefore all too commonly subject to crop failure and become regions of famine.

## Agricultural Regions

THE IMPORTANCE OF AGRICULTURE. It is estimated that three-fourths of the people of China gain their living directly from tilling the land. However, because so much of the area is handicapped by aridity or steep slopes, the area of cultivable land is not great, perhaps not much more than one-seventh the area of the 28 provinces, or one-fourth that of the provinces of greatest agricultural importance. The area of crop land per family is, therefore, extremely limited—only about 3.5 acres. Agriculture is intensive, and not much land is available for the production of crops to be used in the feeding of livestock, even such as are used as work animals. The principal crops are those which can be used directly for human food, especially the grains, beans, and vegetables. Some crops, especially cotton and the mulberry plant, which is used to feed silkworms, help to clothe the population and, together with others less widely grown, are sold from the farm and give the farmer a small cash income. However, the several parts of China differ considerably in the emphasis placed on one or another combination of crops. This is largely because of differences in climatic, surface, and soil conditions (Fig. 280).

NORTH CHINA AND MANCHURIA. The plains of northern China and Manchuria have summers too short and too dry to produce rice as a major food crop. Their principal crops are wheat, millet, a large grain sorghum (called "kaoliang"), and soybeans. Associated with these are many other crops, such as corn, barley, oats, potatoes, and other vege-

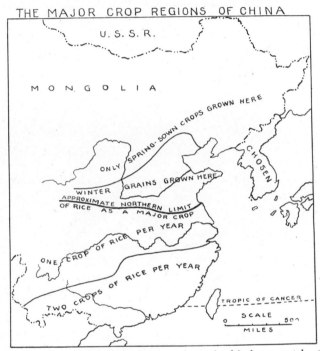

THE MAJOR CROP REGIONS OF CHINA

FIG. 280.—The great crop regions of China are determined in large part by the length of the growing season.

tables. In this part of China the farms are somewhat larger than the average, and there are more farm animals than in the southern regions. Yet the farming is very intensive, compared with American or even European standards, and most of the crops grown are for human food. On the typical farm a large part (more than 75 per cent) of all the food consumed is produced at home. Yet in spite of careful hand cultivation, the yields are not remarkably high, because the soils have been cropped for a long time, there is inadequate fertilizer, and the best seed is not always planted. The leading crop, wheat, is widely grown (Fig. 17). In the plain of North China it is mainly fall sown; but in Manchuria the winters are more severe, and spring-sown wheat is more productive. The flour produced is commonly eaten in the form of an alimentary paste, something like noodles or spaghetti.

Soybeans are the principal cash crop of North China and especially of Manchuria. They have been grown for centuries as a food crop. Like other legumes, their roots add nitrogen to the soil, and the beans are a versatile food resource. The bean is rich in oil and protein; by grinding and pressing them oil is extracted, and the bean meal properly treated yields a sort of milk substitute from which curds and a kind of cheese can be obtained. The meal, produced by grinding the cake that remains after

FIG. 281.—Terraced land in the loess region of North China. Saving soil after the forests are gone. (*Photograph by U.S. Forest Service.*)

the oil is pressed out, is used also as food, as feed for livestock, and as a fertilizer. In Manchuria large numbers of Chinese immigrants, under the stimulus of Japanese management, have in recent decades expanded the soybean crop far beyond local requirements, and large quantities of beans, exceeding 2 million tons per year, together with some bean oil and cake have been exported.

THE DRY NORTHWEST. To the west of the plains of northern China and Manchuria lie the dry plateaus, loess hills, and mountain borders. The larger part of the region is desert and steppe lands, inhabited by nomadic herdsmen who live in tents and graze flocks of sheep, cattle, horses, and camels. On the borders, however, and in oases live some farmers who raise dry-land crops of wheat and millet and, with the aid of irrigation, some more intensive food crops, such as potatoes. The population of the drier part of this large area is comparatively sparse. It is most dense in the region of the loess hills, where terrace agriculture and supplementary irrigation on the fertile soils have made even these dissected lands very productive (Fig. 281).

THE YANGTZE VALLEY. The alluvial plains that border the lower Yangtze River and the rough lands of the Red Basin of Szechwan are densely peopled regions (Fig. 5). Because of their longer growing season, more adequate rainfall, and tillable soils they are able to produce a greater variety of crops than the north. This valley includes some of the most productive land in China, and part of it is made to produce two crops per year during the long growing season. In addition to a crop of winter wheat, rice is grown as a summer crop on the same land. Associated with them are other grains, oilseeds, and supply crops. Such are corn and barley, beans, peanuts and other oilseeds, tea, cotton, and many vegetables. These crops, even including the cotton, are grown in small plots, mainly for home use. However, some cotton, tea, and peanuts are exported. Another important oil export is obtained from the tung tree. This is imported into the United States in large amounts and is used in the paint and varnish industry. The tung tree is now being grown to some extent in southern United States also, especially in northern Florida; but western China, especially Szechwan, is still the largest source of supply. The land of the Yangtze Valley is intensively tilled, with a great expenditure of hand labor, and it is by these means that so large a population is supported. In this region also the mulberry is grown to feed silkworms, and considerable raw silk is produced. The farms average only 2 to 3½ acres in size, and livestock are few, except swine (Fig. 82) and poultry, which can be fed from the waste products of field and household.

THE HILL LANDS OF SOUTH CHINA. The hill lands south of the Yangtze afford only limited areas of tillable soil. The best of them are found in the delta and floodplain of the largest river, the Si Kiang, and in some smaller coastal lowlands. Elsewhere only the narrow valleys of small streams afford level land. But the pressure of population upon the food supply has long enforced the cultivation of the lower valley slopes also. Many of these have been terraced at great expenditure of labor. The upper slopes and more distant hills remain covered with woodlands—brush and bamboo—the result of frequent cutting to secure wood for building, fuel, and other purposes. By means of the terracing, small level fields are created. On these, as on the valley lowlands, crops are grown in rapid succession. The rain is abundant, and, in the far south, the growing season lasts practically the entire year. Rice is the dominant crop. In the warmer and more rainy southern and coastal districts the land is made to produce two rice crops per year and sometimes a winter crop of vegetables also. This is done by growing the young rice in seedbeds and transplanting the second crop to the fields as soon as the first crop is harvested and the land prepared, by tilling and flooding, to receive the plants. The rice grows in standing water furnished by the heavy rains and retained on the level terraces and floodplains. Some of the water is provided by supplementary irrigation.

Another important crop in the hilly region of South China is tea. It is widely grown in this region but is especially important in the districts immediately south of the Yangtze River and westward into the basin of Szechwan. It is grown mainly in small hillside plots on the small farms and serves as a source of cash income for the farmers. The leaves are picked twice in the early summer and once later. By their method of treatment they are manufactured into the green tea that is the characteristic type obtained from China. A century ago this region was the world's principal source of tea, but it has now been far surpassed by the great tea plantations of southern Asia.

Farm animals in this region are even less numerous than in the north (Figs. 80, 81, 82). The water buffalo is the principal draft animal in the muddy rice fields, but even there much of the tillage is performed with spade and hoe.

RURAL SETTLEMENTS.  Farmers in most parts of China do not live on the land that they till but near by in rural villages. These are clusters of houses, some of which contain only a few habitations, though others are of large size. From them the farmers go out to their fields near by. The average farm may be made up of several pieces of land in different directions from the village, and they may include both tillable and untillable land. In northern China the houses are built mainly of earth or brick and are thatched with straw. In the southern provinces there are brick and stone houses also, tile roofed, but there are many others built upon wooden frameworks with walls of bamboo and branches, interwoven and plastered with clay. In only a few special localities do farmhouses stand alone and on the land tilled by their occupants. The inhabitants of the farm villages have little purchasing power, and there are seldom stores or any commercial functions such as are likely to be seen in the smallest American village. In China a commercial town usually is not far away, and the farm village remains almost entirely residential and rural in its connections

## Industrial Resources and Development

FUEL AND INDUSTRIAL POWER.  The era of industrialization has only begun in China. To a large extent the manufactures used in the country either are the products of household industry or are imported.

This is, however, not so much for lack of industrial power resources as for lack of their development and means for their transportation.

China has large resources of coal. They are probably not so large as was once estimated, but they are now believed to exceed those of any other country except the United States or Canada, being considerably greater than those of either Great Britain or Germany. Fortunately, they are also of high quality, since they include much anthracite and even larger amounts of bituminous coal. The largest deposits of good coal

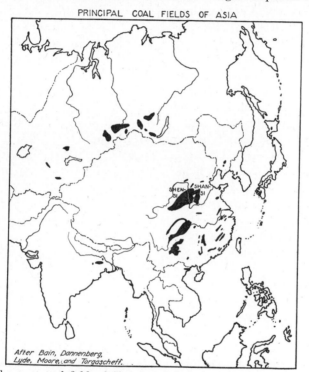

PRINCIPAL COAL FIELDS OF ASIA

After Bain, Dannenberg, Lyde, Moore, and Torgasheff.

FIG. 282.—The great coal fields of Shensi and Shansi are not yet as much used as some of the smaller ones that are more accessible.

are in the dry northwestern provinces of Shensi and Shansi, with smaller amounts in the middle Yangtze Valley (Fig. 282). There are also small amounts in various other districts, as in the Shantung Peninsula and Manchuria. Because they are more accessible, some of these smaller deposits are now more used than are the larger, richer fields. The southern provinces are least abundantly supplied. The total quantity of coal mined in China in recent years is not large in proportion to the reserves, being only a little greater than that produced in Belgium.

Although extensive explorations have been made for petroleum, no important supplies have been discovered. Large parts of the country are underlain by rocks of a geologic age or type in which it is very unlikely that this source of energy ever will be found. Petroleum does not appear to be one of the important resources of China.

The potential water powers of the country are considerable but not large in proportion to its area. They are estimated at considerably less than the comparable figure for the United States. However, the utilization of hydroelectric energy has hardly begun, and China is credited with less developed water power than any other large country, only a small fraction of 1 per cent of its estimated potential resource being now in use.

ORES AND MINERAL RESOURCES. China is a producer of several important mineral ores but is not a leading producer of any except antimony and tungsten. It shares also in the great tin resource of southeastern Asia, but its proportion of the world's output is normally less than 5 or 10 per cent. These metals are vital to certain industrial processes but particularly to such as belong to a type of industrial development beyond that to which China has advanced. Consequently these ores are important to China mainly as export products.

Iron ore, the critical metal of modern industrial development, is found in several places in China but not in quantities proportionate to its resources of good coal. In fact, it appears likely that the supply of ore is not adequate for a large-scale iron and steel industry such as characterizes the United States or western Europe. Most of the known deposits are relatively small in size and of inferior quality. Several types of ore are found. The deposits are mainly in the northern provinces, and the one most used is in southern Manchuria where exploitation under Japanese control has continued for some years. Others of the iron-ore deposits have been worked to some extent, but most of them are not well located with respect to supplies of coking coal. Only a relatively small quantity of raw iron and steel is produced, and that mainly in Manchuria. The per capita output of iron in China was, at its highest, hardly more than 2 pounds, as compared with nearly 650 pounds in the United States. Even that amount has been greatly reduced in recent years because of the war with Japan. It is to be noted, moreover, that most of the better deposits of both coal and iron are within the limits of the territory occupied by the Japanese military forces, and resumption of production must wait upon the outcome of the military struggle and probably upon Japanese initiative.

FORESTS AND TIMBER RESOURCES. A country as densely peopled as China requires a large amount of wood for construction, fuel and many other uses. So long has this demand existed that large sections of the land, believed once to have had forests, have been completely denuded of trees. That is particularly true in the drier and colder northwestern provinces, where timber is now so scarce that houses must be built of mud and where

roots, shrubs, grasses, straw, and even animal manure must be gathered
to supply the demand for household fuel. The use of wood for construction there is limited to minimum essentials such as rafters, window
frames, and doors. The poles and boards so used must be brought long
distances overland or imported from abroad. Not all of China is completely devoid of forest, however. Three principal areas remain. The most
extensive of them is the coniferous forest in the mountainous northern
and eastern borders of Manchuria. In the mountains of the far west also,
beyond Szechwan, there are forests whose products are carried downstream to the Yangtze Valley markets. The third region is made up of
scattered forest remnants in the hill region of southern China. Much of
this latter region has furnished timber for centuries and is being constantly cut over; but in the humid subtropical climate trees grow rapidly,
and a large part of the steeper hill slopes are forest covered. Saw logs are
obtained principally from the more distant slopes, but those near the
settled valleys furnish firewood, poles, bamboo, and camphor wood for
construction, paper manufacture, or the distillation of camphor gum.
Most of the sawmills or other manufactures engaged in timber exploitation are small, some of them being operated exclusively by hand power.

MANUFACTURING INDUSTRIES. It has been noted previously that a
large part of the manufactured wares required in China are produced at
home by hand looms and by local craftsmen such as carpenters, potters,
and metalworkers. However, certain types of manufacture had, prior to
the Japanese occupation, developed to the stage of large factory production. This was notably true of textiles. There were in 1936 about 140
cotton-spinning and weaving mills in the country, of which 88 were
owned by Chinese, 47 by Japanese, and 5 by British interests, and most
of these continued in operation after the Japanese invasion. There were
also numerous silk mills, flour mills, and establishments manufacturing
sugar, matches, cement, clothing, and many other products.

The most important industrial center of China is the lower Yangtze
Plain and especially the city of Shanghai, near the mouth of the river.
In this relatively modern city of more than 3 million inhabitants, and in
its environs, were a large part of the silk and cotton mills, although the
latter were found also in some other cities. The importance of Shanghai
as an industrial city lay in the fact that it was the principal port for the
receipt of foreign cotton and other imported raw materials and that it
was in a position to profit by the trade moving both inland and outward
along the rich Yangtze Valley, the principal commercial thoroughfare of
the country. Upriver from Shanghai were several large cities, including
Nanking and Hankow. The latter was formerly the center of a group of
commercial and industrial towns that included one of the principal iron-
smelting industries, no longer in operation.

The Yangtze industrial region was a principal objective of the Japanese in their attempt to establish control over the political and economic life of China. Its industries have now been in part abandoned; some of its cities are in ruins; and there has been a large but unknown migration of population inland. Its future under the "new order in Asia" can hardly be foretold.

## Transportation and Commerce in China

LAND TRANSPORTATION.   In scarcely any other respect is the development of China more retarded than in its facilities for transportation. In most of the country there are few improved highways. In the northern provinces and Manchuria there are some roads over which it is possible for motor vehicles to pass, especially during the winters, when the ground is dry or frozen, but in the rainy season they are poor. Most of the transporting is done by pack animals, by wheelbarrows, or on the backs of men. The cost of such transport is high even at the low wages prevailing there. In South China the country roads are mainly footpaths along the valley sides and among the rice fields. Goods are commonly carried in baskets suspended from poles resting on the shoulders of human porters. Even lumber and other heavy freight are carried by men or trundled on barrows. Under modern conditions, transportation by automobile truck is growing in popularity, but for the most part the roads are little improved and sometimes impassable. During the years of the current war with Japan, military necessity has required the construction of several improved truck roads to supplement the inadequate railway system. Most famous of these is a long one extending across the southwestern provinces to reach the border of Burma and provide a rear entrance to China for the importation of military supplies. But it was hardly completed or well graded before its military value was much reduced through attack by the Japanese air force. In a land of poor roads, it is not surprising that air transport has risen rapidly in favor for the movement of passengers and valuable commodities. But the scope of air transport is as yet limited principally to military use.

RIVER AND CANAL TRANSPORT.   The importance of the Yangtze River as a means of reaching western China has been noted. In addition there are hundreds of miles of canals mainly in the low delta lands and floodplains of the eastern provinces. Included among them is the Grand Canal, which is about 1,000 miles long, extending from Hangchow northward to Peiping. It was completed about 650 years ago and is much used for local transportation. There are many thousands of miles of local canals in this flat region also that are able to carry small boats and reach innumerable farmsteads and villages, taking the place of country roads. But although they serve a region of dense rural population, they do not reach large portions of the country and cannot provide through transportation for general freight.

RAILROADS. There are not many railroads in China. Their total length of less than 7,000 miles requires that each mile of road serve about 450 square miles of area in the major provinces, and the far northwestern regions have none at all. However, the distribution of the railways even in the major provinces is not uniform, the larger part of the mileage being in the northeast, whereas most of the west and south have little, if any. The principal lines are shown in Fig. 278.

FOREIGN TRADE. The foreign trade relations of China have been almost completely disrupted since the beginning of the struggle with Japan in 1937, and it is to be doubted if they may again return to their former course. Prior to that time the trade was considerable in the aggregate but very small on a per capita basis. It had certain fairly well-defined characteristics that are worthy of note. (1) It was fairly evenly balanced between exports and imports. (2) The export trade was dominated by a few items—soybeans and their products, tung oil, tungsten and tin, silk, cotton and textile manufactures, eggs, and tea. These are mainly the products of farms and mines. (3) Imports were more varied than exports and consisted largely of petroleum products, metalwares, timber, and miscellaneous manufactures. (4) The trade of China proper was most largely with Great Britain, the United States, and Japan; that of Manchuria was dominated by Japan alone. It may be assumed that, if it falls under complete Japanese control, the trade of all China will be directed as largely toward Japan as that of Manchuria now is.

The commercial nations have looked upon China as one of the great markets of the future; but China can become a large purchaser only by improving her own production so that she may have a larger surplus to be exchanged for the products of other countries. An old and populous country like China can hardly be expected to export as much per capita as a country like Argentina which has a large agricultural area and a small population. Such countries produce a great deal more than they need of agricultural staples, but China needs nearly all that it produces. Neither can a people with the low standard of living that prevails in China be expected to make large per capita purchases of foreign goods, yet the total purchases are large. If China could buy from the United States as much per capita as Canada usually does, the value would be many times more than the United States' present exports to the whole world.

IMPORTANCE OF JAPAN'S RELATIONS TO CHINA. Japan has a great advantage over other nations with respect to Chinese affairs. This advantage of proximity and Japan's urgent need make the action of Japan in China a matter of world-wide interest. Japan greatly needs the surplus raw materials of China, especially iron, cotton, and foodstuffs, and almost equally she needs the great potential market of China in which to sell her manufactured goods. This is the reason that she has undertaken to exercise control over the political and economic life of the larger country, taking advantage of the economic disorganization of China· and the political disorganization of Europe as an occasion for enforcing the type of cooperation most advantageous to her. Upon the outcome of this struggle both the political and economic independence of China and her future trade relations with the United States and the rest of the world are likely to depend. Its progress is watched with interest by all other countries.

SELECTED REFERENCES

BAIN, H. FOSTER. "Ores and Industry in the Far East," New York, 1933.
BELDEN, W., and M. SALTER. The Coal Resources of China, *Econ. Geog.*, Vol. 11 (1935), pp. 426–430.
———. The Iron Ore Resources of China, *Econ. Geog.*, Vol. 11 (1935), pp. 304–306.
BERGSMARK, DANIEL. "Economic Geography of Asia," New York, 1935.
BUCK, G. L. *Land Utilization in China*, Chicago, 1937.
BUXTON, L. H. D. "China; a Human Geography," Oxford, 1929.
CHANG YIN-T' ANG, "The Economic Development and Prospects of Inner Mongolia," Shanghai, 1933.
"China Yearbook," Woodhead and Bell, London and Tientsin Press, Tientsin.
CONDLIFFE, J. B. "China Today; Economic," Boston, 1932.
CRESSY, G. B. Agricultural Regions of Asia: Part VI, China, *Econ. Geog.*, Vol. 10 (1934), pp. 109–142.
———. "China's Geographic Foundations," New York, 1934.
FELLNER, F. V. "Communications in the Far East," London, 1934.
JAMES, H. F. Industrial China, *Econ. Geog.*, Vol. 5 (1929), pp. 1–21.
——— (ed.). China, a series of 39 articles on social and economic conditions, *Ann. Am. Acad. Soc. Pol. Sci.*, Vol. 152, November, 1930.
KING, F. H. "Farmers of Forty Centuries," New York, 1927.
LYDE, L. W. "The Continent of Asia," London, 1933.
PEARSE, A. S. "The Cotton Industry of Japan and China," Manchester, 1929.
STAMP, L. D. "Asia; A Regional and Economic Geography," London, 1935.
TREWARTHA, G. T. Field Observations on the Canton Delta of South China, *Econ. Geog.*, Vol. 15 (1939), pp. 1–10.
———. Ratio Maps of China's Farms and Crops, *Geog. Rev.*, Vol. 28 (1938), pp. 102–111.

# Chapter XXX. Japan

AN ISLAND EMPIRE. The land of Japan proper is included in a long and narrow group of islands draped like a giant festoon upon the border of eastern Asia. It is comprised of 4 main islands and more than 450 smaller ones. In addition there are outlying possessions which include the large island of Taiwan (Formosa), which lies far down the China coast, part of Sakhalin Island to the nortward, and several smaller islands. On the mainland of Asia the political control of Japan has been established over the peninsula of Chosen (Korea), and close supervision or military authority is exercised in Manchuria and most of northern China. However, the right of Japan in these two latter regions is not recognized by the United States government.

The area of Japan proper is only about as large as that of Montana, and it is a land of extensive mountains and hills. Hardly one-sixth of its surface is suited to cultivation. Yet it has a population of nearly 75 millions, about one-half of whom depend upon the land for their living. The density of population in the islands as a whole is about 500 per square mile, and there are nearly 3,000 persons per square mile of tillable land. The population is increasing rapidly, and the standard of living is necessarily low. The restricted land area forces many Japanese to seek a living in other ways than agriculture. Such are fishing, forestry, manufacturing, and commercial pursuits; yet farming occupies the greatest number.

THE SURFACE FEATURES OF JAPAN. Insular Japan is, in fact, a partially submerged group of mountain ranges. They have been thrust upward along a zone of instability in the earth's crust. They are bordered on the Pacific side by great ocean deeps and on the continental side by shallow seas. Their instability is evidenced by the presence of numerous volcanoes and by earthquakes so frequent that, on the average, three or four per day occur somewhere in the islands. Some of these have been accompanied by great disasters and loss of life. The rainfall of Japan is abundant, and from the mountain slopes short torrential streams flow to the near-by coasts carrying quantities of sediment. These they have deposited as deltas and alluvial plains, which are the most level and productive lands of the country. The plains are distributed at intervals about the 17,000 miles of coastline, but most of them are small in area and are separated from one another by hilly uplands or mountainous projections. Only a few are of large size, the largest being the Kwanto Plain on which are located the cities of Tokyo and Yokohama. It is about the size of the state of Delaware.

The alluvial lands are of two types, and each has a different agricultural utility. At elevations somewhat above the present sea level lie deposits of older alluvium. These were put down as deltas and floodplains at a time when the coastline was also higher. They now contain leached and porous soils and are not the most productive crop lands. Since the islands have risen somewhat farther above sea level, the streams have cut through these older deposits, dissecting them considerably, and have made new and lower floodplains and deltas of fresh alluvium about their margins. These deposits of new alluvium are the most productive soils in Japan and the most suited to intensive tillage. Although the greater part of the plains are coastal in location, some are found also in the broader interior valleys and mountain basins.

Above the alluvial lands rise the hill and mountain slopes, and these are occupied in large part by the carefully supervised forests of Japan. The forests cover, in fact, nearly two-thirds of the entire country and four times as great an area as the tillable lands. They constitute one of the important resources.

THE CLIMATES OF JAPAN share with eastern China in the monsoon conditions affecting Asia; but since Japan is separated from the great landmass by expanses of water, it is less extreme in its temperatures and has generally a more abundant and better distributed rainfall. The long extent of Japan in latitude, more than 2,000 miles, brings about a considerable difference in climate between the northern and southern parts of the country. Sakhalin, in the far north, has the longest and coldest winters and the least rainfall. Its winters are severe and snowy; its summers have warm days and cool nights, with frequent rains and fogs. It is a climate somewhat like that of the coast of Maine. Hokkaido, the northernmost of the large islands, has somewhat milder middle-latitude conditions. Its climate is somewhat like that of Connecticut or New Jersey. The other islands, and therefore much the larger and more populous sections of Japan, have humid subtropical climate, somewhat like that of the Yangtze Valley or the American cotton region. Because of its marine situation, however, the winters of southern Japan are more humid than those of China and even more mild. There are occasional frosts and, on the northwestern coast, heavy snows, but the summers are hot and humid. The climate of Tokyo is, for example, somewhat like that of Charleston, S. C. This region suffers, as do the coasts of Florida and southern China, from occasional violent storms, called "hurricanes" in America and "typhoons" in Asia. These frequently cause severe floods and are destructive of life and property.

ADVANTAGES OF SITUATION. Insular Japan, with its long coastline and many harbors, has an advantageous commercial position. Like Great Britain, it is the focus of trade and trade routes leading toward the neighboring continent. Like Britain also, it has fishing grounds and a large fishing fleet in which men are trained in seamanship. It has a large merchant fleet and a large navy and is in some ways repeating the maritime history of Great Britain and for similar reasons.

## The Agriculture of Japan

AGRICULTURAL LAND AND RURAL POPULATION. The land is the most important resource of Japan. About half the population is agricultural and lives directly upon the produce of the soil. Yet the islands are so rugged that centuries of the severest toil have rendered only about one-sixth of their total area suitable for tillage. These lands are included mainly in the alluvial basins and deltas previously mentioned. They are intensively utilized and, like the tilled lands of China, are divided into small holdings which average only a little more than 2.5 acres per farm. In the more newly settled regions of the north the farms are larger than the average, but in the south they are generally smaller than the average. Intensive utilization requires the production of more than one crop per year from all the land capable of multiple cropping. This is more widely practiced in the south where the growing season is longer. Thus an average farm in the south, although smaller, may produce enough to support a family. Two crops of rice are possible in Taiwan and in most of the southern part of Japan proper. Moreover, rice is commonly followed by winter crops of unirrigated grain or oilseeds as far north as Tokyo, the proportion of the land so used decreasing as the latitude increases. On the drier, nonrice lands, multiple cropping is even more common, part of the diversity being the result of intertillage, *i.e.*, the growing of two or more crops at the same time in alternate rows. In the northern part of Honshu it is not possible to mature another crop on the irrigated lands after the rice is harvested, and the rice fields lie idle in the winter. In Hokkaido the season is still shorter, and nearly all the crops are planted in the spring.

The farm population in the long-settled, older part of Japan lives mainly in rural villages (Fig. 283). About these lie the numerous small fields, often scattered, that make up the farmer's holding; and from the villages the farmers go out to work. In the productive lowlands the villages are closely spaced, occupying the better drained sites at road junctions or strung out along highways that follow river dikes, beach

FIG. 283.—Rural villages and irrigated rice fields on the alluvial lowlands of Japan. These are in sharp contrast with the forested slopes of the adjacent foothills and mountains. (*U.S. Bureau of Foreign and Domestic Commerce.*)

ridges, or foothill zones. Farmhouses having the scattered distribution common in America are infrequent in the rice-growing districts of Japan but are found to some extent in the mountain districts and in the newer Japan, the pioneer farming areas of Hokkaido.

THE IMPORTANCE OF RICE. Because of its large food-producing ability, rice is much the most important crop in Japan. It occupies more than half of all the cultivable land of Japan proper and the larger part of the newer alluvial lands of the recent floodplains and deltas. It is grown also to some extent on the older and more porous alluvial slopes and upon terraced hillsides. The newer delta lands are preferred for rice, not only because the soils are more productive but also because they are more compact and retain irrigation water more perfectly. This reduces the labor and cost of irrigation, for most of the rice grown requires irrigation. The water is provided from streams, artificial ponds, and wells. Often it is carried to the fields at great expense of labor. In some regions a part of the crop depends for its irrigation upon rainfall alone, but the yields usually are lower. Rice is grown in all the principal islands of Japan except Sakhalin. However, in Hokkaido and northern Honshu the growing season is rather short, and early-maturing varieties are grown. The greater part of the crop is grown, therefore, on the lowlands of southern and middle Japan, both east and west sides, and in Chosen and Taiwan (Fig. 284).

OTHER GRAIN CROPS. Although rice is the principal food crop of Japan, other grains occupy large areas. In the far north they are much more important than rice. Chief among them are wheat, barley, millet, and buckwheat. In part they are grown on the dry or unirrigable lands that are not suited to rice, and in part they are grown without irrigation as winter crops on the rice lands. The yields of grain per acre from these crops are much less than from rice, but they constitute an important supplement to the food supply.

BEANS AND VEGETABLE CROPS. In Japan, as in China, the staple foods of rice and other grains are used in conjunction with numerous vegetables and fruits. Among the more important of these are beans and potatoes. Soybeans are widely grown, and other types of beans also, but they reach their greatest importance in Chosen. The potato crop includes both white and sweet potatoes, the former being most cultivated in the cooler northern regions, and the latter in the subtropical southern portion of Japan proper and in Taiwan.

COMMERCIAL CROPS. Some of the agricultural land of Japan is devoted to commercial crops such as the mulberry plant and tea. The first named is widely distributed in the warmer and more densely peopled parts of the country south of the 39th parallel of latitude. It is grown largely without irrigation on the drier upland soils, and in certain districts it is the principal crop. Mulberry leaves, gathered from the fields, are used to feed silkworms which produce the *silk* that, in raw or manufactured form, constitutes one of the most important single exports of Japan. Many farm families are employed in silk production. It is an industry that can prosper only where experienced and very cheap labor is

JAPAN
RICE
ACREAGE
EACH DOT REPRESENTS 5,000 ACRES

FIG. 284.—Over half of the cultivated land of Japan is devoted to rice. (*U.S. Department of Agriculture.*)

available. The worms require a great deal of care, for they are sensitive to changes of temperature and subject to destructive diseases. For some days after hatching they eat voraciously and grow rapidly, but soon they seek the places prepared for them to attach the cocoons that they spin around themselves. The hairlike filament of silk in each cocoon contains about 300 yards. To prevent the emergence of the moth and the destruction of the filament, the cocoon is heated, and its inmate is killed. Formerly the silk was all reeled from the cocoon in the home, and much of it still is, but in recent decades a large part of the growers sell their cocoons to buyers who take them to factories (called "filatures") where the silk is reeled into skeins by machinery, although much hand labor—mostly by women and girls—is employed in these establishments also. The silk cocoons represent one of the largest sources of agricultural income in the country.

*Tea* is also an important crop in southern Japan and Taiwan. It does not occupy more than one-twentieth so great an area as the mulberry plantings and little more than 1 per cent as much as irrigated rice, yet it is important to Japan because of its wide use. As an export crop it has suffered much, as has that of China, from competition with the great tea plantings of India and the East Indian region. Tea, like silk, requires cheap labor, and it is grown in intensively tilled plots on the hillsides and porous uplands of older alluvium and volcanic ash. The area of greatest tea specialization is in the plain and foothills region just west of Tokyo.

THE ANIMAL INDUSTRIES IN JAPAN. There is but little natural pasture land in Japan, and the animal industries have never had a large place in the prevailing agricultural economy. Most of the inhabitants can seldom afford meat, and they have not acquired a taste for dairy products. Therefore, most of the animals raised are used as work animals. This is true of cattle as well as of horses. There are not many of the latter, but they are relatively more important in northern Japan, whereas cattle are more commonly used in tilling the fields of the warmer south and in Chosen. The water buffalo is also used in Taiwan.

## Resources Other Than the Land

JAPAN'S FORESTS. Nearly two-thirds of Japan is forest covered. Wood is the preferred building material in nearly all parts of the country, and most of the limited heating of houses and the cooking of food is done with firewood and charcoal obtained from the forests that clothe the mountain slopes in all but their highest and most rugged portions. Japan is also a large user of paper. The domestic forests are, however, not sufficient to supply all these needs, and much pulpwood and large amounts of lumber must be imported.

The forests of southern Japan are dominated by species of oaks, with some coniferous trees and groves of bamboo. In the most tropical portions occasional palm trees reflect conditions similar to those of Florida. The evergreen oak, characteristic of the American Gulf and southern Atlantic Coastal Plain, is found also on the subtropical lowlands of Japan as far north as Tokyo. In northern Japan, and at greater altitudes farther south, the hardwoods include such deciduous trees as oak, chestnut, beech, and maple, and there is also a large admixture of pines and other coniferous species. This kind of forest is more nearly like that of the northern Appalachian Highlands and New England. In the far north of Hokkaido and in Sakhalin spruce, fir, and small hardwoods predominate. This is a forest more nearly like that of maritime Canada and Newfoundland.

So long have the forests of densely occupied Japan supplied the requirements of the country that timber suitable for lumber manufacture is found only in the more remote mountain sections and in the sparsely occupied pioneer regions of the north (Fig. 285). Much must be imported

Fig. 285.—Lumbering operations in the mountains of Japan. (*Photograph by U.S. Forest Service.*)

from the United States, Canada, and Siberia. Reforestation has been carried on for many years, but large quantities of small trees must be cut each year to supply charcoal and firewood. Near the densely peopled lowlands are large mountain districts which are used continuously to supply this requirement.

JAPAN'S FISHERIES. The scarcity of meat in Japan and the vast extent of coastline and sheltered seas have conspired to make that country much the most important fishing nation of the world (Fig. 97). Nearly 1½ millions of people engage in the industry, some of them farmers or tradesmen who find only part-time employment in it. Fishing villages dot the coast, and thousands of fishing boats ply the coastal waters. Some larger powerboats fish distant waters and add their quota to the food resource and the national income. Fish canneries also are numerous, and fish in fresh or preserved form is a staple of diet even in remote sections of the islands. Canned fish is also an important item in the list of Japan's exports.

ENERGY RESOURCES. *Coal.* The industrial ambitions of Japan and her great need to employ her surplus population in manufacturing industries are not well supported by large reserves of coal. In this respect her situation is strikingly different from that of Great Britain. The total quantity of coal available is not large, and most of it is of only moderately good quality. Some of the reserves are contained in thin seams and lie at great depths, so that the cost of mining is high and is likely to increase in the future. The production of coal in Japan in recent years has increased

FIG. 286.—Coaling ships by human labor at Nagasaki, Japan. (*U.S. Department of Agriculture.*)

to an annual total exceeding 40 million tons, an amount about equal to that produced in France but less than one-fifth that mined in Great Britain. At that rate of mining her proved reserves would last only about 25 years, but the probable reserves would doubtless extend far beyond that time unless the mining costs became prohibitive. In any case the coal supply is not adequate for a large expansion of industry, especially of the heavy industries. This, as has been previously noted, is one of the reasons why the Japanese government is anxious to gain control of the large coal reserves of China. The most important coal fields of Japan lie in two widely separated districts. They are the extreme southwestern part of the country, north of the city of Nagasaki, and the northern island of Hokkaido. There are also some other smaller deposits (Fig. 286).

*Petroleum* reserves in Japan are even more meager than are those of coal. Limited areas along the western coast of Japan proper and some in Taiwan produce upward of 2 million barrels yearly. This may be compared with an average of nearly 60 million barrels in Rumania, for example, and more than 1 billion barrels in the United States. The small size of its petroleum resource is reason enough why Japan should wish for control over the oil fields of the East Indian region which produce more than thirty times as much.

*Water Power.* Mountainous topography and abundant rainfall in Japan combine to give that country a relatively large potential water power (Fig. 125). The total developable resource is estimated to be larger than that of France, and about half of it is now in use. It has, in fact, four-fifths of all the *developed* water power in Asia, although it has less than one-twentieth of the total water-power reserves of that continent. Shortages in coal and petroleum have encouraged the rapid development of Japanese water powers, and hydroelectric energy is well adapted to the light industries characteristic of Japanese manufacture, particularly to the textile industries.

MINERAL RESOURCES AND INDUSTRIES. *Iron-ore* reserves in Japan proper are scant indeed. The total estimated supply would last the United States hardly one year, and most of it is of low grade. The domestic iron industries are supplied largely by imported ores, by iron produced in Manchuria under Japanese control, and by imports of scrap iron and steel, principally from the United States. The total annual manufacture of pig iron in Japan in recent years has been less than that in Belgium and less than one-tenth that in the United States.

*Copper* is the most important metal mined in Japan and, next to coal, is its most valuable mineral resource. Its output in recent years has been, however, less than 5 per cent of the world's total, as compared with about 30 per cent in the United States.

## Japan's Industrial Development

THE RISE OF INDUSTRY. Only seventy-five years ago factory production was unusual in Japan. Handmade products were the rule. Household industries still are common; but in manufacturing, as in other things, Japan has increasingly adopted European methods. With coal and water power for mechanical energy and an abundance of cheap labor, rapid changes have taken place. European methods were studied; technical schools were established; model factories were set up by the government; and certain industries were subsidized. Some of the largest industries still are carried on in numerous small plants, but their aggregate production is by no means small. Japanese industry not only supplies most of the requirements of the home market but produces an ever-increasing surplus which makes foreign markets a vital necessity.

THE TEXTILE INDUSTRIES. The light industries and especially the textiles are outstanding in Japanese industrial economy. Textile manufacture alone occupies more than a million workers, over one-third of

those occupied in all Japanese manufactures. By far the greater number
of the establishments are of small size, many of them employing less than
five workers. Included in the list are manufactures of cotton, wool, silk,
and rayon.

The cotton-spinning and -weaving industries must depend entirely
on raw material imported from India, China, Egypt, and the United
States. Asiatic cotton mainly is of short staple, and for the manufacture
of fine yarns Egyptian cotton is used for admixture. The bulk of Japanese
cotton cloth is, therefore, of the coarser types and competes for the
cheaper Asiatic markets, especially that of China. In the numerous small
mills the use of electric power is most advantageous.

Woolen textiles also depend upon raw materials which must be
imported from Australia, Europe, and other sources. The output of woolen
textiles has not averaged half the value of that of cotton, which is the
most important of the textile group.

Silk and rayon fibers are the only ones produced at home as the basis
of textile manufacture. Silk raising is an ancient industry in Japan, and
the silk filiature is the first step in silk manufacture. Much the larger
part of Japan's silk is exported in the form of skeins of raw silk as it
comes from the filiature, but there are also spinning and weaving mills
that manufacture silk for home use and for export. The great advance of
rayon and other substitutes for silk in recent years has constituted a
threat to the silk industry that the Japanese have been unable to ignore.
To forestall possible disaster through the ultimate reduction or loss of
their silk markets they have developed a large rayon industry of their
own as a branch of the chemical industries. It has grown rapidly in recent
years and is reported now to exceed even that of the United States in
quantity of fiber produced, making it the largest in the world. However,
the principal raw material of rayon manufacture is woodpulp, and Japan
must import a large part of her requirement. It has come from various
sources, including the United States.

OTHER LIGHT INDUSTRIES. Japan has developed numerous light
industries as a means of employing labor without the use of much mechanical energy. The availability of electric power and certain raw materials,
such as wood, pottery clays, and certain chemicals, has also contributed
to this form of manufacture. Products of the lighter industries include
foods, chemicals and fertilizers, leather, rubber, camphor, lacquered
wares, glassware, and novelties of many kinds. These are in part for
home consumption, but large amounts are exported.

THE HEAVY INDUSTRIES. It has been pointed out that the position
of Japan with respect to coal resources and iron ore is disadvantageous.
However, so large a supply of cheap labor is available that considerable
manufactures of metal and clay products have developed in spite of a
shortage of domestic raw materials.

The pig-iron and steel production of Japan averages less than that of Belgium, yet it is of the utmost importance to Japanese economy. More than one-half of the blast-furnace and steel-mill output is derived from the region of the leading coal field in the island of Kyushu, near Nagasaki. The next largest contributor is Manchuria, whereas northern Japan has only scattered blast furnaces and a minor part of the national production. The domestic supply of iron is augmented by large importations of scrap iron and pig iron. Considerable quantities of iron ore are imported also.

The increased need for iron and steel in Japan rests upon the requirements of a rapidly growing industrialism. Beginning in 1936, manufactures of metals, metal products, vehicles, and machinery as a group exceeded the textile group in value. In this group are included not only the many small wares for the export of which Japan has long been famous but also heavy products, such as textile machinery, electrical equipment, railroad equipment, and ships for the large Japanese merchant marine. There are included also naval craft and arms and equipment for the large Japanese army.

INDUSTRIAL CITIES AND REGIONS.   Japan proper has more than 125 cities, and about one-third of the total population lives in them. However, not all the cities are dominantly industrial. There are about 35 cities of more than 100,000 population each, and several of the largest lie in the area facing the Pacific Ocean and the Inland Sea of southern Japan. This may be called the "industrial belt." It extends from Tokyo and the port of Yokohama westward to the principal coal-mining and iron-smelting region near the city of Nagasaki. In the belt are such large industrial cities as Osaka, Nagoya, Kyoto, and Kobe.

## Transportation Facilities and Trade

LAND TRANSPORTATION.   The modernization of Japan and the development of trade have required the perfection of means of domestic and foreign transport. Unlike China, Japan is well provided with roads. It has, in fact, more roads in proportion to its area than any other country—about 4.5 miles for each square mile of area. Many of the roads are old and narrow, ill-adapted for modern traffic but usable. Some are well improved and in use for automobiles and bus transportation. Even the more remote sections of the islands are readily accessible. In addition to the good roads there is also an excellent railway system. It includes both government-owned and privately owned lines amounting to about 1 mile of railroad for each 10 square miles of land in Japan proper. This, in a land as highly mountainous as Japan, is remarkable, since the density of the rail network is about equal to that in the American South and is greater than that of mountainous California.

WATER TRANSPORTATION.   The extent of roads and railroads in Japan does not give a complete picture of the domestic transportation facilities. In a country comprised of islands it is necessary that much of the local movement of goods and passengers should be carried by water, and a large fleet of boats is employed in that service. Japan's insular position has encouraged the growth of a large merchant marine fleet also. Its rated tonnage in 1938 (5 million tons) was greater than that of any other country except Great Britain and the United States.

## LEADING ITEMS IN JAPAN'S FOREIGN TRADE

PRINCIPAL IMPORTS          PRINCIPAL EXPORTS

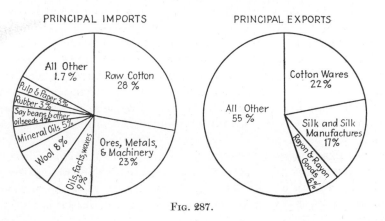

FIG. 287.

FOREIGN TRADE is a necessity to modern Japan. Although it still is an agricultural country, its population has grown beyond the capacity of its land to support by farming alone. Its manufactures have been developed as a means of further employment, but they require large quantities of imported raw materials, and the industrial wares must be marketed in part overseas (Fig. 287). An unfavorable balance in this trade is one of the principal problems in Japanese economy, since the value of the numerous imported products normally exceeds that of the exports. That is true of Great Britain also, but in that country a large income from foreign investments added to the income from ships employed in foreign trade and other sources of outside income has balanced the trade. Japan has ships in foreign trade but no large foreign investments and few other sources of income. It is for this reason that export markets are necessary, markets in which Japanese exports can be absorbed in large quantities relatively free from the competition of foreign manufactures. Such a market could be created in densely populated Asia if it were under Japanese military and political domination.

Proximity to Asiatic markets and sources of raw materials has been the dominant factor in Japanese foreign trade even under the conditions of the period before the struggle with China. A great variety of imports, drawn from China, India, and other Asiatic regions, has comprised more than a third of Japan's total imports, and the same markets have absorbed more than half the country's exports. However, the United States has been the largest single source of Japanese imports and the destination of nearly a quarter of the export trade. The largest items in the list of imports from America have been raw cotton, minerals, metal manufactures, and petroleum and its products. Exports to the United States have been varied, but more than half the total has consisted of raw silk. This fact has received popular attention in connection with recent trade and political negotiations between the two countries.

JAPAN'S PROBLEMS.   Japan has advanced so rapidly and her population has grown so large that the nation is in a difficult situation. Within her own territory she cannot produce either the quantity of food needed by her people or even the larger part of the raw materials necessary for her industries. To maintain the economic position already attained, to say nothing of satisfying her ambitions, Japan must have assured access to food supplies, iron, cotton, and other raw materials and also assured markets in which to dispose of her products. Her debt is large; taxation is heavy; and her whole economic structure is in unstable equilibrium. America, with its great area and resources, its large home market and sources of revenue, can little appreciate the problems that confront Japan. It is the need to secure some of these requirements, particularly a market free from import restrictions, that has led the Japanese to seize a favorable opportunity and to submit to a military regime in a desperate attempt to establish an economic control in China and perhaps in the East Indian region. That is the meaning of the "new order in Asia" of which Japanese statesmen speak.

SELECTED REFERENCES

ALLEN, G. C. "Modern Japan and Its Problems," London, 1928.
DAVIS, D. H. Present Status of Settlement in Hokkaido, *Geog. Rev.*, Vol. 24 (1934), pp. 386–399.
EOPPING, V. P. Expansion of Japan's Foreign Trade and Industry, *U.S. Dept. Commerce, Trade Information Bull.* 836, 1937.
HALL, ROBERT B. Agricultural Regions of Asia, Part VII. The Japanese Empire, *Econ. Geog.*, Vol. 10 (1934), pp. 323–347; Vol. 11 (1935), pp. 33–52, 130–147.
———. Some Rural Settlement Forms in Japan, *Geog. Rev.*, Vol. 21 (1931), pp. 93–123.
"Japan Yearbook," Tokyo (annual).
MOULTON, HAROLD, and JUNICHI KO. "Japan, an Economic and Financial Appraisal," Washington, 1931.
ORCHARD, J. E. "Japan's Economic Position," New York, 1930.
PEARSE, A. S. "The Cotton Industry of Japan and China," Manchester, 1929.
STAMP, L. D. "Asia: A Regional and Economic Geography," London, 1935.
TREWARTHA, G. T. A Geographic Study of Shizuoka Prefecture, Japan, *Ann. Assoc. Am. Geographers*, Vol. 17 (1938), pp. 127–259.
———. "A Reconnaissance Geography of Japan," Madison, Wis., 1934.
———. The Suwa Basin, *Geog. Rev.*, Vol. 20 (1930), pp. 224–244.
YANO, T., and K. SHIRASAKI. "Nippon," Tokyo, 1936.

# Chapter XXXI. Southern Asia and the East Indies

REGIONAL CONTRASTS. The vast expanse of land that extends across southern Asia from Turkey and Palestine eastward to the Pacific Ocean is an area of strong contrasts. From the broad base formed by the core of the continent three large peninsulas project southward—Arabia, India, and Farther India. The last named may be understood to include also the great island group of the East Indies. Among the regions included are some of exceedingly dense population and others in which there are few if any inhabitants (Fig. 5). There are also great differences in the productivity of the land and in the races of people resident there, differences that involve centuries of contrasting cultural and political history. There are fundamental differences also between the physical characteristics of the different parts of southern Asia. High mountains alternate with broad plateaus, alluvial basins, and coastal plains. Southwestern Asia is largely desert. Most of India has hot and humid monsoonal summers alternating with warm, dry winters. The climate of the East Indian area, on the other hand, is mainly of the rainforest type, with abundant precipitation throughout the year. It will be convenient to divide this part of the world for consideration into portions of strong climatic contrast.

## Southwestern Asia

ROUGH LANDS AND ARIDITY. The vast area comprising southwestern Asia is one of the less productive regions of the world. It includes the Arabian Peninsula, Mesopotamia, Persia, Afghanistan, and northwestern India. Only in the high lands of northern Mesopotamia and northwestern India is there sufficient rainfall to give rise to rivers of importance, and 80 to 90 per cent of the region is too dry to grow crops without irrigation. In this region, more than half as large as Europe, geographical conditions are so unfavorable that scarcely enough food can be raised to supply the sparse population, and the external commerce is small and limited to a few items.

THE ARABIAN PENINSULA is a plateau along whose Red Sea margin is a small but settled population, but its interior is a desert, almost unknown except to its nomadic inhabitants and the dwellers in a few oases. The plateau is higher on its western side, and the west-facing slope gets a little more rain than the upland. Facing the Red Sea are tilled lands and famous towns, such as Mecca, the holy city of the Mohammedans, and Mocha. The latter was once the center of the coffee trade, and the hill slopes of Yemen were the world's principal coffee-producing region.

'IRAQ occupies the lowland between northern Arabia and the plateau of Iran (Persia). It includes the region called Mesopotamia, the seat of ancient empires; and its principal population is located close to the two rivers Tigris and Euphrates in whose valleys are irrigated lands, once more extensive than now. Two-thirds of the territory of 'Iraq is desert grazing land inhabited by nomadic Arabs who pasture flocks of sheep, goats, and camels and live almost as did their ancestors in ancient times. They have for export only wool, camel's hair, and a few other products, such as gums and herbs collected from the desert plants. Less than 10 per cent of the total area of the country is under tillage.

In northern 'Iraq, along the western foothills of the Kurdistan Mountains, the winter rainfall is sufficient to produce a crop of wheat, and barley and some other foodstuffs are raised in summer by means of supplementary irrigation. Most of the tilled land of the country, however, lies upon the narrow floodplains bordering the main streams and their few tributaries. In these strips alone can irrigation waters be applied to the land in abundance, and from parts of them only is there drainage to remove accumulations of salt and alkali from the soils, thus making them productive. The staple food crops on the irrigated floodplains also are barley and wheat, but in some districts rice, dates, citrus, and other fruits are grown also. Other crops, such as cotton and sugar beets, could be grown, but the farmers are conservative and produce but little beyond their immediate needs.

In the southern part of 'Iraq the Tigris and Euphrates join before they enter the Persian Gulf as a single stream, called the "Shatt al Arab." There the river level is raised periodically by the backing up of the fresh water due to the rise of the tide in the Gulf. This aids the process of irrigation, and extensive date groves border the stream both above and below the city of Basra. Dates are the most valuable export crop of 'Iraq, and from this region the United States obtains nearly all its large imports of that fruit.

IRAN occupies a mountainous plateau between the Caspian Sea and the Persian Gulf. Among its mountains are numerous oases and foothill slopes used for the cultivation of cereals, cotton, and fruit crops. The larger part of the land is suited only for grazing, however, and there is but little surplus of agricultural products for export. Wool, woven by hand processes into carpets and rugs, is perhaps the most typical and famous of these exports.

PETROLEUM.   Along the shores of the Persian Gulf and the boundary between 'Iraq and Iran lies one of the highly important petroleum fields of the world. British, Dutch, French, and American oil companies have been engaged in a struggle for its control and exploitation. The oil is of vital strategic importance to the British especially, since its supplies ship fuel, by way of the Persian Gulf, to India and the Red Sea ports for cargo ships and naval craft. From northern 'Iraq oil is transported overland westward by two pipe lines to eastern Mediterranean ports, a distance of more than 500 miles. One objective of the Axis Powers in their military and naval operations in the eastern Mediterranean during 1940 was to wrest the control of these pipe lines from the British and thus assure Italy and Germany additional supplies of oil. The combined petroleum output of the various oil regions in the Persian Gulf fields is little more than 5 per cent of the world's total, but the location of these oil supplies gives them a high strategic value. Royalties from their sale are important items in the support of the governments or for the construction of internal improvements in the two countries concerned. More than two-thirds of the total oil produced comes from wells on the Iranian side of the boundary.

TRANSPORTATION.   The location of dry southwestern Asia made of it a great commercial crossroad in ancient times. A number of famous caravan routes crossed it, connecting the Mediterranean and Red seas with the Tigris-Euphrates Valley, the Persian Gulf, Central Asia, India, and even China. Damascus, Baghdad, and other ancient cities were focal points on these routes. Much of the traffic over them has, until recent years, been by caravan. Motor transport has, however, practically ended that ancient and picturesque form of carrying goods. There are not many good roads in the region, but much of the land is dry, unfenced grazing range over which automobiles can seek new routes when the old become too badly worn. Railroads are not extensive either. Before the World War of 1914–1918 German interests were constructing a rail line across Turkey toward 'Iraq—the "Berlin to Baghdad Railway." It was not completed then, but parts of it were in operation for many years. Only in July, 1940, was the final link built in 'Iraq, making possible through rail transportation from Istanbul to Basra. There is now being built in Iran a railroad designed to connect the Caspian Sea with the Persian Gulf.

CONFLICTS OF NATIONAL INTEREST.   Before the First World War the dry land of southwestern Asia was one of the theaters of international conflict of interest on the part of Britain, Germany, France, and Russia, all of which were seeking to control its resources and its natural highways. Since it lies between Europe and India, it lay then in the path of both

German and Russian territorial ambitions. Britain and Russia had divided Iran into spheres of influence, and all four countries were engaged in intrigue for advantages in this struggle. Since that time the active competition has not been so great, but the objectives still remain. In fact the growth of petroleum production and increased knowledge of the probable oil reserves have increased the rivalry. It is likely to appear in new forms and with greater strength at the conclusion of the present European war, if not before.

AFGHANISTAN is a dry, mountainous highland east of Iran, across whose territory lies the direct route from Russia to India. It is inhabited by warlike tribesmen who are occupied mainly in the grazing of sheep and the cultivation of the soil. It has little to export except wool, and its imports are limited. Hence, it has small commercial importance. However, its political importance as a buffer state between Russia and India is great, and political maneuvering there is currently reported, with Britain, Russia, and Germany all participating.

NORTHWESTERN INDIA is part of the Indian territories long under British control. However, in many ways it is more like the adjacent dry lands than it is like the rest of India. It includes the desert of Thar, where camels are an important element in the livestock; the dry Punjab, where wheat and cotton are irrigated crops; and the rugged lands of Baluchistan. It is also one of the sections of India where the Mohammedan religion is predominant. Since, however, it is a part of India, it may conveniently be discussed in that connection.

# India

CULTURAL AND PHYSICAL DIVISIONS. Since the beginning of the seventeenth century the British have had increasing political control over Indian territories which they have organized into the Empire of India. Many provinces and states make up India, some of them directly under British rule and others (native states) under the rule of their native princes, who have British "advisors." Among the many states there is a great variety of languages, religions, and racial groups. There is little cultural unity, and India has not been in historic times united under the rule of its own people.

The surface features of India are divisible into three major groups: (1) the slopes and foothills of the Himalayas and other bordering mountains on the north, northwest, and northeast; (2) the broad alluvial depression south of the mountains, drained by the Indus, Ganges, and Brahmaputra rivers; and (3) the Deccan, or peninsular India. The Deccan is a plateau comprised in large part of ancient crystalline rocks and great lava flows, like those in Washington and Oregon. It is higher on its western edge and slopes gently eastward. The high western margin is much dissected and, especially on its seaward side, appears as mountains which are called the "Western Ghats." The eastern margin is also dissected into hills called the "Eastern Ghats," but they are not high. The Ganges and Indus valleys contain a great depth of alluvium brought down from the bordering mountains. Some of it, like the alluvial lands of Japan, was deposited long ago and has been much leached of its fertility. Included also is a large area of recent alluvium which is inherently fertile, but part of it is badly drained.

The area of India is slightly more than half that of the United States, but its population is two and one-half times as great.

THE IMPORTANCE OF MONSOON CLIMATE. Nowhere else is the monsoon climate so well developed or so important to vast numbers of people as in India. The summer monsoon, blowing off the sea from June to October, inclusive, moves northeastward over India, bringing heavy rains to the seaward slopes of the Western Ghats, to the Ganges lowland, and to the Himalaya front. The direction of the wind then changes, and it moves up the Ganges Valley, leaving less rain as it goes inland. In far northwestern India, as has been noted, the climate is dry or even desert. The surface of the western Deccan, sheltered by the Ghats, is also comparatively dry, having less rain than the bordering lowlands.

The amount and distribution of the rainfall is of the greatest importance to the people of India. Almost nine-tenths of them live by agriculture, and most of them are very poor, so poor that a single crop failure reduces millions to the verge of starvation. Owing to the nature of the monsoon winds they sometimes are delayed or fail to bring rain to certain districts, and formerly great famines resulted. However, under British management, supplementary irrigation has been developed, and railways have been built. Both of these, by giving some security against drought and by enabling the importation of food from other districts, have much reduced the severity of the famines.

The outblowing winter monsoon is dry over most of India; but on the southeastern coast and in Ceylon there is winter rain also, because these northeasterly winds must first cross the Bay of Bengal before they strike the lands. Northwestern India likewise has some winter rain, brought by occasional storms which have traversed the Mediterranean region and the highlands of Iran. It helps in the production of winter wheat.

## AGRICULTURAL REGIONS AND PRODUCTS

REGIONS. Because of its strongly contrasted features of geology, surface, and climate, India may be divided into several agricultural provinces. The divisions, when studied in detail are, in fact, numerous and of complicated pattern. In the interest of simplicity they may be grouped as follows (Fig. 288): (1) the dry northwestern districts, where wheat and cotton are the major crops and irrigation culture is widespread. (2) The rainy west coast, where coconuts occupy the sandy coastal strip, rice is the dominant food crop on all alluvial lands, and spices, bananas, and many other crops reflect a humid tropical environment. (3) The Deccan Plateau, where millet and wheat are the food staples and cotton the principal cash crop. (4) The eastern coastal margin of the peninsula, where rice is dominant on all alluvial lands, especially in the deltas of the several streams flowing from the uplands. Here the climatic conditions require supplementary irrigation for rice, and many valleys on the

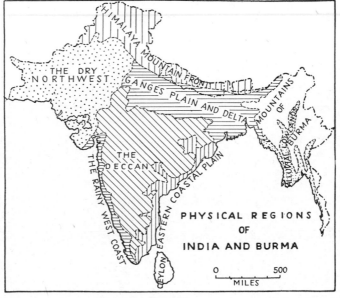

Fig. 288.

plateau margin have been dammed to create reservoirs, or "tanks," to provide the necessary water. (5) The Ganges delta and the floodplains of the Brahmaputra and Ganges. There are the broadest expanses of rich land and the largest region of dense population (Fig. 5). Rice is everywhere the principal food crop, but it is associated with cash crops and others that vary with situation. In the delta proper jute is grown. On the higher lands of the Brahmaputra Valley are the most extensive tea plantations of India. On the Ganges floodplain corn and sugar cane are important crops, grading westward into regions of barley and wheat as the drier climate of the northwest is approached. (6) The foothills and slopes of the Himalaya Mountains, a forested region in which areas of cleared and cultivated land are interspersed among the forested slopes and pastures.

In all the agricultural regions there are some districts of highly inten
sive utilization of land and others where there is little if any tillage. The
latter include marshlands, areas of porous or badly leached upland soils
covered with jungle, steep slopes, thin or stony soils, and desert lands
with salt or alkali soils. Actually, in spite of its dense population, only a
little more than one-third of the land of India is cultivated. Even that is a
fairly high figure, as compared with only about 16 per cent in Japan

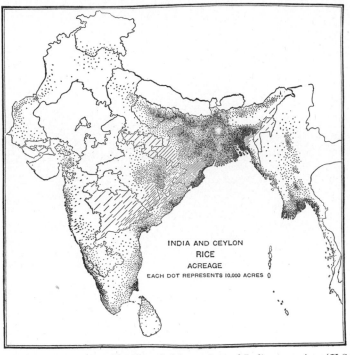

INDIA AND CEYLON
RICE
ACREAGE
EACH DOT REPRESENTS 10,000 ACRES

FIG. 289.—The low, wet, coastal lands and delta regions of India grow rice. (*U.S. Department of Agriculture.*)

and 18 per cent in the United States. However, the yields obtained in
India are generally low. In part this is due to insufficient or erratic
precipitation but in part also to poor methods of cultivation. The size of
the Indian farm averages very small. Few exceed 10 acres, and nearly
half the total number include less than 3 acres. As in China and some
other parts of the Old World, the farmers live mainly in some 600,000
villages from which they work their small and scattered plots, of which
each farm may have a dozen or more, containing a small fraction of an
acre each. The peasants have inadequate tools and no capital; many are
ignorant of progressive methods of agriculture and are bound by tradition. A large part of the farm labor is performed by hand or with the aid

of oxen. It is estimated that three-fourths of the farmers are heavily in debt and have little prospect of ever being able to make repayment. Their standard of living is one of abject poverty, a standard lower than that in almost any other part of the world.

Further understanding of Indian agriculture may be gained by considering the geographical distribution of several of the leading crops that have been mentioned above and the status of the animal industries.

RICE.   About one-third of the cultivated lands of India (80 million acres) is devoted to one crop, rice. Most of it is of the wet-land type, and its production is especially concentrated in the Ganges-Brahmaputra valleys and delta, although the coastal lowlands bordering the Deccan

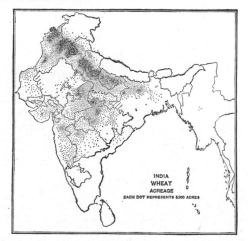

INDIA
WHEAT
ACREAGE
EACH DOT REPRESENTS 5,000 ACRES

FIG. 290.—The dry lands of northwestern India produce most of the wheat as a cool-season crop and, in part, with the help of irrigation. (*U.S. Department of Agriculture.*)

also grow rice as a major crop (Fig. 289). Most of it is required for home consumption; and although there is usually a small exportation, imports exceed the exports in some years.

WHEAT, SORGHUM, AND MILLETS are the leading food grains of the dry lands. Wheat reaches its greatest importance in the Upper Ganges Valley and the northwestern provinces (Fig. 290). It is fall-sown and has the benefit of the winter rains of that region. But that is not moisture enough, and large areas are irrigated both in the Upper Ganges Valley and in that of the Indus. In the tropical climate of the Deccan Plateau, where the winters are dry, wheat does not grow well, and there is not sufficient water or proper soils for rice. In that region the grain sorghums and millets furnish cereal foods for millions of people who seldom eat either rice or wheat flour (Fig. 291).

SUGAR CANE.   India grows more sugar cane and produces more sugar than any other country in the world. In recent years its sugar manufacture has been more than twice that of Cuba. However, it is not an important commercial crop. It is grown mainly in small plots on native farms for home consumption in nearly all parts of the country but particularly under irrigation in the Upper Ganges Plain. The juice is extracted in crude mills and reduced by boiling to a soft brown sugar, called "gur," in which form it is consumed. There is no important export of sugar from India, but a large importation of refined sugar for foreign residents and others who are able to afford it. It comes principally from Java.

VEGETABLES AND OILSEEDS.   A diet of cereals requires supplement. For this purpose many vegetables, including peas, beans, and peppers, are grown. Oils for cooking, for illumination, and for other uses are now

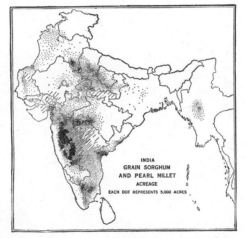

FIG. 291.—Sorghum and millet are important food grains in drier sections of southern India. Compare with wheat and rice. (*U.S. Department of Agriculture.*)

provided by a variety of crops such as sesamum, flaxseed, rapeseed, and peanuts and are valued at many millions of dollars per year.

COTTON is the leading cash crop of India and by far its most valuable export. It has been grown in India for centuries, and that country ranks second only to the United States in both acreage and production of cotton. In fact the acreage planted averages about three-fourths that in the United States, but the crop is much smaller because the yields per acre in India are less than half as great. Cotton is grown in several regions in India, but the western Deccan region is much the most important (Fig. 292). The industry is promoted there by deep, dark-colored clay soils, known as "regur." They are derived mainly from the disintegration of the dark, basaltic lavas which cover a part of the plateau. The summer weather there is hot and has much sunshine interspersed with thundershowers of monsoonal origin. The rainy season is relatively short, but the regur soils have high water-holding capacity and retain enough moisture to mature the crops. In the Indus Valley cotton is grown under irrigation.

JUTE is another of the important fiber crops of India, but, unlike cotton, it is not grown on a large scale in any other part of the world. Jute fiber, from which jute bags and burlap are made to supply the whole world, comes almost exclusively from the Ganges delta. It is the inner bark of a woody plant grown as an annual crop on rich, moist alluvial soils and in hot, humid climate. It requires so much labor and grows in such unpleasant environment that there is no other region having the required physical conditions and the cheap and willing labor to compete with the Ganges delta.

FIG. 292.—India ranks second among the countries in the production of cotton. (*U.S. Department of Agriculture.*)

TEA is a plantation crop in India. Unlike the Chinese, the people of India never employed tea in their native agriculture, and its rise to an important crop awaited outside initiative, capital, and management. This has been supplied by the British, but the abundant cheap labor was recruited from the Indian rural population, and in some areas it was transported from densely settled areas and established in sparsely peopled districts that were suited to tea cultivation. In India proper there are two tea regions (Fig. 293). The more important lies in the far northeast on the valley bottoms and hill slopes of the Brahmaputra Valley in the province of Assam. The hill sites produce better tea but are difficult to maintain under the heavy rainfall, which causes severe soil erosion. The valley-bottom soils are less subject to erosion and yield more tea, but the tea is of lower quality and much expense is required to provide artificial drainage, since the plant requires well-drained soils. The tea leaves can be picked more times per year than in China, where the rainy season is shorter, and under plantation management the leaves can be uniformly treated and graded to produce standard qualities of tea. Practically all the Indian crop is made into black tea. A second, but less important, region is located

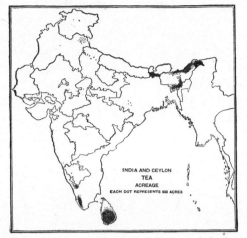

INDIA AND CEYLON
TEA
ACREAGE
EACH DOT REPRESENTS 500 ACRES

FIG. 293.—The principle tea-growing districts of India and Ceylon. (*U.S. Department of Agriculture.*)

in southern peninsular India. In the hills of Ceylon, however, is a region almost as productive of tea as is Assam. It also has extensive plantations under British management. This region has one advantage over that farther north. Because of rains from both the summer and the winter monsoons it has no pronounced dry seasons to retard the growth of the tea bushes; hence the leaves can be picked at frequent intervals throughout most of the year. India and Ceylon furnish a large part of the world's commercial tea supply (Fig. 294).

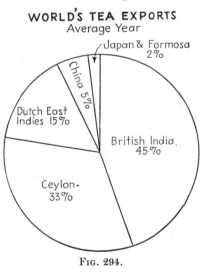

WORLD'S TEA EXPORTS
Average Year

Japan & Formosa 2%

China 5%

Dutch East Indies 15%

British India 45%

Ceylon 33%

FIG. 294.

LIVESTOCK IN INDIA. Unlike the densely peopled regions of China and Japan, India has great numbers of domestic animals, mainly cattle and goats. It has three times as many cattle as the United States or Russia and more than one-fourth of all in the world. Yet the Indian people make little use of their cattle for meat and only to a slight extent for milk, the milk of goats and water buffaloes being preferred. The principal Hindu religion opposes the killing of animals, and devout Hindus will starve rather than kill a cow for meat. About one-fifth of the Indian population adheres to the Mohammedan faith, in which there is no scruple against the use of beef or mutton, yet in India they also refrain from meat to avoid giving offense to the Hindus. Departure from this practice is not an infrequent cause of trouble or even of serious riots. The cattle of India are of the zebu type and, together with the buffaloes, are used almost entirely as work animals. However, a large number are aged or weak from undernourishment and are unable to work, and still others are tolerated in idleness through religious veneration. It is estimated that a third of the total number exist as best they can on badly overgrazed

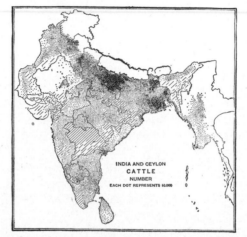

Fig. 295.—India has three times as many cattle as the United States on little more than half as much area. (*U.S. Department of Agriculture.*)

pastures and constitute a burden upon the resources of the land. Even the common work cattle are small and undernourished, yet they are necessary to the tillage of the soil, and the greatest numbers are found in the regions of most productive land (Fig. 295). After death the animals of all kinds are skinned; and cowhides, goatskins, and leather are among the important exports of India.

## MINERAL AND OTHER RESOURCES

ENERGY RESOURCES.   India has comparatively little coal or petroleum. There are several small deposits of coal in various parts of the Deccan highland. They are contained in pocketlike structures of coal-bearing rocks enfolded among the hard rocks of the plateau and thus protected from erosion. The total reserve is not great, and present production is less than that in Japan or Belgium. The most productive coal region is a district in the northeastern corner of the plateau, a belt of some 200 miles long, northwest of Calcutta (Fig. 281).

There is little petroleum in India proper, but an appreciable quantity is obtained from Burma. The total output of India and Burma is, however, only about one-half of 1 per cent of the world's total. There is, therefore, a relative scarcity of fuels in India, but at present the need is correspondingly small. Little fuel is required for household use in a tropical climate, and the industrial development of India has not progressed far enough to require fuel in great quantity.

The water-power resources of India are comparatively large but are as yet only slightly developed. Exceedingly heavy rainfalls on the mountain slopes of the Himalayas, Ghats, and other highlands give rise to potential powers estimated to be somewhat greater than those of the United States (Fig. 125). Of this resource less than 2 per cent is developed, as compared with more than 50 per cent in the United States. The developed water power of India is much greater than that of China but only one-eighth of that in use in Japan.

MINERAL RESOURCES. India was reputed in ancient times to be a land rich in gold and precious stones, but these substances are of small present importance. Several other types of minerals are produced, but only a few have large world significance, either actual or potential. Among these are ores of iron and manganese. Although the smelting of iron on a small scale is an exceedingly old industry in India, abundant iron ores are of relatively recent discovery there. The largest deposits lie about 250 miles west of Calcutta on the margin of the plateau and not far from the best coal. The ores are hematite of high grade. They are of great extent and are so near the surface that some, at least, are capable of being mined in open pits, as are the Mesabi ores in Minnesota. The quantity of Indian ore mined is small compared with that in the United States; but it is increasing, as the domestic smelting capacity increases. The ore is not exported. If this large reserve of ore could be used in conjunction with the large coal resource of China and the cheap labor available in both countries, it might be the basis of one of the greatest centers of heavy manufacture in the world. However, high mountain barriers, long sea routes, inadequate transportation, and political obstacles separate these basic resources, and the chance of their being brought together seems remote.

India is, next to Russia, the world's principal source of manganese ore. All the mines are located in the plateau region—some in the northeast, near the coal and iron, others in the central and southern parts of the Deccan. India produced in 1937 about one-sixth of the world's manganese supply. The larger part of it is exported, the largest markets being normally in Great Britain, the other iron-smelting centers of northwestern Europe, Japan, and the United States.

FOREST RESOURCES. Although India is densely peopled, nearly 10 per cent of its area still is forest covered. However, aside from supplies of firewood and timber for local uses the forest resource is not great. On the rainy slopes of the Western Ghats and in the eastern Himalayas and the borders of Burma are dense forests of the tropical rainforest type. They do not contain many trees usable for lumber manufacture. The forests of the drier monsoonal type and of the higher mountain slopes, above the frost line, are better. The latter include pine and cedar, and the former contain the highly valuable teakwood, which is the principal timber export of India. The teak forests are found principally in Burma and in the western and other moderately rainy portions of the Deccan Plateau.

## INDIAN MANUFACTURES

Handicrafts of remarkable skill have long existed in India. They produced textiles, pottery, and wares of intricate design in metal and wood. Some of these crafts still persist in various parts of the country, but they tend to die out under the competition of imported wares and the development of factory production at home.

TEXTILE MANUFACTURE. The most highly developed of the factory industries is in the making of textiles. There are more than 350 cotton-spinning and -weaving mills in the country, the greatest concentration of them being in or near Bombay, on the west coast, adjacent to the Deccan cotton-growing region. The mills produce mainly the cheaper grades of cloth from the short-staple Indian cotton, and they consume nearly one-half the cotton grown in the country. They do not entirely supply the home market, and there are large imports of cotton goods from Britain, Japan, and elsewhere. Yet there are also some exports of Indian cotton textiles.

The next most important textile industry is based upon the domestic production of jute fiber. The jute mills, of which there are about 100, are located mainly in the Calcutta region, near the jute-growing district. About two-thirds of the value of the jute exported from the country is in the form of burlap and jute bags.

The wool produced in India is, unlike jute, exported largely in unmanufactured form. The leading wool manufactures are located in the far northwest and tend to be of the type produced in the homes or small shops rather than in large mills. Rugs and carpets are the principal items exported.

IRON AND STEEL MANUFACTURE. Among the heavy industries of India, iron manufacture stands practically alone. Several blast furnaces and steel mills are located in the region of the iron and coal mines, west of Calcutta. These, because of low costs of labor and mining, are reputed to produce about the cheapest steel in the world. However, the $1\frac{1}{2}$ million tons of iron produced annually in recent years supplies only about 60 per cent of the domestic requirement, and the total output is marketed at home. The industry has shown a steady growth, even when foreign iron-manufacturing centers were adversely affected by economic depression.

## TRANSPORTATION AND COMMERCE

INLAND TRANSPORTATION in India is largely by railroad. Improved public roads are few, and during the rainy season most of the roads are difficult to traverse. There are neither many motor vehicles nor horses, and rural transport is accomplished mainly by bullock carts. The rivers are little used for navigation. With respect to railroads, however, the situation is different. Only two Asiatic countries are well equipped with railroads; they are Japan and India, and the latter owes its railroads to British initiative. Nearly half the mileage, mainly in branch lines and in hill regions, are of narrow gauge. But most of India is well served, since there is an average of 1 mile of railway for every 38 square miles of land in the country. The areas of greatest density of rail net are the Ganges Valley and the western portions of the Deccan. The rail lines focus principally upon the leading ports, Calcutta, Madras, Bombay, and Karachi.

FOREIGN COMMERCE. The total foreign trade of India is large—nearly 1½ billion dollars per year. Yet in consideration of the large population, it is a very small amount per capita. The Indian peasant and worker produces but a small surplus for sale, and he is unable to supply more than the most limited of needs by purchase from abroad. Five groups of products, all of them basically agricultural, make up the greater part of the exports—cotton and its manufactured products; jute and its products; tea; vegetable oilseeds; and hides, skins, and leather. About 75 per cent of the imports consist of manufactured goods, an evidence of the limited manufactural development of the country. The direction of the foreign trade reflects the colonial relation of India to Great Britain, since about one-third of Indian exports go to Britain and a similar proportion of the imports come from that source. The next most important, source of Indian imports and destination of exports includes all other British colonies, such as Australia or Canada. Formerly the British exports to India considerably exceeded India's exports to Britain, thus making India a most important market. In recent years, however, that situation has changed, owing in part to the rise of manufactures in India; and now India sells more to Britain than it purchases in return. The only important non-British trade of India is with Japan and the United States. The principal American imports from India are manganese ore and jute.

# Ceylon

The productive and populous island of Ceylon, at the southern tip of India, has nearly as many people as Australia. It is governed separately from India but is a British dependency. The southern part of the island is mountainous, but that is its most productive portion. On its marginal plains the flat lands are planted in rice, the principal food of the inhabitants. Associated with rice are coconut plantings, some that are the small groves of native growers and others that are commercial plantations. In the better drained foothills are large rubber plantations, and higher in the mountains are extensive plantations of tea (Fig. 293). Large areas in the mountains still are forested, and on the eastern and northern sides of the island are ill-drained districts with but small populations. The chief port, Colombo, is one of the important ports of call on the Suez route from Europe to the Far East. It has also a relatively large export trade in the produce of the island's plantations.

## Farther India and Malaysia

FARTHER INDIA. Set apart from India by mountainous barriers and by population differences is that broad peninsular extension sometimes called "Farther India." It is a region of broad, alluvial river basins separated from one another by mountain ridges. In climate the region is monsoonal, with abundant summer rainfall—heavy on the forested mountain slopes but less heavy in the sheltered valleys. Farther India is divided politically to include Burma, Thailand (Siam), and Indo-China. The whole region is much less densely populated than most of India or China (Fig. 5), and in the more remote forest regions are some tribes who have not advanced in agriculture beyond the primitive stage of shifting from one forest clearing to another. In the more accessible regions, however, agriculture is relatively intensive, but mainly it is of the self-sufficient type in which there is little commercial surplus and little requirement for imported goods. On the alluvial lowlands, such as the deltas of the Irrawaddy in Burma (Fig. 288), the Menam in Thailand, and the Mekong in Indo-China, rice is everywhere the dominant crop. Because these regions are accessible and less densely peopled than most rice-growing regions, they usually have a surplus of rice for export. Rice is, in fact, much the most important export of each of these three countries. Other than rice the leading exports are the products of mines, forests, and plantations, mostly developed by outside capital and initiative. The minerals include petroleum and lead ores from Burma and tin and tungsten ores from Thailand and Indo-China. In northeastern Indo-China there is also a deposit of coal, a significant resource of considerable use for steamship fuel in a region that generally is lacking in coal. The forest and plantation products include teakwood and rubber. The leading imports of all three countries are the same—textiles and metal manufactures, including machinery.

## Malaysia

REGIONAL CONTRASTS. The insular and peninsular region that lies southeast of Asia has, like the West Indies, certain broad similarities among all its parts but also some striking contrasts. The entire insular region is one of mountainous or hilly interiors with bordering lowlands and alluvial valleys. It is, as a whole, included in the East Indian region of tropical rainforest climate. However, not all its parts have equally heavy rainfall; and some districts, such as the lowland of northeastern Java, for example, have a pronounced dry season. Cultural contrasts are indicated by differences in density of population, intensity of land utilization, and degree of commercial development. In many of the hill districts isolated tribes still live in their wild state, by shifting tillage in forest clearings. Some whole islands are but little developed, and it may be that some of them have poorer soils or smaller resources and are not so capable of development as others. The large island of New Guinea, for example, has an average population of only 5 per square mile. Java and Madoera, in contrast, are highly developed, and their density of population exceeds 800 per square mile. In some of the rice-producing districts of the lowlands of Java the population exceeds 1,200 per square mile. Most of the larger islands are heavily forested, with the exception of Java, which has less than 25 per cent of its original woodlands remaining. Even the widespread plantation agriculture of some of the districts has not greatly modified the forested appearance of the land, since it has only substituted cultivated trees for wild ones in limited areas that are flanked by the original forests. Some of the forested mountain valleys are so isolated that they are as yet unexplored by Europeans, whereas other localities in this island realm not only are accessible but are like Singapore, which lies at a busy crossroads in the highway of world commerce.

The whole Malayan-East Indian region is one of actual or potential richness. Its resources have thus far been developed under the supervision of Dutch and British colonial authorities with the aid of native, Indian, and Chinese labor. But other nations, especially the Japanese, look with favor upon the unoccupied lands, the raw materials, and the potential markets of these insular empires. It is not improbable that great changes are about to occur in the political adherence and commercial relations of this region.

AGRICULTURE IS DOMINANT. Most of the people in Malaya and the East Indies depend upon agriculture for a living. It has been indicated already that, in some districts, the farming is of an exceedingly primitive type. The native agriculture is everywhere dependent on rice, corn, bananas, coconuts, and vegetables. Native agriculture of a more intensive subsistence type includes the tillage of rice on terraced floodplains and foothills, where it is irrigated either by the copious rainfall or with the help of supplementary irrigation works of native design. In Java and Madoera, the most highly developed of all the islands, 60 per cent of the entire area is occupied by native farmers, 23 per cent by government forests, and only 8 per cent by large plantations. More than 40 per cent of the land tilled by native farmers is irrigated, most of that part being rice fields. Altogether more than one-fourth of the entire area of these two islands is irrigated. In the more accessible localities the native farmers produce a surplus of certain crops, especially coconuts, the meats of which they dry into copra by primitive means and sell on the commercial market. They are therefore commercial farmers, at least in a small way.

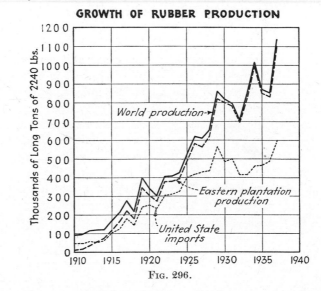

FIG. 296.

Large-scale commercial agriculture is, however, conducted mainly upon a plantation basis. The plantation crops for which this region has become famous are rubber, sugar, coconuts and other oilseeds, tea, coffee, tobacco, and spices.

RUBBER PLANTATIONS. Since 1914, when the supply of cultivated rubber first exceeded that of wild rubber on the world's markets, a revolution has taken place in the rubber industry. What was formerly a forest industry in Brazil has become an agricultural industry in Malaya and the East Indies, which now supply more than 95 per cent of the world's requirements (Fig. 296). In large part it is a plantation industry, but to some degree, also, rubber trees have been set out by natives in their abandoned forest clearings. The advantages of this part of the world for rubber growing include (1) rainforest climate, similar to that to which the Brazilian rubber tree is native; (2) European capital and

management; (3) abundant, cheap, and dependable labor; (4) a high
degree of accessibility, since few plantations in this insular area need be
more than a few miles from the coast or a port. The regions of principal
rubber planting are shown in Fig. 297. A belt of well-drained soils back
from the coastal swamps of western Malaya produces about half the
world's total rubber crop, and it could produce much more if it were not
for an interregional agreement to restrict production. Other East Indian
rubber-producing districts include a central belt in Sumatra, parts of
western and southern Java, and northern Borneo. Considerable plantation rubber is grown also in Ceylon, southern India, Burma, and Thailand.

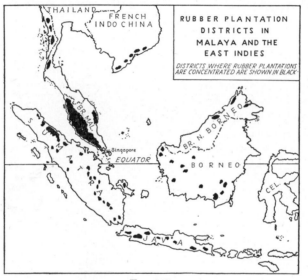

FIG. 297.

After clearing the forest and preparing the land, small rubber trees
are planted from 12 to 20 feet apart in rows—100 or more trees to the
acre. Within about 6 years the tree grows to a diameter of 6 inches and
is ready for tapping. This consists in cutting through the outer bark,
whence a milky fluid (latex) flows slowly for several hours and is caught
in little cups attached to the tree. A new cut is made, and latex gathered
each day—about three-fourths of a teacupful from an average tree. About
35 per cent of the latex is rubber, and the balance is water. These small
collections are assembled in large cans and transported to the central
factory of the plantation, where the rubber is coagulated by a process
much like churning butter and is washed, dried, and prepared for market.
About half the world's rubber is consumed in the United States, and the
fact that so large a part of the supply is produced in Malaysia is cause
for some concern in America over the political destiny of that part of Asia.

SUGAR.   Java ranks next after Cuba among the commercial producers
of cane sugar (Fig. 186). The crop is much more intensively cultivated
than in Cuba because of the abundance of labor and the pressure of
population upon the land supply. It is grown in sheltered upland basins
and on the northern plain, where a dry season promotes the maturing,
harvesting, and milling of the cane. So much land is required to produce
food for a total population of about 42 millions in an island not quite so
large as the state of Pennsylvania that sugar is not grown in large blocks
of land and ratooned year after year as it is in Cuba. Instead, it is grown
in fields of small size associated with others that produce rice, cassava,
sweet potatoes, and the many other food staples, and it generally is
replanted each year, since larger yields are obtained in that way. Numerous sugar mills are distributed within the areas of sugar planting, and
their managers supervise the cultivation and harvesting of the crop, which
largely is grown on land leased to small farmers. Plantations in the other
islands average larger than those in Java because of their smaller populations and less intensive culture.

OILSEEDS.   Coconuts are widely grown in Malaysia, especially in the
coastal districts, and the Dutch East Indies rank with the Philippine
Islands among the largest producers of copra and coconut oil. Other
important vegetable oilseeds grown are peanuts, soybeans, and the oil
palm. The latter is especially significant because it is a relatively new
industry which has been established here on a plantation basis and is
increasing rapidly. The oil palm is native to West Africa, which is still
the largest source of supply. However, the same advantages that have
enabled Malaysia to take the rubber industry away from Brazil seem
likely to promote the extension of oil-palm culture there; and Malaysia
may, in the near future, dominate in its production also. In the 10 years
between 1929 and 1939 the area planted to the oil palm in the Netherlands
Indies increased threefold, and the exports of its products rose from 5 per
cent of the world's total to 25 per cent.

THE BEVERAGE CROPS.   Tea planting in the highland of western
Java has the same advantages of climate enjoyed by the industry in
Ceylon. Tea has become an important export. Coffee was in former times
a large crop also, but for many years the industry was practically ruined
by diseases that destroyed the trees. It is being reconstituted in southeastern Java by the use of varieties of coffee that are native to the hot
and humid regions of western Africa rather than the original Arabian
type grown in Latin America (Fig. 210). Cacao is grown only to a small
extent, although climatic and labor conditions would seem to favor the
crop. Its failure is also attributed to diseases that affect the tree in
Malaysia.

OTHER PLANTATION CROPS that have been successfully established in
the East Indian region include tobacco, cinchona, spices, and pineapples.
Tobacco is grown in Sumatra and Java, and the former is noted for its
production of high-quality leaf used as cigar wrappers. Cinchona is the
bark of a small tree native to Peru. It is the source of quinine, the medicine
used in relief of tropical fevers. It is cultivated in the tea region of western
Java and is important because that is now practically the world's only
source of supply.

Spices, especially black pepper, cinnamon, and nutmegs, were among
the crops that attracted the early European traders to the East Indian
region, and these areas still supply
most of the world's markets. Their
actual production is on a larger scale
than in the period of their greatest
fame, because world consumption is
larger, but their relative importance
has been dwarfed by the new and
larger industries established there.

### MINERAL RESOURCES

PETROLEUM. The Malaysian region produces several minerals, but
only two of world importance—petroleum and tin. The oil fields of this
region, together with those of less importance in Burma, are the only
sources of petroleum in eastern Asia
and have on that account great strategic value. The productive districts

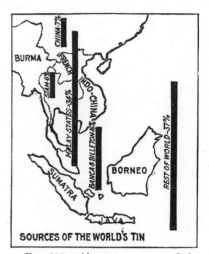

SOURCES OF THE WORLD'S TIN

FIG. 298.—About 65 per cent of the
world's tin comes from southeastern
Asia and near-by islands.

are located at several points on the coast of Borneo, the most productive
of the islands, and also in Java and Sumatra. The total average yield of
the Malaysian region is only about 3 per cent of the world's oil supply
(Fig. 118), but it is more than half that of the Mesopotamian region and
a quarter that of Russia. It is one of the regional features most attractive
to Japan.

TIN is one of the metals not widely distributed in the rocks of the
earth—one of those of which the United States has no domestic supply.
The largest known deposits of tin ore lie in an extensive geological formation that begins in southwestern China and extends southward through
the northwestern edge of Indo-China and eastern Burma into Thailand,
the Malay Peninsula, and especially the three small East Indian islands
of Banka, Billiton, and Singkep, east of Sumatra. These deposits are

mainly near the surface and are mined by placer methods. The entire Asiatic region, including China, produces about 65 per cent of the tin mined in the world, but about two-thirds of it is obtained near the southern end of the belt, in the Malay Peninsula, and the small islands mentioned above (Fig. 298). The political control of this resource also is of vital concern to the United States which is a large user of tin.

CITIES AND COMMERCE.  The peoples of Malaysia are dominantly agricultural, and the manufacturing industries are of the simplest type, being mainly those required to process the native products for use or for

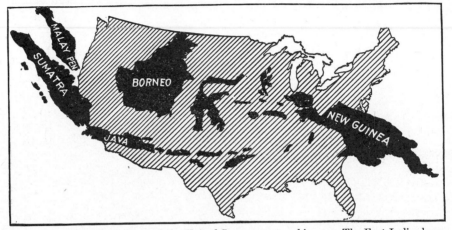

FIG. 299.—The East Indies and the United States compared in area. The East Indies have an east-west extent of between 4,000 and 5,000 miles.

export. These include rubber and tea factories, sugar and rice mills, and the like. They are located in the rural districts, and the region has no great industrial cities. A few cotton mills and some other local manufactures are seen in the larger towns; but in the main, these towns are commercial, their port functions being more important than manufacture. There are many towns that are ports of call on the very long coast lines of this insular region (Fig. 299). They are connected by rivers, roads, or short rail lines with interior producing regions. Only a few of them are large cities. Such, however, are Soerabaja and Batavia on the north coast of Java, and particularly Singapore at the tip of Malaya. Singapore is, in fact, the focus and strategic center of the whole region and of southeastern Asia. It is a fortified naval base and commands the flow of traffic between the Orient, India, and the Suez Canal. The control of Singapore is necessary to the control of eastern Asia.

SELECTED REFERENCES

ANSTEY, V. "The Trade of the Indian Ocean," London, 1929.
BERGSMARK, D. R. "Economic Geography of Asia," New York, 1935.

"Blue Book for the Straits Settlements," Singapore (annual).

BROEK, J. O. M. The Economic Development of the Outer Provinces of the Netherlands Indies, *Geog. Rev.*, Vol. 30 (1940), pp. 187–200.

BOESCH, HANS H. El'-Iraq, *Econ. Geog.*, Vol. 15 (1939), pp. 325–361.

CASTRO, E. RAY. Economic Geography of Palestine, *Econ. Geog.*, Vol. 13 (1937), pp. 235–259.

COLTON, C. W. E. "Handbook of Commercial Information for India," Calcutta (annual).

MATHESON, M. C. "Indian Industry," London, 1930.

MUKERJEE, R. "The Rural Economy of India," London, 1926.

MURPHY, MARIAN. Geography of Burma, *Jour. Geog.*, Vol. 30 (1931), pp. 17–33.

PEARSE, A. S. "The Cotton Industry of India," Manchester, 1930.

PUGH, M. A. Economic Development of Siam, *U.S. Dept. Commerce, Trade Information Bull.* 606, 1929.

REDECKER, S. B. Sumatra: Economic and Commercial Survey, *Trade Information Bull.* 452, Washington, 1927.

SIMKINS, E. The Coastal Plains of South India, *Econ. Geog.*, Vol. 9 (1933), pp. 19–50, 136–159.

STAATS, J. R. India East Coast, *Jour. Geog.*, Vol. 31 (1932), pp. 93–111.

STAMP, L. D. "Asia: A Regional and Economic Geography," London, 1935.

"Statistical Abstract for British India," London (annual).

STRAIN, W. The West Coast of India, *Jour. Geog.*, Vol. 31 (1932), pp. 1–20.

SVEC, MELVINA. The Dry Lands of Sind and Western Rajputana in Northwestern India, *Jour. Geog.*, Vol. 34 (1935), pp. 45–60.

TREWARTHA, G. T. The Tea Crop, *Jour. Geog.*, Vol. 28 (1929), pp. 1–25.

VAN VALKENBURG, SAMUEL. Agricultural Regions of Asia, *Econ. Geog.*, Vol. 9 (1933), pp. 1–18, 109–135; Vol. 10 (1934), pp. 14–34; Vol. 11 (1935), pp. 325–337; Vol. 12 (1936), pp. 27–44.

———. Java, The Economic Geography of a Tropical Island, *Geog. Review*, Vol. 15 (1925), pp. 563–583.

# Chapter XXXII. Africa

A CONTINENT OF COLONIAL EMPIRES. In spite of the fact that northern Africa was the seat of a very early civilization, the continent was latest to be explored, has remained to be developed under the colonial dominion of European governments, and is without any strong independent states of its own. Several conditions inherent in the land of Africa help to explain this condition. (1) The unhealthfulness of long stretches of the African coast and of large parts of its equatorial interior have deterred Europeans from settling there in large numbers. (2) The coastline of Africa is exceptionally regular, and the deep, protected indentations and the many peninsulas and islands that have done so much for the commercial progress of Europe are lacking on the African coast. (3) The continent is, in the main, a plateau, and the rivers, flowing over the edge of the plateau to the sea, nearly all have rapids and falls in their lower reaches, rendering them unnavigable from the seaward side. This retarded exploration and commercial penetration. (4) Nearly half the continent is in the trade-wind desert belts. (5) Unlike South America, the continent of Africa was already inhabited by a fairly dense population of negro tribes, a part of whom were settled agricultural peoples or pastoralists. They could not readily be, and have not been, dislodged and replaced by Europeans in large numbers.

POLITICAL CONTROL IN AFRICA. Several European powers have exercised colonial control over parts of Africa (Fig. 300). As a result of the World War of 1914–1918 there were territorial revisions which extended the British and French possessions at the expense of the German holdings. Britain, France, Portugal, and Belgium have dominated the continent in recent years, with Italy and Spain occupying minor positions. Now again war in Eruope brings to colonial possessions in Africa, as elsewhere, an uncertainty regarding their future status that only the events of the war and the terms of its settlement can end.

MAJOR REGIONS OF AFRICA. South of the Mediterranean fringe of northern Africa, which has been touched upon already (Chap. XXVII), are many geographical subdivisions of the continent. These may be grouped for brief description upon a basis that is in large part climatic

(Fig. 301). The great majority of the people of Africa, both black and white, live by agriculture or pastoralism, and their occupations are im-

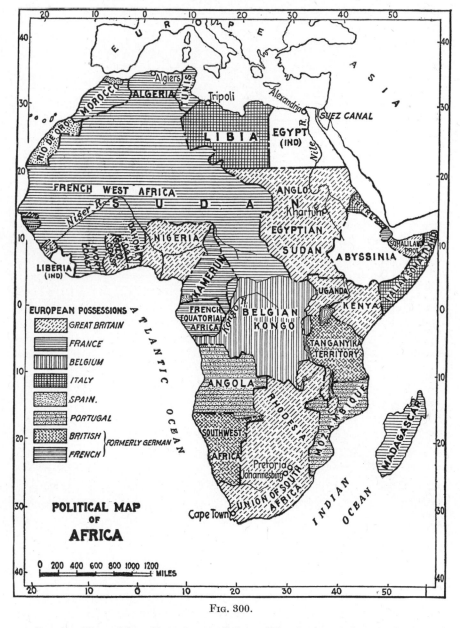

FIG. 300.

mediately affected by climatic conditions. The major regions to be noted are (1) Egypt and the Sahara, (2) the native farm and grasslands of the

Sudan, (3) the forest lands of the Guinea Coast and the Congo Basin, (4) South Central and East African native farmlands and pioneer white plantations, and (5) the subtropical farm and grazing lands of South Africa.

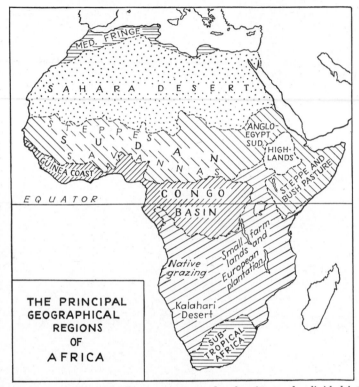

Fig. 301.—Africa is vast and its features are complex, but it may be divided into a few regions with some degree of internal unity.

## Egypt and the Sahara

EGYPT AND THE NILE. Egypt, one of the two nominally independent states of Africa, is practically coincident with the floodplains and delta of the Nile River. Were it not for the Nile, its floods, and the irrigation water that it supplies, Egypt would not differ from the rest of the Sahara. It is in fact a giant oasis. Of the large area within the political boundaries, only 3½ per cent is irrigated and cultivated, yet on this small irrigated area (13,600 square miles) about 15 million people live, the greater part of them by agriculture. The density of population on the delta exceeds 1,500 per square mile of crop land, probably the most dense agricultural population in the world.

The Nile floods are due mainly to the periodic rise of two large tributaries which enter the Nile from Ethiopia, where heavy downpours of tropical summer rain greatly increase the volume of the rivers. The Nile Valley is a narrow cleft in the rocky plateau. Only a part of the valley width is capable of irrigation, and the cultivated part is a narrow ribbon of green 1 to 9 miles wide, dotted with agricultural villages (Fig. 302).

IRRIGATION. Formerly the river was uncontrolled, and irrigation was accomplished naturally by the summer flooding of the river, which brought

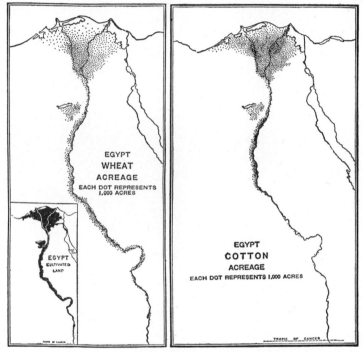

FIG. 302.—Crops, in Egypt, can be grown only on the irrigated lands of the delta and floodplain of the Nile. (*U.S. Department of Agriculture.*)

great quantities of enriching silt and saturated the ground so that crops could be grown during the autumn. Now the river is controlled, and water is stored for continuous irrigation by a series of great dams, but the settlement of mud behind these dams removes from the land much of its former source of renewed fertility. By means of gates the stored waters and part of the rich silt that they carry are released, and by means of canals they are led upon the fields as needed. This practice permits the growth of two and even three crops per year and enables the crops to utilize the growing weather of the hot summer.

THE CROPS OF EGYPT. Warm climate, rich soil, and intensive tillage make the irrigated lands of Egypt highly productive. Cotton is the leading commercial crop. Most of it is of special long-staple varieties developed in Egypt. These bring a high price and are used in all the important cotton-spinning regions of the world. The other important crops are raised mainly for food, and they include wheat, corn and other grains, beans, and vegetables. Dates are grown in large quantities; but the home requirement is great, and few are exported. Much land is devoted also to a kind of clover used as forage for work animals and sheep. The farms are very small, more than two-thirds of them being less than 1 acre in size. Cotton, which makes up two-thirds of all Egyptian exports, moves downriver through the largest city, Cairo, at the head of the delta and is loaded at Alexandria, the principal port.

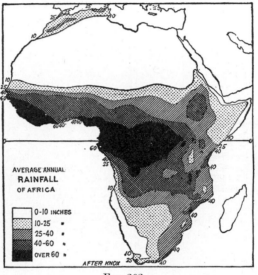

AVERAGE ANNUAL
**RAINFALL**
OF AFRICA

- 0-10 INCHES
- 10-25 "
- 25-40 "
- 40-60 "
- OVER 60 "

AFTER KNOX

FIG. 303.

THE SUEZ CANAL, completed in 1869, is a sea-level canal connecting the Mediterranean and the Red Sea and greatly shortening the route from Europe to the Orient. Its control has been in the hands of a company owned by British and French interests. Its vital importance to Italy has made it a point of particular strategy in the Mediterranean campaign of Italy against British forces, and its future status remains to be determined.

THE SAHARA. West of the Nile lies the larger part of Sahara, the largest of the tropical deserts of the world (Fig. 303). Most of it consists of broad uplands having a sparse vegetation of shrubs and grasses suited only to the use of wandering herds of camels, sheep, and goats. Locally there are expanses of rocky plain, or "hammada," having little if any plant life. There are also areas of drifting sands, called "ergs," of almost equally low productivity. Yet only about one-eighth of the desert is covered with sand. Oases of various types, where underground water comes to the surface as springs or filters through the alluvial soils of dry stream beds, are fairly numerous, and some of them are large, affording room for many villages. These are occupied by dense populations (Fig. 267). Grains, vegetables, and fruits are grown in the oases, and especially date palms, of which there are several varieties. Formerly there were many caravan routes across the Sahara, reaching from oasis to oasis, and goods of large value were carried by caravans that numbered thousands of camels. However, the commercial penetration of the Sahara by motor transport and by railroads from both north and south has reduced the caravan trade to a small fraction of its former value. The greater part of the Sahara has long been under French and Italian dominion, and the wild desert tribes have largely been brought under control.

## The Sudan

NATURE AND EXTENT. Extending across Africa from the Atlantic to the Indian Ocean, south of the Sahara, is a belt of steppe and savanna lands called "the Sudan." It lies between the aridity of the desert and the equatorial rainforest. Its tropical climate alternates between a rainy summer and a dry winter, as the belt of equatorial rains moves north and south. It includes a northern belt of subhumid steppe where the summer rains are of short duration. This is bordered on the south by savanna grasslands, and that, in turn, has a southern margin of bush and open forest where the rainy season is long. Its people are a medley of races with negroes in the majority but including also Arabs, Berbers, Ethiopians, and others. Much of the Sudan is remote from the sea, and the inhabitants of the interior regions have little outside contact. The commercial produce of the Sudan reaches the markets of the world largely through the Niger and Nile valleys, both of them having been penetrated by railroads which have greatly stimulated agricultural productivity.

CLIMATE AND AGRICULTURE. The natives of the Sudan are for the most part primitive farmers and herdsmen, and only in a few localities is there permanent and settled agriculture of importance. The herdsmen are more numerous on the dry northern margin of the Sudan belt and in those areas least touched by modern transportation. Over most of the area a shifting cultivation is practiced which provides sorghum or millet for local food and some cotton and other minor crops.

It is in the districts where European influence, coupled with means of transportation, has become most effective that commercial agriculture is important. There are several of these areas. In the west, the natives of Gambia, Senegal, and the French Sudan have been induced to take up the culture of peanuts for export. In the same region also, but more especially in northern Nigeria, cotton culture has been promoted. However, this industry has not expanded so greatly as was once hoped it would expand. One of the reasons for this is the climatic instability that afflicts this and most other regions of marginal rainfall. Years or cycles of ample rainfall alternating with periods of severe drought discourage the cultivation of commercial crops upon which the farmer comes to depend for a cash income.

The region immediately east of Lake Chad is perhaps the least touched by the elements of modern commerce, and it has little progressive agriculture. Still farther east, however, is the Anglo-Egyptian Sudan, which has an outlet northward by rail and boat down the Nile and by rail eastward to the Red Sea. This also is a region where the British colonial authorities have promoted cotton culture, and with some success.

Ethiopia lies in the general belt of the desert-forest borderland, but it is a mountainous region with a highland climate and greater rainfall than the Sudan. Its population is more dense, and there is a higher proportion of tilled land, in spite of its rough surface. There is also a greater diversity of crops, and much livestock is grazed on the mountain pastures. One of its provinces, Khaffa, is reputedly the native habitat of the Arabian type of coffee, which still grows there wild.

SETTLEMENTS. In a region characterized by primitive agriculture and seminomadic pastoralism it is not to be expected that there will be many large towns. Some of those in the Sudan, such as Timbuktu at the great bend of the Niger, derive their importance from the time when they were the terminals of caravan routes across the Sahara. Others have grown in more recent years as market towns at the ends of the short railroads reaching in from the coast. Examples of the latter type are Bamako in the French Sudan, Kano in Nigeria, and Khartoum in the Anglo-Egyptian Sudan.

## The Equatorial Rainforest Region

LAND AND RESOURCES. The rainforest region of Africa includes the Guinea Coast and the Congo River Basin, a region of heavy rainfall which merges by slow transition into the open savanna forests on all sides (Figs. 301, 303). The Congo Basin is included in the broad plateau of central Africa and rises from an elevation of about 1,000 feet near the coast to about 3,000 feet in the interior. Most of it is heavily forested, as is also the Guinea Coast region.

The principal natural resources of the region are those of the forests and the mines and water powers. The forests yield mahogany and other tropical woods, together with other products collected by its primitive inhabitants. Most of the region has a geological foundation of sedimentary rocks which do not yield important mineral resources. But there are some notable exceptions. In the southeastern part of the Belgian Congo and extending across into Rhodesia is a copper-bearing formation of remarkable richness and extent. After only a comparatively few years of development this Katanga region produces nearly half as much copper as all the mines of the United States, or about 15 per cent of the copper mined in the world. Diamond production in the Belgian Congo and in the Guinea Coast region each now exceeds that of South Africa, making this section of Africa the largest diamond-mining region in the world. More than half the total output now comes from the Belgian Congo alone.

The greatest of the natural resources of equatorial Africa probably is its water power (Fig. 125). However, this is very little used as yet. It is estimated to be the greatest potential resource of water power possessed by any region in the world. Its concentration here may be attributed to (1) the great volume of water carried by the Congo and by other streams that flow through or head in the equatorial region, (2) the regulation of their flow by uniformly distributed precipitation, and (3) the fact that these great streams must leave the plateau over falls and rapids where the powers may one day be economically developed.

AGRICULTURE AND SETTLEMENT. The inhabitants of the African rainforest region are most numerous on the accessible Guinea Coast but are very unevenly distributed over the Belgian Congo (Fig. 5). As a whole the region is sparsely peopled, having an average density varying from 2 to 10 persons per square mile. The proportion of negro to white population is very high, ranging from as low as 100 negroes to 1 white person in some districts to as high as 3,000 negroes to 1 white in others.[1] The negroes belong to many tribes, but all are forest dwellers, and all make the principal part of their living by a shifting forest agriculture, by collecting forest products, or by hunting.

The forest products and those of primitive cultivation in the forest clearings include both food crops and some of commercial value. Among the former are manioc, corn, bananas, beans, yams, and a little rice. The latter include cacao, palm nuts, and a little rubber.

Cacao planting reaches its highest development in the Guinea Coast region, and there the native cacao producers have in some districts approached the status of settled farmers. Because cacao raising is itself a semiforest industry, requiring no high skills or great persistence at labor, it is well adapted to the requirements of these people. It has increased in recent decades until the West African region as a whole takes first rank among the cacao-producing areas of the world. However, African cacao is generally rated as being somewhat inferior to that of South America in quality. The African oil palm is native to this region,

[1] SHANTZ, H. L. Agricultural regions of Africa, *Econ. Geog.* Vol. 16 (1940), pp. 1–47, 122–161.

where its fruits are gathered from wild trees and from those which have been planted in old forest clearings. Although it still furnishes the major part of the world's supply of this product, West Africa is in danger of losing its position to the plantations of the East Indies, as has been previously noted. With the exception of American plantations in Liberia, comparatively little cultivated rubber is grown in equatorial Africa. A small amount of wild rubber is collected.

The natives of the forest region live in primitive villages, some of fairly large size. But they are not very permanent centers of population. One of the reasons for their impermanence is disease. Sleeping sickness, a disease carried and spread by the tsetse fly, sometimes becomes epidemic and practically depopulates villages and even whole districts. The survivors then abandon their settlements in favor of others less afflicted. This disease is believed to be one of the reasons for the very uneven distribution of people over the region generally. It may also be one of the reasons for the backwardness of agriculture and commerce. The same disease afflicts cattle and horses, which might otherwise have been of greater aid in agriculture and transportation.

COMMUNICATIONS IN CENTRAL AFRICA. It has been noted already that railroads have been built from the coast to various productive districts in the hinterland. Most of those form the west coast are relatively short lines, but the eastern Belgian Congo is reached also by the main line from the south, a part of the "Cape to Cairo" route.

The Congo River and its tributaries form important transportation routes in central Africa also, but the Congo is far from a satisfactory river for navigation. This is due not only to the falls near the river's mouth but to other rapids in its middle course, to its curved and indirect route to the sea, and to its great seasonal changes in depth. If, for example, copper from the Katanga region were to seek an outlet to the sea by way of the Congo, it would have to be loaded on cars and steamers eight times and unloaded eight times before it reached the ocean. However, a railway has been completed from the copper-mining regions to the west coast of Africa through Angola.

## South-central and East Africa

LAND AND CLIMATE. From the Portuguese colony of Angola, in western Africa, a broad plateau stretches eastward. It reaches through the Rhodesian provinces northeastward into the lake region of equatorial Africa. Little of this vast upland lies at an elevation less than 3,000 feet above sea level. Much of it, especially in the east, exceeds 4,500 feet; and above its higher portions rise great mountain masses topped by the snow-capped peaks of ancient volcanoes. Within its eastern portion also lie broad basins and deep trenches, produced by the fracturing of the earth's crust. Within these depressions lie the great lakes such as Nyasa, Tanganyika, and Victoria.

Although the climate of this whole region is tropical, its temperatures are considerably modified by altitude and are made more endurable for white residents. Over a large part of the area the climatic conditions are those of tropical savannas, with hot weather and abundant rainfall from October to April, whereas drier weather and more variable temperatures prevail during the balance of the year. However, the great differences in surface relief induce great local variations in climate. In large sections of the plateau frosts are experienced during some nights of the dry season, and there are also local differences in the quantity and seasonal distribution of rain, some districts being very rainy and others semiarid.

AGRICULTURE AND SETTLEMENT. The highlands of this great region are occupied by moderate populations of negro tribes who are primitive farmers and by a small number of white planters or estate owners. So far as white settlement is concerned, this part of Africa still is in the pioneer stage. The density of the total population averages generally between 5 and 15 per square mile, and only in a few districts does it exceed 30 to 50 per square mile. In most of the region the ratio of negro to white inhabitants exceeds 50 to 1, and in the northeastern portion it exceeds 100 to 1. The population is, however, very unevenly distributed, the greatest density being in certain sections of the eastern highlands and lake region.

The native agriculture is largely of the shifting type, designed to produce food for local consumption. The crops most raised include millet, sorghum, corn, beans, sweet potatoes, and peanuts. Livestock are raised also, especially in the higher regions which are more free from disease. In some of the provinces large areas have been set aside as native reserves which are not open to white settlement, but in no part is native agriculture restricted to these reservations. The native farmers are widely scattered, and not a few of them find employment as laborers on the estates of the white planters. Most of them live in villages consisting of simple dwellings of thatch, and some find employment in other than agricultural labor, particularly in mines.

White settlement in the highland is most advanced in Rhodesia and the highlands of Kenya, but it is not uniformly distributed. It has advanced particularly along railway lines, from which it has spread into adjacent districts that are particularly suited to plantation agriculture by reason of climate, soil, or markets in mining centers. Farming by white settlers is mainly on a scale requiring considerable capital, and there are few small farms of the poorer type. Plantations of commercial crops and livestock ranches both are found, the outstanding crops varying with the characteristics of environment and market outlets. The leading crop in the region of Lake Victoria is cotton, particularly in Uganda; but coffee in the highlands of Kenya, sisal in the drier areas, and several other crops are grown also. In Southern Rhodesia ranching is more common, with cattle and corn as principal sources of income.

MINERAL RESOURCES of various types are found in the highland region, more in the central and southern provinces than in the eastern. The great Katanga copper region, previously mentioned, extends into Northern Rhodesia. Small deposits of gold are numerous, and there are resources of zinc, coal, and other valuable earth materials. None of these is of great world importance except the copper, but they have had a significant affect on settlement in that the mining centers have required supplies and thus have provided markets for the farmers of their respective localities. In many places the development of mining and farming has progressed together.

TRANSPORTATION in the highlands of central and eastern Africa is served largely by a few important railroads. The main line of the Cape to Cairo route crosses the Rhodesian provinces, and the eastern highland is served by two railroads that reach ports on the Indian Ocean. Branch lines are few, however, and large districts are lacking in modern transport facilities. The great lakes, nearly as large as the American Great Lakes, are navigated by steamships that make connection with rail lines both east and west. Yet these lines of communication, valuable as they are, form a very meager system for so vast a country. There are rural highways, but only a few are sufficiently improved to permit heavy all-season motor traffic.

## Subtropical South Africa

LAND AND CLIMATE. The Union of South Africa, including the four major provinces of the Cape of Good Hope, Natal, the Orange Free State, and the Transvaal, has conditions more suited to European occupance than any other section of the continent (Fig. 301). Like most of Africa, it is not densely peopled, having an average density of only about 20 persons per square mile. However, the proportion of people of European descent to those of native, mixed, and Asiatic origin is higher than in any other part, being about one white to three or four of all others.

The surface features of South Africa include (1) the southern end of the great interior plateau of the continent and (2) the slopes that descend from the plateau margin to the sea. The plateau is high and increases in altitude southward toward its bounding rim. The rim is dissected into several ranges of mountains, of which the Drakensberg, in the southeast, are highest. In the north, on the borders of Rhodesia, the plateau appears as a broad plain with a general elevation of 3,000 to 4,000 feet above sea level. Southward and southeastward it rises to 6,000 feet as the mountainous rim is approached. This broad upland is not abundantly supplied with moisture. Its eastern portion, in the Transvaal, is most humid, having in excess of 30 inches of average annual rainfall in the highlands. But the quantity decreases westward, with decreasing elevation, to about 15 inches in the central portion and to 5 on the western plateau margin (Fig. 303). The latter region lies within the realm of the Kalahari Desert. Over most of the plateau the season of maximum rainfall is the summer, and the winters are dry and cool. Frosts are of frequent occurrence in the higher parts of the upland in the Transvaal and the Orange Free State. The higher, cooler, and more humid part of the plateau is a temperate grassland, known as the "High Veld." This grades off northward and westward into mixed shrub vegetations, called "Bushveld," on the dry-land margins.

The slopes leading from the plateau rim to the sea are of two types as to both surface features and climate. The whole coastal strip may therefore be divided for consideration into a southeastern and a southwestern section. On the southeast, especially in Natal province, a narrow coastal plain is flanked in the rear by a foothill belt, and that in turn rises rapidly toward the crest of the Drakensberg Range. Facing the southeasterly trade winds thus, the whole area, both slope and plain, receives abundant rainfall with a summer maximum. This is a humid subtropical type of climate, comparable with that of Florida or southern Brazil. In the southern and southwestern coastal region, the ascent from the sea to the veld is not so regular as in the southeast. The rise is rather by a series of steps, of which there are three: the coastal belt, the Little Karroo, and the Great Karroo. Each step has at its back a range of hills, and there are also several included ranges and valleys. North of Capetown the several steps are less apparent, and the rise from the coast to the plateau is abrupt. The climatic conditions of the coastal portion of southwestern Africa are subtropical. They are, however, of the dry subtropical, or Mediterranean, type, the season of maximum rainfall being the winter. The climatic contrast between Capetown and Durban is therefore comparable with that between Los Angeles and Jacksonville, Fla. Northward from Capetown the aridity of the coastal district becomes severe, and the desert descends to the sea (Fig. 303).

AGRICULTURE AND SETTLEMENT. Agriculture in the Union of South Africa is carried on largely by white farmers, the colored races being employed mainly as wage earners except in certain large districts or reservations set apart for them. Three regions of somewhat different types of agriculture may be noted. These are related to regional characteristics of surface and climate. They are (1) the livestock-ranching and the corn- and livestock-farming region of the veld; (2) the sugar-planting and live-stock-farming region of the southeast; and (3) the Mediterranean fruit, wheat, and livestock region of the southwest.

*Agriculture on the veld* varies in intensity with the rainfall. On the western desert margin a sparse population of ranchmen graze sheep and cattle, but the productive capacity of the range is low, and the number of animals and of people per square mile is small. East of the 15-inch rainfall line, in the Transvaal and the Orange Free State, the forage is better, and the density of livestock population greater. In this region, also, the ranch type of livestock raising is replaced by a more intensive use of land involving the dairy industry and the production of crops. Most important of the crops is corn (maize), which is a staple food of the negro inhabitants, is used to some extent in feeding livestock, and also is exported in large amounts. Corn is widely grown, both in the humid veld and in the southeast, but its main region of commercial production is in a large triangle which lies in southern Transvaal and northern Free State. It is an area of heavy, dark soils of grassland origin. Other crops, such as grain sorghums and tobacco, are grown also; and in the more humid and tropical northern Transvaal cotton, peanuts, and oranges are produced for export. Farms in the veld region average large, many exceeding 1,500 acres in size. They are operated by resident farmers with the aid of several negro workmen. Many of the farmers are "Boers," the descendants of the Dutch farmers who were the original settlers in South Africa.

*Agriculture in Natal* centers about the production of sugar cane in the coastal lowlands and the raising of livestock in the rougher inland districts. Corn and cotton are common crops also, but they are not so important as they are in the veld. Crops of local importance are pineapples and oranges. The livestock industry includes both sheep and cattle. Few sheep are found in the low and humid coastal belt, but they are numerous in the rough lands of the interior. Cattle are more abundant in the southeast than in any other part of South Africa. They are mainly beef cattle and work animals, but the dairy industry is well established also. The farms average somewhat smaller than is typical of the veld but still are large as compared with American farms.

*Agriculture in the Mediterranean southwest* includes sheep grazing on the dry and rough lands, cattle ranching, and wheat farming under winter rainfall on the tillable lands near Capetown. Its most distinctive aspects are, however, those associated with horticultural crops produced on irrigated lands and a dairy industry supported by irrigated alfalfa pastures. It is very much the California type of agriculture, modified by a lack of large domestic markets and by the separation of a long sea journey from the markets of Europe. The more important horticultural crops are grapes and oranges. Some grapes are marketed fresh in Europe, since they ripen in March, when European grapes are not available. Some quantities, grown in the drier interior valleys, are made into raisins also. But by far the larger part of the crop is manufactured into wine. There are several districts of considerable local fame for their particular varieties of wine. The irrigated citrus fruits, like those of California, have good keeping quality, and some of them also are shipped to Europe. Other fruits, such as peaches, apricots, figs, and olives, are grown also; and the surplus is either shipped fresh under refrigeration or dried, canned, and preserved for exportation. Two phases of the animal industry found in the dry region of southwestern district are not common to the others. These are the raising of Angora goats for their mohair and the raising of ostriches. Ostrich farming on irrigated alfalfa pastures in the Little Karroo was formerly a major industry, but changes in style have so reduced the market for ostrich feathers that the industry has declined to small proportions. The demand for mohair continues, however, and South Africa is one of its important sources (Fig. 304).

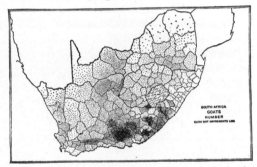

Fig. 304.—Some of the many goats that graze the rough or dry lands of South Africa are of the Angora breed, but a larger number are common goats, the property of native owners. (*U.S. Department of Agriculture*.)

MINERAL RESOURCES OF SOUTH AFRICA. The settlement and development of South Africa has depended upon its mineral resources as well as upon its farm land. The variety of minerals obtained from its mines is not great, but in two of them it takes high rank in world production. These two are gold and diamonds.

*The Gold Mines.* In the Transvaal, near the city of Johannesburg, is a range of granitic hills, called the "Witwatersrand," or "the Rand," which is the greatest gold-producing region that has ever been known. About one-third of all the gold mined in the world comes from that source (Fig. 305). The ore does not contain a large amount of gold per ton, but it is remarkably uniform and dependable. In 1938 the value of the gold produced from the Witwatersrand district was more than 350 million dollars. This is not a large amount compared with the value of certain agricultural products, but the industry employs a large number of workmen and supports a number of towns.

*The Diamond Mines.* Over 95 per cent of the world's diamond supply comes from Africa. Formerly the principal mines were in the vicinity of

Kimberley and Pretoria in South Africa. Although this region continues to be an important producer, its output has been exceeded by that of mines in the Belgian Congo and in the Guinea Coast region. Some of the diamonds are obtained from alluvial deposits, but the larger part comes from deep mines in rock that appears to be of volcanic origin. The rock is mined and spread on the surface to disintegrate through the action of weathering, and the diamonds are separated from the earthy residue by washing and sorting.

*Coal* is one of the important resources of South Africa. The reserve supply is not large, and most of the coal is of only fair quality. However,

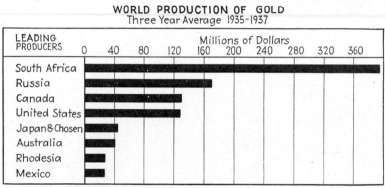

WORLD PRODUCTION OF GOLD
Three Year Average 1935-1937

FIG. 305.

other parts of Africa are so poor in coal that the South African supply has a high strategic value. The principal fields lie in the eastern highland region, mainly in Natal and the Transvaal (Fig. 306). The amount produced is not large. It about equals that of the state of Indiana and is less than half that mined in Japan. However, it has been of great benefit to the development of the mining industries of South Africa, the beginnings of manufacture, and the growth of railroad transportation. It has also been of the utmost importance as steamship fuel. It can be supplied almost directly from the mines through the port of Durban in Natal, and much is shipped by the longer rail haul to the port of Capetown. Of petroleum the Union of South Africa has no known resource, and of water power comparatively little (Fig. 125).

TRANSPORTATION IN SOUTH AFRICA. The railroad system of South Africa is the most developed of any in the continent. Since the interior lies nearly a mile above sea level and the face of the plateau rises steeply from the coast, railway entrance to the interior is difficult. A half dozen lines, however, connect ports on the south and east coasts with cities on the veld. The average density of the rail pattern in the Union of South Africa is about 1 mile of railroad to each 55 miles of area, but in this figure are included large areas of the dry lands which have few railroads. The network in the humid regions is, therefore, much more dense. One of the principal rail lines is that which comprises the southern part of the transcontinental route. It climbs the first escarpment east of Capetown, crosses the Little Karroo and the Great Karroo, then rises to the High Veld and sets out upon the long traverse through Kimberley to the Rhodesias and the Belgian Congo. Thence by steamer and by rail one may make the 7,000-mile traverse of the continent from Capetown to Cairo and the Mediterranean.

South African Trade. The foreign trade of South Africa is peculiarly unbalanced. Its sales of ordinary merchandise overseas are less than half as valuable as its purchases of foreign goods. The difference is made

PRINCIPAL COAL FIELDS OF SOUTH AFRICA AND AUSTRALIA.

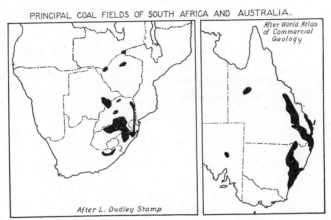

After World Atlas of Commercial Geology

After L. Dudley Stamp

Fig. 306.—In both Africa and Australia the principal coal deposits are near the southeastern coasts.

up by exports of gold and diamonds. The value of these is more than twice that of all other commodities sold. Aside from the produce of the mines, the exports of South Africa are almost exclusively agricultural. Much the most important of these is wool. Next in rank are fruits, both fresh and preserved. In some years also there are large exports of corn. South African imports are mainly manufactures, including even considerable quantities of foods not produced at home. However, the leading items in the list are manufactures of iron and steel, such as machinery, automobiles, steel plates, bars, and wire. Next most important is the textile group including cloth and manufactured clothing. Smaller items include wood, paper products, and chemicals. South Africa trades more with the United Kingdom than with any other country, about 40 per cent of its exports of merchandise being sold in Britain and nearly one-half its imports being derived from that source. Other leading export markets have been the countries of western Europe. The United States is normally but a small purchaser of the products of South Africa, since they are, like those of Argentina, competitive with those grown in America. As a source of South Africa's imports, however, the United States ranks next after Britain. American automobiles, mining machinery, and farm equipment are of types suited to South African requirements.

### SELECTED REFERENCES

BEAVER, S., and L. D. STAMP. "A Regional Geography, Pt. II: Africa," London, 1934.

FAULKNER, O. T., and J. R. MACKIE. "West African Agriculture," Cambridge, 1933.

FITZGERALD, W. "Africa," London, 1934.

HAILEY, LORD. "An African Survey," London, 1938.

HARRIS, RALPH S. Egypt's Place in the World Cotton Drama, *Jour. Geog.*, Vol. 36 (1937), pp. 278–282.

LIGHT, RICHARD, and MARY LIGHT. Contrasts in African Farming: Aerial Views from the Cape to Cairo, *Geog. Rev.*, Vol. 28 (1938), pp. 529–555.

SCHWARTZ, L. J. Cocoa in the Cameroons under French Mandate and in Fernando Po, *U.S. Dept. Commerce, Trade Promotion Series* 148, 1933.

———. Cocoa in the Ivory Coast, *U.S. Dept. Commerce, Trade Promotion Series* 125, 1931.

SHANTZ, H. L. Agricultural Regions of Africa, *Econ. Geog.*, Vol. 16 (1940), pp. 1–47, 122–161.

WHITFORD, N. N., and ALFRED ANTHONY. Rubber Production in Africa, *U.S. Dept. Commerce, Trade Promotion Series* 34, 1926.

WINSHIP, NORTH. Anglo-Egyptian Sudan, A Commercial Handbook, *U.S. Dept. Commerce, Trade Promotion Series* 49, 1927.

# Chapter XXXIII. Australia and New Zealand

## The Commonwealth of Australia

THE SITUATION OF AUSTRALIA. Australia is on the opposite side of the earth and 12,000 miles distant from the great population centers and markets of Europe. This has had a notable effect upon its settlement and development. The long and expensive sea voyage naturally has deterred many prospective immigrants from going there, and the cost of transportation has a constant influence upon the kinds of products that can be produced and exported to Europe. The much shorter distance to the densely peopled countries of Asia holds comparatively little advantage for Australia. The low purchasing power of these countries does not make them large buyers of most of the things that Australians produce in surplus. On the other hand, that close distance to centers of Asiatic population is a reason for some anxiety. Australia is not densely peopled, and undoubtedly it could accommodate many more people if they were content with a lower standard of living. But the Australians do not want a lower standard of living; neither do they want any Asiatic immigration.

THE POPULATION OF AUSTRALIA. The total population of Australia, after a century of white settlement, is only 7 millions, just about the same as that of New York City. It is more than 99 per cent European, largely of British descent. The aboriginal black race was small in numbers, was more primitive than the black races of Africa, and lived entirely by hunting. They number at present no more than 55,000 and are hardly so important an element in the labor supply of Australia as are the American Indians in that of the United States. The labor question is important. The climate of Australia is largely tropical or subtropical, and the land is the principal resource. It is difficult for a people of European origin with a high standard of living to work the land under tropical climate. Yet so concerned are they to keep a "white Australia" that they have enacted laws forbidding the importation of colored or Asiatic laborers. This has a notable effect upon the characteristic use of the land and the principal types of Australian farm products.

The population of Australia is sparse—only about 2.3 persons per square mile—and it is very unequally distributed (Fig. 5). The principal concentration is in the southeastern seaboard region. The state of Victoria has 21 persons per square mile, whereas Northern Australia has only 1 person per 10 square miles on the average. Vast spaces in the central and northwestern parts of the country are practically uninhabited, save for a few aboriginals.

LAND AND CLIMATE IN AUSTRALIA. Australia is the smallest of the continents, but its area is almost exactly equal to that of the United States. Its surface configuration is that of a broad and very shallow basin. Low mountain ranges border the eastern margin of the continent, and the west and northwest are occupied by a broad but low plateau. The east-central portion is a plain, its lowest portion, Lake Eyre, being about

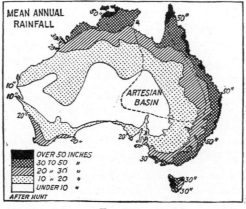

FIG. 307.

40 feet below sea level. The eastern mountains are locally rugged, but in the main they are hardly as much of a physical barrier as the Appalachians are in America. The remainder of the continent is, with a few local exceptions, comprised of level or rolling lands which offer no surface obstacle to cultivation. Yet the area of land in crops, fallow, and orchards in the entire country is only about 1½ per cent of the total, an area equal to less than that devoted to harvested crops in Texas alone. The land of Australia that is actually in tilled crops is less than that in Iowa. This is mainly due to lack of rain, for most of interior and western Australia is semiarid or desert (Fig. 307). The continent has the misfortune to be situated in the latitudes dominated by the southeastern trade winds and the Southern Hemisphere belt of high atmospheric pressures which are characteristically dry. The southeastern highlands receive moisture from the trade winds, and the narrow coastal slopes on that side are well watered. West of the mountains, however, the rainfall decreases rapidly

with distance inland. The northern coasts get summer rainfall of monsoonal origin; but especially in the northwest it is undependable in quantity, and the winters are warm and dry. Only the southern extremities of the continent project far enough poleward to receive moisture from the storms of the westerly winds of middle latitudes, and that comes only in the winter season, from May to September. These southern districts, and especially those which face westward, have, therefore, the

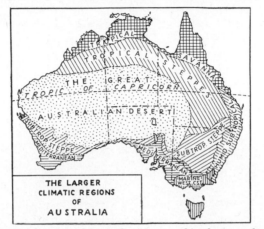

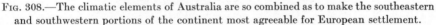

FIG. 308.—The climatic elements of Australia are so combined as to make the southeastern and southwestern portions of the continent most agreeable for European settlement.

Mediterranean type of climate. Southern Victoria and the island of Tasmania project farthest south and have a marine type of climate somewhat like that of southern England or western Oregon. The distribution of the major climatic types in Australia is shown in Fig. 308. More than one-third of the land is complete desert, and another third has too little rainfall for raising crops. If Australia, with its vast stretches of level land and its mild winters, had ample rainfall, it could be one of the greatest food-producing regions of the world.

### AUSTRALIAN AGRICULTURE

THE SHEEP INDUSTRY. Vast areas of semiarid land, a small population, and great distance from the world's markets have combined to make livestock grazing the principal industry of Australia. The sheep industry was first established because wool was a valuable and imperishable product which could stand the long hauls overland to the ports and the even longer and slower shipment to the world's markets by the means of transportation that existed during the middle of the past century. Sheep, and particularly the fine-wooled Merino sheep, found a most suitable environment on the grasslands of the undulating plains of the "back slopes" west of the eastern Highlands. Even now few sheep are kept in the humid eastern coastal districts. The best of the "back-slopes" pastures are in the cooler southern section, in New South Wales and Victoria, and the larger part of the sheep still are there (Fig. 309). However, as the industry expanded, sheep were grazed farther west into the margin of the desert and farther northward into the tropical steppe lands of Queensland. The pasturable lands of Western Australia were utilized also. On the desert margin the forage is a shrub vegetation (Fig. 310) rather than grass; it is able to support fewer sheep; and in

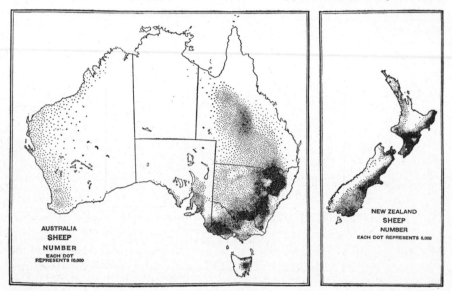

Fig. 309.—The principal sheep lands of Australia are the rolling surfaces of the "back slopes" of the mountains; drier than the coast, but not desert. (*U.S. Department of Agriculture.*)

some years severe droughts so reduce the food supply that either sheep must be got out of the area, or large numbers die of thirst and starvation. In past decades millions did die, but two changes have tended to reduce the losses. One is the construction of several railway branches out toward the desert edge (Fig. 314). Some of these were built to reach mining districts, but they also facilitate the removal of livestock in emergency. The other change is the development of artesian water. Underneath the northern part of the "back-slopes" region and the desert margin is an artesian basin whose intake area lies in the rainy northeast highlands (Fig. 307). Hundreds of wells drilled into this water-bearing rock provide water for livestock far out in the desert, but the quantity is not adequate for irrigation.

During the past century the largest supply of fine Merino wool in the world came from Australia, but the advent of refrigerator transport wrought a change in the Australian sheep and wool industry, just as it did in that of the United States or Argentina. When it became possible to ship mutton as well as wool, the heavy English breeds of sheep with their medium or coarse fleeces were introduced, and crossbred lambs were produced. The 110 million sheep now grazed in Australia are twice the number kept in the United States and more than that in any other country in the world. Wool constitutes more than 40 per cent of Australia's exports, and her exports of lamb and mutton are about one-tenth

Fig. 310.—Sheep on salt-bush range on the dry margin of the "back slopes" in central New South Wales. (*U.S. Department of Agriculture.*)

as valuable as those of wool, an additional item of importance to the country.

CATTLE AND THE DAIRY INDUSTRY. Cattle ranching was not an important industry in the early period of Australian agriculture, because cattle yielded no exportable products except hides and tallow. However, they were raised in large numbers for local supply and as work animals. Heavy wagons drawn by many yoke of oxen carted wool from the back country to railway towns or even to distant ports. With the advent of refrigeration, beef could be shipped in frozen form; but by reason of the great distance the beef grower still was handicapped in his competition for the English market. This was particularly true with respect to the more desirable form of chilled beef. Moreover, the sheep industry was so

FIG. 311.—Beef cattle in the humid coastal district of Queensland, near Brisbane. (*U.S. Department of Agriculture.*)

well established on the back slopes that the cattle industry was not able to compete in that most desirable region. It developed, therefore, along the more humid eastern coast, and in the tropical grasslands of the north. On the cooler southeastern coast, cattle raising presently was evolved into a dairy industry, leaving for the beef industry mainly the more tropical grasslands of the country. Of these there are two principal sections. In the rainy, forested districts of eastern Queensland beef cattle are raised on large farms, some of them in conjunction with tropical crop agriculture (Fig. 311). West of the highlands, however, are the great cattle ranges. They lie in the savanna and tropical steppe lands and extend westward across Queensland and northern Australia (Fig. 308). They are bounded on the north by the more humid, semiforested coastal savannas, where the grass is coarse and unnutritious, and on the south by the desert margin. This is a region of huge cattle ranches. Several of them are as large as the entire state of Connecticut, and there is at least one as large as the combined areas of Massachusetts and Connecticut, or more than 8 million acres.[1] Some of these larger ranches have as many as 50,000 head of cattle, but their management may be centered in a number of small "stations," each of which has a staff consisting of perhaps one or two white men and a few of the aborigines employed as horsemen. The existence of these ranches does not much increase the population density of the region. The great disadvantages that affect the cattle industry in this vast area are three: tropical cattle diseases, such as the Texas fever; the erratic and undependable rainfall, which sometimes damages the pasture; and the meager transportation facilities, which require long drives to get the cattle to market.

*The dairy industry* is most highly developed in the marine and humid subtropical coastal regions of the southeast (Fig. 308). There is some dairying in other regions also, especially near the larger towns. The main dairy belt, however, lies east of the highlands and extends from Melbourne, Victoria, to some distance beyond Brisbane in southern Queensland. Eastern and northern Tasmania are an important part of the dairy belt also. The region thus defined includes the areas of most uniformly distributed and dependable rainfall, lowest summer temperatures, largest population, and greatest crop diversity. The rainfall of even this region is subject to considerable variation, however, and droughts are not infrequent. The dairy industry is not highly intensive, and its most important export products are butter and condensed milk. The value of the butter exported is ten times greater than that of condensed milk and twenty-five times greater than that of the cheese exports.

WHEAT THE LEADING CROP. It has already been pointed out that wheat is a crop well adapted to subhumid grassland regions and to the

[1] Conigrave, C. P. "North Australia," p. 306, London, 1936.

pioneer farming economy of areas far from markets. Like the sheep industry, wheat farming in Australia was first attempted in the humid eastern coastal district, but it met with equally poor success. On the back slopes, however, and in the Mediterranean climatic sections of South and West Australia it has become well established (Fig. 312). These areas have average rainfalls of 15 to 25 inches, with a winter maximum over much of the area. In part, also, they have old grassland soils, high in nitrogen. The cultivation of wheat there has required the plowing of some of the best sheep pastures, and sheep and wheat farming are carried on together, as they are in Argentina and parts of the western plains of the

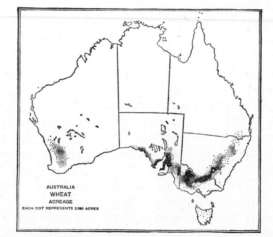

Fig. 312.—The wheat belt of Australia lies in the regions of Mediterranean climate and in the more humid part of the "back slopes" of New South Wales. (*U.S. Department of Agriculture.*)

United States. Wheat is much the most important crop in Australia, occupying 60 per cent of the cultivated land. This emphasizes the predominantly extensive character of Australian agriculture, in spite of the fact that some localities are given over to crops of a more intensive type.

OTHER GRAIN CROPS are of comparatively small importance in Australia. Oats and barley are grown but largely to be cut for hay in the Mediterranean regions where the dry summers cause a shortage of pasture. Corn is also grown, but corn for livestock feed is little needed in a country where there is pasture all the year. Also, there is no large native population, as in Africa, whose labor is available for producing the crop or whose low standard of living accepts corn as a food grain. A large part of the corn grown is therefore fed green or used as silage to supplement pasture in the dairy districts.

TROPICAL CROPS IN QUEENSLAND. The humid tropical climate of the coast of Queensland has encouraged the cultivation of several tropical crops for home supply. These include sugar, cotton, bananas, pineapples, and others. Sugar is the most important of the group. It is confined to the coastal district where there are more than 40 inches of annual rainfall of the summer monsoon type. It is grown near all the important towns between the 15th and 30th parallels of latitude, and most of the towns have sugar mills. The land planted to sugar cane is only 3 per cent as extensive as that sown to wheat, but it supplies the Australian market with sugar and provides an exportable surplus of several million dollars worth per year. Cotton culture is found in southeastern Queensland also, both in the coastal districts and in the upland, which is not very high in that region. The quantity of cotton produced is not large (about 15,000 bales), insufficient even for domestic requirements. However, the cotton and sugar industries of the Queensland area are interesting because they demonstrate the ability of white farmers to live under humid tropical conditions and (under the protection of a tariff) to produce these crops which, in so large a part of the world, seem to require the labor of races more adapted to tropical climate. The coast of far northern Queensland, in the Cape York Peninsula, produces bananas sufficient for the Australian market.

FRUIT FARMING IN THE AUSTRALIAN SOUTH. The Mediterranean climatic regions of South and West Australia, like those of the United States, Europe, and South Africa, have fruit industries. The most important of these is the production of grapes. Vineyards are particularly extensive on irrigated lands in the vicinity of Adelaide and in the Murray River Valley, where large irrigation projects have been completed. The grapes provide fresh fruit for the limited Australian market, and some are dried for raisins, but the larger part of the crop is made into wine. The principal raisin-growing district is near Renmark, east of Adelaide, in a dry interior locality. The wine industry is faced with a serious difficulty. Because of the small size of the home demand, much of the product seeks an export market. Most of it goes to Great Britain or to other British possessions where it finds empire preference, but even then the Australian government finds it necessary to help the wine producers by means of an export bounty. Some grapes are grown in the Mediterranean climatic region of southwestern Australia also, especially near Perth.

Citrus fruits are grown under dry subtropical climate near Adelaide and under humid conditions near Sidney. This contrast, as has been noted previously in connection with South America and South Africa, is comparable with the contrast between the citrus districts of California and Florida.

In southern Victoria and southwestern Tasmania, the climatic conditions resemble those of the Willamette Valley of Oregon. In this region likewise there is a large deciduous fruit industry including apples, pears, and small fruits. It is interesting to note the favorable influence of increasing latitude and cooler summers on the production of apples in Australia. During the 1939–1940 season, tropical Queensland produced only 150,000 bushels of apples; subtropical New South Wales produced 1 million; Victoria, with a still cooler climate, nearly 2 million; and the island of Tasmania, 6 million bushels. Normally about 4.8 million bushels of Australian apples are exported, principally to Great Britain. The small fruits, however, cannot stand long-distance shipment, and many canning and preserving factories are established to prepare them for shipment to Britain. This also is comparable to the fruit-canning and -preserving industry in the Williamette Valley.

## NATURAL RESOURCES

FOREST RESOURCES. So much of Australia is arid that its forest resources are limited to about 5 per cent of its area. However, some of the more humid and cooler districts originally contained trees of great size and economic value. The best of these were in Victoria and Tasmania and in the extreme southwestern corner of the continent. There are even more extensive forests in Queensland and the tropical northern coast region, but in the main they are comprised of species having little commercial value. The gum forests of the southeast were excellent for lumber, and there were other species resembling mahogany and ebony. These have been used as cabinet woods.

ENERGY RESOURCES. Australia is fortunate in the possession of a fairly abundant supply of coal, some of it reputed to be the best coal in the Southern Hemisphere. The principal deposits lie near the coast of New South Wales not far from Sydney, the largest city and principal port (Fig. 306). Practically the entire coal supply lies near the eastern seaboard. Some of the mines at Newcastle, the largest mining center, are at the water's edge, and coal can be loaded directly from the mine into waiting ships. The quantity mined (about 15 million tons) is less than half that mined in Japan, but it has great value for the growing Australian manufacturing industries and as steamship fuel. Also, since coal is scarce in the Southern Hemisphere, nearly half a million tons are exported.

Australia has no domestic supply of petroleum, and because of its general aridity and low relief its potential water powers are small in proportion to its area (Fig. 125).

MINERALS. Gold is the most important mineral produced in Australia, exceeding in value even the coal output. It has had, moreover, a great influence on the settlement and development of the country. It was discovered in Australia in 1857, shortly after the California gold rush. Before that date Australia had attracted few voluntary settlers. The total white population in 1850 did not reach a half million. But no matter how remote the land, men will flock to it if gold in promising quantities is discovered. The Australian gold was found in placer deposits of remarkable richness; many nuggets weighing 5 pounds or more were discovered; one of them was worth $50,000. Within 10 years, two of the gold fields had yielded nearly 500 million dollars. The early discoveries were made in central New South Wales and Victoria, and population in the southeast increased rapidly. Many who failed at mining remained to take up other occupations. The mines of Victoria have, in the 90 years since gold discovery, produced the largest total quantity; but the most productive sources of the east have long since been exhausted, and gold mining turned to the arid west. In the ancient rocks of the southwest, about 350 miles east of Perth, new gold discoveries were made, and the famous mining towns of Kalgoorlie and Coolgardie were built in the desert where even the water supply had to be piped in. This region still is the most productive of gold of any in Australia, but it also has ceased to be of great importance among the world's gold producers. All the gold mined in Australia does not comprise much more than 4 per cent of the world's total, and that continent is far surpassed in output not only by South Africa but also by the United States, Canada, and Russia (Fig. 305).

In addition to gold, Australia has been a producer of several other minerals. Large quantities of silver, lead, and zinc are mined there; and smaller quantities of copper and tin also. In the Broken Hill mining district, located in the desert of extreme western New South Wales, the three first named are found together. This has been one of the richest mining regions of Australia in recent years, and it still is a large producer, especially of lead.

The Australian resource of iron ore is not large, but it is believed sufficient for 50 years at the present rate of use. It is contained in two principal deposits. The first is readily available to water transportation which can move the ore to the eastern coal region. It is situated near the head of Spencer Gulf in South Australia. The other deposit is situated on the coast of West Australia and has little present importance, except possibly for export to Japan.

## CITIES AND INDUSTRIES

URBAN CENTERS. In view of the fact that Australia has so small a population in so large an area it is surprising that only a little more than one-third of the people are rural. Nearly half live in the larger cities. It is the more surprising in consideration of the dominant agricultural interests of the country and the relatively small development of the manufacturing industries. Perhaps it merely emphasizes the fact that Australian agriculture is very extensive. In most of the rural regions a small number of people engaged in livestock and wheat farming can manage a large area of land. The city population is employed in trade, shipping, and manufacture. There are six cities having more than 100,000 inhabitants each, and Sydney and Melbourne each exceeds 1 million. Thus, nearly as many people live in those two cities alone as in all the rural areas of the country.

All the largest cities are ports. Sydney and Melbourne lie on exceedingly spacious and well-protected harbors; few great ports are better situated, and they serve the most densely settled part of the continent (Fig. 313). Perth, on the west coast, together with its neighbor Free-

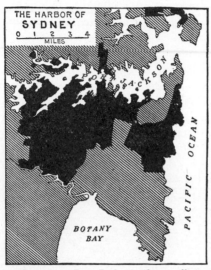

Fig. 313.—Port Jackson, the excellent harbor of Sydney, Australia. City area of Sydney shown in black.

mantle, which is the actual port, is one of the four largest cities. It has an advantageous location for shipping but a poor and arid hinterland. Because of its location, practically all the ships plying between southeastern Australia and either the Suez Canal or Capetown touch there, the route south of the continent being shorter than that to the north. As many ships call at Freemantle per year as at Sydney, although it has much less cargo to be moved.

Ports that have a large trade employ many people in freight handling, brokerage offices, wholesale merchandising, and many other commercial pursuits. They also attract manufacturing industries, as has been noted before. The Australian ports are no exception to this rule. In some respects the manufactures of Australia are like those of Argentina. They include flour milling, meat packing, wool scouring, mineral reduction, and other processes required in preparing agricultural, pastoral, or mineral raw materials for shipment overseas or for home use. They include also many infant industries that have sprung up since the First World War. The great distance to England and the dangers of wartime shipping started a movement toward industrial independence during that time, and several factors have fostered it since, especially a protective tariff. These industries are attempting to furnish a great variety of materials to a small nation of high purchasing power. Their manufactures include textiles and clothing, furniture, shoes, rubber goods, chemicals, and a variety of iron- and steelwares.

The iron and steel industry is so significant as to require special comment. This is one important respect in which the Australian industrial development is unlike that of Argentina, since the latter has neither coal nor iron ore, and Australia has both. In Australia, as in the United States, the iron ore tends to move to the coal region for smelting, and other industries that use iron and steel as raw materials gravitate to the same locality. It is, therefore, in the neighborhood of Sydney and Newcastle and of their coal fields that heavy industry has developed. The total steel production of Australia is not large— about the same as that produced in Canada. Yet on a per capita basis it is high—about 325 pounds per capita as compared with 100 pounds in Japan, for example. The domestic iron

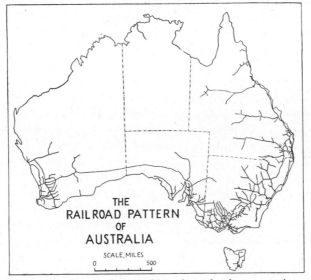

THE
RAILROAD PATTERN
OF
AUSTRALIA

SCALE, MILES
0      500

FIG. 314.—Most of the railroads of Australia end on the desert margin and only one is transcontinental.

and steel is transformed into many wares, including railway steel and equipment, agricultural and mining machinery, wire fencing, heating equipment, and many other things. The whole range of Australian manufactures employs more than half a million workers, and the iron and steel industries account for more of them than any other industrial group.

AUSTRALIAN TRANSPORTATION faces a problem somewhat like that of Canada in that its eastern and western regions of settlement are separated by a vast extent of unproductive territory. The railway problem is further complicated by the fact that the rail systems of the several states have not adopted the same gauge of track. That, as in Argentina, hinders the free internal movement of goods. In all Australia there is less than 1 mile of railroad for every 100 square miles of land, but that figure means no more than does such a figure for Canada or Siberia. There are large areas having no transportation facilities other than motor trucks following desert tracks or the airplane. The density of the rail network in the more settled areas reaches a fairly high figure. That of the most uniformly settled state of Victoria, for example, is 1 mile of railroad for about each 15 square miles of area, a ratio comparable with that of Nebraska. A comparison of Figs. 307 and 314 will show the peculiar features of the Australian railway pattern and its relation to the margins of the desert. The rivers of Australia do not permit of any important navigation. The highway system is made up largely of unimproved dirt roads. There is estimated to be about 1 mile of road of some kind for every 6.5 square miles of area. In the United States the comparable ratio is about 1 to 1. Of the Australian roads, and especially of the paved roads, a large part are in the two states of New South Wales and Victoria.

FOREIGN TRADE. The principal exports of Australia all are the products of farms and mines. Wool is much the most important, making up about half the total. Others, in the order of decreasing importance, are wheat and flour; gold; meat and meat products; dairy produce; lead and zinc; and fruits, both fresh and preserved. The imports, on the other hand, are almost entirely manufactures or raw materials for manufacture, except for petroleum and its products. The leading import items are vehicles and machinery, textiles, and petroleum products. It is perhaps an indication of the part that distance plays in the daily life of the Australians, as well as of their high standard of living, that the two single items of highest value in the list of imports are automobiles and gasoline. The direction of Australian trade, like that of South Africa, is evidence of Empire solidarity supported by preferential tariff arrangements. About 43 per cent of Australia's imports come from the United Kingdom, and nearly 50 per cent of the exports go to the mother country. Next most important in both the import and export lists are other British colonies. Beyond these areas, imports are derived more largely from the United States than from any other source. Machinery and petroleum products are the larger items in the list. Of Australia's non-Empire export trade, however, the larger part goes to Japan.

## The Dominion of New Zealand

THE LAND AND THE PEOPLE. New Zealand is almost exactly on the opposite side of the earth from the British Isles, and consequently it is very remote from Europe and from eastern United States. It began its development somewhat later than Australia (about 1840). The long voyage that has prevented many settlers from going there has also made it necessary for New Zealand to specialize in concentrated products for export. The area of the islands is about equal to that of England, Scotland, and Wales combined, but the population is only a little more than 1½ millions.

The climate of New Zealand is of a mild, marine type, somewhat like that of the coastal slopes and valleys of Oregon and Washington. It has no desert lands. Much of the surface is hilly or mountainous; and the west side of the South Island is rainy, rugged, and deeply fiorded, like that of Norway, British Columbia, or southern Chile. It is a region of superb scenery. However, nearly 25 per cent of the land of New Zealand is used for pasture, and nearly 3 per cent for crops. Presumably much more could be tilled if it were necessary. The food-producing possibilities of New Zealand are probably equal to those of Japan with its 70 million people.

Nearly all the people are of British extraction, and they sometimes boast of being more British than the British themselves. Auckland, the largest city, has a population of more than 200,000; and, as is true of Australia, more than half the people of New Zealand live in cities and towns.

A LAND OF PASTURES, CATTLE, AND SHEEP. The fact that less than 3 per cent of the land of New Zealand is tilled is evidence of the newness of the country, its small population, and the small local requirements for the kind of food crops that must be raised at home. In fact the only important field crop is wheat, which is grown on the Canterbury plain, the driest section of the eastern lowland of South Island. On this loess-covered glacial plain the soils are fertile, but the summers are dry, and supplementary irrigation for pasture and crop land is planned. Other crops, especially oats, potatoes, and peas, are grown; but the areas occupied by them are small. The large remainder of the improved land—nearly seven-eighths—is in grass, devoted to the pasturage of more than 30 million sheep and $4\frac{1}{3}$ million cattle. Swine are relatively unimportant.

There are three main reasons why New Zealand is distinctly a pastoral country: (1) Its mild, moist climate favors the growth of grass and permits cattle and sheep to graze in the open all the year around. (2) The labor supply is small in proportion to the extent of the country; and this condition favors the pastoral industry, which requires less labor than does agriculture. (3) Animal products—wool, meat, butter, and cheese—are concentrated products of high value per unit of weight and can stand the cost of a long journey to market.

ANIMAL PRODUCTS AND NEW ZEALAND'S EXPORTS. Sheep raising is the major pastoral industry of the country. British breeds of sheep predominate, and wool and frozen mutton make up nearly half the exports. Sheep are found in all parts of the islands except the rainy and forested southwest, but they are most numerous on the drier eastern slopes of both islands (Fig. 309). They are grazed on large farms, some of which have farmsteads much like those of English country estates. They have large houses, fine gardens, and hedges, even though they may be many miles from neighbors or towns.

Cattle are raised in New Zealand both for beef and for their dairy products, but the dairy industry is much the more valuable. Beef cattle, like sheep, are found to some extent in nearly all parts of the islands, but they are much more abundant in the warmer North Island than in the south. They are also relatively more numerous than sheep on the western, more humid side of that island and also in the low, subtropical Auckland Peninsula, which constitutes its northern extremity. Chilled and frozen beef are important but not major items in the list of exports.

The dairy industry of New Zealand has attracted international fame because of the large quantities of butter and cheese exported. The quantity produced is not so large as in some other of the world's dairy regions; but the local market is restricted because of the small population of the country, and there is a large surplus for export. The dairy industry reaches its maximum development in four somewhat separate districts. These are (1) the environs of Auckland; (2) the rainy slopes of Mount Egmont, on the west side of North Island; (3) the undulating farm lands of the southern part of North Island; and (4) the cool eastern slopes of South Island, especially its southern portion. Unlike the sheep industry, dairying does not occupy the hilly back-country districts but has developed on the accessible plains and gentler slopes. Moreover, it is not conducted on great estates but mainly on farms that average only about 100 acres in size.

As compared with the dairy industry in Europe or northern United States, that of New Zealand has several advantages with which to offset the disadvantages of great distance from the European markets. Principal among these are a very favorable climate and cheap land. The mild, moist, and uniform climate provides excellent forage; permits of winter grazing; requires but a small amount of labor for the raising of hay crops; and makes expensive barns for the housing of cattle and hay unnecessary. Labor costs in New Zealand are high, but most of the dairy farms are managed by their owners with little hired help. To accomplish this the industry is highly mechanized, milking machines and other labor-saving devices being employed to a larger extent even than in the United States. Butter and cheese are made in large factories under close supervision and have had an excellent reputation on the European market. Of the total value of New Zealand's exports butter has, in recent years, comprised nearly 30 per cent, and cheese nearly 10 per cent.

OTHER INDUSTRIES IN NEW ZEALAND. Although the principal business of New Zealand is dependent upon its pastures, there are other resources than the land. There are forest and energy resources and some domestic manufactures. A small supply of coal on the west coast of South Island is mined to the extent of more than 2 million tons per year, and the country has nearly twice as much potential water power as Australia and nearly three times as much of it in use. Its potential water powers are, in fact, about equal to those of Switzerland, although only 12 per cent as much has been developed. With coal and water power available, small manufacturing industries have been established that provide for the processing not only of agricultural raw materials but also those of forests and mines and for the manufacture of shoes, clothing, and other local needs to a moderate extent. Many of these requirements are still supplied by importation, however, and especially from Great Britain. No other of the larger British dependencies has traded with the mother country and the other members of the British Empire so exclusively as has New Zealand (Fig. 315).

### THE DIRECTION OF NEW ZEALAND TRADE, 1934-1936

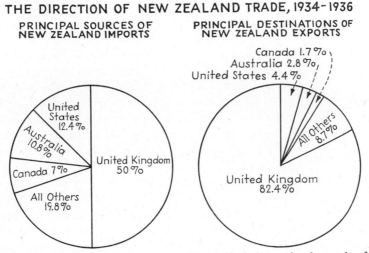

PRINCIPAL SOURCES OF NEW ZEALAND IMPORTS

PRINCIPAL DESTINATIONS OF NEW ZEALAND EXPORTS

Canada 1.7 %
Australia 2.8 %,
United States 4.4 %

United States 12.4 %
Australia 10.8%
Canada 7%
All Others 19.8%
United Kingdom 50 %

United Kingdom 82.4 %
All Others 8.7%

FIG. 315.—The United Kingdom has more than half of the trade of even her farthest dominion.

SELECTED REFERENCES

ANDREWS, JOHN. The Present Situation in the Wheat-growing Industry in Southeastern Australia, *Econ. Geog.*, Vol. 12 (1936), pp. 109–135.

Australian Raisin and Currant Industry. *U.S. Dept. Commerce, Trade Information Bull.* 699, 1930.

BELSHAW, H. Dairying Industry of New Zealand, *Econ. Geog.*, Vol. 3 (1927), pp. 281–296.

CHAPMAN, EMMETT A. Australia: Survey of Its Resources and Foreign Trade, *U.S. Dept. Commerce, Trade Information Bull.* 390, 1926.

COPLAND, D. P. (ed.). "An Economic Survey of Australia," Philadelphia, 1931.

HANCOCK, W. K. "Australia," New York, 1931.

KNIBBS, G. H. Official Yearbook of the Commonwealth of Australia (annual).

MAYNARD, R. S. "Australian Dairyman's Handbook," Sydney, 1931.

New Zealand, Official Yearbook (annual).

TAYLOR, G. Agricultural Regions of Australia, *Econ. Geog.*, Vol. 6 (1930), pp. 109–134, 213–242.

ZIERER, C. M. The Australian Iron and Steel Industry as a Functional Unit, *Geog. Rev.*, Vol. 30 (1940), pp. 649–659.

# APPENDIX

TABLE 1.—AREA AND POPULATION OF PRINCIPAL COUNTRIES

Rounded figures are approximate only. Density is computed on basis of latest population figures even when these are estimates. Asterisk (*) indicates the capital of the country. The world totals are published by the League of Nations. (From Foreign Commerce Yearbook, 1938.)

| Country | Area, square miles | Latest census Year | Latest census Population (thousands) | Official estimates Year | Official estimates Population (thousands) | Density per square mile | Largest city | Estimated population (thousands) |
|---|---|---|---|---|---|---|---|---|
| Total, world............. | 51,177,000[1] | .... | ....... | 1937 | 2,115,800 | 41.3 | | |
| North America: | | | | | | | | |
| United States (continental) | 3,088,519 | 1940 | 131,669 | .... | ......... | 42.6 | New York | 7,380 |
| Per cent of world total. | 5.1 | .... | 6.2 | | | | | |
| Alaska................. | 586,400 | .... | 72 | .... | ......... | 0.1 | Juneau | 5 |
| Hawaii................ | 6,407 | .... | 423 | .... | ......... | 66.0 | Honolulu | 179 |
| Canada................ | 3,466,793[1] | 1931 | 10,377 | 1937 | 11,120 | 3.2 | Montreal | 819 |
| Newfoundland and Labrador................ | 152,734 | 1935 | 290 | .... | ......... | 1.9 | *St. John's | 55 |
| Mexico................ | 760,290 | 1930 | 16,553 | 1937 | 19,154 | 25.2 | *Mexico, D. F. | 1,029 |
| Central America: | | | | | | | | |
| British Honduras........ | 8,598 | 1931 | 51 | 1936 | 56 | 6.5 | *Belize | 17 |
| Costa Rica............. | 23,000 | 1927 | 472 | 1936 | 540 | 23.5 | *San José | 64 |
| Guatemala............. | 42,364 | 1927 | 2,005 | 1937 | 3,008 | 71.0 | *Guatemala | 167 |
| Honduras.............. | 46,250 | 1935 | 962 | .... | ......... | 20.8 | *Tegucigalpa | 43 |
| Nicaragua............. | 49,500 | 1920 | 638 | 1938 | 1,000 | 20.2 | *Managua | 115 |
| Panama............... | 32,380 | 1930 | 467 | 1936 | 535 | 16.5 | *Panama | 83 |
| El Salvador............ | 13,176 | 1933 | 1,550 | 1936 | 1,632 | 123.9 | *San Salvador | 99 |
| West Indies: | | | | | | | | |
| Cuba.................. | 44,164 | 1931 | 3,962 | 1936 | 4,109 | 93.0 | *Habana | 552 |
| Dominican Republic...... | 19,332 | 1935 | 1,478 | 1937 | 1,581 | 81.8 | *Ciudad Trujillo | 71 |
| Haiti................. | 10,204 | 1918 | 1,631 | 1937 | 2,700 | 264.6 | *Port-au-Prince | 105 |
| Puerto Rico............ | 3,435 | 1935 | 1,724 | 1938 | 1,806 | 525.8 | *San Juan | 137 |
| Bermuda.............. | 19 | 1931 | 28 | 1937 | 32 | 1,684.2 | *Hamilton | 4 |
| British West Indies...... | 12,611 | 1931 | 2,023 | 1937 | 2,204 | 174.8 | Kingston (and suburb) | 141 |
| French West Indies...... | 1,114 | 1936 | 551 | .... | ......... | 494.6 | Fort-de-France | 48 |
| Curaçao (Netherlands West Indies).......... | 403 | .... | ....... | 1936 | 91 | 225.8 | *Willemstad | 28 |
| South America: | | | | | | | | |
| Guiana, British......... | 89,480 | 1931 | 318 | 1936 | 333 | 3.7 | *Georgetown | 66 |
| Guiana, French[2]........ | 35,100 | 1936 | 37 | .... | ......... | 1.1 | *Cayenne | 11 |
| Surinam (Netherlands Guiana)............... | 54,305 | .... | ....... | 1936 | 169 | 3.1 | *Paramaribo | 53 |
| Colombia.............. | 448,741 | 1928 | 7,851 | 1936 | 8,665 | 19.3 | *Bogotá | 340 |
| Venezuela.............. | 352,143 | 1936 | 3,428 | .... | ......... | 9.7 | *Caracas | 203 |
| Argentina............. | 1,076,966 | 1914 | 7,885 | 1937 | 12,762 | 11.8 | *Buenos Aires | 2,318 |
| Brazil................. | 3,286,170 | 1920 | 30,636 | 1937 | 43,247 | 13.2 | *Rio de Janeiro | 1,802 |
| Paraguay.............. | 176,000 | 1899 | 656 | .... | 900 | 5.1 | *Asunción | 95 |
| Uruguay.............. | 71,172 | 1908 | 1,043 | 1937 | 2,093 | 29.4 | *Montevideo | 693 |
| Bolivia................ | 506,793 | 1900 | 1,767 | 1937 | 3,283 | 6.5 | *La Paz | 202 |
| Chile................. | 286,396 | 1930 | 4,287 | 1937 | 4,597 | 16.1 | *Santiago | 696 |
| Ecuador.............. | 276,007[3] | .... | ....... | 1937 | 2,757 | 10.0 | Guayaquil | 140 |
| Peru.................. | 482,258 | 1876 | 2,699 | 1936 | 6,500 | 13.5 | *Lima (and suburbs) | 285 |
| Europe: | | | | | | | | |
| Sweden................ | 158,394[1] | 1937 | 6,285 | .... | ....... | 39.7 | *Stockholm | 557 |
| Norway[4].............. | 119,148[1] | 1930 | 2,814 | 1937 | 2,907 | 24.4 | *Oslo | 253 |

[1] Land area. World total is approximate only.

[2] Including Territory of Inini.

[3] Boundaries unsettled. Figures are those of the Ecuadoran government.

[4] Not including outlying possessions.

TABLE 1.—AREA AND POPULATION OF PRINCIPAL COUNTRIES.—(Continued)

| Country | Area, square miles | Latest census | | Official estimates | | Density per square mile | Largest city | Estimated population (thousands) |
|---|---|---|---|---|---|---|---|---|
| | | Year | Population (thousands) | Year | Population (thousands) | | | |
| Europe: (Continued) | | | | | | | | |
| Denmark[4] | 16,575 | 1935 | 3,706 | 1937 | 3,764 | 227.1 | *Copenhagen (Kö-benhavn) | 843 |
| United Kingdom | 94,281 | 1931 | 46,189 | 1935 | 47,029 | 498.8 | *London (Greater)[5] | 8,203 |
| Ireland (formerly Irish Free State). | 26,601 | 1936 | 2,966 | | | 111.5 | *Dublin (Baile Atha Cliath). | 468 |
| Belgium | 11,754 | 1930 | 8,092 | 1937 | 8,361 | 711.3 | *Brussels (Bruxelles) | 910 |
| Luxembourg | 999 | 1935 | 297 | 1937 | 298 | 298.3 | *Luxembourg | 58 |
| France | 212,722 | 1936 | 41,906 | | | 197.0 | *Paris (and suburbs) | 4,963 |
| Netherlands | 13,515 | 1930 | 7,936 | 1938 | 8,635 | 638.9 | Amsterdam | 788 |
| Austria | 32,377 | 1934 | 6,760 | | | 208.8 | *Vienna (Wien) | 1,874 |
| Czechoslovakia | 54,244 | 1930 | 14,730 | 1937 | 15,263 | 281.4 | *Prague (Praha) | 962 |
| Hungary | 35,936 | 1930 | 8,688 | 1937 | 9,035 | 251.4 | *Budapest | 1,059 |
| Germany | 181,743[6] | 1933 | 66,029 | 1936 | 67,587 | 371.9 | *Berlin | 4,251 |
| Switzerland | 15,944 | 1930 | 4,066 | 1937 | 4,174 | 261.8 | Zürich | 321 |
| Estonia | 18,359 | 1934 | 1,126 | 1938 | 1,131 | 61.6 | *Tallinn (Reval) | 146 |
| Finland | 134,547 | 1930 | 3,667 | 1936 | 3,807 | 28.3 | *Helsinki (Helsing-fors) | 284 |
| Latvia | 25,402 | 1935 | 1,951 | 1937 | 1,965 | 77.4 | *Riga | 385 |
| Lithuania (including Klai-péda district) | 21,474 | 1923 | 2,170 | 1938 | 2,550 | 118.7 | *Kaunas (Kovno) | 108 |
| Poland | 149,957 | 1931 | 32,133 | 1938 | 34,500 | 230.1 | *Warsaw (Warszawa) | 1,261 |
| U.S.S.R. | 8,176,054 | 1933 | 165,748 | 1934 | 170,500 | 20.9 | *Moscow (Moskva) | 3,642 |
| Italy | 119,764 | 1936 | 42,445 | 1938 | 43,786 | 365.6 | *Rome (Roma) | 1,251 |
| Portugal (including Azores and Madeira) | 35,582 | 1930 | 6,826 | 1936 | 7,275 | 204.5 | *Lisbon (Lisboa) | 650 |
| Spain (including Canary Islands) | 195,258 | 1930 | 23,564 | 1935 | 24,849 | 127.3 | Barcelona | 1,061 |
| Bulgaria | 39,825 | 1934 | 6,078 | 1938 | 6,280 | 157.7 | *Sofia (Sofiya) | 350 |
| Greece | 50,270 | 1928 | 6,205 | 1937 | 7,000 | 139.2 | *Athens | 494 |
| Rumania | 113,887 | 1930 | 17,889 | 1937 | 19,646 | 172.5 | *Bucharest (Bucur-esti) | 643 |
| Yugoslavia | 95,576 | 1931 | 13,934 | 1937 | 15,400 | 161.1 | *Belgrade (Beograd) | 242 |
| Asia: | | | | | | | | |
| Arabia | 1,000,000 | | | 1933 | 7,000 | 7.0 | Mecca | 85 |
| Iran (Persia) | 628,000 | | | 1936 | 12,000 | 19.1 | *Tehran | 310 |
| 'Iraq | 175,094 | 1934 | 3,561 | | | 20.3 | *Baghdad | 300 |
| Palestine | 8,800 | 1931 | 1,036 | 1937 | 1,402 | 157.9 | Tel-Aviv | 141 |
| Afghanistan | 251,000 | | | | 7,000 | 27.9 | *Kabul | 80 |
| Nepal | 54,000 | | | | 5,600 | 103.7 | *Katmandu | 80 |
| Syria and Lebanon | 79,000 | | | | 3,250 | 41.1 | Aleppo | 250 |
| Turkey (including European) | 294,492 | 1935 | 16,201 | | | 55.0 | Istanbul | 741 |
| India | 1,575,307 | 1931 | 338,171 | | | 214.7 | | |
| British Provinces | 862,799 | 1931 | 256,860 | | | 297.7 | Calcutta (and sub-urbs) | 1,419 |
| Indian States | 712,508 | 1931 | 81,311 | | | 114.1 | *Hyderabad | 346 |
| Burma[7] | 233,492 | 1931 | 14,667 | | | 62.8 | *Rangoon | 399 |
| Malaya, British | 53,243 | 1931 | 4,351 | 1937 | 5,137 | 96.5 | Singapore | 446 |
| Ceylon | 25,332 | 1931 | 5,313 | 1937 | 5,780 | 228.2 | *Colombo | 315 |
| Netherlands Indies | 735,268 | 1930 | 60,727 | 1935 | 64,450 | 87.7 | *Batavia (including Meester Cornelis) | 533 |

[4] Not including outlying possessions.

[5] The area of Greater London is 693 square miles. The area of registration of London is 117 square miles, and the population 4,396,821. Neither population figure is closely comparable with New York.

[6] Including Saar district.

[7] Separated from India Apr. 1, 1937.

TABLE 1.—AREA AND POPULATION OF PRINCIPAL COUNTRIES.—(*Continued*)

| Country | Area, square miles | Latest census | | Official estimates | | Density per square mile | Largest city | Estimated population (thousands) |
|---|---|---|---|---|---|---|---|---|
| | | Year | Population (thousands) | Year | Population (thousands) | | | |
| Asia: (*Continued*) | | | | | | | | |
| Indo-China, French...... | 284,900 | 1936 | 23,030 | .... | ........ | 80.8 | *Saïgon and Cholon | 256 |
| Philippine Islands....... | 114,400 | 1918 | 10,315 | 1935 | 13,099 | 114.5 | *Manila | 353 |
| Thailand (Siam) ........ | 200,148 | 1937 | 14,464 | .... | ........ | 72.3 | *Bangkok | 886 |
| China (Dominion)....... | 4,500,000 | .... | ........ | 1937 | 466,786 | 103.7 | Shanghai (and suburbs) | 3,490 |
| Hong Kong............. | 391 | 1931 | 841 | 1936 | 988 | 2,526.9 | Victoria | 378 |
| Japan, Empire........... | 260,758 | 1935 | 97,698 | .... | ........ | 374.7 | | |
| Japan Proper.......... | 147,701 | 1935 | 69,254 | 1937 | 71,253 | 482.4 | *Tokyo | 6,274 |
| Chosen (Korea)........ | 85,239 | 1935 | 22,899 | .... | ........ | 268.6 | *Keijo (Seoul) | 322 |
| Taiwan............... | 13,885 | 1935 | 5,212 | .... | ........ | 374.4 | Taihoku | 196 |
| Africa: | | | | | | | | |
| Algeria[8]................. | 851,300 | 1936 | 7,235 | .... | ........ | 8.5 | *Algiers (Alger) | 264 |
| Tunisia................. | 60,200 | 1936 | 2,608 | .... | ........ | 43.3 | *Tunis | 220 |
| Libya.................. | 677,000 | 1936 | 889 | .... | ........ | 1.3 | *Tripoli | 99 |
| Egypt[9]................: | 386,000 | 1937 | 15,905 | .... | ........ | 41.2 | *Cairo | 1,307 |
| Morocco, French........ | 154,010 | 1936 | 6,296 | .... | ........ | 40.9 | Casablanca | 257 |
| Ethiopia (Abyssinia)[10].... | 400,000 | .... | ........ | .... | 6,000 | 15.0 | *Addis Ababa | 167 |
| Eritrea[10]............... | 85,000 | 1931 | 601 | 1936 | 1,000 | 11.8 | *Asmara | 19 |
| Italian Somaliland[10]...... | 270,000 | 1931 | 1,022 | 1936 | 1,300 | 4.8 | *Mogadiscio | 30 |
| Anglo-Egyptian Sudan.... | 969,600 | .... | ........ | 1936 | 5,950 | 6.1 | Omdurman | 111 |
| French West Africa[11]..... | 1,815,000 | 1936 | 14,702 | .... | ........ | 8.1 | *Dakar | 93 |
| Liberia................. | 43,000 | .... | ........ | .... | 2,000 | 46.5 | *Monrovia | 10 |
| Gold Coast............. | 78,802 | 1931 | 2,870 | 1936 | 3,269 | 41.5 | *Accra | 71 |
| Sierra Leone (including protectorate)......... | 27,925 | 1931 | 1,768 | 1935 | 1,890 | 67.7 | Freetown | 62 |
| Gambia (including protectorate)............... | 4,068 | 1931 | 200 | .... | ........ | 49.2 | *Bathurst | 14 |
| Nigeria[11]............... | 338,593 | 1931 | 19,131 | 1936 | 19,365 | 57.2 | Ibadan | 387 |
| French Equatorial Africa.. | 960,000 | 1936 | 3,423 | .... | ........ | 3.6 | *Brazzaville | 47 |
| Uganda................. | 80,588 | 1931 | 3,552 | 1936 | 3,687 | 45.8 | Kampala | 6 |
| Kenya................. | 219,730 | 1931 | 3,041 | 1936 | 3,262 | 14.8 | Mombasa | 43 |
| Belgian Congo.......... | 902,000 | .... | ........ | 1937 | 10,067 | 11.2 | *Leopoldville | 32 |
| Tanganyika............. | 366,632 | 1931 | 5,064 | 1936 | 5,147 | 14.0 | Dar es Salaam | 23 |
| Angola (Portuguese West Africa)............... | 481,350 | .... | ........ | 1933 | 3,098 | 6.4 | S. Paulo de Luanda | 18 |
| Rhodesia, Northern...... | 287,950 | 1931 | 1,345 | 1935 | 1,378 | 4.8 | Broken Hill | |
| Rhodesia, Southern...... | 150,354 | 1931 | 1,109 | 1935 | 1,289 | 8.6 | *Salisbury | 33 |
| Mozambique (Portuguese East Africa)........... | 297,731 | 1930 | 3,996 | 1937 | 4,006 | 13.5 | *Lourenço Marques | 43 |
| Madagascar (including dependencies)......... | 238,000 | 1936 | 3,798 | .... | ........ | 16.0 | *Tananarive | 105 |
| Union of South Africa.... | 472,550 | 1936 | 9,589 | 1937 | 9,797 | 20.7 | Johannesburg | 519 |
| Oceania: | | | | | | | | |
| Australia............... | 2,974,581 | 1933 | 6,631 | 1937 | 6,867 | 2.3 | Sydney | 1,279 |
| New Zealand........... | 103,934 | 1936 | 1,574 | 1937 | 1,602 | 15.4 | Auckland (and suburbs) | 212 |

[8] Including desert and thinly populated areas (southern territories), with area of 770,300 square miles and population of 642,651.

[9] The area of occupied lands in Egypt is only about 13,600 square miles; the density of population for this area is 1,169 per square mile.

[10] Italian statistics of areas administered as Italian East Africa.

[11] Excluding mandated areas.

### TABLE 2.—STATE AND TERRITORIAL STATISTICS

| States, etc. | Capitals | Largest cities | Area, square miles | Population, 1930 | Population, 1940 |
|---|---|---|---|---|---|
| Alabama | Montgomery | Birmingham | 51,998 | 2,646,248 | 2,832,961 |
| Arizona | Phoenix | Phoenix | 113,956 | 435,573 | 499,261 |
| Arkansas | Little Rock | Little Rock | 53,335 | 1,854,482 | 1,949,387 |
| California | Sacramento | Los Angeles | 158,297 | 5,677,251 | 6,907,387 |
| Colorado | Denver | Denver | 103,948 | 1,035,791 | 1,123,296 |
| Connecticut | Hartford | Hartford | 4,965 | 1,606,903 | 1,709,242 |
| Delaware | Dover | Wilmington | 2,370 | 238,380 | 266,505 |
| District of Columbia | Washington | Washington | 70 | 486,869 | 663,091 |
| Florida | Tallahassee | Jacksonville | 58,666 | 1,468,211 | 1,897,414 |
| Georgia | Atlanta | Atlanta | 59,265 | 2,908,506 | 3,123,723 |
| Idaho | Boise | Boise | 83,888 | 445,032 | 524,873 |
| Illinois | Springfield | Chicago | 56,665 | 7,630,654 | 7,897,241 |
| Indiana | Indianapolis | Indianapolis | 36,354 | 3,238,503 | 3,427,796 |
| Iowa | Des Moines | Des Moines | 56,147 | 2,470,939 | 2,538,268 |
| Kansas | Topeka | Kansas City | 82,158 | 1,880,999 | 1,801,028 |
| Kentucky | Frankfort | Louisville | 40,598 | 2,614,589 | 2,845,627 |
| Louisiana | Baton Rouge | New Orleans | 48,506 | 2,101,593 | 2,363,880 |
| Maine | Augusta | Portland | 33,040 | 797,423 | 847,226 |
| Maryland | Annapolis | Baltimore | 12,327 | 1,631,526 | 1,821,244 |
| Massachusetts | Boston | Boston | 8,266 | 4,249,614 | 4,316,721 |
| Michigan | Lansing | Detroit | 57,980 | 4,842,325 | 5,256,106 |
| Minnesota | St. Paul | Minneapolis | 84,682 | 2,563,953 | 2,792,300 |
| Mississippi | Jackson | Jackson | 46,865 | 2,009,821 | 2,183,796 |
| Missouri | Jefferson City | St. Louis | 69,420 | 3,629,367 | 3,784,664 |
| Montana | Helena | Butte | 146,997 | 537,606 | 559,456 |
| Nebraska | Lincoln | Omaha | 77,520 | 1,377,963 | 1,315,834 |
| Nevada | Carson City | Reno | 110,690 | 91,058 | 110,247 |
| New Hampshire | Concord | Manchester | 9,341 | 465,293 | 491,524 |
| New Jersey | Trenton | Newark | 8,224 | 4,041,334 | 4,160,165 |
| New Mexico | Santa Fe | Albuquerque | 122,634 | 423,317 | 531,818 |
| New York | Albany | New York | 49,204 | 12,588,066 | 13,479,142 |
| North Carolina | Raleigh | Charlotte | 52,426 | 3,170,276 | 3,571,623 |
| North Dakota | Bismarck | Fargo | 70,837 | 680,845 | 641,935 |
| Ohio | Columbus | Cleveland | 41,040 | 6,646,697 | 6,907,612 |
| Oklahoma | Oklahoma City | Oklahoma City | 70,057 | 2,396,040 | 2,336,434 |
| Oregon | Salem | Portland | 96,699 | 953,786 | 1,089,684 |
| Pennsylvania | Harrisburg | Philadelphia | 45,126 | 9,631,350 | 9,900,180 |
| Rhode Island | Providence | Providence | 1,248 | 687,497 | 731,346 |
| South Carolina | Columbia | Charleston | 30,989 | 1,738,765 | 1,899,804 |
| South Dakota | Pierre | Sioux Falls | 77,615 | 692,849 | 642,691 |
| Tennessee | Nashville | Memphis | 42,022 | 2,616,556 | 2,915,841 |
| Texas | Austin | Houston | 265,896 | 5,824,715 | 6,414,824 |
| Utah | Salt Lake City | Salt Lake City | 84,990 | 507,847 | 550,310 |
| Vermont | Montpelier | Burlington | 9,564 | 359,611 | 359,231 |
| Virginia | Richmond | Richmond | 42,627 | 2,421,851 | 2,677,773 |
| Washington | Olympia | Seattle | 69,127 | 1,563,396 | 1,736,191 |
| West Virginia | Charleston | Huntington | 24,170 | 1,729,205 | 1,901,974 |
| Wisconsin | Madison | Milwaukee | 56,066 | 2,939,006 | 3,137,587 |
| Wyoming | Cheyenne | Cheyenne | 97,914 | 225,565 | 250,742 |
| Part of Great Lakes | .......... | .......... | 61,730 | | |
| Main body of U.S. | .......... | .......... | 3,088,519 | 122,775,046 | 131,669,275 |
| Outlying territory | | | | | |
| Alaska | Juneau | Fairbanks | 590,884 | 59,278 | 72,000 |
| Hawaii | Honolulu | Honolulu | 6,449 | 368,336 | 423,329 |
| Puerto Rico | San Juan | San Juan | 3,435 | 1,543,913 | 1,869,245 |
| Philippine Islands | Manila | Manila | 115,026 | est. 12,252,594 | est. 13,099,000 |
| Tutuila, etc. | Pago Pago | Leone | 77 | 10,055 | 12,908 |
| Guam | Agaña | .......... | 210 | 18,509 | 22,290 |
| Panama Canal Zone | .......... | .......... | 527 | 39,467 | 51,827 |
| Virgin Islands of U.S. | St. Thomas | St. Thomas | 132 | 22,012 | 24,889 |
| In U.S. service abroad | .......... | | | 89,453 | |
| Total outlying | .......... | .......... | 716,740 | 14,403,617 | 15,575,488 |
| Total U.S., etc. | Washington | New York | 3,805,259 | 137,178,663 | 147,244,763 |

TABLE 3.—POPULATION OF LARGE CITIES OF THE UNITED STATES

| | 1940* | 1930 | 1920 | 1900 | 1880 | 1860 |
|---|---|---|---|---|---|---|
| New York, N. Y. | 7,380,259 | 6,930,446 | 5,620,048 | 3,437,202 | 1,911,698 | 1,174,779 |
| Chicago, Ill. | 3,384,556 | 3,376,438 | 2,701,705 | 1,698,575 | 503,185 | 109,260 |
| Philadelphia, Pa. | 1,935,086 | 1,950,961 | 1,823,779 | 1,293,697 | 847,170 | 565,529 |
| Detroit, Mich. | 1,618,549 | 1,568,662 | 993,678 | 285,704 | 116,340 | 45,619 |
| Los Angeles, Calif. | 1,496,792 | 1,238,048 | 576,673 | 102,479 | 11,183 | 4,385 |
| Cleveland, Ohio | 878,385 | 900,429 | 796,841 | 381,768 | 160,146 | 43,417 |
| Baltimore, Md. | 854,144 | 804,874 | 733,826 | 508,957 | 332,313 | 212,418 |
| St. Louis, Mo. | 813,748 | 821,960 | 772,897 | 575,238 | 350,518 | 160,773 |
| Boston, Mass. | 769,520 | 781,188 | 748,060 | 560,892 | 362,839 | 177,840 |
| Pittsburgh, Pa. | 665,384 | 669,817 | 588,343 | 451,512 | 235,071 | 77,923 |
| Washington, D. C. | 663,153 | 486,869 | 437,511 | 278,718 | 177,624 | 61,122 |
| San Francisco, Calif. | 629,553 | 634,394 | 506,676 | 342,782 | 233,959 | 56,802 |
| Milwaukee, Wis. | 589,558 | 578,249 | 457,147 | 285,315 | 115,587 | 45,246 |
| Buffalo, N. Y. | 575,150 | 573,076 | 506,775 | 352,387 | 155,134 | 81,129 |
| New Orleans, La. | 492,282 | 458,762 | 387,219 | 287,104 | 216,090 | 168,675 |
| Minneapolis, Minn. | 489,971 | 464,356 | 380,582 | 202,718 | 46,887 | 2,564 |
| Cincinnati, Ohio | 452,852 | 451,160 | 401,247 | 325,902 | 255,139 | 161,044 |
| Newark, N. J. | 428,236 | 442,337 | 414,524 | 246,070 | 136,508 | 71,941 |
| Kansas City, Mo. | 400,175 | 399,746 | 324,410 | 163,752 | 55,785 | 4,418 |
| Indianapolis, Ind. | 386,170 | 364,161 | 314,194 | 169,164 | 75,056 | 18,611 |
| Houston, Tex. | 386,150 | 292,352 | 138,276 | 44,633 | 16,513 | 4,845 |
| Seattle, Wash. | 366,847 | 365,583 | 315,312 | 80,671 | 3,533 | |
| Rochester, N. Y. | 324,694 | 328,132 | 295,750 | 162,608 | 89,366 | 48,204 |
| Louisville, Ky. | 318,713 | 307,745 | 234,891 | 204,731 | 123,758 | 68,033 |
| Denver, Colo. | 318,415 | 287,861 | 256,491 | 133,859 | 35,629 | 4,749 |
| Portland, Ore. | 307,572 | 301,815 | 258,288 | 90,426 | 17,577 | 2,874 |
| Columbus, Ohio | 304,936 | 290,564 | 237,031 | 125,560 | 51,647 | 18,554 |
| Oakland, Calif. | 304,909 | 284,063 | 216,261 | 66,960 | 34,555 | 1,543 |
| Atlanta, Ga. | 302,538 | 270,366 | 200,616 | 89,872 | 37,409 | 9,554 |
| Jersey City, N. J. | 301,012 | 316,715 | 298,103 | 206,433 | 120,722 | 29,226 |
| Dallas, Tex. | 293,306 | 260,475 | 158,976 | 42,638 | 10,358 | |
| Memphis, Tenn. | 291,312 | 253,143 | 162,351 | 102,320 | 33,592 | 22,623 |
| St. Paul, Minn. | 288,023 | 271,606 | 234,698 | 163,065 | 41,473 | 10,401 |
| Toledo, Ohio | 281,096 | 290,718 | 243,164 | 131,822 | 50,137 | 13,768 |
| Birmingham, Ala. | 264,151 | 259,678 | 178,806 | 38,415 | 3,086 | |
| Providence, R. I. | 253,214 | 252,981 | 237,595 | 175,597 | 104,857 | 50,666 |
| San Antonio, Tex. | 253,143 | 231,541 | 161,379 | 53,321 | 20,550 | 8,235 |
| Akron, Ohio | 243,130 | 255,040 | 208,435 | 42,728 | 16,512 | 3,477 |
| Omaha, Neb. | 223,185 | 214,006 | 191,601 | 102,555 | 30,518 | 1,883 |
| Dayton, Ohio | 211,456 | 200,982 | 152,559 | 85,333 | 38,678 | 20,081 |
| Syracuse, N. Y. | 205,637 | 209,326 | 171,717 | 108,374 | 51,792 | 28,119 |
| Oklahoma City, Okla. | 204,517 | 185,389 | 91,295 | 10,037 | | |
| San Diego, Calif. | 202,038 | 147,995 | 74,683 | 17,700 | 4,324 | 731 |
| Worcester, Mass. | 193,402 | 195,311 | 179,754 | 118,421 | 58,291 | 24,960 |
| Richmond, Va. | 190,341 | 182,929 | 171,667 | 85,050 | 63,600 | 37,910 |
| Ft. Worth, Tex. | 177,748 | 163,447 | 106,482 | 26,688 | 6,663 | |
| Jacksonville, Fla. | 174,336 | 129,549 | 91,558 | 28,429 | 7,650 | 2,118 |
| Miami, Fla. | 170,877 | 110,637 | 29,571 | 1,681 | | |
| Youngstown, Ohio | 167,426 | 170,002 | 132,358 | 44,885 | 15,435 | 2,759 |
| Nashville, Tenn. | 167,415 | 153,866 | 118,342 | 80,865 | 43,350 | 16,988 |
| Hartford, Conn. | 166,329 | 164,072 | 138,036 | 79,850 | 42,015 | 29,152 |
| Grand Rapids, Mich. | 164,061 | 168,592 | 137,634 | 87,565 | 32,016 | 8,085 |
| Long Beach, Calif. | 163,441 | 142,032 | 55,593 | 2,252 | | |
| New Haven, Conn. | 160,257 | 162,655 | 162,537 | 108,027 | 62,882 | 39,267 |
| Des Moines, Iowa | 159,155 | 142,559 | 126,468 | 62,139 | 22,408 | 3,965 |
| Flint, Mich. | 151,275 | 156,492 | 91,599 | 13,103 | 8,409 | 2,950 |
| Salt Lake City, Utah | 150,019 | 140,267 | 118,110 | 53,531 | 20,768 | 8,236 |
| Springfield, Mass. | 148,989 | 149,900 | 129,614 | 62,059 | 33,340 | 15,199 |
| Bridgeport, Conn. | 146,900 | 146,716 | 143,555 | 70,996 | 27,643 | 13,299 |
| Norfolk, Va. | 143,275 | 129,710 | 115,777 | 46,624 | 21,966 | 14,620 |
| Yonkers, N. Y. | 142,404 | 134,646 | 100,176 | 47,931 | 18,892 | 11,848 |
| Tulsa, Okla. | 141,750 | 141,258 | 72,075 | 1,390 | | |
| Scranton, Pa. | 140,393 | 143,433 | 137,783 | 102,026 | 45,850 | 9,223 |
| Paterson, N. J. | 139,651 | 138,513 | 135,875 | 105,171 | 51,031 | 19,586 |
| Albany, N. Y. | 130,447 | 127,412 | 113,344 | 94,151 | 90,758 | 62,367 |
| Chattanooga, Tenn. | 128,138 | 119,798 | 57,895 | 30,154 | | |
| Trenton, N. J. | 124,685 | 123,356 | 119,289 | 73,307 | 29,910 | 17,228 |
| Spokane, Wash. | 122,462 | 115,514 | 104,437 | 36,848 | | |
| Kansas City, Kans. | 121,258 | 121,857 | 101,177 | 51,418 | 3,200 | |

* Preliminary.

TABLE 4.—LARGEST CITIES OF THE WORLD*

| City | Year | Population | City | Year | Population |
|---|---|---|---|---|---|
| London (Greater) | 1931 | 8,203,000 | Cairo | 1937 | 1,307,000 |
| New York | 1940 | 7,380,000 | Peiping | 1927 | 1,297,000 |
| Tokyo | 1937 | 6,274,000† | Sydney | 1937 | 1,279,000† |
| Berlin | 1938 | 4,299,000† | Warszawa (Warsaw) | 1938 | 1,261,000 |
| Moscow (Moskva) | 1936 | 3,642,000† | Rome (Roma) | 1938 | 1,251,000 |
| Shanghai area | 1935 | 3,490,000 | São Paulo | 1937 | 1,217,000† |
| Chicago | 1940 | 3,385,000 | Nagoya | 1937 | 1,187,000† |
| Osaka | 1937 | 3,213,000† | Milan (Milano) | 1938 | 1,181,000 |
| Paris (without suburbs) | 1936 | 2,830,000 | Bombay | 1931 | 1,161,000 |
| Leningrad | 1936 | 2,739,000† | Kyoto | 1937 | 1,134,000† |
| Buenos Aires | 1937 | 2,318,000† | Hamburg | 1937 | 1,097,000† |
| Philadelphia | 1940 | 1,935,000 | Glasgow | 1931 | 1,088,000 |
| Vienna (Wien) | 1934 | 1,874,000 | Barcelona | 1933 | 1,061,000† |
| Rio de Janeiro | 1937 | 1,802,000† | Budapest | 1937 | 1,059,000† |
| Detroit | 1940 | 1,619,000 | México, D. F. | 1930 | 1,029,000 |
| Hankow area | 1927 | 1,500,000 | Melbourne | 1937 | 1,024,000† |
| Los Angeles | 1940 | 1,497,000 | Madrid | 1933 | 1,015,000† |
| Calcutta | 1931 | 1,419,000 | Birmingham, England | 1931 | 1,002,000 |

* U.S. Department of Commerce and estimates for cities of China from The World Almanac.
† Latest official estimate.

TABLE 5.—CITIES OF THE WORLD HAVING OVER 500,000 POPULATION*

| City | Year | Population | City | Year | Population |
|---|---|---|---|---|---|
| Alexandria | 1937 | 682,000 | Łódź | 1938 | 665,000 |
| Amsterdam | 1938 | 788,000† | London (Greater) | 1931 | 8,203,000 |
| Baku | 1935 | 670,000† | Los Angeles | 1940 | 1,497,000 |
| Baltimore | 1940 | 854,000 | Lyon | 1936 | 570,000 |
| Bangkok | 1937 | 886,000 | Madras | 1931 | 646,000 |
| Barcelona | 1933 | 1,061,000† | Madrid | 1933 | 1,015,000† |
| Batavia | 1930 | 533,000 | Manchester, England | 1931 | 766,000 |
| Berlin | 1938 | 4,299,000† | Marseille | 1936 | 914,000 |
| Birmingham, England | 1931 | 1,002,000 | Melbourne | 1937 | 1,024,000† |
| Bombay | 1931 | 1,161,000 | México, D. F. | 1930 | 1,029,000 |
| Boston | 1940 | 770,000 | Milan (Milano) | 1938 | 1,181,000 |
| Breslau | 1937 | 625,000† | Milwaukee | 1940 | 590,000 |
| Brussels (Bruxelles) | 1937 | 910,000† | Montevideo | 1937 | 693,000† |
| Bucureşti (Bucharest) | 1936 | 643,000† | Montreal | 1931 | 819,000 |
| Budapest | 1937 | 1,059,000† | Moscow (Moskva) | 1936 | 3,642,000† |
| Buenos Aires | 1937 | 2,318,000† | Munich (München) | 1937 | 756,000† |
| Buffalo | 1940 | 575,000 | Nagoya | 1937 | 1,187,000† |
| Cairo | 1937 | 1,307,000 | Naples (Napoli) | 1938 | 908,000 |
| Calcutta | 1931 | 1,419,000 | New York | 1940 | 7,380,000 |
| Canton, China | 1926 | 535,000 | Odessa | 1935 | 509,000† |
| Chicago | 1940 | 3,385,000 | Osaka | 1937 | 3,213,000† |
| Cleveland | 1940 | 878,000 | Paris (without suburbs) | 1936 | 2,830,000 |
| Cologne (Köln) | 1937 | 762,000† | Peiping | 1927 | 1,297,000 |
| Copenhagen (Köbenhavn) | 1935 | 843,000 | Philadelphia | 1940 | 1,935,000 |
| Detroit | 1940 | 1,619,000 | Pittsburgh | 1940 | 665,000 |
| Dortmund | 1937 | 540,000† | Praha (Prague) | 1937 | 962,000† |
| Dresden | 1937 | 637,000† | Recife (Pernambuco) | 1937 | 510,000† |
| Düsseldorf | 1937 | 515,000† | Rio de Janeiro | 1937 | 1,802,000† |
| Essen | 1937 | 662,000† | Rome (Roma) | 1938 | 1,251,000 |
| Frankfurt (on Main) | 1937 | 551,000† | Rosario | 1937 | 504,000† |
| Genoa (Genova) | 1938 | 647,000 | Rotterdam | 1938 | 606,000† |
| Glasgow | 1931 | 1,088,000 | St. Louis | 1940 | 814,000 |
| Gorki (Nizhni Novgorod) | 1935 | 513,000† | San Francisco | 1940 | 630,000 |
| Habana | 1936 | 552,000† | Santiago, Chile | 1930 | 696,000 |
| Hamburg | 1937 | 1,097,000† | São Paulo | 1937 | 1,217,000† |
| Hangchow | 1927 | 1,000,000 | Shanghai area | 1935 | 3,490,000 |
| Hankow area | 1927 | 1,500,000 | Sheffield | 1931 | 512,000 |
| Hongkong | 1927 | 849,000 | Stockholm | 1937 | 557,000 |
| Istanbul (Constantinople) | 1935 | 741,000 | Sydney | 1937 | 1,279,000† |
| Johannesburg | 1936 | 519,000 | Tashkent | 1935 | 565,000† |
| Kharkov | 1935 | 625,000† | Tientsin | 1927 | 839,000 |
| Kiev | 1936 | 625,000† | Tokyo | 1937 | 6,274,000† |
| Kobe | 1937 | 964,000† | Toronto | 1931 | 631,000 |
| Kyoto | 1937 | 1,134,000† | Turin (Torino) | 1938 | 675,000 |
| Leipzig | 1937 | 698,000† | Vienna (Wien) | 1934 | 1,874,000 |
| Leningrad | 1936 | 2,739,000† | Warszawa (Warsaw) | 1938 | 1,261,000 |
| Lisbon (Lisboa) | 1936 | 650,000† | Washington, D. C. | 1940 | 663,000 |
| Liverpool | 1931 | 856,000 | Yokohama | 1937 | 760,000† |

* U.S. Department of Commerce and estimates for cities of China from The World Almanac.
† Latest official estimate.

### TABLE 6.—PER CAPITA TRADE, BY COUNTRIES*
### (Calendar year, 1937)

| Country | Population estimates (thousands) | Per capita trade (current dollars) Imports | Exports | Country | Population estimates (thousands) | Per capita trade (current dollars) Imports | Exports |
|---|---|---|---|---|---|---|---|
| **North America:** | | | | **Europe—continued:** | | | |
| United States (customs areas) | 131,514 | 25.10 | 22.90 | Lithuania | 2,550 | 14.00 | 13.75 |
| Canada | 11,120 | 72.65 | 88.85 | Netherlands | 8,635 | 98.80 | 73.20 |
| Newfoundland† | 290 | 82.55 | 93.45 | Norway | 2,907 | 110.45 | 69.25 |
| Mexico | 19,154 | 9.15 | 12.95 | Poland | 34,500 | 6.85 | 6.55 |
| **Central America:** | | | | Portugal | 7,275 | 14.25 | 7.45 |
| Costa Rica | 592 | 20.05 | 19.45 | Rumania | 19,423 | 4.80 | 8.25 |
| Guatemala | 3,008 | 6.95 | 5.35 | U.S.S.R. | 170,500 | 1.55 | 2.00 |
| Honduras | 962 | 10.80 | 10.00 | Spain (1935) | 24,849 | 11.55 | 7.65 |
| Nicaragua | 1,000 | 5.60 | 7.05 | Sweden | 6,285 | 85.10 | 81.10 |
| Panama | 535 | 40.85 | 7.60 | Switzerland | 4,174 | 98.75 | 70.55 |
| El Salvador | 1,632 | 6.10 | 9.50 | United Kingdom | 47,029 | 108.20 | 54.85 |
| British West Indies | 2,204 | 4.00 | 3.20 | Yugoslavia | 15,400 | 7.85 | 9.40 |
| Cuba | 4,109 | 31.55 | 45.30 | **Asia:** | | | |
| Dominican Republic | 1,581 | 7.40 | 11.45 | Ceylon | 5,780 | 15.65 | 20.00 |
| Haiti | 2,700 | 3.40 | 3.30 | China | 466,786 | .60 | .55 |
| **South America:** | | | | Chosen | 22,899 | 10.85 | 8.60 |
| Argentina | 12,761 | 36.75 | 59.35 | India | 338,171 | 1.80 | 2.25 |
| Bolivia | 3,283 | 1.85 | 3.25 | Indo-China, French | 23,030 | 2.70 | 4.40 |
| Brazil | 43,247 | 4.60 | 4.85 | Iran (Persia) | 12,000 | 4.40 | 11.40 |
| Chile | 4,597 | 19.15 | 42.50 | 'Iraq | 3,561 | 13.30 | 7.75 |
| Colombia | 8,665 | 11.10 | 12.00 | Japan (Proper) | 71,252 | 15.25 | 12.85 |
| Ecuador | 2,757 | 4.35 | 5.40 | Malaya, British (1936) | 5,137 | 77.45 | 101.45 |
| British Guiana | 337 | 34.95 | 41.15 | Netherlands Indies | 64,450 | 4.20 | 8.10 |
| French Guiana (1936) | 48 | 56.35 | 31.70 | Palestine | 1,402 | 56.10 | 20.50 |
| Surinam (Netherland Guiana) (1936) | 166 | 24.40 | 15.25 | Philippine Islands | 13,099 | 8.30 | 11.55 |
| Paraguay | 900 | 9.45 | 9.20 | Thailand (Siam) | 14,464 | 3.40 | 5.45 |
| Peru | 6,500 | 9.10 | 14.15 | Syria | 3,250 | 13.35 | 6.40 |
| Uruguay | 2,093 | 20.35 | 25.05 | Taiwan (Formosa) | 5,212 | 16 90 | 21.60 |
| Venezuela | 3,428 | 15.65 | 56.80 | Turkey | 16,201 | 5.65 | 6.80 |
| **Europe:** | | | | **Oceania:** | | | |
| Austria | 6,760 | 44.30 | 37.10 | Australia | 6,866 | 65.15 | 83.15 |
| Belgium-Luxemburg | 8,659 | 106.25 | 99.00 | New Zealand | 1,574 | 139.15 | 160.35 |
| Bulgaria | 6,280 | 10.10 | 10.25 | **Africa:** | | | |
| Czechoslovakia | 15,263 | 25.10 | 27.35 | Anglo-Egyptian Sudan | 5,950 | 5.35 | 6.95 |
| Denmark | 3,749 | 99.90 | 94.60 | Algeria | 7,235 | 22.95 | 23.95 |
| Estonia | 1,131 | 26.40 | 25.20 | Belgian Congo | 10,067 | 3.85 | 8.35 |
| Finland | 3,807 | 53.40 | 53.85 | Egypt | 15,905 | 12.10 | 12.30 |
| France | 41,906 | 40.50 | 22.80 | French West Africa | 14,703 | 4.20 | 3.45 |
| Germany | 67,587 | 32.50 | 35.15 | Gold Coast | 3,614 | 16.85 | 16.70 |
| Greece | 6,205 | 19.65 | 12.35 | Kenya-Uganda | 6,949 | 7.00 | 7.95 |
| Hungary | 9,035 | 15.50 | 19.20 | Madagascar | 3,798 | 4.95 | 6.15 |
| Ireland | 2,966 | 73.55 | 37.10 | Morocco, French | 6,296 | 11.20 | 7.25 |
| Italy | 43,786 | 16.80 | 12.65 | Nigeria | 20,191 | 3.60 | 3.65 |
| Latvia | 1,951 | 23.15 | 26.20 | Tanganyika | 5,147 | 3.75 | 4.30 |
| | | | | Tunisia | 2,608 | 20.30 | 17.50 |
| | | | | Union of South Africa | 9,797 | 48.60 | 60.55‡ |

* From the *U.S. Dept. Commerce Foreign Commerce Yearbook*, 1938.
† Fiscal year ending June 30, 1936.
‡ Including gold bar.

TABLE 7.—TRADE OF LEADING COUNTRIES WITH THE UNITED STATES*

| Country | Exports to the United States | | | | Imports from the United States | | | |
|---|---|---|---|---|---|---|---|---|
| | Thousands of dollars | | Percentage of total exports | | Thousands of dollars | | Percentage of total imports | |
| | 1930 | 1937 | 1930 | 1937 | 1930 | 1937 | 1930 | 1937 |
| Argentina.............. | 49,639 | 96,687 | 9.7 | 12.8 | 136,204 | 76,829 | 22.1 | 16.4 |
| Australia.............. | 24,608 | 28,452 | 4.1 | 4.8 | 147,534 | 76,540 | 23.1 | 15.2 |
| Belgium............... | 35,946 | 65,484 | 5.1 | 7.6 | 86,339 | 80,527 | 10.0 | 8.8 |
| Brazil................. | 126,316 | 126,328 | 40.6 | 36.3 | 60,638 | 76,410 | 24.2 | 23.1 |
| Canada................ | 349,661 | 352,599 | 43.7 | 35.7 | 584,407 | 489,997 | 64.5 | 60.6 |
| Ceylon................ | 16,742 | 18,085 | 15.7 | 15.6 | 3,439 | 2,325 | 3.0 | 2.6 |
| Chile.................. | 40,804 | 43,918 | 25.4 | 22.5 | 56,609 | 25,711 | 33.5 | 29.1 |
| China................. | 60,665 | 68,523 | 14.7 | 27.6 | 106,907 | 55,291 | 17.5 | 19.8 |
| Colombia.............. | 88,459 | 66,799 | 81.3 | 64.1 | 27,536 | 46,394 | 45.4 | 48.3 |
| Cuba.................. | 116,051 | 150,158 | 69.3 | 80.7 | 127,051 | 88,847 | 58.8 | 68.6 |
| Czechoslovakia......... | 28,918 | 38,839 | 5.6 | 9.3 | 23,270 | 33,576 | 5.0 | 8.8 |
| Denmark.............. | 2,791 | 6,576 | .6 | 1.9 | 52,057 | 20,490 | 11.2 | 5.5 |
| Egypt................. | 9,768 | 7,890 | 6.1 | 4.0 | 11,030 | 10,864 | 4.7 | 5.6 |
| France................ | 95,449 | 61,326 | 5.7 | 6.4 | 238,710 | 160,713 | 11.6 | 9.5 |
| Germany.............. | 163,218 | 84,237 | 5.7 | 3.5 | 311,272 | 113,506 | 12.6 | 5.2 |
| India, British.......... | 90,407 | 77,715 | 9.8 | 10.6 | 55,326 | 39,406 | 8.2 | 6.4 |
| Italy.................. | 69,712 | 41,184 | 10.9 | 7.5 | 133,451 | 79,496 | 14.6 | 10.9 |
| Japan................. | 249,968 | 188,090 | 34.4 | 20.6 | 218,739 | 365,502 | 28.6 | 33.6 |
| Malaya, British†....... | 220,235 | 172,216 | 42.2 | 47.1 | 18,417 | 5,454 | 3.7 | 1.9 |
| Mexico................ | 126,079 | 139,823 | 58.3 | 56.3 | 112,579 | 109,850 | 68.2 | 62.7 |
| Netherlands Indies...... | 56,901 | 97,853 | 12.2 | 18.7 | 35,983 | 27,482 | 10.4 | 10.2 |
| Netherlands........... | 19,531 | 31,848 | 2.8 | 5.1 | 84,943 | 75,052 | 8.7 | 8.8 |
| New Zealand.......... | 10,301 | 18,987 | 4.7 | 7.2 | 36,847 | 27,626 | 17.6 | 12.4 |
| Norway............... | 14,777 | 20,024 | 8.1 | 9.8 | 27,596 | 27,399 | 9.7 | 8.5 |
| Peru.................. | 34,684 | 20,422 | 39.3 | 22.1 | 18,646 | 20,976 | 37.2 | 35.3 |
| Philippine Islands....... | 105,342 | 120,743 | 79.1 | 79.8 | 78,183 | 63,302 | 63.5 | 58.1 |
| Poland................ | 2,458 | 19,097 | .9 | 8.6 | 30,386 | 28,223 | 12.1 | 11.9 |
| Spain‡................. | ...... | 18,179 | .... | 9.5 | ...... | 47,966 | .... | 16.8 |
| Sweden............... | 43,206 | 56,107 | 10.4 | 11.0 | 61,439 | 75,728 | 13.8 | 14.0 |
| Switzerland........... | 27,826 | 25,768 | 8.3 | 8.8 | 39,528 | 28,944 | 8.1 | 7.0 |
| U.S.S.R............... | 21,080 | 26,882 | 3.9 | 7.8 | 136,162 | 48,861 | 25.0 | 18.2 |
| Union of South Africa.... | 5,831 | 6,306 | 3.9 | 3.4 | 44,959 | 97,819 | 15.7 | 20.6 |
| United Kingdom........ | 139,693 | 209,386 | 5.0 | 7.1 | 747,545 | 564,847 | 14.7 | 11.1 |
| Venezuela.............. | 34,275 | 33,625 | 23.8 | 13.7 | 35,199 | 45,452 | 51.1 | 52.8 |

* Bureau of Foreign and Domestic Commerce.
† Values and percentages are for 1929 and 1936.
‡ Values and percentages are for 1935.

TABLE 8.—TRADE OF THE UNITED STATES WITH WORLD REGIONS*
(In thousands of dollars)

| Region | United States exports to | | United States imports from | |
|---|---|---|---|---|
| | 1931–1935 average | 1937 | 1931–1935 average | 1937 |
| Canada and Newfoundland................ | 300,147 | 518,873 | 235,536 | 406,683 |
| Middle America.......................... | 196,025 | 408,745 | 255,902 | 362,019 |
| South America, West Coast............... | 24,448 | 53,913 | 31,493 | 68,568 |
| South America, East Coast............... | 83,036 | 176,764 | 134,022 | 274,484 |
| Northern Europe........................ | 848,514 | 1,244,013 | 440,904 | 739,646 |
| Mediterranean lands.................... | 119,263 | 126,806 | 78,138 | 111,061 |
| Eastern Asia............................ | 245,127 | 374,596 | 203,686 | 320,744 |
| Southern Asia.......................... | 104,784 | 205,376 | 287,223 | 646,517 |
| Africa (except Mediterranean)............ | 54,758 | 140,950 | 29,360 | 84,770 |
| Australia and New Zealand............... | 48,031 | 97,398 | 15,067 | 65,907 |

* Bureau of the Census.

### TABLE 9.—EXPORTS OF LEADING COMMODITIES FROM THE UNITED STATES
(Values in millions and tenths of millions of dollars)

| Commodity | Quantity | | Value | |
|---|---|---|---|---|
| | 1931–1935 | 1937 | 1931–1935 | 1937 |
| Cotton, unmanufactured (in million pounds)........ | 3,875 | 3,223 | 366.5 | 368.7 |
| Petroleum and products........................... | .... | .... | 231.4 | 376.2 |
| Refined oils (in million barrels)................ | 71 | 93 | 176.2 | 253.4 |
| Crude oil (in million barrels)................... | 36 | 67 | 38.2 | 96.4 |
| Machinery*....................................... | .... | .... | 212.5 | 479.1 |
| Electrical and apparatus........................ | .... | .... | 62.6 | 112.6 |
| Agricultural and implements..................... | .... | .... | 26.8 | 75.3 |
| Industrial...................................... | .... | .... | 94.7 | 240.5 |
| Automobiles, parts and accessories................ | .... | .... | 146.5 | 346.9 |
| Wheat, including flour (in million bushels)......... | 37 | 39 | 39.2 | 64.0 |
| Wheat grain (in million bushels)................. | 32 | 35 | 19.5 | 38.7 |
| Packing-house products (in million pounds)......... | 712 | 270 | 63.1 | 41.9 |
| Meats (in million pounds)....................... | 216 | 124 | 28.7 | 24.7 |
| Fats and oils, edible (in million pounds)......... | 496 | 146 | 34.4 | 17.2 |
| Lard (in million pounds)........................ | 444 | 136 | 31.0 | 16.0 |
| Iron and steel mill products....................... | .... | .... | 62.9 | 300.1 |
| Copper, including manufactures (in million pounds).. | 493 | 701 | 39.9 | 93.6 |
| Tobacco, unmanufactured (in million pounds)....... | 442 | 435 | 103.7 | 134.5 |
| Coal and coke (in million tons)................... | 11 | 14 | 51.7 | 67.4 |
| Fruits and nuts................................... | .... | .... | 84.8 | 82.2 |
| Cotton manufactures.............................. | .... | .... | 36.4 | 43.6 |
| Cloths, duck, tire fabric (in million square yards).. | 291 | 236 | 26.3 | 28.3 |
| Sawmill products................................. | .... | .... | 37.5 | 53.7 |
| Boards and planks (in million board feet)......... | 1,002 | 1,095 | 31.2 | 45.8 |
| Iron and steel, advanced manufactures............. | .... | .... | 27.2 | 52.1 |
| Chemicals (coal tar, medicinal, industrial).......... | .... | .... | 57.7 | 87.9 |
| Rubber and manufactures......................... | .... | .... | 23.0 | 32.1 |
| Automobile casings (in thousands)............... | 1,150 | 1,016 | 11.0 | 13.2 |
| Leather.......................................... | .... | .... | 17.1 | 17.3 |
| Wood manufactures (advanced)..................... | .... | .... | 13.7 | 20.3 |
| Furs and manufactures............................ | .... | .... | 17.2 | 17.9 |
| Pulpwood and woodpulp, paper, paper manufactures. | .... | .... | 24.0 | 54.7 |
| Naval stores, gums and resins..................... | .... | .... | 14.7 | 22.1 |
| Oil cake and meal (in thousand tons).............. | 294 | 380 | 7.6 | 11.5 |
| Photographic goods............................... | .... | .... | 15.8 | 22.5 |
| Books and printed material........................ | .... | .... | 14.1 | 22.8 |
| Pigment, paints, and varnishes.................... | .... | .... | 13.6 | 21.6 |
| Fish............................................. | .... | .... | 10.3 | 13.7 |
| Dairy products................................... | .... | .... | 6.2 | 5.1 |
| Leather manufactures............................. | .... | .... | 4.3 | 8.0 |

* Includes office appliances and printing machinery.

TABLE 10.—IMPORTS OF LEADING COMMODITIES INTO THE UNITED STATES
(Values in millions and tenths of millions of dollars)

| Commodity | Quantity | | Value | |
|---|---|---|---|---|
| | 1931–1935 | 1937 | 1931–1935 | 1937 |
| Silk, raw (in million pounds)..................... | 70 | 58 | 115.1 | 106.6 |
| Rubber, crude (in million pounds)............... | 1,015 | 1,339 | 74.6 | 247.5 |
| Coffee (in million pounds)....................... | 1,622 | 1,697 | 141.2 | 150.6 |
| Sugar, cane (in million pounds).................. | 5,972 | 6,392 | 113.1 | 166.2 |
| Paper and manufactures......................... | | | 95.5 | 137.1 |
| Newsprint (in million pounds)................. | 4,098 | 6,634 | 84.8 | 122.5 |
| Petroleum and products......................... | | | 51.0 | 44.6 |
| Crude oil (in million barrels)................... | 38 | 27 | 27.3 | 20.8 |
| Refined oils (in million barrels)................ | 24 | 33 | 22.3 | 22.4 |
| Hides and skins (in million pounds).............. | 261 | 312 | 39.8 | 71.1 |
| Furs and manufactures.......................... | | | 43.1 | 86.2 |
| Paper base stocks.............................. | | | 69.6 | 117.9 |
| Woodpulp (in thousand tons)................... | 1,606 | 2,395 | 59.5 | 98.3 |
| Copper, including manufactures (in million pounds).. | 422 | 455 | 29.7 | 52.6 |
| Vegetable oils, expressed....................... | | | 45.0 | 112.0 |
| Tin-bars, blocks, pigs (in million pounds).......... | 120 | 197 | 43.8 | 104.3 |
| Wool and mohair (in million pounds).............. | 136 | 326 | 18.7 | 96.3 |
| Fertilizers, (in thousand tons).................... | 1,236 | 2,046 | 28.7 | 46.7 |
| Oilseeds....................................... | | | 26.6 | 63.3 |
| Flaxseed (in thousand bushels)................. | 13,619 | 28,032 | 12.7 | 35.2 |
| Cotton manufactures............................ | | | 31.7 | 51.7 |
| Tobacco, unmanufactured (in million pounds)....... | 61 | 72 | 27.1 | 31.9 |
| Wool manufactures.............................. | | | 15.0 | 24.5 |
| Diamonds (in thousand carats)................... | 702 | 2,501 | 15.9 | 44.1 |
| Chemicals (coal tar, industrial, medicinal).......... | | | 32.3 | 49.7 |
| Cocoa or cacao beans (in million pounds).......... | 484 | 619 | 21.5 | 52.3 |
| Cotton, unmanufactured (in million pounds)........ | 65 | 134 | 7.4 | 16.6 |
| Silk manufactures............................... | | | 8.6 | 11.1 |
| Tea (in million pounds).......................... | 88 | 95 | 15.7 | 21.4 |

TABLE 11.—SELECTED UNITED STATES MANUFACTURING INDUSTRIES*

| Products | Value of products, 000 omitted | | |
|---|---|---|---|
| | 1929 | 1935 | 1939 |
| Motor vehicles, bodies and parts................ | $5,260,723 | $3,942,014 | $4,040,930 |
| Iron and steel, blast furnaces, and rolling mills.... | 4,137,214 | 2,305,970 | 3,341,222 |
| Slaughtering and meat packing, wholesale........ | 3,434,654 | 2,362,369 | 2,648,325 |
| Clothing...................................... | 2,986,000 | 1,936,731 | 2,156,614 |
| Foundry and machine-shop products............ | 2,791,462 | 1,438,042 | |
| Printing and publishing....................... | 2,760,196 | 1,891,639 | 2,233,843 |
| Petroleum refining............................ | 2,639,665 | 1,838,622 | 2,461,126 |
| Electrical machinery, apparatus, and supplies..... | 2,300,916 | 960,430 | |
| Lumber and timber products.................. | 2,062,233 | 932,343 | 1,484,888 |
| Railway-car construction and repair............ | 1,598,137 | 520,639 | |
| Bread and other bakery products............... | 1,526,111 | 1,235,073 | 1,412,187 |
| Cotton goods................................. | 1,524,177 | 861,170 | 917,854 |
| Smelting and refining, copper, lead, zinc, excluding gold, silver, platinum....................... | 1,451,683 | 617,250 | |
| Tobacco and its products...................... | 1,246,242 | 1,093,400 | 1,322,188 |
| Paper and woodpulp........................... | 1,206,114 | 879,002 | 1,273,046 |
| Butter, cheese, and condensed and evaporated milk........................................ | 1,066,173 | 771,655 | 810,183 |
| Flour and other grain-mill products............. | 1,060,269 | 853,219 | 649,943 |
| Boots and shoes (not rubber).................. | 965,923 | 643,872 | 734,673 |
| Woolen and worsted goods.................... | 827,006 | 685,273 | 698,467 |
| Rubber tires and inner tubes................. | 770,177 | 446,092 | 580,928 |

* Bureau of the Census.

# INDEX

Pages on which maps appear are in **boldface** type

633